ADVANCED BIOLOGY IN CREATION

the HUMAN BODY

fearfully and wonderfully made!

BODY

2nd EDITION

Marilyn M. Shannon, M.A.
Rachael L. Yunis, M.S., M.A.

Technical Editorial Contributions:
Laura C. Chase, DDS

Bible Reference Editorial Contributions:
Scott Cureton, M.Div.

Biochemistry Editorial Contributions:
Mary Manson McManamy, Ph.D.

Ear, Nose, and Throat Editorial Contributions:
J. Robert Silver, M.D.

The Human Body: Fearfully and Wonderfully Made!
2nd Edition
Advanced Biology in Creation

Published by
Apologia Educational Ministries, Inc.
1106 Meridian Plaza, Suite 220/340
Anderson, Indiana 46016
apologia.com

The Human Body, 2nd Edition, is revised and updated from a previous
edition coauthored by Dr. Jay L. Wile and Marilyn M. Shannon

Printed by Bang Printing, Brainerd, MN

Manufactured in the USA

Second Printing: August 2014

ISBN: 978-1-935495-72-7

Cover: Doug Powell
Book Design: Doug Powell and Jade Novak

NEED HELP?

Apologia Educational Ministries, Inc. Curriculum Support

If you have any questions while using Apologia curriculum,
feel free to contact us in any of the following ways:

 By Mail: Curriculum Help
Apologia Educational Ministries, Inc.
1106 Meridian Plaza, Suite 220/340
Anderson, IN 46016

 By E-MAIL: help@apologia.com

 On The Web: http://www.apologia.com

 By FAX: (765) 608 - 3290

 By Phone: (765) 608 - 3280

the
HUMAN
BODY *fearfully and wonderfully made!*
2nd EDITION

Have you ever watched a robot perform a task? Robots are becoming more and more popular in today's industries, because they can perform repetitive tasks in a fast, efficient manner, and they never get bored with the work! Well, if you've ever watched a robotic arm perform a task over and over again, you probably were amazed at what you saw. After all, it boggles the mind to think of the design, engineering, and computer power it takes to make something like that work.

If you are amazed by something like that, you will be thoroughly astounded by what you learn in this course. Although robotics and computers probably represent the pinnacle of today's science and technology, they pale in comparison to the organic machine that we call the human body. In this course, you will learn the 11 major systems that make up this organic machine. Each system has its own tasks to complete, and each system interacts with the other systems as well. The efficiency with which each system works, and the seamless integration of one system with the others represents a feat of engineering and design prowess that will never be matched by modern technology. The awesome design and engineering that you will see in the human body tells us that we are, indeed, "...fearfully and wonderfully made!"

PEDAGOGY OF THE TEXT

This text contains 16 modules. Each module should take you about two weeks to complete, as long as you devote an hour or more of every school day to studying this course. At this pace, you will complete the course in 32 weeks. Since most people have school years that are longer than 32 weeks, there is some built-in "flex time." You should not rush through a module just to make sure that you complete it in two weeks. Set that as a goal, but be flexible. Some of the modules might come harder to you than others, especially the ones that contain a lot of organs to memorize. On those modules, take more time on the subject matter.

To help you guide your study, there are several student exercises that you should complete.

- The "On Your Own" questions should be answered as you read the text. The act of answering these questions will cement in your mind the concepts you are trying to learn. Complete solutions to these questions appear at the end of the module. Once you have answered an "On Your Own" question, turn to the back of the module and check your work. If you did not get the correct answer, study the solution to learn why.

- The Study Guide should be completed *after* you have finished the module. It will allow you to review all of the important concepts in the module. If you have a good command of the concepts in the study guide, you should do well on the test.

The separate Solutions Manual has the solutions to the study guide, tests, and test solutions.

EXPERIMENTS

The experiments in this course are designed for you to complete as you are reading the text. We recommend that you keep a notebook of these experiments. This notebook serves two purposes. First, as you write about the experiment in the notebook, you will be forced to think through all of the concepts that were explored in the experiment. This will help you cement them into your mind. Second, certain colleges might actually ask for some evidence that you did, indeed, have a laboratory component to your human anatomy and physiology course. The notebook will not only provide such evidence but will also show the college administrator the quality of your human anatomy and physiology instruction. We recommend that you perform your experiments in the following way:

- When you get to the experiment during the reading, read through the experiment in its entirety. This will allow you to gain a quick understanding of what you are to do.

- Once you have read the experiment, start a new page in your laboratory notebook. The first page should be used to write down all of the data taken during the experiment and perform any calculation explained in the experiment.

- When you have finished the experiment, write a brief report in your notebook, right after the page where the data and calculations were written. The report should be a brief discussion of what was done and what was learned. You should not write a step-by-step procedure. Instead, write a brief summary that will allow someone who has never read the text to understand what you did and what you learned.

- PLEASE OBSERVE COMMON SENSE SAFETY PRECAUTIONS. The experiments are no more dangerous than most normal, household activity. Remember, however, that the vast majority of accidents do happen in the home. Chemicals should never be ingested; hot beakers and flames should be regarded with care; and OSHA recommends that all experiments be performed while wearing some sort of eye protection such as safety glasses or goggles.

LABORATORY EQUIPMENT

This course contains laboratory exercises and coloring book exercises for the student to perform. The laboratories come in three types: microscope labs, dissection labs, and household labs. The coloring book is a detailed coloring book commonly used in college courses. It is an excellent means of reviewing the anatomy that the student needs to learn.

The microscope experiments require a prepared slides kit, which contains several prepared slides of human tissue. Since this is your second biology course, we assume that you already have a high-school quality microscope with which to view the slides. The prepared slides kit also contains a blood-typing kit.

The dissection experiments require a dissection specimens set. Once again, since this is your second biology course, we assume that you already have dissection tools, a pad, and a pan.

The coloring book contains detailed drawings of all the anatomy that you need to learn in this course and more. As you color the pictures, you are reviewing the anatomy that is covered in the course. Of all the laboratory items available with the course, this is probably the most important. The review provided by the coloring exercises is invaluable, and it is also a way that you can see *different illustrations* for the same situation. Also, the coloring book contains a *lot more* anatomy than what we cover in the course. Thus, if you want to learn more bones, muscles, nerves, or blood vessels, you can use the coloring book to do so.

LEARNING AIDS

There is a special website for this course that you can visit. The website contains links to web-based materials related to the course. These links are arranged by module, so if you are having trouble with a particular subject in the course, you can go to the website and look at the links for that module. Most likely, you will find help there. If you are enjoying a particular module in the course and would like to learn more about it, there are links which will lead you to advanced material related to that module. To visit the website, go the following address:

www.apologia.com/bookextras

When you get to the address, you will be asked for a password. Type the following password into the password box:

Wonderfullymade

Be sure that you do not put spaces between any of the letters and that the first letter is capitalized.

Apologia Educational Ministries, Inc. produces multimedia companion CDs to accompany its courses. When available, this CD also contains additional materials for the course.

TABLE OF CONTENTS

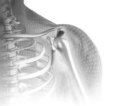

WELCOME

Have you ever sat quietly and contemplated who you are, how you came into being, and how your body functions? Have you ever been fascinated by the realization that you started life as a single cell that was smaller than the dot at the bottom of this question mark?

> I knew you before I formed
> you in your mother's womb.
> —Jeremiah 1:5, NLT

Do you realize that this one cell contained all of the information your body would ever need to develop not only into who you are today, but who you will be later in your life?

heart of the matter

"We often think that when we have completed our study on one, we know all about two, because two is one *and* one. We forget that we have still to make a study of *and.*" —Arthur Eddington

This textbook is not just a compilation of facts and figures for you to memorize. This textbook is written to take you on a remarkable journey that involves facts about the human body, figures to help you understand the materials, and truth from your Creator.

So God created human beings in his own image. In the image of God he created them; male and female he created them. —Genesis 1:27, NLT

> You saw me before I was born. Every day of my life was recorded in your book.
> Every moment was laid out before a single day had passed.
> —Psalm 139:16, NLT

Your life's journey began as a single cell, which then divided into two cells and then became four, eight, sixteen, thirty-two cells and more until something incredible happened so that you are not just a ball of trillions of cells.

> You watched me as I was being formed in utter seclusion,
> as I was woven together in the dark of the womb.
> —Psalm 139:15, NLT

You are a functioning human being with bones, muscles, skin, eyes, teeth, and blood. Even more incredibly, you have everything that you need to be a human being who lives, thinks, and creates. You are the human body, fearfully and wonderfully made!

Saint Augustine was right when he said, "Men go abroad to wonder at the height of mountains, at the huge waves of the sea, at the long courses of the rivers, at the vast compass of the ocean, at the circular motion of the stars; and they pass by themselves without wondering." We at Apologia pray that this text will enable you say:

> I praise you because I am fearfully and wonderfully made;
> your works are wonderful, I know that full well.
> —Psalm 139:14, NIV

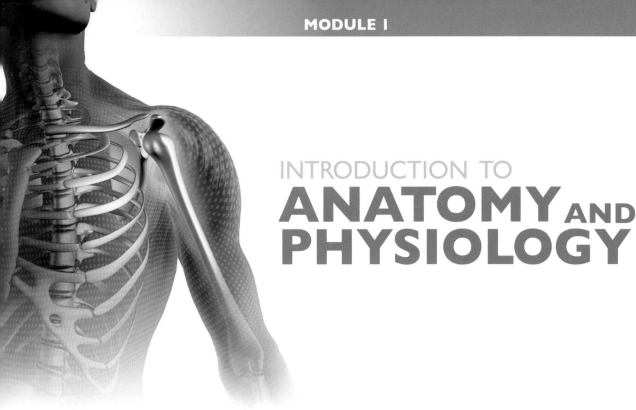

INTRODUCTION TO
ANATOMY AND PHYSIOLOGY

The human body is a complex organism that functions at many different levels. This module provides a broad prospective on what the rest of this text will cover in detail. It is important that you achieve a complete understanding of each module before you move on to the next.

Anatomy is the study of the structure of the body and its parts, while physiology is the study of how those parts function and work together to make the human body the wonder that it is. There are many different ways that anatomy can be studied.

heart of the matter

Each of your cells is its own incredible world, containing basic knowledge of how to survive. Instead of living for itself, however, each cell cooperates with other cells to form and sustain the anatomy and physiology of your body. You are probably not even aware of your cells' individual presences. As you read through this chapter, take a few moments to contemplate how complex your body is and how no part functions entirely on its own.

Developmental anatomy is the study of the changes that begin in the human body at conception and proceed into adulthood. Embryology is the subdivision of developmental anatomy that covers the first eight weeks following conception. This time period is filled with amazing moment-to-moment changes.

Surface anatomy is used for diagnosis. When a physician feels your skin to determine whether your glands are swollen or if there are any suspicious lumps or bumps on your body, the physician is using surface anatomy.

Regional anatomy means analysis of specific parts of the body. Have you ever been to a podiatrist (foot doctor)? Podiatrists treat diseases of the feet, including warts, infected toenails, and aches and pains of the many joints within the feet. Podiatry is a good example of an application of regional anatomy. The podiatrist needs to know the precise location of blood vessels, nerves, muscles, tendons, ligaments, and bones. How else could the podiatrist, for example, safely inject an anti-inflammatory medication into a patient's painful foot?

In this course, the majority of study will focus on gross anatomy. *Gross* in this context means large, so you will be studying systems that you can see. The term macroscopic anatomy is also used to mean gross anatomy. To understand how an organism functions, however, you sometimes have to see it up close. Microscopic anatomy is the study of structures so small that you will be required to use a microscope to see them. As necessary, we will cover microscopic anatomy.

This text concentrates on systemic anatomy, which means anatomy of the organ systems—groups of organs related by shared functions. One example of systemic anatomy is the digestive system. The organs—teeth, tongue, esophagus, stomach, intestines, liver, pancreas, and others—all cooperate as a system to provide a common function, which is digesting food. Systemic anatomy is the best approach when both anatomy and physiology are being studied at the same time.

Comparative anatomy refers to the anatomy of nonhuman species, and it can be used to assist in the study of the human body. Your dissection labs are a comparative anatomy study. For example, the bones of some animals are homologous (huh mol' uh gus), which means that they are similar.

As demonstrated by figure 1.1, comparative anatomy is truly a fascinating study. The human forearm is made of two bones called the radius and the ulna. A porpoise's flipper also has a radius and ulna, and the bones that form a bird's wing include a radius and ulna. Thus, we could say that a porpoise swims with its "arms" and a bird flies with its "arms." A bat's "arm" also contains a radius and an ulna, but they are small. Bones that are similar to human finger bones (phalanges) form the bat's wings. Thus, we can say that the bat flies with its "fingers."

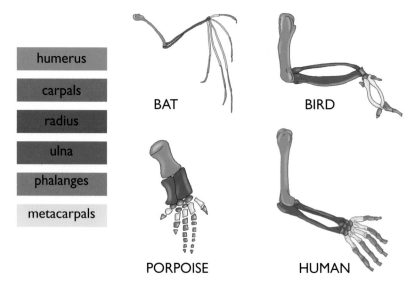

humerus

carpals

radius

ulna

phalanges

metacarpals

BAT

BIRD

PORPOISE

HUMAN

FIGURE 1.1
Comparative Anatomy of Upper (Fore) Limbs
Illustration by Megan Fruchte

Do not worry about memorizing the bones in this figure. For right now, just notice that even though bats, birds, porpoises, and people are quite different from one another, they have similar bones. In other words, these bones are homologous.

ORGANIZATIONAL LEVELS OF THE HUMAN BODY

The first thing you need to be familiar with is that the human body is organized on several different levels. The highest level of organization is the entire person, or whole **organism**. The entire person, of course, is made up of a single human body. When we look at that human body from a scientific point of view, what do we see? First, *we can divide the entire body into eleven different organ systems.*

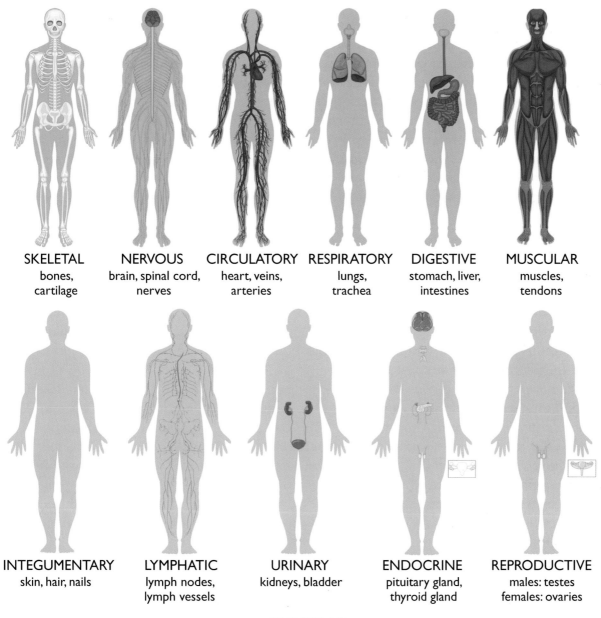

SKELETAL
bones,
cartilage

NERVOUS
brain, spinal cord,
nerves

CIRCULATORY
heart, veins,
arteries

RESPIRATORY
lungs,
trachea

DIGESTIVE
stomach, liver,
intestines

MUSCULAR
muscles,
tendons

INTEGUMENTARY
skin, hair, nails

LYMPHATIC
lymph nodes,
lymph vessels

URINARY
kidneys, bladder

ENDOCRINE
pituitary gland,
thyroid gland

REPRODUCTIVE
males: testes
females: ovaries

FIGURE 1.2
The Eleven Organ Systems in the Human Body with Examples of Organs
Illustrations: first eight © Matthew Cole, last three by Megan Fruchte

An organ system is a group of organs that work together to perform related functions. As you will learn, some organs belong to more than one organ system.

The skeletal system is made up of the bones in your body and their associated cartilages, ligaments, and joints. It provides support, as in the leg bones, and protection, as in the skull and ribs. It gives shape to the body, and its joints allow the body to move. It also produces blood cells.

The nervous system is composed of the brain, spinal cord, nerves, and all of your body's sensory receptors, including vision, hearing, smell, taste, and touch receptors. It detects sensations and controls movement, and it controls intellectual function. It regulates the other organ systems, and so is "in charge" of many physiological processes, both conscious and unconscious. It is capable of very rapid responses.

The circulatory system is composed of the heart, blood vessels, and blood. It transports gases, nutrients, waste products, hormones, and many other molecules throughout your body. It has an active role in your immune system and also aids in the regulation of your body temperature.

The respiratory system contains your lungs, respiratory passages, and diaphragm. It enables the exchange of oxygen and carbon dioxide between your blood and the air. It also has a role in regulating your blood pH.

The digestive system is perhaps the most familiar of all the organ systems. Your mouth, esophagus, stomach, intestines, liver, gallbladder, pancreas, appendix, and rectum are all part of it. It breaks down the foods you eat so that they can be absorbed out of the intestines into the blood, and it eliminates waste products.

The muscular system consists of the muscles of your body. It powers the movements of your skeleton and maintains your posture when you stand still. It enables internal organs such as the heart, diaphragm, stomach, and intestines to move. It is also used to generate heat, as when you shiver.

The integumentary system consists of skin, hair, sweat glands, oil glands, and nails. Its purpose is to protect your body, regulate your body temperature, prevent water loss, and aid in the production of vitamin D.

The lymphatic system consists of a multitude of organs, including your spleen, thymus gland, lymphatic vessels, and lymph nodes. It is sometimes called the immune system, because it gets rid of foreign substances such as bacteria, viruses, and fungi that may invade your body. But in addition to fighting disease, its thin-walled lymphatic vessels maintain the right amount of fluid around your cells, and these vessels also absorb fat from your digestive tract.

The urinary system consists of your kidneys, urinary bladder, ureters, and urethra. It removes waste products from your blood, and it regulates blood pH, ion balance, and water balance.

The endocrine system is made up of a number of organs that secrete signal molecules called hormones. The hypothalamus, pineal gland, pituitary gland, thyroid gland, parathyroids, thymus, adrenals, pancreas, ovaries (female), and testes (male) are all typical hormone glands.

However, the heart, stomach, small intestine, and kidneys also secrete hormones, even though we usually classify them with other organs systems. Along with the nervous system, the endocrine system regulates other organ systems. This system influences metabolism, growth, reproduction, and many other unconscious internal functions of your body. It generally acts more slowly than does the nervous system.

The reproductive systems are made up of the female ovaries, vagina, uterus, and mammary glands; or the male testes, penis, prostate gland, and other internal organs.

The female reproductive system produces oocytes for fertilization, provides a place for fetal development, and produces milk for the newborn. The male reproductive system produces and transfers sperm for fertilization. Both the female ovaries and male testes produce important reproductive hormones.

This is the big picture of what you will study throughout this course. By the time you are done, you will have greater knowledge of each of these organ systems.

We've mentioned the term *organ* a few times, but we really have not defined it yet.

COLORING BOOK EXERCISE 1.1
In the laboratory supplies for this course, we have included *The Anatomy Coloring Book* by Kaplan. This is an excellent tool for remembering anatomy. We recommend reviewing what you have just learned by coloring in the organ systems found on pages 9-13 in this coloring book.

Organ—A group of tissues specialized for a particular function

Examples of organs include the liver, lungs, kidneys, heart, skin, and many others that you could list. Of course, the definition of an organ does not do much good without a definition of tissues. Tissues are like building materials that can be assembled in multiple ways to build the structures of your body.

Tissues—Groups of cells forming various building materials of the body

Now, here is an amazing thing. There are eleven organ systems in your body, and each of those systems is made up of many different organs. Thus, there are a *lot* of organs in your body, and some organs are members of more than one organ system. You would, therefore, expect there to be a multitude of tissues in the body; however, *there are only four basic kinds of tissue in the entire human body!*

The first basic kind of tissue is nervous tissue. It makes up the brain, spinal cord, and nerves. Nervous tissue has the ability to conduct electrical signals.

Muscular tissue comprises the muscles that enable your skeleton to move, your heart to beat, and your other internal organs to push food or fluid along.

The third type of tissue is connective tissue, which makes up bone, cartilage, the deeper layer of the skin, and the bindings or connectors around and between organs. The bridge of your nose and the flexible part of your ears are

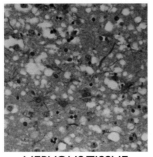
NERVOUS TISSUE

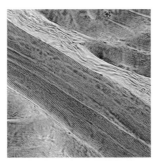
MUSCULAR TISSUE

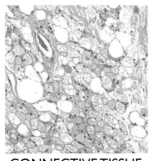
CONNECTIVE TISSUE

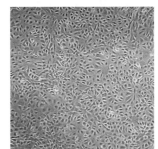
EPITHELIAL TISSUE

FIGURE 1.3
Four Types of Tissue
Photos (clockwise from top left): Public Health Image Library, APHIS, PD; Department of Histology, Jagiellonian University Medical College, cc-by-sa 3; Nephron cc-by-sa 3; Subclavian, PD

cartilage. Even your body fat and your blood are connective tissues.

The last of the four basic kinds of tissue is epithelial (ep uh theel' ee uhl) tissue. The surface of your skin is epithelial tissue, as is the inner lining of your respiratory passages, digestive tract, urinary tract, and reproductive tract. Glands, including your thyroid gland, liver, and many others, are also made of epithelial tissue.

Are you beginning to see a pattern here? The human body is organized into organ systems. Each organ system is composed of specific organs, which do one or more jobs to achieve common goals. Each organ is composed of tissues. Notice, then, that we have already discussed four levels of organization in the human body: whole body, organ system, organ, and tissue. The first three levels are part of the study of gross anatomy.

Tissues are best studied at the level of microscopic anatomy because each tissue is composed of specific cells. The cell is the basic unit of life. The trillions of living cells that make up your body are themselves composed of membrane-bound organelles, which means little organs. Thus, even your cells are composed of smaller units! Beyond this level is biochemistry. Organelles are formed from incredibly complex molecules, such as proteins, fatty acids, and carbohydrates. Finally, these molecules are a combination of atoms; see figure 1.4.

COLORING BOOK EXERCISE 1.2

The levels of organization are illustrated and discussed on page 5 of your coloring book. Use this as a review for what you have just learned. Note that the coloring book refers to these levels as the hierarchy of the body.

ON YOUR OWN

1.1 Certain muscles are attached to your skeleton by tendons. Of the four tissue types, which kind makes up tendons?

1.2 Which three levels of organization in the human body are studied in gross anatomy?

1. The <u>Whole Organism</u> is made up of eleven organ systems.

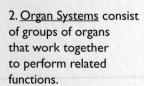

2. <u>Organ Systems</u> consist of groups of organs that work together to perform related functions.

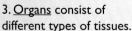

3. <u>Organs</u> consist of different types of tissues.

4. <u>Tissues</u> consist of similar types of cells and the materials around them.

5. <u>Cells</u> are made up of organelles.

6. <u>Organelles</u> are the "little organs" of the cell. They are made of molecules.

7. <u>Molecules</u> that cells make include DNA, RNA, proteins, fatty acids, and carbohydrates. Molecules consist of complex arrangements of atoms.

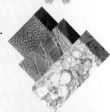

FIGURE 1.4
Seven Levels of Organization

think about this

HOMEOSTASIS

We have briefly introduced to you the anatomy (structure) of the body, which underlies the physiology (function) of the human body. What is the goal of physiology? *The goal is to maintain life and health in spite of the many changes, inside and out, that are always occurring.*

Energy must be expended constantly to maintain life, so energy must be acquired from outside the body in the form of food. That food must be processed, delivered to each cell, and then used by those cells as building materials or as an energy source. For example, the molecules that make up your organelles deteriorate and must be replaced, a process that requires both materials and energy. In thousands of ways, moment by moment, the organ systems maintain the body so that it can continue to live and be healthy. We could say that the goal is to keep the body working "normally" or "with stability" despite constant external and internal changes. The scientific term for this ongoing stability despite ongoing change is homeostasis (ho' me oh stay' sis).

Homeostasis—A state of dynamic equilibrium in the body with respect to its internal environment and functions

Let's analyze that definition for a minute. Equilibrium means balance or stability, and dynamic refers to energy. The "internal environment" in this usage means the surroundings of the cells that make up the body. "Functions" might be defined as the tasks the cells perform. So, homeostasis means the ability of your body to maintain itself in a stable balance despite the fact that energy must be used to do so. That healthy stability is maintained internally around the cells. That environment is far different from the external environment, outside the body.

Homeostasis is *the* big idea of physiology, and we will help you to gradually develop your understanding of it. Yes, we need to have a stable environment within our bodies, and there are many different variables within, such as temperature, acid-base balance, nutrient levels, blood pressure levels, oxygen levels, and waste levels, that must be controlled. What keeps us alive is the ability to maintain these variables and many more around some normal level, which we call a set point. These variables can change somewhat, but only within certain limits. If they would change too much, serious problems, illness, or death would result. Each of the organ systems illustrated in Figure 1.2 is responsible for maintaining some aspect of homeostasis for the entire person.

Set point—Ideal normal value of a variable around which homeostasis is maintained through a normal range of values that are acceptable to the body

Blood pressure is a variable that offers a good example of how homeostasis is maintained. Your blood pressure can go up under certain conditions (such as when you exercise), and it can go down under other conditions (such as when you are asleep), but it is controlled within a normal range. Thus, your body is constantly working to ensure that your blood pressure stays in equilibrium around the set point. That is a practical application of the concept of homeostasis.

Your body temperature is another variable that must be controlled. Whether your external environment is really cold or really hot, the temperature of your internal environment does not vary much. Even when you have a fever, your body temperature is still not out of control. Your body has merely increased the set point for body

FIGURE I.5
Homeostasis
Your body constantly monitors its temperature and adjusts to maintain homeostasis. This child is sweating (integumentary system) because he is too hot. If this child were to get too cold, he would start to shiver (muscular system). The motion of the muscles would produce heat, warming the body.
Photo © iStockphoto/TerryJ

temperature to deal with an infection. There are many variables within the body that must be controlled in order for the body to work properly. When those variables are within the normal range of acceptable values, the body is in a state of homeostasis. It is healthy!

Your body requires mechanisms to maintain homeostasis because the outside world (the external environment) and the needs of the body itself subject your body to stress. Now when you hear the term stress, you probably have a specific idea in mind. For example, studying for a hard test might cause you stress. In this course, however, we use the term in a much broader sense. Stress is an imbalance in the internal or external environment that causes one or more variables to move away from its set point. This causes your body to react to return the variable to an acceptable value. If the variables are not corrected, your health will be affected. In other words, stress is an imbalance that must be corrected to maintain homeostasis.

> **Stress**—A factor that causes one or more physiological variables
> to move away from its homeostatic set point

The common cold is an example of a stress. Colds are caused by viruses that have invaded your body. You might not think that a cold is very bad but that's because you have an organ system (the lymphatic system) which creates uncomfortable symptoms as it combats the virus and rids it from your body, restoring homeostasis. Without your lymphatic system, the common cold probably would be called *the fatal cold*.

The organ systems in the body, each in their own ways, contribute to homeostasis. The urinary system maintains acid-base balance; the respiratory system maintains oxygen and carbon dioxide balance, and so on, as you will learn throughout this course. Each organ system counteracts particular stresses so as to maintain the body's normal balance. Some physiologists propose that there is one exception among the eleven organ systems, however. Can you guess which one? It is the reproductive system, which is designed to propagate the human race. We will discuss this in a later chapter.

CONTROL OF HOMEOSTASIS: FEEDBACK SYSTEMS

Let's look for a moment at the control mechanisms of homeostasis. You will see that the issue of control will come up again and again throughout this course. It is one of the most fundamental aspects of physiology. Two organ systems, the nervous system and the endocrine system, are responsible for "deciding" if a variable is moving away from a state of homeostasis. They then initiate a message to correct the imbalance. The brain and spinal cord, together called the central nervous system, act as the nervous system's control center. Endocrine glands also serve as control centers. They secrete chemical messengers called hormones that signal the proper organs to respond in such a way as to maintain homeostasis.

think about this

Did you know that the simple act of standing up after lying down is actually a major change for your body? When you stand up after you have been lying down, your blood pressure drops as gravity pulls your blood away from your head. Your body quickly compensates for this change through a negative feedback mechanism. Otherwise, if you stood up suddenly, you would faint, because your blood pressure would be too low. Have you ever gotten light-headed after standing up too quickly? That happened because your negative feedback system took a little too long to raise your blood pressure.

Control center—The part of the body, either central nervous system or endocrine gland, that receives information about a variable, determines the set point, and signals a response to correct imbalances

Here's an example of how homeostasis works. Earlier, we told you that blood pressure must not get too high or too low. A "happy medium" keeps you healthy. Your body's blood pressure is detected by sensory receptors located in arteries near the heart and in the neck. When these receptors sense high blood pressure, nerves associated with them send a message to your brain, the control center, indicating that your blood pressure is too high.

Receptor—A structure in the body that monitors the values of your body's variables

Your brain, however, can't directly lower blood pressure. In order to get the job done, it sends a message via nerves to an effector. The effector makes the change. In this example, the effector is the heart, which slows down in order to lower your blood pressure.

Effector—A structure in the body that can change the value of a variable in response to a signal from the control center

As the definition indicates, the effector can change the blood pressure. In this example, the brain sends a message via nerves to the effector, and the effector then lowers the blood pressure. The effect, called the "response," is that your blood pressure drops. This, then, is an example of how your body detects and counteracts stress. What we have here is a really useful process called a negative-feedback system, which is illustrated in figure 1.6.

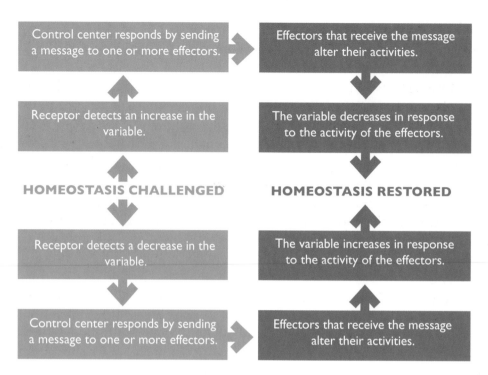

Control center responds by sending a message to one or more effectors.	Effectors that receive the message alter their activities.
Receptor detects an increase in the variable.	The variable decreases in response to the activity of the effectors.
HOMEOSTASIS CHALLENGED	**HOMEOSTASIS RESTORED**
Receptor detects a decrease in the variable.	The variable increases in response to the activity of the effectors.
Control center responds by sending a message to one or more effectors.	Effectors that receive the message alter their activities.

FIGURE 1.6
The Body's Negative-Feedback System

Negative-Feedback System—A control mechanism consisting of receptors, control center, and effectors through which homeostasis in the body is maintained by regulation of the body's organ systems. It is called negative feedback because the control system *opposes* or *reverses* the original stress.

Now think of the blood pressure example we just gave you in terms of the upper part of figure 1.6. An increase in blood pressure is detected by the receptors in your arteries. Those receptors send signals about the blood pressure that your brain (the control center) monitors. If the brain senses that your blood pressure is getting too high, it sends a message via nerves to one or more effectors. In our example, we used only one effector, the heart. Your heart changes its activity (it slows down), and the result is that your blood pressure decreases. Thus, an *increase* in blood pressure detected by the control center produced a reaction that caused a *decrease* in the blood pressure.

The opposite can happen as well. Look at the lower portion of figure 1.6. Remember, blood pressure that is too low is also a stressor. If the receptors in your arteries detect a decrease in blood pressure, they will relay that information to the brain. As the control center, the brain will recognize that your blood pressure is getting too low, and it will send a message to your heart (the effector). The message will be for your heart to speed up, and the result will be that your blood pressure increases. So, in this case, a *decrease* in blood pressure produces a reaction that will *increase* blood pressure. That's what negative feedback means—the feedback system detects a change and initiates the *opposite* effect. *Negative* in this usage means "opposite."

Let's go through one more example. As you know, the level of glucose in your blood is closely regulated, whether you have just eaten a big meal or whether you have not eaten for many hours. Blood glucose is sensed by receptors in your pancreas. If your pancreas (the control center in this case) receives information from its receptors that blood glucose levels are too high, it releases the hormone insulin (in' suh lin) into your blood. Insulin affects most of the cells in your body. They respond to the insulin by taking in glucose. This removes glucose from your blood, which results in a decrease in the blood glucose level. This is negative-feedback because the response *reverses* the stress.

What body system is the control center in this negative feedback mechanism? The *endocrine* system. Hormones are secreted by the endocrine system. Thus, *if a hormone is involved, the endocrine system must be involved.*

In summary, homeostasis is controlled by negative-feedback mechanisms. Both the nervous system and the endocrine system are used as control centers to maintain homeostasis within the body. This is no small feat given that these systems coordinate homeostasis for trillions of cells!

Before we end this discussion, we should mention positive-feedback systems. That sounds great, does not it? *Positive* means "good," right? Well, not when it comes to feedback mechanisms! Positive-feedback systems are naturally unstable and *escalate* the imbalance, moving the body farther and farther away from homeostasis. They can lead to disease or death unless they are interrupted.

Nevertheless, there are certain times when positive-feedback systems are important in human physiology. When we study the reproductive process toward the end of this course, you will see an example of a positive-feedback system that is necessary for childbirth. However, that positive-feedback system is *eventually* interrupted by the birth of the baby, and a negative-feedback system takes its place. Thus, even the positive-feedback systems that are necessary in the body (there are not many of them) must eventually be interrupted.

ON YOUR OWN

We already have discussed shivering as a response to the body being cold. Here's how it works. Receptors in the skin send temperature information to the hypothalamus (hi poh thal' uh mus), a structure in the brain. If the hypothalamus "decides" that the temperature is too low, it can send signals via the nerves to the muscles. These signals cause the muscles to start moving rapidly, which we observe as shivering. This increased movement produces heat, which warms the body.

1.3 Is this a negative- or positive-feedback system? Why?
1.4 What is the control center for the system?
1.5 What is the effector?
1.6 Based on this description, is the endocrine system involved in this process?

A REVIEW OF CELL STRUCTURE AND ORGANELLE FUNCTION

So far, in terms of organization in the human body, we have talked about the organism, the organ systems, and the organs. In the next module, we will discuss tissues, so we will not talk about that level of organization here. Instead, we will jump down to the next levels of organization: the cell and its organelles. We will not spend too much time on this subject. The majority of your anatomy and physiology study will occur at the tissue level and above.

Figure 1.7 is a drawing of an idealized animal cell. All members of kingdom Animalia, including human beings, have this basic kind of cell. You have to realize, however, that there is probably no cell in the human body that looks exactly like the illustration in the figure. Indeed, some cells (such as neurons) look quite different from what you see here. Nevertheless, the features that you find in various cells throughout the body are woven together into this idealized representation of a typical animal cell.

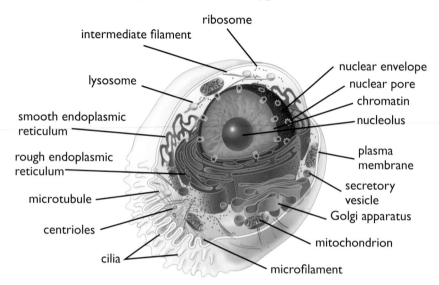

FIGURE 1.7
An Idealized Animal Cell
Illustration: Jennifer Fairman

Of course, not every cell will have all of the features pointed out here. The key is that all of the features pointed out exist in at least some cells. For example, mature red blood cells do not have a nucleus. Nevertheless, most of your other cells do. Cells that line your trachea (the airway to your lungs) are an example of cells with cilia, but most of your cells do not have cilia.

Remember, tissues are composed of cells, and cells are composed of organelles. In order to understand cells, you need to know the major organelles and their functions. Let's start with the plasma membrane. The plasma membrane is the boundary of the cell. It holds the cell together and controls entry and exit of substances. It has many receptors on it, allowing it to determine what substances are transported into the cell and what substances are allowed out of the cell.

The next organelle to consider is the nucleus. It's wrapped in a nuclear membrane called the nuclear envelope. It is actually a double membrane, which is quite porous. The nucleus contains the genetic material, which is DNA (deoxyribonucleic acid). Except during cellular reproduction, the DNA is "spread out" in the nucleus. We usually use the term chromatin (kro' muh tin) to identify it. During cellular reproduction, the DNA forms chromosomes (krom' uh sohms). We will go over that in a later section of this module. The nucleus can be thought of as the control center of the cell because the DNA is there. The DNA codes for all the proteins that the cell produces.

Between the nucleus and the cell membrane, cytoplasm (sigh' toh plaz uhm) is found. The fluid part of the cytoplasm, called cytosol, contains many dissolved chemicals,

think about this

including ions, proteins, and other molecules. These chemicals are used for various processes, including the breakdown of sugars and fats, as well as for the production of other chemicals that the cell needs.

If we think of the nucleus as the control center of the cell, the ribosomes (rye' buh sohms) can be thought of as tiny kitchens within the cell. Proteins are synthesized in the cell's ribosomes. The proteins that a cell produces are a major part of determining what the cell does for the body. So, the ribosomes are an essential part of the cell. Because they are so tiny, they are represented by dots in the figure. Sometimes, the ribosomes stand alone. If so, they are called free ribosomes. You may also find ribosomes attached to the next organelle that we will to discuss, the endoplasmic (en' doh plaz' mik) reticulum (re tik' you luhm).

The prefix *endo* means "within," and *plasmic* refers to the cell's cytoplasm. The word *reticulum*, from the Latin, means "network." Thus, the endoplasmic reticulum is the network within the cell's cytoplasm. There are two types of endoplasmic reticulum: smooth endoplasmic reticulum and rough endoplasmic reticulum. The smooth endoplasmic reticulum is a series of tubes that are used in intracellular transport (transport within the cell) as well as in the production of lipids and carbohydrates. Rough endoplasmic reticulum is also used for intracellular transport, but it is rough in appearance because it has ribosomes on it. Because of these ribosomes, rough endoplasmic reticulum is used in protein synthesis as well as intracellular transport of proteins. The amount of smooth and rough endoplasmic reticulum can give you a clue as to the function of the cell. Cells with large amounts of smooth endoplasmic reticulum usually specialize in the production of lipids and carbohydrates. Cells with large amounts of rough endoplasmic reticulum specialize in protein synthesis.

The Golgi (gol' jee) apparatuses can be thought of as the cell's packaging plants. They take various chemicals and package them for many purposes, especially secretion. This packing may involve chemical modification. Nervous system cells, called neurons, have many Golgi apparatuses. That should tell you something about what they do. They secrete chemicals. When you eat, your salivary glands secrete saliva. This is done by the Golgi apparatuses within the salivary glands' cells.

The secretory (sec' ruh tor ee) vesicle in figure 1.7 came from the Golgi apparatus. When the Golgi apparatus has packaged a chemical for secretion, it puts the chemical into a secretory vesicle, which is a tiny membrane-bound sac. The vesicle then pinches off the Golgi apparatus and travels through the cytoplasm to the plasma membrane, where its contents can be released outside the cell. Often, a cell will build up secretory vesicles, but those vesicles will not release their chemicals until the cell gets a signal. For example, in our earlier discussion of blood glucose level, we mentioned that the pancreas releases insulin when the blood glucose level increases. That is done by cells in the pancreas whose Golgi apparatuses produce secretory vesicles full of insulin. However, those cells do not release their insulin

science and creation

until they get a signal to do so. So, the vesicles tend to build up until the cells get the signal to release the insulin.

The lysosome (lie' so sohm) is a kind of vesicle, and its main function is to break down lipids, proteins, polysaccharides, carbohydrates, and nucleic acids. What makes the lysosome interesting is that, in order to do its job, it must contain certain enzymes. These enzymes are very damaging to other parts of the cell and can easily kill the entire cell if released from the lysosome.

Have you ever heard that you can only live four to eight minutes without oxygen? Do you know why? After four to eight minutes without oxygen, the lysosomes of the neurons can't hold themselves together. They then burst, dumping their lethal contents into the cell. This kills the neurons.

The rupturing of lysosomes is sometimes actually a *good* thing. When we need to get rid of diseased or damaged tissues, the lysosomes provide a way for these cells to, in effect, self-digest. White blood cells, for example, are full of lysosomes. Have you ever had a cut that got infected? Typically, an infected cut produces white pus. That white pus is from white blood cells (we will talk about these cells in more depth in a later module) that burst their lysosomes. This kills the white blood cell, but it also kills the foreign invader. Isn't that amazing?

Centrioles (sen' tree olz) are found in the centrosome (sen' truh sohm), which is the center of microtubule formation for the cell. Microtubules are spiral strands of proteins that form a rope-like structure. They influence the movement and shape of the cell. Centrioles are important in cellular reproduction.

Cilia are like tiny hairs formed from an intricate arrangement of microtubules. In your first-year biology course, you studied paramecia and perhaps other ciliates. They are examples of microscopic organisms with cilia. What you might not realize, however, is that there are cells in your body with cilia. For example, ciliated cells are in the back of your nose, down your trachea, and all the way down your larger airways. Their cilia beat upward, pushing mucus toward your throat. The mucus typically has dust and other foreign particles that it traps. Once the cilia-containing cells push the mucus far enough upward, it can be swallowed or blown out your nose.

Microfilaments also contribute to movement. They enable certain cells to contract. Muscle cells, for example, do their job by contracting and relaxing. The microfilaments in the muscle cells take care of this function. Your cells also have intermediate filaments, which are responsible for strengthening and supporting the cells. This allows them to maintain their normal shape.

Mitochondria (my tuh kahn' dree uh) are the major site of ATP synthesis in the cell. ATP (adenosine triphosphate) is the "currency" in which cellular energy is stored. As a result, we call the mitochondria the powerhouses of the cell. It is important to remember that not all ATP (and therefore not all cellular energy) is produced in the mitochondria. The first stage of cellular respiration (called glycolysis) actually occurs in the cytoplasm, so some ATP is made there. However, the vast majority of cellular energy is produced in the mitochondria.

Although most of the DNA in a cell is stored in its nucleus, there is actually some DNA in the mitochondria. This DNA, called mitochondrial DNA, codes for the production of certain proteins necessary for the mitochondrion (singular of mitochondria) to do its job. Not only is DNA present in the mitochondria, but ribosomes are as well. With both DNA and ribosomes, a mitochondrion can produce its own proteins. Interestingly enough, however, a mitochondrion cannot produce all of the proteins it needs. Some proteins vital for the mitochondria are still produced by DNA in the nucleus, and the ribosomes in the cytoplasm. Those proteins are then transported to the mitochondria.

COLORING BOOK EXERCISE 1.3

An overview of the cell and its organelles can be found on page 21 of your coloring book. Color and label sections a-p.

ON YOUR OWN

1.7 A microbiologist is looking at a cell under a microscope. It has a large number of Golgi apparatuses in it. What, most likely, is the cell's major function?

1.8 Substances regularly are transported into and out of cells. If a substance is transported into a cell, what is the first structure it must pass through?

A REVIEW OF PROTEIN SYNTHESIS

Proteins are large molecules formed by the joining of amino acids. The type and number of amino acids joined together, along with the order in which they join, determine the properties of the protein. For example, some proteins, called enzymes, act as catalysts. Catalysts are molecules that speed up chemical reactions without being either reactants or products. Other proteins act as hormones. Some act as antibodies, which fight infections. There are thousands and thousands of proteins involved in the processes of life.

Protein synthesis in the cell takes place in two steps, transcription and translation. A transcription is a written representation of something. Historically, scribes were the persons who copied documents—keep that in mind. Translation is the process of rendering the meaning of one thing (transcription) into something else (protein).

For all of its complexity, understanding DNA is rather simple. DNA is similar to the alphabet, except that it has only four letters, not twenty-six. These letters, called bases, are adenine (A), thymine (T), cytosine (C), and guanine (G). Just as the twenty-six letters of the alphabet are combined to form words of communication, these four bases, in groups of three, form "words" that make up genes. Genes are like sentences in that they state complete thoughts. Simply put, a cell can transcribe a gene and then translate that copy into a complete protein.

Here is an analogy to explain transcription and translation: Imagine that you would like a recipe for an old-fashioned johnny cake. You go to the library to a set of encyclopedias and look up "johnny cake." There you find a recipe, but of course, you cannot take the encyclopedia set out of the library. On the other hand, you do not need the whole set, and you do not even need the whole book. You just need the recipe. What do you do? You jot the recipe down on a piece of paper and take the information home. Once you get to your kitchen, you use the recipe to get the right amounts of the correct ingredients together, and then you use them to make the johnny cake.

The library with its encyclopedias is like the nucleus of a cell. You can think of the library as having two sets of encyclopedias, each with twenty-three volumes. They are from different publishers, but they cover the same material, though perhaps with a different perspective. Those two sets represent the twenty-three pairs of chromosomes in your cells, one set of each pair inherited from each parent. They contain *all* the information for *everything* every cell in the body can do.

Of course, no one cell needs anywhere near all that information, and it is enclosed in the cell nucleus anyway. When you opened up one volume to the correct page and made a copy on paper, that was transcription. Some of the DNA from one DNA molecule "unwound," so that a copy could be made of just that part. Your paper with the correct information copied from the book is messenger RNA (mRNA).

The mRNA, like a recipe, has the information you need, and it is small enough to leave the nucleus. The ribosomes where proteins are made are like the kitchen. When the mRNA is used to call up the right amino acids in the right order to make a protein, that process is called translation. Transfer RNA (tRNA) brings the correct amino acids to the ribosome to make the protein. Figure 1.8 illustrates this process.

think about this

You are now a fully developed, mature person, but you started life as a single cell. At each cell division, your DNA copied itself so that each of your cells contains your entire DNA "encyclopedia." Throughout this process, your cells specialized according to their functions. Using the encyclopedia analogy, we could say, for example, that your muscle cells may operate from "volume four," and your nerve cells use "volume six," but they all have a complete set of DNA instructions. Now you might wonder how your DNA protects its information from mutations, which are abrupt changes in the DNA sequence. A very common kind of mutation is produced when the chemical machinery that copies DNA makes a mistake and uses the wrong nucleotide base. This, of course, will change the codon that is formed in transcription, which could result in a change in the protein, and that might be a real problem for the cell. However, since many codons refer to the same amino acid, many mutations don't result in a change in the protein because the new codon produced by the mutation still refers to the same amino acid to which the old codon referred. This is called redundancy, and it is very important in any kind of coding system. The more redundant the code, the less prone it is to random error. Interestingly enough, when two researchers (Freeland and Hurst) analyzed the genetic code of DNA in terms of how well it uses its redundancy to reduce random error, they found that it is significantly better than codes that scientists could devise. Indeed, the title of the paper by Freeland and Hurst in which they published their results is "The Genetic Code Is One in a Million."
—Freeland and Hurst, 1998

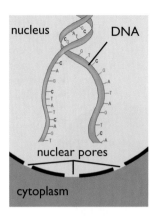

In the nucleus of the cell, DNA unwinds.

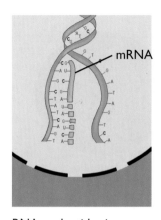

RNA nucleotides in the nucleus bind to the exposed DNA nucleotides, forming a strand of mRNA. The mRNA copies only a a small part of the DNA's information.

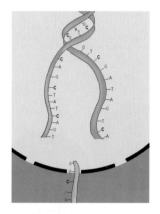

The smaller mRNA then leaves the nucleus through a nuclear pore and goes to a ribosome, where there are plenty of tRNA molecules and the associated amino acids.

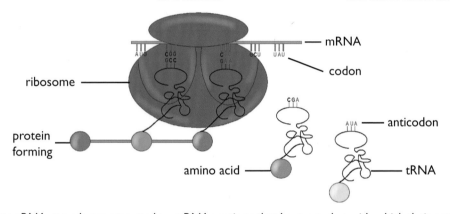

In the ribosome, tRNA strands are attracted to mRNA sections that have a codon with which their anticodon can bind. They bind to that section of the mRNA, dragging their amino acids along with them. This results in amino acids sitting next to each other. The amino acids chemically bond, and after this happens many, many times, a protein is formed.

FIGURE 1.8
A Schematic Describing Protein Synthesis in Cells
Illustration by Megan Fruchte

A REVIEW OF CELLULAR MITOSIS

Before we move on to information that will be new, a review of one more thing about cells is in order. One of the most fundamental processes that a cell must undergo is reproduction. Indeed, you started your life as a single cell. In order to develop into the person you are today, that single cell and all of its *daughter cells*, as they are called, had to reproduce over and over again. In addition, most of the cells in your body must reproduce so that you can grow and repair injuries.

Cells reproduce according to a process known as mitosis (mye toh' sis). This process takes place in four broad steps: prophase, metaphase, anaphase, and telophase. When a cell is not undergoing mitosis, it is said to be in interphase, which is the normal state for a living cell. All of these phases of a cell's life are summarized in figure 1.9. In the figure, the only organelles shown are the nucleus and the centrioles. Those are the most important

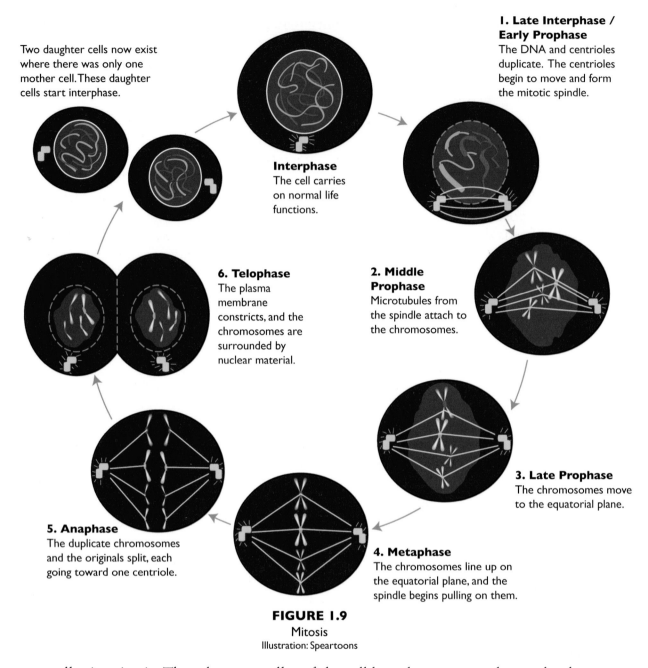

Two daughter cells now exist where there was only one mother cell. These daughter cells start interphase.

1. Late Interphase / Early Prophase
The DNA and centrioles duplicate. The centrioles begin to move and form the mitotic spindle.

Interphase
The cell carries on normal life functions.

6. Telophase
The plasma membrane constricts, and the chromosomes are surrounded by nuclear material.

2. Middle Prophase
Microtubules from the spindle attach to the chromosomes.

3. Late Prophase
The chromosomes move to the equatorial plane.

5. Anaphase
The duplicate chromosomes and the originals split, each going toward one centriole.

4. Metaphase
The chromosomes line up on the equatorial plane, and the spindle begins pulling on them.

FIGURE 1.9
Mitosis
Illustration: Speartoons

organelles in mitosis. The other organelles of the cell have been removed to make the illustration easy to understand.

Notice that in interphase, there are no distinguishable chromosomes. That's because the DNA is spread throughout the nucleus, and it is called chromatin. During prophase, four things happen. The centrioles duplicate and begin to form a spindle of microtubules between them. They also move toward opposite ends of the cell so that the spindle spreads across the cell. Also, replicated DNA forms chromosomes, which are thick and condensed and can be seen easily under a microscope. Those chromosomes move toward the center of the cell. That place in the center is the equatorial plane.

Once the chromosomes reach the equatorial plane, the cell is in metaphase. The spindle attaches to the chromosomes right at the point where each replicated chromosome is attached to its partner. At that point, the spindle begins to pull so that the duplicates and originals are pulled apart, which is the beginning of anaphase. During anaphase, the duplicates and originals separate and are pulled to opposite ends of the cell.

In the last phase, telophase, one set of chromatin is on one side of the cell, and another set is on the other side. The plasma membrane constricts to pinch the cell in two. The result, then, is two daughter cells that go back to interphase.

Before moving on, note that the X shapes that you see for the chromosomes during prophase and anaphase exist because the chromosome has been replicated (duplicated). A chromosome that has not been replicated does not have the X shape that most people think of when they think of chromosomes. Instead, a normal chromosome before replication looks more like what is shown in the illustration of telophase, and it is called chromatin.

Although most of the cells in your body are able to reproduce via mitosis, there are three types of cells that cannot: *mature neurons, mature skeletal muscle cells, and mature cardiac muscle cells.* These cells lack centrioles and cannot form the spindle for mitosis. This means that if skeletal muscle or cardiac muscle cells die, you lose them forever and cannot get new ones! On the other hand, if a part of your liver gets injured, your remaining liver cells can undergo mitosis and repair that injury.

Since neurons cannot undergo mitosis, scientists thought until recently that once you were past infancy, you could never produce any more neurons. So, if some of your neurons died, you simply lost them forever. We now know that is not true in at least some regions of the brain. These special regions do produce new neurons each year; however, they are not produced via mitosis. They are produced via processes we will discuss when we cover the brain in detail.

ON YOUR OWN

1.9 A human cell has 46 chromosomes. If the illustration in figure 1.9 were of a human cell, how many X shapes would there be in the prophase and metaphase illustrations?

THE PLASMA MEMBRANE

We've been reviewing a lot about the organization of the cell. Before we end this module, however, we do want to go one level deeper in organization. The best way to do this is to examine one aspect of the cell in detail. Since it has so much to do with the physiology of the human body, we have chosen to discuss the details of the plasma membrane. This will probably be new to you. When you look at the plasma membrane of the cell, you are going to find a beautiful relationship between structure and function. That is, you can look at how it is put together and what it is made of, and then you can see how it works. It is truly amazing what the cell membrane does and how well it works!

The cell membrane, of course, holds the cell together. That is not all it does, however. The plasma membrane is incredibly important to the life of the cell because it restricts what goes in and out of the cell, and it lets the cell communicate with its environment. First, let's look at its structure, as illustrated in figure 1.10.

The first thing that you should notice about the figure is that the cell membrane is largely made of a phospholipid bilayer. What's that? A phospholipid is composed of two fatty acids and a phosphate group. The result is a molecule that is polar (water-soluble) on one side and nonpolar (lipid-soluble) on the other. In the figure, the yellow balls represent the polar region of each phospholipid. The two stems coming out of each ball represent two fatty acids, which make up the nonpolar region of the phospholipid. So, that defines the phospholipid part. Bilayer means, as you can see, two layers: a set of phospholipids on top and a set on the bottom.

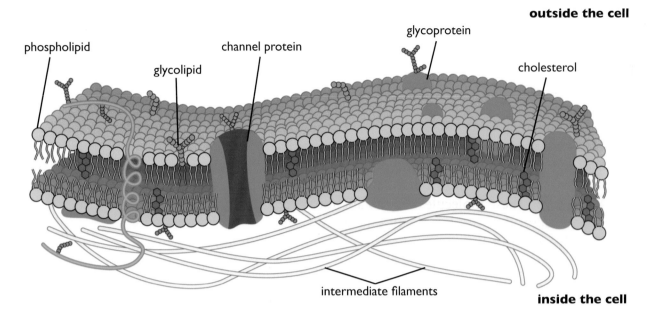

FIGURE 1.10
The Plasma Membrane
Illustration: Speartoons

Phospholipids are interesting molecules. They have a head and two tails. The heads are water-soluble because they are polar. Sometimes, biologists use the word hydrophilic instead of water soluble because hydrophilic means "water loving." The other end of the molecule (with the tails), however, is nonpolar. This means it will dissolve in oil (another nonpolar substance) but not in water. Biologists often call this hydrophobic, which means "water hating."

Because phospholipids have this remarkable property (water-soluble on one end, lipid-soluble on the other), the plasma membrane can automatically re-form if it gets disturbed for some reason. This will happen because the nonpolar tails of each layer are attracted to one another and because the polar heads of each layer are attracted to the water outside the cell and the water of the cytoplasm inside the cell. So, the phospholipids, even if they are moved and disoriented, will reorient themselves so that the heads of the phospholipids on the bottom point in toward the cell and the heads of the phospholipids on the top point out toward the watery environment surrounding the cell. The tails of each phospholipid, then, are pointed toward each other. This results in a stable arrangement because the tails are attracted to one another.

It is important to realize that the overall nature of the plasma membrane is *lipid solubility*. It acts as a lipid barrier between two very different water-based fluids—the intracellular fluid within the cell and the extracellular fluid around the cell. The water-soluble heads of the phospholipids serve to orient the phospholipid, but again, the plasma membrane is largely a lipid-soluble barrier.

Of course, phospholipids are not the only substances we find in the plasma membrane. Floating within the phospholipid bilayer, like icebergs in a sea, are proteins. Remember, proteins are large molecules. You can see several in figure 1.10, and they have different functions. Some are channel proteins. They have a little channel to let water and small water-soluble molecules in and out. Some are glycoproteins. The prefix glyco means "glucose." A glycoprotein is a protein that has a carbohydrate chain attached to it. Glycoproteins typically act as markers, allowing cells to recognize each other. For example, your immune system's cells must identify both cells that belong to you and foreign cells that must be destroyed. The glycoproteins allow for such identification. There are also receptor proteins that receive messages from other cells. For example, in order for a neuron to tell a skeletal muscle cell to contract, it must release a chemical that will bind to the receptor protein on the muscle cell. The chemical binds to the receptor. The muscle cell responds by contracting.

Additionally, glycolipids are found in the plasma membrane. Just as a glycoprotein is a protein that has a carbohydrate attached to it, a glycolipid is a lipid with a carbohydrate attached to it. These molecules help to anchor some membrane proteins in place and provide structural support to the plasma membrane.

Another molecule that is found within the plasma membrane is cholesterol. Fully one-third of the lipid part of the membrane is cholesterol. Now, cholesterol is lipid-soluble, which means it is nonpolar. So, cholesterol is found among the nonpolar tails of the phospholipids. It is important to realize that cholesterol is critical to the plasma membrane. Some people still have the idea that cholesterol is a toxin. It is not. It is true that your body can make cholesterol, and some people benefit by restricting their cholesterol intake, but cholesterol is a necessary substance that every cell membrane in every cell of our body uses for stabilization of the cell membrane. You see, the phospholipids by themselves just would not hold together for any reasonable length of time. Cholesterol gives the membrane the right degree of firmness.

This description of the plasma membrane is called the fluid mosaic model. The word fluid refers to the phospholipid bilayer. Remember, phospholipids, like all lipids, are oil-soluble molecules, so, the phospholipids form a kind of fluid. The word mosaic refers to the fact that there are many different kinds of chemicals floating within the phospholipid bilayer, especially proteins. Finally, remember that the overall nature of the plasma membrane is lipid solubility.

FUNCTIONS OF THE PLASMA MEMBRANE

What are the functions of the plasma membrane? First, it delimits the cell; that is, it holds the cell together. Second, it provides receptors so that the cell can sense its environment. These receptors are extremely important. You have probably heard of diabetes. There are two types of diabetes. In Type 1 (insulin-dependent) diabetes, the person lacks the ability to make the hormone **insulin**. Insulin signals the plasma membrane to allow glucose to enter the cells. In Type 2 (non-insulin-dependent) diabetes, which is much more common than Type 1, the receptors are not responding. There is more than enough insulin in the body, yet the cells do not respond to the insulin because the receptors either do not work correctly or are reduced in number. As a result, glucose cannot enter the cells. You can see from this example that the plasma membrane's receptors are essential to cells. The example of diabetes actually leads to the third function of the plasma membrane: selective permeability.

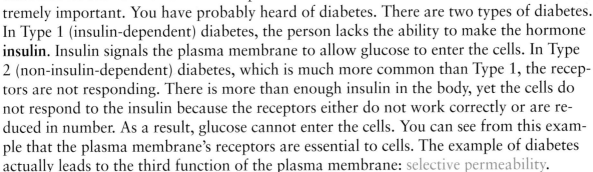

ON YOUR OWN

1.10 Suppose you placed a cell in a nonpolar fluid. Suppose furthermore that the plasma membrane was disturbed. In this kind of environment, could the plasma membrane reassemble? Why or why not?

Selective permeability—The ability to let certain materials in or out while restricting others

The definition is easy if you think of the individual words. Selective means that some things will be selected; others will not. Permeability is the ability to go through. Therefore, selective permeability is the ability to let certain materials in or out of the cell while restricting others.

What gives the plasma membrane selective permeability? There are several factors. Let's start with the easiest one first. Lipids are fats, and therefore nonpolar. Polar dissolves polar, and nonpolar dissolves nonpolar, but nonpolar cannot dissolve polar. Now, when you think of the cell membrane, think of it as largely lipid (largely oily) because the majority of it is formed by the tails of the phospholipids. So, suppose a cell encounters a small fat molecule. The fat will dissolve into the oily plasma membrane because nonpolar dissolves nonpolar. So, the fat can travel through the plasma membrane and get into the cell. As a result, fatty molecules can get into the cell rather easily (unless they are quite large). This is applicable practically. Have you heard of a nicotine patch that can help people quit smoking? This patch works by putting a drug that reduces craving for nicotine into a bandage. The patch is placed on the skin, and the skin cells absorb the drug. Why? Because the drug is nonpolar! It can travel through the plasma membranes of the closely packed skin cells.

The second reason that the plasma membrane has selective permeability is also easy to understand. It has to do with the *size* of the molecule that approaches the plasma membrane. Remember, one type of protein you find in the plasma membrane is a channel protein. As the name implies (and figure 1.10 illustrates), a channel protein has a channel running through it. Small molecules can travel through that channel. Practically speaking, that means that water, which is one of the smallest of molecules, easily moves into and out of cells. If there is too much water outside the cell, water will move in. If the cell has too much water inside, water will move out. Large molecules (such as proteins) cannot get into the channel of a channel protein, so they cannot penetrate the plasma membrane easily. There are, however, other processes that allow certain proteins into the cell. We will discuss those in a moment.

Now, the third factor that affects permeability is charge. There are various ions (charged atoms or molecules) that cells need. There are also ions that they must release. So, ions need to move into and out of cells. Small ions can go in and out through the channel proteins, as we just discussed. However, here is an amazing design. Many channel proteins are oriented so that their amino acids form a positive or negative charge within the channel. Now think about that for a moment. If the channel inside a channel protein is negatively charged, what ions will it attract? It will attract *positive* ions. If a channel protein has a positively charged channel, however, it will attract *negative* ions. So, channel proteins not only allow small molecules into and out of the cell they also can attract certain ions. Sodium ions (Na^+), for example, are important for neurons. These ions enter neurons through channel proteins whose channels are negatively charged.

While all of this is amazing, these three aspects of the plasma membrane's selective permeability are simply the easy ones. At this point, we need to talk about a more complicated aspect. For example, there are certain chemicals that cells have to have, which are slightly too big to fit into channel proteins. We are not talking about huge molecules like proteins. Instead, we are talking about molecules that are about the size of amino acids or glucose. Glucose is the favored fuel for most cells. It is the only fuel that brain cells normally use. However, glucose is too big to get into the cells through channel proteins. The fact that you are conscious (we hope!) right now means that there is a mechanism for glucose to get into cells. How does this happen? It happens with the help of carrier proteins. Carrier proteins allow certain molecules into the cell through a process called mediated transport. The best way to explain mediated transport is to start with figure 1.11.

In mediated transport, a carrier protein is designed to accept a molecule with a specific shape. More than one molecule might have that general shape, so the carrier protein may work with more than one type of molecule. In order to work, however,

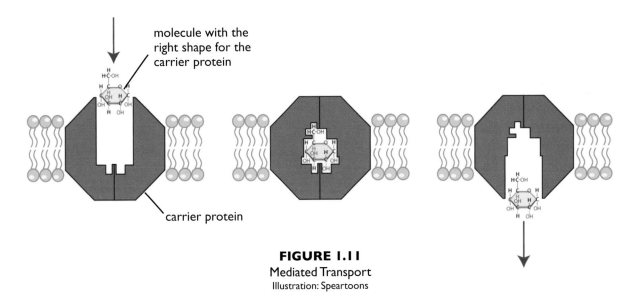

molecule with the right shape for the carrier protein

carrier protein

FIGURE 1.11
Mediated Transport
Illustration: Speartoons

the molecule must have the shape for which the carrier protein is designed. Because the molecule fits into the carrier protein, the carrier protein accepts it. In chemical terms, we say that the carrier binds to the molecule. Then, the carrier protein changes its shape so as to release the molecule on the other side of the plasma membrane. In the end, then, a molecule that could not get through the plasma membrane via a channel protein or by dissolving into the membrane can get through with the help of a carrier protein.

Although the process of mediated transport works very well, there are three conditions that must be considered: specificity, competition, and saturation. First, let's discuss specificity. The carrier protein is made for a *specifically shaped molecule*. For every molecule that must get into the cell via mediated transport, you need carrier proteins into which the molecule can fit. In other words, you need a carrier that is designed for that molecule's shape. Let's give an analogy. Suppose you needed to go to church. You might be able to walk there, but most likely, you would ride in a car. Suppose you had a pet giraffe and wanted him to come along. Could he? Of course not! A car is designed specifically to carry people, not giraffes. You can therefore think of a car as a carrier, but a carrier for people. If your church wants to attract giraffes, it would have to have carriers designed for giraffes in order to get them to church. It is the same way with carrier proteins. If the cell wants glucose, it needs carrier proteins designed to accept glucose. That is specificity.

The next consideration is competition. Suppose your neighbor's car is broken down and he asks you to take his family to church. Let's say that there are five persons in your family and three persons in his, and let's say that the car can hold six persons. If, in a very unChristian manner, everyone starts to run for the car at once, the car will fill up after six persons get into it. That will leave two persons with no way to church. That is competition. Eight persons competed for six spaces. Now, consider this. Which family will, most likely, have the best representation at church? Your family will, most likely, since it had more members. Your family had a better chance at getting into the car simply because there were more of you. The same thing happens in mediated transport. Similarly shaped molecules can compete for the same carrier protein. Remember, it is the shape that determines whether or not the carrier will bind to the molecule. If two different molecules have very similar shapes, they will be able to compete for the same carrier. Similar amino acids, for example, compete for the same carrier proteins. This is why you must eat foods that have the proper proportions of amino acids. Otherwise, competition can cause problems! Typically, whichever molecule has a high concentration will tend to win the competition because more molecules means more chances to meet up with the carrier.

Finally, let's discuss saturation. Remember, in our car analogy there is room for only six persons. If you could walk to church, all of your family and all of your neighbor's family could go. However, after six persons, the car is saturated (full). Thus, having a carrier (the car) limits the number of individuals who can be transported. In the same way, if a molecule must enter the cell through mediated transport, there is a limit to how many molecules can get into the cell within a certain period of time. When the carrier is constantly busy transporting molecules through the membrane, we say that it is saturated, because there is no way to get more molecules in any faster. On the other hand, if a carrier protein meets few molecules that can bind to it, it is not saturated and if more molecules suddenly become available, they can get inside quickly.

In the end, then, there are several factors that lead to the selective permeability of the plasma membrane. First, there is its lipid-soluble nature, which allows fat-soluble molecules to travel into the cell. Second, there are channel proteins that allow small molecules to travel through the cell membrane. Third, those channel proteins can have an overall electrical charge in their channels. That leads to channeling of specifically charged, small ions. Finally, there are carrier proteins that can transport slightly larger molecules through the membrane.

Now you should have noticed something. We have not yet told you how the cell allows in *proteins*. We have talked about carbohydrates and ions, but not proteins. Cells make their own proteins, according to the protein synthesis process discussed earlier. However, sometimes they must bring proteins in from the outside. They can certainly do that, and the plasma membrane is certainly involved, but the transport of proteins into and out of the cell involves more than just the properties of the plasma membrane. We will discuss this in the next section.

ON YOUR OWN

1.11 In each of the cases below, indicate which path (dissolving through the phospholipids, channel proteins, charged channel proteins, or carrier proteins) the molecules will take to enter the cell.

a. Chloride ions
b. Simple sugars
c. Fatty acids
d. Water molecules

MEMBRANE TRANSPORT PROCESSES

In the previous section, we noted the path by which certain molecules can get into and out of cells, but we did not discuss what causes this kind of transport to occur. That is what we will cover now. Along the way, we will also discuss how huge molecules like proteins are transported through the plasma membrane.

There are two basic kinds of transport through the membrane: passive transport and active transport. Let's talk about passive transport first. There are two basic passive processes: diffusion and facilitated diffusion. Diffusion is the movement of ions or molecules from an area of higher concentration to an area of lower concentration. The best example of diffusion in cells is probably Na^+. When we discuss the nervous system, you will see that cells are in an environment that has a greater concentration of Na^+ than what is found inside the cell. Recall that Na^+ can travel through channel proteins, typically ones with negatively charged channels. Since molecules and ions diffuse from areas of higher concentration to lower concentration, the Na^+ can travel through the channel proteins and into the cell. That is how diffusion works. In the case of another important cellular ion, potassium ions (K^+), there is a higher concentration of K^+ *inside* the cell than outside. K^+ will diffuse through channel proteins in the other direction, leaving the cell.

Now remember, this is a passive process. What does that mean? It means that the process does not require cellular energy. It simply happens as a matter of course. As mentioned previously, cells store energy as ATP. ATP is the abbreviation for adenosine (uh den' uh seen) triphosphate (try fahs' fate). Cells make ATP by taking ADP, adenosine diphosphate, and adding a phosphate. This stores energy, much like a compressed spring stores energy. When the cell needs energy, it breaks an ATP molecule back into ADP and a phosphate. That breakup releases energy, which the cell can then use for any number of tasks. Of course, that uses up an ATP molecule, and the cell will have to make another ATP molecule to replace the broken-down one. So, we often use the term ATP instead of energy when we talk about the cell. In the case of diffusion, then, we can say that the cell does not need to use any ATP.

It is not difficult to see that diffusion can work through a channel protein. You can probably even imagine how it can work if fatty molecules are simply dissolving through the membrane. What you might not realize is that diffusion will also occur with mediated transport as well. When that happens, we call it facilitated diffusion. Now think about this for a moment. Look back to figure 1.11. It is easy to see how the molecule in question gets through the membrane, but wait. Why did the molecule go into the cell? If the carrier protein can transport through the membrane, it can transport either way. Molecules can *enter or leave* the cell through mediated transport. If the direction of transport occurs according to the dictates of diffusion (the molecules are moving from a higher concentration to a lower concentration) and a carrier is required, that is facilitated diffusion.

What is so special about facilitated diffusion? Well, if the carrier protein is sending the molecules from an area of high concentration to an area of low concentration, no energy is required. It happens as a matter of course. *So, facilitated diffusion is mediated transport that requires no ATP.* In general, when glucose enters a cell, it does so via facilitated diffusion. There is almost always a higher concentration of glucose outside of the cell than inside because the cell constantly uses glucose as a fuel. The glucose molecules travel into the cell via a carrier because they are too big to enter any other way. However, since they are doing so according to the dictates of diffusion, the cell spends no ATP on the process.

Active transport is transport that requires cellular energy. The cell must break down ATP in order to get the transport to work. One of the more common modes of active transport uses a carrier, but the carrier transports substances *against* the concentration gradient; that is, from lower concentration to higher concentration. Remember, diffusion happens naturally. However, if the cell needs to move a substance from an area of lower concentration to an area of higher concentration (against the dictates of diffusion), it can do so, but that costs ATP!

Consider the following example. Remember, Na^+ travel through channel proteins and that the concentration of Na^+ is higher outside the cell than inside. As a result, the Na^+ can diffuse into the cell. This creates a problem. Cells cannot stand a high concentration of Na^+; it kills them. Therefore, even though Na^+ are constantly moving into the cells by diffusing through channel proteins, cells often need to get the Na^+ right back out again. Of course, the outside of the cell is exactly where the Na^+ do not "want" to go. After all, they diffused into the cell because molecules or ions tend to move from areas of higher concentration to areas of lower concentration. The cell must get rid of the Na^+, even though they do not "want" to leave. The only way to force the Na^+ out is to expend energy by breaking down some ATP molecules. That energy will force the Na^+ out, even though they "want" to diffuse in.

Biologists often refer to this kind of active transport as pumping. When you pump water, you are typically trying to send it the opposite way that gravity will take it. You need to spend energy pumping the water. In this kind of active transport, the cell is forcing the ions to travel opposite of the way diffusion demands, so the cell must pump the Na^+ out. This requires a carrier. The carrier binds the Na^+ and pushes them out of the cell. That takes energy, so the cell expends ATP in the process. However, it has to or the cell will die.

Let's look at the opposite situation. Cells like to have K^+ within them; in other words, they like a high concentration of K^+ inside. The concentration of K^+ outside cells is quite low. Because of this, K^+ tend to diffuse out of the cell. To counteract this, cells are constantly pumping in K^+. This requires ATP because the K^+ are going the opposite way that they would normally go. This, then, is another example of active transport. Interestingly, as you will learn when we study the nervous system, in the case of Na^+ and K^+, a single carrier, powered by ATP, pushes Na^+ out of the cell while simultaneously pulling K^+ inside, a remarkably efficient design!

There are still two more types of active transport processes to discuss. The first is called endocytosis (en' doh sigh toh' sis). Endo means "within," and cytosis means "cell." So, the definition is straightforward.

Endocytosis—The process by which large molecules are taken into the cell

We can divide endocytosis into pinocytosis (pin' oh sigh toh' sis) and phagocytosis (pha' goh sigh toh' sis). Pinocytosis, which means "cell drinking," is the process that allows proteins to enter into the cell. The proteins are dissolved in fluid around the cell. If a cell needs to take in a protein, the plasma membrane folds inward until it pinches off a vesicle. The vesicle, with the protein inside, can then travel in the cell to where the protein is needed. Pinocytosis is illustrated in figure 1.12.

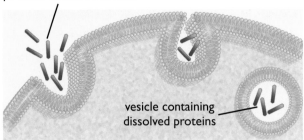

proteins dissolved in fluid

vesicle containing dissolved proteins

FIGURE 1.12
Pinocytosis
Illustration: Speartoons

Phagocytosis means "cell eating." Compared to pinocytosis (cell drinking), then, you can see that phagocytosis is used to ingest particles rather than fluids containing dissolved proteins. In phagocytosis, the cell engulfs what it is trying to take in. Not all cells can perform phagocytosis. White blood cells are probably the cells that use phagocytosis the most. They do this in order to kill foreign cells or to get rid of dead cells in our bodies. Figure 1.13 is a series of photomicrographs showing a white blood cell engulfing a yeast cell.

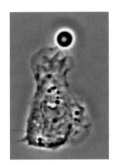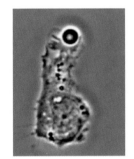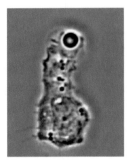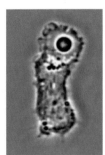

FIGURE 1.13
A White Blood Cell Ingesting a Yeast Cell
Photos © James A. Sullivan, CELLS Alive!

The last active transport process that we will discuss is exocytosis. This, as its name implies, is the opposite of endocytosis.

Exocytosis—Transportation of material from inside the cell to outside the cell using vesicles: also called secretion

The Golgi apparatus often plays a role in exocytosis. Remember, we already mentioned that the Golgi apparatus packages chemicals so they can be sent outside the cell. Well, if a cell must secrete something, this is usually started in the Golgi apparatus, as illustrated in figure 1.14.

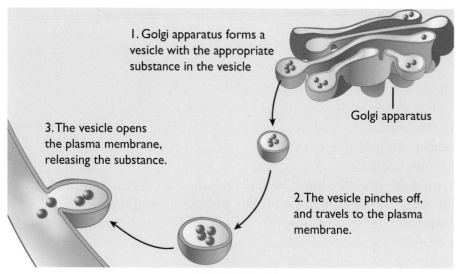

1. Golgi apparatus forms a vesicle with the appropriate substance in the vesicle

Golgi apparatus

3. The vesicle opens the plasma membrane, releasing the substance.

2. The vesicle pinches off, and travels to the plasma membrane.

FIGURE 1.14
Exocytosis
Illustration by Fairman Studios

Many cells use exocytosis to secrete important chemicals for the body's use. We already discussed cells in the pancreas that secrete insulin, which controls the facilitated diffusion of glucose by most body cells. Insulin-secreting cells use exocytosis to release their insulin.

Endocytosis (pinocytosis and phagocytosis) and exocytosis require ATP, but not because of movement from lower concentrations to higher, as in active transport of Na$^+$ or K$^+$. It is the size of the molecules that causes the cell to need ATP energy. Think of it by analogy: If someone tries to move a grand piano into or out of your living room, extra effort will need to be expended because of the sheer size of it. That extra effort has nothing to do with how many grand pianos are already inside or outside of your home.

COLORING BOOK EXERCISE 1.4

An illustration of the plasma membrane can be found on page 21 of your coloring book. Many of the different structures mentioned in your text are visible. It would be a good review to color sections q-w.

ON YOUR OWN

1.12 A chemical travels into a cell via a carrier protein. If that process required no ATP, what can you say about the relative concentration of the chemical inside and outside of the cell?

1.13 A cell uses exocytosis to secrete a hormone. This process requires ATP. What can you say about the relative concentration of the hormone inside and outside of the cell?

There is one other thing to consider when it comes to endocytosis and exocytosis. Both of them involve a breakdown of the plasma membrane. After all, consider pinocytosis. When the folded portion of the membrane pinches off, the plasma membrane is broken. What happens then? Well, remember, the phospholipids of the plasma membrane allow it to automatically reassemble. Thus, exocytosis and endocytosis work only because the plasma membrane has been so well designed. If it were not for both the polar and nonpolar property of phospholipids, the plasma membrane could never reassemble, and exocytosis (or endocytosis) would destroy the cell!

Before we end this module, please take a moment to think about what we have just discussed. In the first module alone, we have touched on several wonderfully designed processes that occur in the human body. The plasma membrane of the cell is, by itself, a wonder of chemical engineering. The processes of endocytosis and exocytosis are both incredibly complex, requiring the concerted effort of dozens of chemical reactions. All of this works smoothly over and over again in every cell of your body! As the psalmist wrote, you are truly "fearfully and wonderfully made" (Psalm 139:14, NIV)!

ANSWERS TO THE "ON YOUR OWN" QUESTIONS

1.1 Connective tissue attaches one tissue to another in your body. That's what the tendons are doing: attaching muscles to the skeleton. So, tendons are made of connective tissue.

1.2 Gross anatomy is the anatomy we can study with the unaided eye. Cells and organelles must be studied with a microscope. Even though you can see tissues with the unaided eye, to study their structures, you need a microscope. So, gross anatomy covers the whole organism, organ systems, and organs.

1.3 This is clearly a negative-feedback system because the stress (temperature decrease) results in the opposite effect (temperature increase).

1.4 The control center is the hypothalamus. Please note that you do not need to know anything about the hypothalamus to answer this question. The first paragraph tells you that the hypothalamus is part of the brain and receives information from receptors and "makes a decision." That's what the control center does.

1.5 The effector is the structure that actually causes the change that is opposite of the stress. The muscles are the effectors because they generate the heat.

1.6 In this description, no hormones are mentioned. So, based on this description, the endocrine system is not involved.

1.7 The Golgi apparatuses package chemicals to send outside the cell. Cells tend to have large numbers of particular organelles that they use frequently. So, the cell secretes chemicals.

1.8 The plasma membrane is the boundary of the cell. Therefore, it is the first structure encountered by any substance attempting to enter the cell.

1.9 Remember, each X is a chromosome and its duplicate. The replication happens during interphase, and the X shape is a result of that. In the end, then, there will be only one X shape for every chromosome, so there will be 46 chromosomes.

1.10 The plasma membrane would not reassemble. Remember, the reason the plasma membrane can reassemble is because the polar parts of the phospholipids orient toward the inside and outside of the cell because the cell's watery interior is polar, as is the watery fluid outside the cell. In this hypothetical case, the outside is nonpolar, so the phospholipids on the outer part of the membrane would not orient correctly.

1.11 a. The chloride ions, since they are charged, will go through charged channel proteins. Specifically, they will go through channel proteins carrying the *opposite* charge.

b. Simple sugars are slightly too large to readily enter cells. Glucose is an example. Since we talked about glucose needing carrier proteins, it should make sense that simple sugars need carrier proteins.

c. Fatty acid molecules are, of course, oil-soluble. So, they will dissolve through the phospholipids.

d. Water molecules go through channel proteins.

1.12 If the process required no ATP, it used no energy, which means it is passive transport. That only happens if the motion is consistent with the dictates of diffusion. So, the chemical had to move from a region of *higher* concentration to one of *lower* concentration. Therefore, the concentration of the chemical inside the cell is lower than it is outside the cell. You also could have said that the concentration of the chemical is higher outside the cell than inside.

1.13 This is a trick question. Exocytosis always requires ATP, regardless of the relative concentration of the chemical inside and outside the cell. So, you can't say anything about the concentrations.

STUDY GUIDE FOR MODULE I

1. Define the following terms:

    a. Gross anatomy

    b. Microscopic anatomy

    c. Physiology

    d. Histology

    e. Organ

    f. Tissues

    g. Homeostasis

    h. Effector

    i. Selective permeability

    j. Endocytosis

    k. Exocytosis

2. If this course taught you only the name of each organ and where it is in the body, would this be an anatomy course or a physiology course?

3. What are the seven levels of organization in a living organism?

4. Suppose you are using a 40x, 100x, 400x, 1000x microscope to study the human body. What levels of organization would you be studying?

5. What are the four types of tissue?

6. Identify the type of tissue that makes up the following:

    a. The lining of a blood vessel or your sinuses.

    b. The trapezius muscle

    c. The cartilage in your joints

    d. The frontal lobe of the brain

7. What is the general term for the processes in the environment that threaten homeostasis?

8. Suppose your heart rate began to increase significantly. If the body initiated a negative-feedback response, would your heart rate go up or down? If the body initiated a positive-feedback response, would your heart rate go up or down?

9. What two organ systems are most involved in controlling the negative-feedback systems of the body?

10. When you exercise, your blood glucose levels tend to drop because you are using the glucose for energy. To counteract that effect, the pancreas monitors your blood glucose level. If the pancreas "decides" that the blood glucose level is too low, it can release a hormone called glucagon. This hormone stimulates the liver to release glucose into the blood.

    a. What is the stress in this situation?

    b. What is the control center?

    c. What is the effector?

    d. Is the endocrine system involved?

11. List the organelles discussed in module 1, and briefly state the main function of each.

12. List the phases of mitosis in order.

13. In which phases of mitosis do chromosomes have the X shape that most people associate with chromosomes?

14. What property of phospholipids gives the plasma membrane the ability to automatically reassemble?

15. What is the function of a glycoprotein in the plasma membrane?

16. What is the function of a receptor protein in the plasma membrane?

17. The model of the plasma membrane that we discussed is the fluid mosaic model. What is the "fluid?" To what does "mosaic" refer?

18. There are essentially four basic ways a substance can get through the plasma membrane. What are they? If you get specific, you will end up listing six. That is fine, too.

19. For each of the following substances, indicate how they will get through the plasma membrane and into the cell. In this case, consider channel proteins and charged channel proteins to be different, and use the two more precise terms for endocytosis.

    a. water   c. a Mg^{2+} ion   e. an invading bacterium

    b. a protein   d. a monosaccharide (simple sugar)   f. a lipid

20. A protein enters a cell. The outside of the cell has a higher concentration of that protein than the inside of the cell. Did the protein enter through active transport or a passive transport process?

21. A glucose molecule enters a cell. The concentration of glucose inside the cell is lower than the concentration of glucose outside the cell. Did the cell use ATP to get the glucose inside?

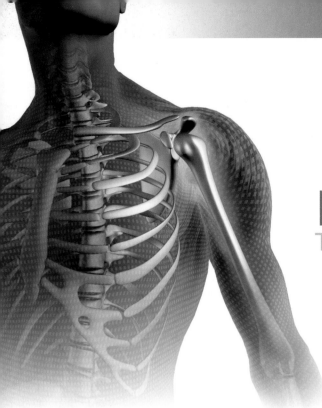

HISTOLOGY
THE STUDY OF TISSUES

Look around the room you are in and think for a minute about the building materials of which it is made. First, the room is probably lined with ceiling tiles, drywall, and perhaps carpet or floor covering. Chances are you can't see the underlying *framework* of wooden studs and joists, concrete blocks, or poured concrete. The room is probably *wired* with electricity for the lights, appliances, and so forth. If you happen to be in a library or bookstore, there might be an escalator with special steps that *move* people. What does all of this have to do with the topic of this module on tissues?

heart of the matter

Each part of your body was designed with a purpose. Your feet were designed to transport you, while your hands were made for different reasons. Yet, they are still part of your whole body. Likewise, your eyes, nose, and ears have different functions, but they work together to help you interact with your world. Your Creator arranged each part to create a whole person. Try to understand how each function contributes to who you are.

Tissues are the building materials of your body. They are groups of cells that are specialized for a particular function, as well as the extracellular material that surrounds them.

There are only four tissue types. Epithelial tissue makes up the linings of organs and forms glands. Examples include the outer layer of your skin and the linings of your mouth and stomach, and your thyroid gland, pancreas, and liver. Connective tissue supports, binds, and insulates. Examples include bone, cartilage, tendons, and fat. Nervous tissue sends and receives signals. It makes up the brain, spinal cord, and nerves. Muscle tissue allows for movement. Can you match each tissue type to the analogy of the building materials in your room? In this module, we will only discuss the first two types of tissue. The others will be addressed in later modules.

EPITHELIAL TISSUE

Let's use an analogy to begin our discussion of epithelial tissue, which covers the surfaces of many parts of your body. Imagine a tile floor made up of tiles that stick to a wooden floor below them. The tiles themselves can be thought of as cells. When those cells come together, they make *two* surfaces. The first surface is obvious; it is the surface upon which you walk. The underside of the tiles, however, makes another surface. That surface is glued to the wooden floor beneath the tiles.

In epithelial linings, cells are attached close together and form two surfaces. The first surface is like the top surface of the tile floor. It is called the free surface, and it is open to its surroundings. Anything that is passing by can come into contact with the free surface. The other surface (the underside of the cells) is called the basal surface. Just like the underside of the tile floor, the basal surface is attached to something else by some kind of glue." The epithelial cells secrete this "glue," which is called the basement membrane. Figure 2.1 has a simplified sketch and an actual photo of one type of epithelial tissue.

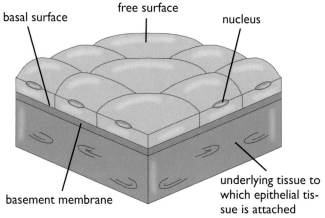
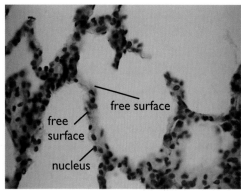

FIGURE 2.1
Simple Squamous Epithelium
Illustration: Megan Fruchte, Photo: John Skipper.

Don't worry about the figure's title for now; just look at the drawing on the left. The free surface can be thought of as the "top" of the epithelial tissue. The cells form the free surface as well as the basal surface. The basal surface is then attached to the tissue below it with the basement membrane. It is important to note that the basement membrane is avascular. What does that mean? When discussing the human body, the term vascular refers to blood vessels. The term avascular means, "lacking blood vessels." Since the basement membrane is avascular, *there are no blood vessels in the basement membrane or in the epithelial tissue!*

A question should immediately come to mind. Remember, cells are alive, and they need energy, nutrients, and oxygen in order to live. How do epithelial cells get these things if there are no blood vessels to provide them? The tissue to which the basement membrane is attached has blood vessels. These vessels release oxygen and nutrients, which then diffuse across the basement membrane and into the cells. This leads to an interesting effect in certain epithelial tissue, which we will discuss shortly.

Epithelial cells often die at a rapid rate. Consider skin cells. They constantly flake off of your skin. Dandruff, for example, is composed of dead epithelial cells from the skin of your head. These dead cells must be replaced, and that happens through mitosis. Even though the epithelial lining of your stomach, for example, is only one cell layer thick, it is replaced very rapidly by mitosis. *The ability to repair itself by mitosis is one very important characteristic of epithelial linings.*

We can classify all epithelial linings by looking at two things: the number of layers and the shape of the cells that make up those layers. If there is one layer, it is called a simple epithelium (ep uh theel' ee uhm). If there are several layers, it is called stratified epithelium. Stratified means "layered," so that name describes the many layers. If the cells in the tissue are flat, they are called squamous (skway' mus) epithelium. Squamous means "flat," or low to the ground. If the cells are shaped like a cube, they are called cuboidal epithelium. If they are tall like a column, they are called columnar epithelium. The names are all describing the shapes of the cells. Given this information, you can see how figure 2.1 gets its title. The epithelium is only one cell thick. That makes it simple epithelium. The cells are also squatty, so it is a simple squamous epithelium.

Now look at the photograph on the right of figure 2.1, which was taken with a microscope. Notice that the photograph is not nearly as easy to interpret as the drawing. This is typical in the study of human anatomy and physiology. Drawings are idealized representations that are easy to understand. The real world, however, is not so simple. First you have to realize that the ovals with no tissue in them represent open space. So, the strip of tissue being pointed out in the photo is composed of two layers of simple squamous tissue that are stuck to one another. As a result, there are two free surfaces—one facing each open space on each side of the thin strip of tissue. Also, notice that it is hard to distinguish all the parts that are shown in the drawing. That is also not unusual when it comes to looking at actual photo micorgraphs, as such photos are called.

Now, does the epithelium in figure 2.1 look like something that is going to offer a lot of protection? No. Does it look like there can be a lot of cellular machinery in there? No. Simple squamous epithelium, then, cannot be used for protection or complex tasks. However, in certain locations, simple squamous epithelium is perfect. Our blood vessels, for example, are lined with simple squamous epithelium. The tiny air sacs of the lungs are also made of simple squamous epithelium. In fact, the photo in figure 2.1 is of the air sacs of the lungs, which is why the large open spaces are visible. What's the function of simple squamous epithelial tissue? The function is to allow for diffusion. In other words, the tissue offers just a minimal barrier through which diffusion of oxygen and nutrients can occur. In our lungs, for example, oxygen moves into the blood vessels strictly by diffusion through this very delicate simple squamous epithelium. Carbon dioxide diffuses out of the blood vessels. The tissue does not offer much of a barrier, but that is by design. The thinner tissue allows more effective diffusion, so simple squamous epithelial tissue is perfectly suited for its function.

Now, let's look at another type of epithelial tissue, as illustrated in figure 2.2. Notice the difference between these cells and the ones drawn in figure 2.1. The cells are not squatty. They are shaped more like cubes. The tissue is still only one cell thick, so it is still simple epithelial tissue, but the cells are cube shaped. So, this is a simple cuboidal epithelium. Since the cells are thicker in this kind of tissue, there is more room for cellular machinery such as mitochondria, Golgi apparatuses, endoplasmic reticulum, and so forth.

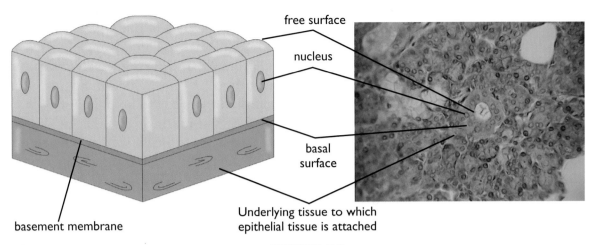

FIGURE 2.2
Simple Cuboidal Epithelium
Illustration: Megan Fruchte, Photo: John Skipper.

As a result, the function of simple cuboidal epithelium is to allow not only diffusion, but also absorption and secretion. For example, in order to cleanse your blood, your kidneys are absorbing certain substances and secreting others constantly. The tissue that you find in the kidneys is mostly simple cuboidal epithelium.

Notice also that because the cells in simple cuboidal epithelium are larger than the cells in simple squamous epithelium, you can more easily distinguish them in the photograph. The photograph is of tissue from the salivary glands, which produce saliva. This tissue cannot be made of simple squamous tissue, as the cells need the cellular machinery such as rough endoplasmic reticulum and Golgi apparatuses, to make and secrete saliva.

The next type of epithelial tissue is illustrated in figure 2.3. Notice how tall the cells are compared with the previous two types of epithelial tissue discussed.

Even though the cells are very tall, the tissue is still only one layer thick. Those tall cells are shaped like columns; therefore, this is a simple columnar epithelium. Since the cells are so much taller, there is room for even more cellular machinery. As a result, this

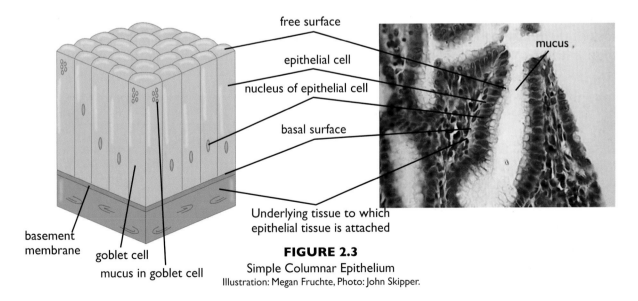

FIGURE 2.3
Simple Columnar Epithelium
Illustration: Megan Fruchte, Photo: John Skipper.

kind of tissue can perform more complex secretion and absorption tasks than simple cuboidal epithelium. Notice also that there is a new type of cell in this tissue. These cells are called goblet cells, and their main job is to produce mucus, which you can to see in the photo. Mucus is a complex mixture of fluids, proteins, and carbohydrates that covers, protects, and lubricates a free surface within the body.

Where do you find a simple columnar epithelium in the body? The lining of your stomach and intestines comes to mind right away. Your stomach fluid is very acidic because of the acid its glands secrete. This acid is necessary to begin digestion of food.

Nevertheless, stomach acid would immediately kill the epithelial cells if they were not protected. The mucus protects the epithelial lining from being damaged by the acid. So, the thick blanket of mucus secreted by the goblet cells forms a coating over the free surface, protecting your stomach. The photo on the right side of figure 2.3 is of tissue from the small intestine. You can see how tall the cells are compared with the other photos you have seen so far, and the mucus covering the free surface is also easy to see.

Before we move on to the next kind of tissue, you need to understand the beauty of histology. When we look at tissue, analyzing the structure of the tissue helps us determine its function. In simple squamous tissue, the cells are not thick enough to provide much protection. They cannot hold much cellular machinery, so squamous cells can perform only simple tasks, such as providing a thin barrier for diffusion. Cuboidal cells are larger and can, therefore, hold more cellular machinery. This increase in cellular machinery allows the cells to do more complex tasks, such as active transport and exocytosis (secretion). Finally, the tall cells of columnar tissue can perform the most complex tasks because their increased size allows for more cellular machinery.

In the end, then, you can look at tissue on the microscopic level and see the kind of task that the tissue must do. This is an incredible testament to the design ingenuity of God. He has formed just the right tissue for each function necessary in the body!

think about this

In some parts of the body, the simple columnar tissue has cilia, as well. For example, when you study human reproduction, you will learn that the egg is moved from the ovary to the uterus via the fallopian tube. The simple columnar epithelium in the fallopian tube has cilia, and the beating of those cilia moves the mucus covering the epithelium. The egg, then, is moved along with it. The cilia in a mother's fallopian tubes play a critical role in life's beginnings.

From birth I have relied on you; you brought me forth from my mother's womb. I will ever praise you.
—Psalm 71:6, NIV

COLORING BOOK
EXERCISE 2.1

Examples of simple epithelia (the plural of epithelium) can be found in your coloring book on page 23. Take this time to review what you have just learned. Color in the illustrations labeled a, b, and c.

ON YOUR OWN

2.1 A simple epithelial tissue sample has cells that produce mucus. Which type of simple epithelial tissue is it?

2.2 Order the three simple epithelial tissue types in terms of increasing distance between the free surface and the basal surface.

STRATIFIED EPITHELIAL TISSUE

Now let's move on to stratified epithelial tissue. As mentioned before, stratified epithelial tissue is layered. Figure 2.4 is an illustration of a stratified squamous epithelium.

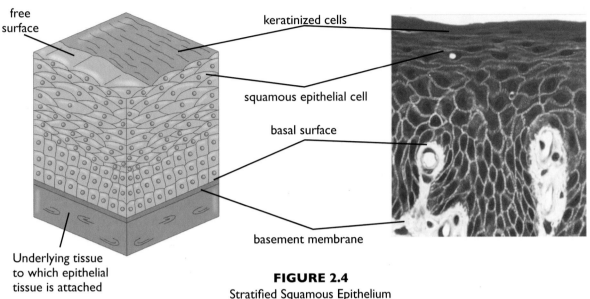

FIGURE 2.4
Stratified Squamous Epithelium
Illustration: Megan Fruchte, Photo: © Dr. Gladden Willis / Visuals Unlimited, Inc.

Notice that this tissue has several layers of cells. That is why it is called stratified. Notice also that the cells closest to the free surface are squamous cells. The deeper cells are cuboidal, but the tissue is named for the cells at the free surface. The deeper cells are called basal cells because they are nearer to the basal surface. Have you ever heard of basal cell carcinoma, a type of skin cancer? The term basal cell refers to the deepest skin cells of the epithelial layer of the skin, so basal cell carcinoma is a cancer of the skin cells close to the basal surface. Notice also that the basement membrane here is not flat, but undulates (it goes up and down like waves).

Where do you find stratified squamous epithelium? You find it in your skin! There are actually two layers to your skin. Only the top layer, the epidermis (ep uh dur' miss), is made of epithelial tissue. This tissue makes up the part of the skin that you can actually see.

What's the function of this tissue? It forms a barrier. Your skin, for example, is a formidable barrier against many things. When you soak in the bathtub, you don't worry that you will swell up from your body absorbing water. Why? Your skin is a barrier against the taking on or losing of water. It is also a powerful barrier against pathogenic microorganisms. In addition, it protects you against ultraviolet radiation.

Have you ever wondered how skin is made? The basal cells in skin are dividing by the process of mitosis, and as division takes place, the cells get pushed upward. As a result, the newer cells tend to stay near the bottom of the epithelial tissue, and the older cells get pushed upward and eventually are lost as they flake off. The cells flake off because they are dead by the time they reach the free surface of the tissue. These dead cells contain a waterproofing protein called keratin (kehr' uh tin), so, skin is called a keratinized (kuh' rat uh nized) membrane.

Why are the surface cells of the skin dead? Remember, the basement membrane is avascular. The nutrients and oxygen that keep cells alive must diffuse through the basement membrane and up into the cells of the epithelium. In a stratified epithelium, the upper cells are often too far away to get enough oxygen and nutrients, so they die. This is not always the case in a stratified squamous epithelium, however.

Although skin is an example of stratified squamous epithelial tissue that forms a keratinized membrane, there is other stratified squamous epithelial tissue whose surface cells are still alive. This kind of tissue is called moist stratified squamous epithelium because the surface cells are covered with mucus. These cells do not produce keratin, so this type of epithelium is also called nonkeratinized. The epithelial tissue in your mouth is an example of a moist stratified squamous epithelium. Even though the surface cells are alive, they still are much less active than the deeper cells because they are farther away from the source of the diffusing oxygen and nutrients.

As you might expect, the body also has stratified cuboidal epithelial tissue and stratified columnar epithelial tissue. We don't want to dwell on them, since they are really just layered versions of the simple cuboidal and simple columnar tissue, and since they are uncommon in the body. Both of these tissues offer protection and tend to be used for secretion. Stratified cuboidal epithelium is found, for example, in parts of the salivary glands that secrete saliva into your mouth, and stratified columnar epithelium is found in your larynx.

A very interesting type of stratified epithelial tissue is the stratified transitional epithelium. The word transitional in this usage means it is changeable. This tissue offers good protection because it is multilayered, but it is remarkable because it stretches. Figure 2.5 illustrates this kind of tissue.

On the left side of figure 2.5, the tissue is drawn as if it is relaxed; on the right side, the tissue is drawn as if it is stretched. Now, think about your body and where it would need protective, stretchy tissue. Where do you think this kind of tissue can be found? It is found in your urinary bladder. Your urinary bladder holds urine until you are ready to expel it from your body. When it is empty, your urinary bladder is only a little bigger than

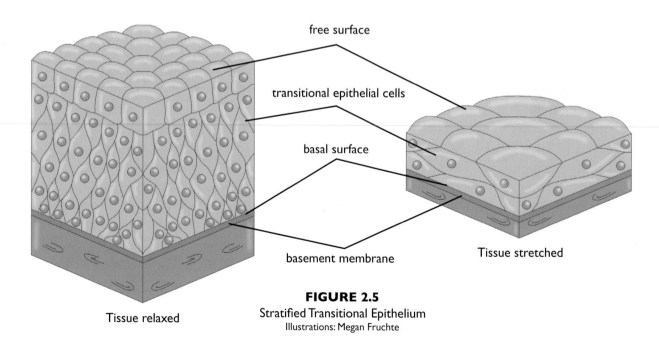

free surface

transitional epithelial cells

basal surface

basement membrane

Tissue stretched

Tissue relaxed

FIGURE 2.5
Stratified Transitional Epithelium
Illustrations: Megan Fruchte

think about this

your thumb. When it is full, it is much larger, depending on the individual. The tissue needs to be protective, but it also must be able to stretch. Notice from the figure that the tissue has many layers when it is relaxed and fewer layers when it is stretched. That should make sense. After all, when stretched, most things get thinner. It is the same with stratified transitional epithelial tissue. The cells slide with respect to one another, allowing the tissue to stretch and become thinner.

The last kind of epithelial tissue that we want to discuss is pseudostratified epithelium.

The name tells you the most important feature of this kind of tissue. Pseudo means "false," and stratified means "layered." So, this tissue is falsely layered. Looking at the figure, you can see that all of the cells touch the bottom, the basement membrane. In a truly stratified epithelium, only the cells at the bottom touch the basement membrane. The other cells are on upper layers and cannot touch the basement membrane. In simple epithelial tissue, all of the cells touch the basement membrane because they are all in just one layer. So, in some ways, this tissue is like simple epithelial tissue. Unlike simple epithelial tissue, however, some of the cells are shorter than others. As a result, not all of the cells touch

COLORING BOOK EXERCISE 2.2

Examples of stratified epithelia can be found in your coloring book on page 25. Follow the coloring directions for both a and b.

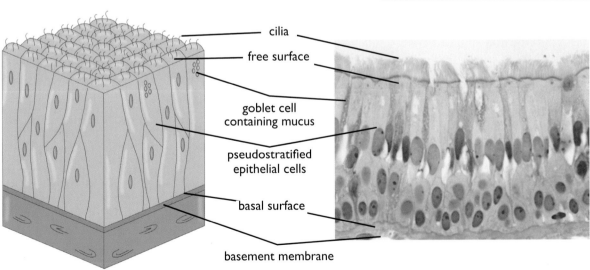

cilia

free surface

goblet cell containing mucus

pseudostratified epithelial cells

basal surface

basement membrane

FIGURE 2.6
Pseudostratified Epithelium
Illustration: Megan Fruchte; Photo: © Dr. Gladden Willis / Visuals Unlimited, Inc.

the free surface. That is more like stratified tissue. So, it is called pseudostratified. Pseudostratified epithelium has goblet cells and often has cilia.

Where do you find this kind of tissue? It is very common in the nasal passages, the air sinuses of the skull, and in the airways of the lungs. Now remember, we already told you that you find simple squamous epithelial tissue in the lungs, but that is deep in the lungs where oxygen and carbon dioxide get exchanged in the blood. In the larger airways of the lungs (the tubes through which the air travels), you find pseudostratified epithelium. What does the tissue do there? The mucus from the goblet cells traps particles from the air, and the cilia then move the particles out of the airways. This air-cleaning function is absolutely necessary to keep the lungs clean and allows for the most efficient exchange of gases farther down in the lungs.

Before we go on to the next subject, we want to give you a chance to look at some of these tissues under the microscope, provided you have a microscope. Looking at drawings and photos is good, but it is even better to have the ability to look at many different sections of tissue to see how they vary from place to place. If you have a microscope and the slide set for the course, please perform the following experiment.

GLANDULAR EPITHELIUM

In this section, you will learn what a gland is and how it works as you study the epithelial tissue found in glands. First of all, there are two types of glands: exocrine glands and endocrine glands. The prefix exo means "out of," so exocrine glands have ducts that allow them to secrete a product out to a surface. Endocrine glands, on the other hand, have no ducts. They secrete chemicals called hormones directly into the bloodstream.

Exocrine glands—Glands that secrete substances outward through a duct

Endocrine glands—Ductless glands that secrete hormones into the bloodstream

Experiment 2.1
Epithelial Tissues

Supplies:

- Microscope
- Prepared slide: human lung
- Prepared slide: human stomach
- Prepared slide: human skin (not the one with hairs or follicles)

Purpose: To explore examples of epithelial tissue

Procedure:

1. Start with the human lung slide. You should definitely see simple squamous epithelium in this slide. Depending on your slide, you might see pseudostratified epithelium as well.

2. To see the simple squamous epithelium, look at the slide under 40x magnification first. At this magnification, you should see what looks like webbed tissue: thin strands of red around large, white holes. If you see thick red tissue surrounding a round hole, do not look there. You will look there in a moment. You need to start with the thin tissue that looks like it forms webbing.

3. Once you have found one of these thin strands, increase magnification to 100x, center the thin strand of tissue, and focus.

4. Increase magnification to 400x. When you focus now, you should see that these strands of tissue have small, slightly darker circles in them. Those are the nuclei of the cells in the tissue. Notice that there are not a lot of circles piled on top of each other. There is one layer of circles in each strand. That tells you the tissue is composed of one layer of cells. The cells are small (you will see bigger ones in a moment), so this is simple squamous epithelial tissue. Draw an example of this kind of tissue in your lab notebook.

5. Go back to 40x and look for a section on the slide with thick, dark red tissue surrounding a circle. It should look quite distinct from the webbed tissue you were just observing. The tissue will be surrounding a circular white area, and the tissue will be thicker than the strands you were just examining. Your slide might not have this kind of tissue, but most will.

6. Center the tissue and increase magnification to 100x. Center it again and focus.

7. Increase the magnification to 400x and focus. Now look at the tissue surrounding the white circle. Once again, you should see darker areas that are roughly circular. Those are the cell nuclei.

8. Notice first how much taller these cells are than the ones you were looking at before. These cells are part of the pseudostratified epithelium, and because the white circle is one of the airways in the lung. The side of the cells touching the white area is the free surface. You might see what look like thin lines sticking up from the free surface of the cells. Those are cilia. The other side of the cells forms the basal surface. Notice the smooth "trail" under the basal surface. That's the basement membrane. Once again, draw a picture of this tissue.

9. Now move to the human skin slide. As mentioned in the "supplies" section, do not use the one that says "with follicles" or "with hairs."

10. Start at 40X again. Look for a wavy, purplish line in the tissue. That's the top of the dermis. The pink tissue above the line is the epidermis, which has keratinized cells. Center and focus on the purplish line of tissue at 40X.

11. Increase magnification to 100X, center, and focus.

12. Increase magnification to 400X and focus. Start examining this epithelium by looking at the free surface (top). Notice that the cells near the free surface are significantly thinner than those below. The cells below are cuboidal, and the cells above are squamous. Notice that above the line of purplish tissue, the cells do not even have nuclei. That is because those cells are filled with keratin and are dead.

13. Now look at the bottom of this purplish tissue. You should see a distinct difference between the cuboidal cells and the tissue below them. That is where the basement membrane is. Notice that the basement membrane is nowhere close to straight. Instead, it forms a "wiggly" line. You will learn more about that when we study the skin in detail.

14. Draw a picture of this stratified squamous tissue.

15. Finally, move to the human stomach slide. This slide will be harder to work with, because the tissue is harder to find on this slide.

16. Start at 40x. At this magnification, you should see red tissue and then oblong, purplish structures. Center one of those oblong, purplish structures.

17. Increase magnification to 100x, center, and focus.

18. Increase magnification to 400x, center, and focus.

19. Now look at the tissue. At this magnification, you should once again see cell nuclei. It should look to you like the oblong shapes you saw at 40x are made of long cells with a white stripe running down the middle. Because staining these cells is hard, you might not see a white stripe running down the middle of the oblong shape. Move the slide around until you find one of these oblong shapes with a white stripe running down the middle.

20. When you find that, look at the cells that surround this white stripe. Notice that the cells are tall, and that there is one cell in the layer. If the white stripe is not there, the cells have run together and there will be two layers of cells. That is just because the staining job was not done well. Once you find an oblong structure with a white stripe, in the middle, you will see that the tissue is one cell thick.

21. Draw an example of this simple columnar epithelium.

22. Put everything away!

COLORING BOOK EXERCISE 2.3

Take this time to review what you have just learned. An example of pseudostratified epithelia can be found in your coloring book on page 23. Color and label d-h.

ON YOUR OWN

2.3 If the surface cells of stratified squamous epithelial tissue are alive, is the tissue moist (nonkeratinized) or keratinized?

2.4 If the number of cells between the basal and free surfaces in stratified epithelial tissue changes, which kind of epithelial tissue is it?

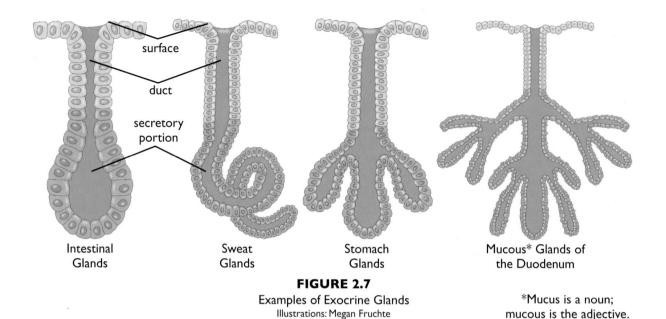

surface

duct

secretory
portion

Intestinal   Sweat   Stomach   Mucous* Glands of
Glands   Glands   Glands   the Duodenum

FIGURE 2.7
Examples of Exocrine Glands
Illustrations: Megan Fruchte

*Mucus is a noun;
mucous is the adjective.

Let's start with exocrine glands. There are many exocrine glands in the body, and they come in different shapes and sizes, as illustrated in figure 2.7. Despite their different shapes and sizes, however, they have a basic structure. They all have a secretory portion, which contains the cells that do the secreting, and they all have a duct, through which the chemicals travel to reach the surface.

The purpose of the figure is to show you the various shapes that exocrine glands can have. You need not memorize the figure. Note that regardless of the shape, they all have secretory regions and ducts through which the chemicals travel. The next figure is more important for you to learn, because it details how these exocrine glands do their jobs.

Some exocrine glands, such as mammary glands, secrete to a surface on the outside of the body. In the case of mammary glands, milk is secreted onto the surface of the skin, so an infant can ingest it. Other exocrine glands, like the ones in the stomach, secrete to a surface inside the body. For example, stomach glands secrete onto the surface inside the stomach so that their secreted chemicals can be used in digesting what is in the stomach. There are three ways that an exocrine gland can secrete chemicals, and that provides a means by which we can classify exocrine glands.

Merocrine glands—Exocrine glands that secrete without losing cellular material

Apocrine glands—Exocrine glands that have cytoplasm in their secretions

Holocrine glands—Exocrine glands that have secretions made up of disintegrated cells

Don't worry if you find these definitions hard to understand. Figure 2.8 illustrates these different modes of secretion.

Notice how the secretion occurs in the different kinds of exocrine glands. In merocrine (mer' uh krin) glands, the cells excrete the products via exocytosis, as described in module 1. Mero means "part," and crine means "secretion."

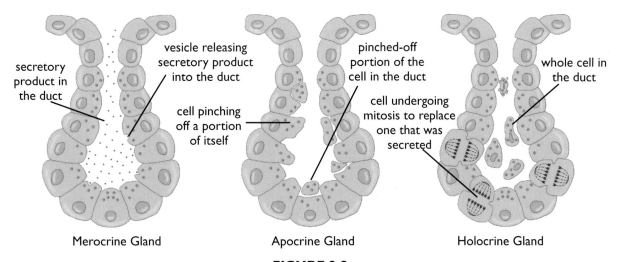

FIGURE 2.8
Merocrine, Apocrine, and Holocrine Glands
Illustrations: Megan Fruchte.

Apocrine (ap' uh krin) glands, on the other hand, actually pinch off the tip of the epithelial cell. Apo"means "apex," or "tip." That cellular material then becomes part of the secretion. That's why the definition says that cytoplasm is a part of an apocrine gland's secretions.

The holocrine (hol' uh krin) glands actually release entire cells into the duct. Holo means "whole." Those cells rupture, spilling their contents, including the nuclei, into the duct. The cells are then replaced by mitosis. So, holocrine glands actually lose cells as a result of how they work, and those cells must be replaced continually. This is not the case for the other two kinds of exocrine glands.

Where do we find examples of these exocrine glands? The sweat glands found all over your body are an example of merocrine glands. They secrete sweat, a substance with water, salt, and other products in it. Mammary glands are apocrine glands. That explains why a mother's milk is such a nutritious food. It does not just contain the chemicals made by the cell; it contains actual fragmented cell parts. The sebaceous glands of the skin are holocrine cells. They secrete oil, which conditions the skin and, at a certain time in your life, is responsible for acne since bacteria can live on these rich secretions.

Now, let's leave exocrine glands for a moment and turn our attention to endocrine glands. These are glands that secrete messenger chemicals called hormones into the blood. Remember, they have no ducts. They secrete directly into the blood. From there, the hormones can be taken rapidly all over the body in the bloodstream. So, the hormones from the thyroid gland, for example, go into the blood and can affect cells far away from the thyroid. In a future module, we will talk about how hormones can cause profound changes in cells. For now, we just want to stress how different their microscopic anatomy is compared to exocrine cells. One way to see that is to look at an illustration of cells in the pancreas, which contains both endocrine and exocrine glands.

In an endocrine gland, cells are packed close to cells. That is typical of epithelial tissue. The big difference between endocrine and exocrine glands is that there are no ducts in endocrine glands. Instead, there are just tiny blood vessels called *capillaries* running

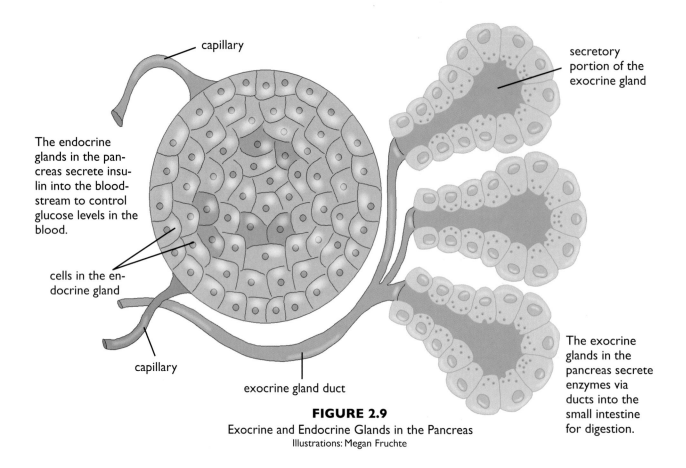

capillary

secretory
portion of the
exocrine gland

The endocrine
glands in the pan-
creas secrete insu-
lin into the blood-
stream to control
glucose levels in the
blood.

cells in the en-
docrine gland

capillary

The exocrine
glands in the
pancreas secrete
enzymes via
ducts into the
small intestine
for digestion.

exocrine gland duct

FIGURE 2.9
Exocrine and Endocrine Glands in the Pancreas
Illustrations: Megan Fruchte

through the cells. The blood takes oxygen and nutrients to the cells, but it also picks up anything the cells secrete. The endocrine cells secrete their hormones by exocytosis, as described in module 1, and the blood in the capillaries quickly carries the hormones throughout the body.

COLORING BOOK
EXERCISE 2.4
A review of glands discussed in this section can be found on page 27 of your coloring book. Please take the time to color and label a-g.

ON YOUR OWN
2.5 The secretions of an exocrine gland are examined, and it is determined that there is cytoplasm in the secretions. This narrows the type down to two. Which two types could it be?

2.6 What analysis could be done to determine which of the two types of exocrine gland is most likely being studied in the question above?

In order to get an idea of what glands look like in tissue samples, perform the following microscope experiment (If you have a microscope and slide set for this course).

Experiment 2.2
Microscopic Anatomy of
the Salivary Glands

Supplies:

- Microscope
- Prepared slide: human salivary gland

Purpose: To identify the ducts and secretory regions of the salivary glands in a tissue cross section

Procedure:

1. The salivary gland is a branched gland, somewhat like the stomach glands illustrated in figure 2.7. Under the microscope, you do not see the whole gland because you can only look at the cross section of the tissue. However, you can find the secretory portion and the ducts if you look carefully.

2. View the prepared slide at 40x. You will see strands of tissue that form a web. Look for white circles or ellipses with a thin line of dark tissue surrounding them. Center on one and focus.

3. Increase magnification to 100x and focus. You should see clusters of tiny nuclei now. Some of the nuclei will just be packed together. Others will be lined up so that they outline a white region in the tissue. They might outline a circle or shape that is more oblong. You may have to search a little, but find a line of cells that outlines an oblong, white region. Center and focus on one.

4. Increase to 400x and focus. At this magnification, you will still see clusters of cells, as well as oblong or circular regions lined with cells. The clusters of cells are the secretory portions of the glands, while the outlined white regions are ducts. Draw the duct and the secretory cells.

5. Scan the slide, looking for different ducts. You will see that either a single layer of cells or a double layer of cells lines each duct. The cells are all cuboidal, so if there is one layer of cells surrounding the duct, you are looking at simple cuboidal epithelium. If you see two layers of cells surrounding the duct, you are looking at stratified cuboidal epithelium.

6. Draw a duct and its surrounding epithelium. If you can find one with simple and one with stratified epithelium, draw both.

7. Put everything away!

CONNECTIVE TISSUE

We have spent so much time on epithelial tissue that you might have forgotten that there are three other types of tissue in the human body! If you think about it, the main functions of epithelial tissue are diffusion, absorption, secretion, and in some cases, protection. Connective tissue is quite different.

Connective tissue forms your infrastructure. In other words, connective tissue is a binding and supporting tissue that holds you up, holds you together, or binds tissues together. It can also insulate. Connective tissue has cells, just like any other tissue, but it is very different from epithelial tissue because extracellular material secreted by its cells is what gives it its special abilities. You see, connective tissue cells secrete a number of products outside of themselves. As a result, the cells are relatively far apart, with a great deal of extracellular material in between them. This is called the extracellular matrix. That makes it markedly different from epithelial tissue, which contains cells packed tightly together.

Extracellular matrix—The chemical substances located between connective tissue cells

The extracellular matrix contains a chemical mixture called the ground substance. This mixture contains special proteins that the cells secrete. In most connective tissues, these proteins attract water to make the ground substance gel-like. Also, many of these cells secrete proteins that form fibers, often called protein threads. Have you heard of collagen? One-third of bone tissue is collagen. It is a thread-like protein fiber that helps hold connective tissue together. The deep part of the skin has collagen in it that makes it firm. As collagen breaks down, the skin sags, making wrinkles. To get an idea of what connective tissue looks like under the microscope, examine figure 2.10.

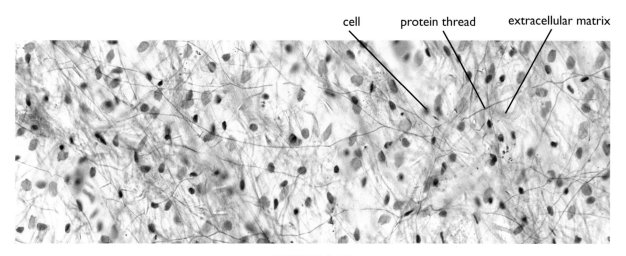

cell   protein thread   extracellular matrix

FIGURE 2.10
Connective Tissue
Photo: © Jubal Harshaw

How do we classify connective tissue? We classify it based on what the extracellular matrix is like because the extracellular material gives it its function. Is it hard? Is it flexible? Is it stretchy? Connective tissue is one of four basic types: connective tissue proper, cartilage, bone, and blood. Yes, blood is a connective tissue. You might find that a little odd, but it is true! Isn't connective tissue supposed to bind and support? Yes, and blood does do that. Just get a cut, and you will see that blood has the ability to bind. It forms a clot that stops the blood. Blood is a connective tissue because it does help hold us together. An extensive dicussion of bones and blood will follow in a later module.

CONNECTIVE TISSUE PROPER

Let's start with connective tissue proper. There are four basic types of connective tissue proper: loose connective tissue, adipose tissue, dense irregular connective tissue, and dense regular connective tissue. Loose connective tissue is illustrated in figure 2.11.

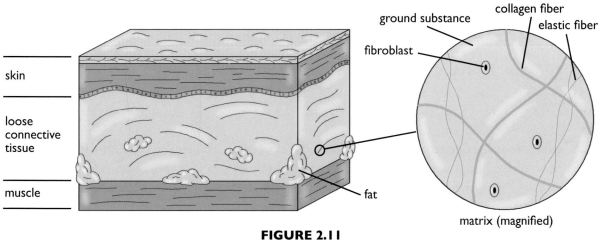

skin

loose connective tissue

muscle

fat

ground substance   collagen fiber   elastic fiber

fibroblast

matrix (magnified)

FIGURE 2.11
Loose Connective Tissue
Illustrations: Megan Fruchte

53

Loose connective tissue is characterized by a ground substance that is gel-like. It has some protein, some fluid, and collagen fibers. Collagen is also a protein, but it is very important in connective tissue, so we usually mention it separately from other proteins. There are also elastic fibers that are made of protein, and they are like rubber bands. They allow the connective tissue to be stretched. Now remember, this entire extracellular matrix (the proteins, fluid, and collagen) comes from the cells that make up the tissue. We call these cells fibroblasts.

Fibroblasts—Spindle-shaped cells that form connective tissue proper

As a minor point of terminology, a connective tissue cell is actually a fibroblast only while the connective tissue is developing. Once the fibroblast is completely surrounded by the matrix, it is called a fibrocyte.

The function of loose connective tissue is light-duty binding. It is not very strong, but it is flexible. If you pull on your skin, the force you feel pulling back is the loose connective tissue that connects the skin to the underlying muscle. So, this connective tissue holds things together in all directions, but just very lightly. By analogy, it is like the thin material that forms nylon hose. As you might guess, a bassett hound with its saggy, baggy skin has very little loose connective tissue holding that skin on!

The skin itself has another type of connective tissue proper: dense irregular connective tissue, illustrated in figure 2.12.

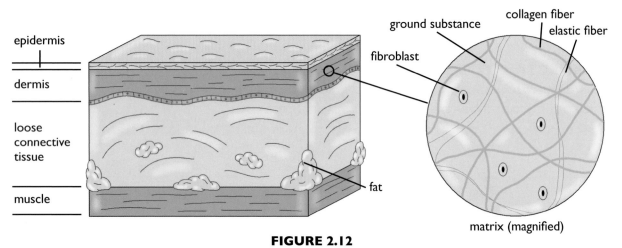

FIGURE 2.12
Dense Irregular Connective Tissue of the Dermis
Illustrations: Megan Fruchte

The skin can be divided into two layers: the epidermis of stratified squamous epithelium and the dermis. The loose connective tissue just discussed is often called the hypodermis, but it is not a part of the skin. The dense irregular connective tissue *is* part of the skin, and it is the dermis. The term dense in "dense irregular connective tissue" is the opposite of loose. It has to do with how many collagen fibers there are. You can see from the last two figures that the main difference between dense irregular connective tissue and loose connective tissue is that the former has significantly more collagen than the latter. The term irregular refers to the fact that the collagen fibers are oriented in all directions.

What is the function of dense irregular connective tissue? Well, it has strength in all directions. Think about the cloth in a pair of jeans. You can pull cloth this way, you can pull it that way, you can pull it the other way, and it won't tear. Your skin also does not tear very easily. The dense irregular connective tissue in the dermis gives your skin strength in all directions. You will also find dense irregular connective tissue in capsules around organs. Many organs, such as the kidneys, will have a thin, but tough, capsule. Think of it as the fibers going in all direction, giving the organ strength this way, that way, and the other way.

As you might expect, dense regular connective tissue (illustrated in figure 2.13) is similar to dense irregular connective tissue. The term regular, however, means that the collagen fibers are lined up mostly in the same direction. You can see that from the magnified sketch of the matrix in the figure. Also, although there are fibroblasts in this tissue, there are no elastic protein fibers in dense regular connective tissue. That is because strong binding is the main function for this kind of tissue, so it provides rope-like strength. Now how is a rope strong? Obviously, you cannot stand something on top of the cut end of a rope. The rope cannot bear weight and will bend. When you pull on a rope, however, it is very, very strong. That is called tensile strength.

Where do you think you need this type of tissue? Well, one place you need it is in your tendons. As illustrated in figure 2.13, tendons hold muscle to bone. It is really hard to pull a tendon off the bone. You can injure it a little, and when you do, it hurts! But tendons are very strong. Dense regular connective tissue also forms your ligaments. Ligaments attach bone to bone. Once again, you need something strong holding your bones together, so dense regular connective tissue is used to make your ligaments. Of course, there is some give in your tendons and ligaments. That is because the collagen fibers are wavy when relaxed, but not because there are elastic fibers.

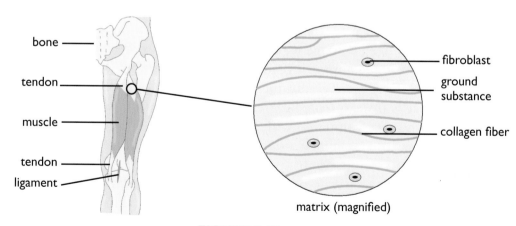

FIGURE 2.13
Dense Regular Connective Tissue
Illustrations: Megan Fruchte

The final type of connective tissue proper is adipose (ad' ih poce) tissue. Adipose tissue, illustrated in figure 2.14, is the technical term for fatty tissue.

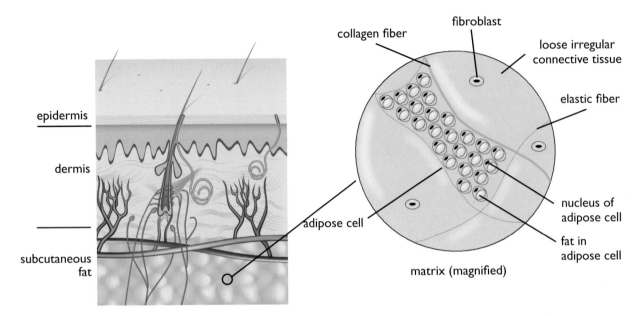

FIGURE 2.14
Adipose Tissue
Illustrations: Megan Fruchte

Adipose tissue is actually most similar to loose connective tissue. It has all of the materials of loose connective tissue, but the cells are adipocytes, or fat cells. The fat cells fill with a droplet of oil, enlarging them, and then pushing them close to one another. As a connective tissue, its functions are support, protection, and insulation. Even if you are quite thin, you have a substantial amount of fat supporting each kidney. That way your kidneys are held firmly in place and are well protected. Adipose tissue can also be found under the skin, where it acts as insulation against the outside temperature. Think of it as Bubble Wrap. It supports and protects what it covers, and it also insulates it from temperature changes!

Although it seems like everyone wants as little fat as possible, adipose tissue has a metabolic function beyond supporting, protecting, and insulating. It is a compact way of storing nutrients for future energy production because the oils stored in each fat cell are energy-rich. If fat cells instead stored carbohydrates as future fuel, it would take about three times as much space compared with fat (oil) storage. All of its functions are crucial to the body, and too little fat can be a dangerous thing. Of course, too much fat can be dangerous, too, so you should not have too much or too little!

Before we leave this discussion of connective tissue proper, we want to make a point about how connective tissue heals. If you have ever injured a tendon or a ligament, you know that such tissue heals very slowly. Why? Look at the cells (the fibroblasts) in the previous drawings. They have to produce a large amount of extracellular material. As a result, it takes longer to heal connective tissue proper than epithelial tissue. In epithelial tissue, all the cells can undergo mitosis and heal. In connective tissue, the cells have a big job to do in producing new extracellular matrix. As a result, it can take a long time to heal even a minor injury to connective tissue proper.

ON YOUR OWN
2.7 Name the connective tissue proper which has a function similar to these household items below:

a. Duct tape
b. Masking tape
c. A thick, warm blanket
d. The string on a kite

CARTILAGE

Feel the bridge of your nose. Bend your outer ear. Bend from the waist. You are dealing with the three types of cartilage: hyaline (hi' uh lin) cartilage, elastic cartilage, and fibro-cartilage. What do they have in common? They have chondrocytes (kon' droh sights), which are the cells that produce special extracellular material. Chondro is the root word meaning cartilage, so chondrocytes are mature cartilage cells.

Cartilage is firmer than connective tissue proper. The bridge of your nose, the outer part of your ear, and the disks between your backbones are all made with cartilage. Since cartilage matrix is firm, the cell cannot live directly in the matrix. Instead, there are small, hollowed-out spaces in which the cartilage cells live, and each space is called a lacuna (la' koon uh). Notice the difference between the cartilage and the other tissue in the picture taken through a microscope of tissue from the trachea (windpipe).

cartilage

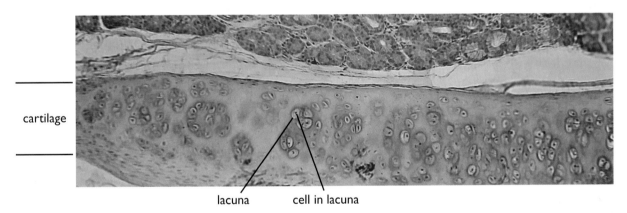

lacuna   cell in lacuna

FIGURE 2.15
Cartilage in the Trachea
Photo: © Jubal Harshaw

The extracellular matrix of cartilage is different from that of connective tissue proper. First, connective tissue proper is vascular; cartilage is avascular. That is, it has no blood supply. This means it has to be thin because chondrocytes are living cells, which need to receive oxygen and nutrients. Since there are no blood vessels in the matrix, oxygen and nutrients must diffuse through it, so the extracellular matrix cannot be very thick. If it gets very thick, it dies. In fact, what most often happens is that it is replaced by bone, and bone has a blood supply that it brings along with it.

Like connective tissue proper, the cartilage matrix contains collagen. The first type of cartilage, hyaline cartilage, is illustrated in figure 2.16.

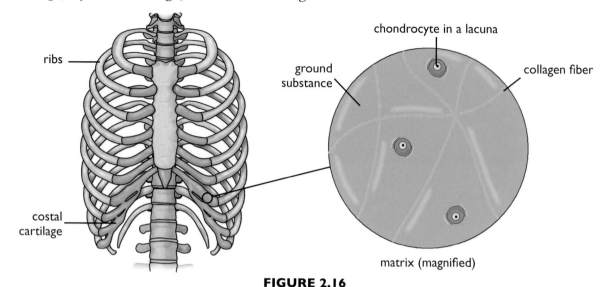

FIGURE 2.16
Hyaline Cartilage
Illustrations: © blamb (left); Megan Fruchte

Even though we now know that hyaline cartilage has collagen in it, the collagen is hard to see under the microscope. It does not stain easily in a slide, and when the light shines through it, you cannot see it. Nevertheless, it is there, which is why it is drawn in the figure. The collagen gives the hyaline cartilage its resiliency. As we already mentioned, its ground substance is firm. So, we have a tissue that is both firm and resilient. In fact, it functions like hard plastic. It can form a hard, but resilient, framework.

Where do we need this kind of tissue? Well, the bridge of your nose and the framework of your larynx contain it. You can feel it in both. As illustrated in Figure 2.16, it also makes up the costal cartilage of the ribs, which connects the ribs to the sternum. Finally, its smoothness makes it ideal to form caps on bones within movable joints. This allows the joints to move without friction, as smooth hyaline cartilage slips against smooth hyaline cartilage with only a lubricant in between.

Now let's look at fibrocartilage in figure 2.17. As the name implies, it is packed with collagen. Notice that the collagen fibers are mostly parallel to one another. The magnified matrix looks much like dense regular connective tissue, but there are differences. One big difference is that in dense regular connective tissue, the cells do not have to be in lacunae (the plural of lacuna). That's because the matrix is not firm in dense regular connective tissue as it is in cartilage.

Fibrocartilage is found in the joints between each vertebra of the backbone, as shown in figure 2.17. What is the function? Fibrocartilage provides tough binding and resilient support. Perhaps the best analogy is the soles of your shoes. If they are rubber or some rubber-like material, they are quite tough. The soles are attached firmly to the upper part of your shoe and do not wear out as you walk across rough surfaces, such as gravel. At the same time, however, they provide a certain amount of cushioning, or resiliency. That is what we need in the joints of the backbone. The vertebrae must be bound together with a tough binding, but there must be enough resiliency to cushion your spinal column as you walk, bend, or jump.

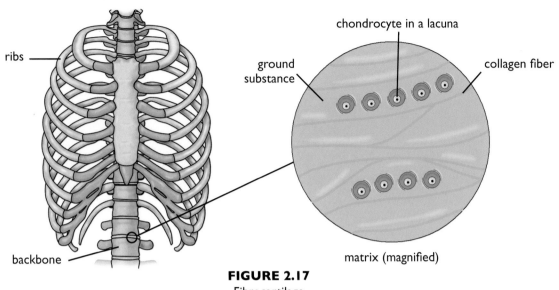

FIGURE 2.17
Fibrocartilage
Illustrations: © blamb (left); Megan Fruchte

Elastic cartilage is different from the other two types of cartilage because there is not as much collagen in it. Instead, the fibers in elastic cartilage are (you guessed it) elastic fibers.

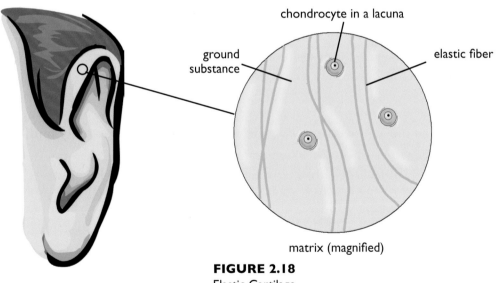

FIGURE 2.18
Elastic Cartilage
Illustrations: © blamb (left); Megan Fruchte

The elastic fibers in elastic cartilage are stretchy, like a rubber band. That gives elastic cartilage the characteristics of soft plastic. Its function, then, is highly flexible support, as in the outer ear. The very tip of the nose is also made of elastic cartilage. Wiggle it (with your fingers, of course). If you have ever owned a puppy whose floppy ears gradually became erect as it grew older, you were observing the slow growth of connective tissue: in this case, elastic cartilage.

**COLORING BOOK
EXERCISE 2.6**
A review of our discussion on cartilage can be found in your coloring book on page 33. Make time to review, color, and label sections a-g.

ON YOUR OWN
2.8 If you are looking under the microscope and are having a hard time distinguishing between cartilage and connective tissue proper, what one thing could you find to positively identify the tissue as cartilage?

BONE AND BLOOD

Although we are going to concentrate on bone tissue and blood in later modules, we do want to spend just a moment on them now. Bone tissue, which is a connective tissue, is properly known as osseous tissue. Like any other connective tissue, osseous tissue contains cells that are far from one another. These cells secrete ground substance, fibers, collagen, and fluid. The ground substance in bone is unusual in that it becomes hardened through a process called calcification.

Blood is properly known as vascular tissue, and it is definitely a connective tissue. It fits the criteria perfectly. It has cells (red and white blood cells), which are not packed tightly together like epithelial cells are, a ground substance (the proteins in blood), and fluid (blood plasma). Blood even has fibers. Normally, the blood proteins that form fibers are small and round, but if stimulated by an injury, they can join together like strings of beads to form long, tangled fibers, creating blood clots.

MEMBRANES

Let's take the two main tissue types you have studied so far and put them together by discussing membranes. Membranes are made of epithelial tissue, as well as connective tissue. Consider, for example, your skin, the cutaneous membrane. The top layer of your skin, called the epidermis, is stratified squamous epithelial tissue. The lower layer, called the dermis, is dense irregular connective tissue. Below those layers, we usually find another connective tissue, loose connective tissue.

We can divide the membranes in the body into three categories: mucous membranes, synovial (sih no' vee al) membranes, and serous (seer' us) membranes. Mucous membranes line the entire digestive tract from the mouth to the anus. They line the respiratory tract, the urinary tract, and the reproductive tracts. What do all of these have in common? They all open to the outside of the body. The digestive system opens to the outside at both ends: the mouth and anus. The respiratory system opens to the outside at the nose and mouth, and so on.

So, the function of mucous membranes is to line tubes that open to the outside of the body. What does this accomplish? It protects the body. Consider, for example, the membranes of the respiratory tract. When you breathe in air, there may be dust and dirt that come in with the air. The mucous membranes in your respiratory tract trap these foreign particles and move them back out of your body. Synovial membranes are found around the movable joints and are also used for lubricating. The bones in a joint are covered with a cap made of hyaline cartilage. Hyaline cartilage is quite smooth, so it allows the bones of the joint to move without bone rubbing against bone. Even though hyaline cartilage is smooth, our joints must be very efficient in their use of energy during movement. Since the bones in a joint must move easily, the hyaline cartilage is lubricated by synovial fluid. The synovial fluid is secreted by the synovial membranes, which form a little sac around the sides of the joints.

Serous membranes are probably less familiar to you. However, it is easy to see what they do. Think about what happens when you move. When you twist and turn, for example, the organs in your abdomen move over each other. In fact, there is a lot of motion in most of your organs. When you bend over, for example, you actually shove your liver around! Think about your heart. It is always moving. Your lungs are moving every few seconds. Your stomach churns food, and your intestines squeeze digested food along. Now, there are some organs that do not move much, such as your kidneys. They are held firmly in place with adipose tissue. However, there is a surprising amount of organ movement within the chest and abdomen.

With all of this movement going on, the organs are going to rub up against each other quite a bit! What happens when surfaces rub against each other? Friction! If there were not something lubricating the organs as they rubbed up against each other, they would quickly get rubbed raw. So, now you know the function of serous membranes. They form thin, double layers around organs and secrete a small amount of lubricating fluid into the space between the layers. This reduces the friction between organs. Not surprisingly, we find them around the heart, the lungs, and many abdominal organs.

Now, stop and think about all that you have learned so far in this module. Epithelial tissue and connective tissue have been perfectly designed in many different ways to do very specific jobs in the body. Some epithelial tissue is thin (where it needs to be thin); other epithelial tissue is thick (where it needs to be thick). Some stratified epithelial tissue is keratinized (where it needs to be), and other stratified epithelial tissue has living cells on the surface (where it needs to have living cells). Then, there is connective tissue. Connective tissue is designed to be flexible where it needs to be flexible, strong where it needs to be strong, and resilient where it needs to be resilient.

These two incredibly well-designed tissues work together to form membranes that protect and lubricate the body as needed. Suppose you had all of the muscles and joints in your body, but your organs were not covered with serous membranes. You could move, but it would be incredibly painful. If the tips of the bones in your joints were not covered with hyaline cartilage, the bones would rub together in a painful way! If the joints were not self-lubricating via synovial membranes, you could move,

think about this

In order to understand just how amazing your body is, compare the joints in your body to the moving parts in an automobile that rub up against each other, much like the bones in a joint rub up against each other. Those parts are not cushioned like bones are, however. If they were, the automobile would not break down and need replacement parts nearly as often. Also, automobiles use oil, like joints use the secretions of the synovial membranes, to lubricate the moving parts. However, automobiles do not make their own oil! Even a marvel of technology like an advanced automobile is primitive compared to the human body!

ON YOUR OWN

2.9 Indicate what kind of membrane you would find lining the surface of each of the following structures:

a. The heart
b. The elbow joint
c. The colon, which leads to the anus

but how painful it would be! And, you would die rather quickly if your mucous membranes were not protecting you from the hazards of the outside world. Finally, without your wonderful cutaneous membrane, you would dehydrate before the end of the day!

As you read this text, remember that you began life as a single cell. Stop and contemplate for one moment your wonderful Creator. That single cell underwent mitosis to form many cells. Those cells each received instructions on how to differentiate and specialize so that they could form the tissues and membranes that are perfectly designed for their individual tasks.

TISSUE REPAIR

The last topic we want to tackle in this module is tissue repair. Most of us got our introduction to how this works when we were little kids. We looked at our little knees, which we skinned when we fell down. Over a period of days, we watched confidently as they healed. This is probably the most amazing process in the human body! It is a process that human science cannot duplicate. Imagine what we could do with a machine that repairs itself! Unfortunately, what is commonplace in our bodies is still out of reach for human technology!

Tissue repair obviously means replacing damaged tissue, but you need to realize that there are different kinds of repair. When an individual survives what laymen call a heart attack, it means that the blood supply has been cut off to a part of the heart, and some heart cells have died. Will the person then be left with a hole in his or her heart? No, of course not. If the person survives, the heart will repair itself. However, the damaged part is replaced by scar tissue. It will not contract like healthy heart tissue does. When you have an ordinary cut on your skin, however, it heals right up, and that part of the skin will be just as good as new. So, there are actually two different kinds of tissue repair. There is the kind of repair in which you get function back (like when you cut your skin), and there is the kind of repair in which you get scar tissue, which does not function like the original tissue.

You can understand these two different kinds of repair if you make a distinction between two different kinds of cells: stromal (stroh' muhl) cells and parenchymal (pair en ky' muhl) cells.

Stromal cells—"Supporting" cells that provide structure or support for parenchymal cells

Parenchymal cells—"Performance" cells that provide the actual function of the tissue

We can say that tissues are generally made up of structural cells that form the infra-structure. Those are the stromal cells. The parenchymal cells, on the other hand, actually do the work that that tissue is designed to do. For example, the liver does many, many things. One of the many things it does is secrete bile. The kinds of cells that secrete bile are parenchymal cells. Meanwhile, there is a delicate network of connective tissue that is produced by stromal cells in the liver. This allows the liver to hold its shape. Now, suppose the liver is damaged. What kinds of cells need to be restored in order for the liver to continue doing its job? The parenchymal cells.

In order for function to be restored to an organ, the parenchymal cells need to be restored. If stromal cells end up repairing the damage, it will be better than nothing at all, but the organ will not function as well as it used to. By analogy, if a windstorm damages the roof on your house, it could be fixed with a piece of plywood, or it could be covered with the exact type of shingles that blew off. Which is better? The shingles of course! That is parenchymal repair. Yet, stromal repair (scar tissue) is better than nothing, just as repairing the roof with plywood is better than no repair at all.

What determines whether parenchymal or stromal cells get restored? Well, the cells in different tissues have different abilities to regenerate. Generally, we can say that a cell will fall into one of three categories when it comes to regeneration.

Labile cells—Cells that undergo mitosis regularly and quickly

Stable cells—Cells that do not regularly undergo mitosis but are able to if the need arises

Permanent cells—Cells that cannot undergo mitosis

The cells of epithelial tissue are always undergoing mitosis and are therefore labile cells. So, if you get a little sore in your mouth for some reason or other, it does not take months to heal. The mouth is lined with epithelial tissue that regenerates quickly due to the constant mitosis that is taking place.

The cells in your bones are examples of stable cells. Once a bone is formed, the cells generally just stay put. However, if you break a bone, the damage and the loss of blood supply will kill bone cells. Clearly, the dead bone cells cannot undergo mitosis, but their neighbors can. They will undergo mitosis to repair the injury.

The cells of nervous tissue are examples of permanent cells. After babyhood, they cannot undergo mitosis. Skeletal and cardiac muscle cells are also examples of permanent cells.

Now, let's get back to the two examples we mentioned earlier. When someone survives a heart attack, some heart cells die. Can they regenerate? No, they are permanent cells. As a result, there is no mitosis of neighboring cells to replace the damaged muscle cells. Instead, replacement with fibroblasts occurs, which produce connective tissue. This does heal the wound, but it does not heal it in a functional way. In the end, then, a certain amount of function is lost. Now, can people have restoration of good health after a heart attack? Yes. The remaining cells can be strengthened through exercise, but what's gone is gone. However, when you cut your skin, you are cutting labile cells. These cells undergo mitosis constantly, so neighboring cells will start reproducing so as to replace the cells lost.

Let's put this in terms of the vocabulary just learned. In the heart, the parenchymal cells are permanent cells. So, when they are destroyed, they cannot be replaced. As a result, they are replaced with stromal cells. This heals the wound, but since stromal cells replace parenchymal cells, function is lost. In the skin, the parenchymal cells are labile. So, when you lose parenchymal skin cells, they are replaced with parenchymal skin cells, and no function is lost. Bone and glands contain stable cells that can undergo mitosis if necessary.

ON YOUR OWN

2.10 Suppose a structure in the body is injured, but, after a fairly long time, it heals so that it is 100 percent functional again. Are its parenchymal cells most likely labile, stable, or permanent?

Tissue repair can also be affected by other factors. Better circulation leads to better tissue repair. Why? Blood brings in nutrients and oxygen, takes away the wastes, and brings in the white blood cells to fight infection. The better the circulation is, the better the healing. Better nutrition also means better tissue repair. Proteins and vitamins are critical for proper tissue repair. Later on in the course, you will learn about which vitamins affect which tissues. For right now, consider vitamin C. It is required for the production of collagen. So, if you need connective tissue repair, you need vitamin C.

Age is another factor that affects tissue repair. Children have growth on their side. Adults in the prime of their lives heal very well, but as we all know, as old age approaches, the healing process is much slower. Nevertheless, healing ability a testament to the power and forethought of the Creator who made your body.

ANSWERS TO THE "ON YOUR OWN" QUESTIONS

2.1 If it has mucus, it is simple columnar epithelium. That is the only type of simple epithelial tissue that has goblet cells.

2.2 In simple epithelial tissue, the distance between the free surface and the basal surface is determined by the size of the cell. So, the order is: simple squamous, simple cuboidal, simple columnar.

2.3 If the cells are alive, the tissue is moist (nonkeratinized).

2.4 Stratified transitional epithelium can stretch because the cells slide relative to one another. This causes the cells to spread out, meaning that there are fewer cells between the two surfaces.

2.5 If there is cytoplasm, it could be an apocrine gland or a holocrine gland. Both put cellular material into the secretion. In apocrine glands, it is just a part of the cell. In holocrine glands, it is the whole cell. Since both put cellular material in the secretions, and since cytoplasm is everywhere in the cell, they both have cytoplasm in their secretions.

2.6 To determine whether the gland is apocrine or holocrine, look for remnants of DNA in the secretions. If there are significant amounts of DNA, it is holocrine, since the whole cell is dumped into the secretion. In apocrine glands, the nucleus is never a part of the secretion, so there would not be easily detectable amounts of DNA in the secretion.

2.7 a. Duct tape is used to hold things together tightly, no matter what direction from which they are pulled. This is like dense irregular connective tissue, which provides strength in all directions.

   b. Masking tape allows for light-duty binding. That is like loose connective tissue.

   c. A thick, warm blanket insulates you from the cold. That is like adipose tissue.

   d. A string has tensile strength that holds the kite. That is like dense regular connective tissue.

2.8 Look for the cells residing in small pockets (lacunae). Remember, the ground substance in cartilage is firm, so the cells need lacunae in which to live.

2.9 a. Organs are typically surrounded by serous membranes for movement.

   b. Joints are surrounded by synovial membranes for lubrication.

   c. Tubes that open to the outside are covered with mucous membranes.

2.10 The parenchymal cells are stable. Since it heals to 100 percent functionality, they cannot be permanent. They are not labile, however, or the healing would be rather quick.

STUDY GUIDE FOR MODULE 2

1. Define the following terms:
   a. Exocrine glands
   b. Endocrine glands
   c. Merocrine glands
   d. Apocrine glands
   e. Holocrine glands
   f. Extracellular matrix
   g. Fibroblasts
   h. Chondrocytes
   i. Stromal cells
   j. Parenchymal cells
   k. Labile cells
   l. Stable cells
   m. Permanent cells

2. What are the four basic types of tissue?

3. What two factors determine the distance from the free surface to the basal surface in epithelial tissue?

4. What is the basement membrane?

5. Is the basement membrane vascular or avascular? How do the epithelial cells get oxygen and nutrients?

6. Identify each epithelial tissue drawing below. Give the tissue's main function and at least one place it can be found in the body.

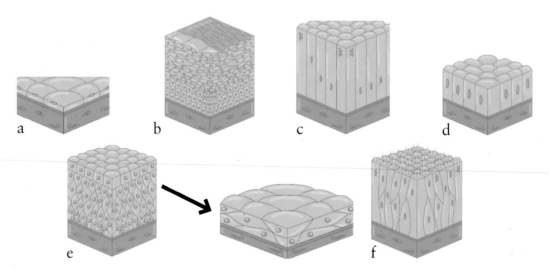

7. Which kind of exocrine gland has no cytoplasm in its secretion?

8. What are the four types of connective tissue?

9. What protein is found in all connective tissue proper?

10. Identify the connective tissue proper by the sketch of its microscopic structure. Give its function and one place in the body where it is found.

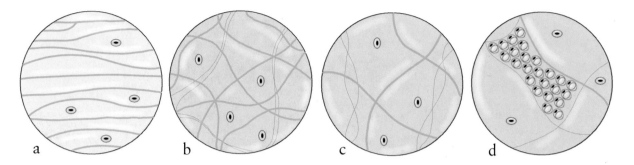

11. Why do chondrocytes need a lacuna?

12. Identify the cartilage by the sketch of its microscopic structure. Give its function and one place in the body where it is found.

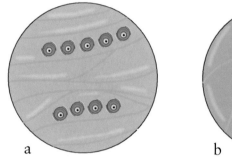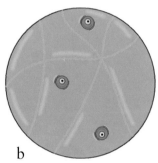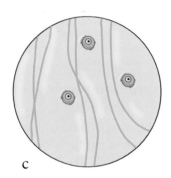

13. Where, in general, will you find serous membranes? What about mucous membranes? What about synovial membranes? What does each type of membrane accomplish?

14. An organ's parenchymal cells are labile. If the organ is damaged, will it be as good as new once it heals?

15. In general, are connective tissue cells parenchymal or stromal?

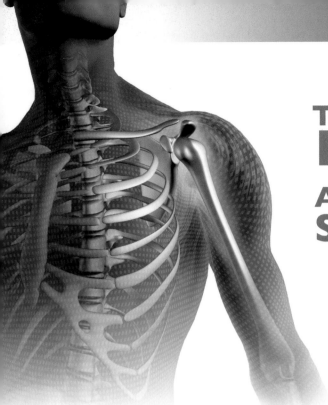

THE INTEGUMENTARY AND SKELETAL SYSTEMS

ow that you have an overview of your body's organization and know something about your body's tissues, it is time for us to begin discussing the organ systems one by one. Although there are other ways by which human anatomy and physiology can be taught, we think that this approach makes the most sense. In our "tour of the organ systems," we want to start with a discussion of skin. Although you might not think about it that way, skin is, indeed, an entire organ system. It is called the integumentary (in teg' you men' tuh ree) system.

heart of the matter

You were created with many different sense organs, but most of them are confined to a specific area of your body. Your skin, however, monitors many different stimuli every moment, and it does this for your entire body! It is strong enough to withstand vigorous activities such as running, and yet sensitive enough to feel the slightest breeze on a warm summer day. With just the tips of your fingers, you can distinguish between cold and hot, smooth and rough, soft and hard. Sometimes our eyes can be fooled, but proof can be tangible with touch.

If you think about all of the things that your skin does for you, it is truly amazing! Skin provides protection from the sun, thermal stress, and infections. It is thin but very tough. It is the thinnest over the eyelids, where it is about 0.02 of an inch thick, and it is thickest on your back and shoulders, where it is about 0.2 of an inch thick. It also has "pleats" and "allowances" so that it doesn't rip when you bend your elbow or your knee. Your skin is waterproof, so that when you want to take a long soak in the bathtub, you do not gain a few pounds of water weight! It is also self-conditioning throughout. Now, sometimes the self-conditioning fails a little in cold weather. When that happens, your skin cracks. However, that brings up another feature of the skin: It is self-mending throughout. Even though it can crack or be cut, it does mend itself! It can even cool off the rest of the body through the process of sweating. It comes in a variety of shades (all of them beautiful), but the lighter shades are more easily damaged by ultraviolet rays if not cared for properly. On the other hand, those ultraviolet rays enable the skin to begin the manufacture of the "sunshine vitamin," vitamin D. New research shows that in addition to vitamin D's well-known ability to help get calcium into the body, it also has important anti-inflammatory and even anti-cancer effects. That's the skin—a truly wonderful organ system!

THE BASIC STRUCTURE OF SKIN

The integumentary system is made up of the skin and the appendages to the skin: the glands, the hair, and the nails. Figure 3.1 illustrates the structure of this system.

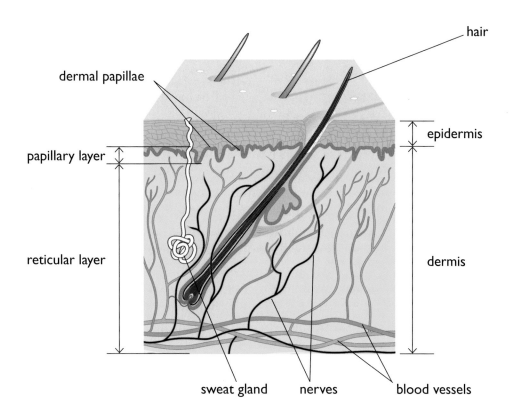

FIGURE 3.1
The Structure of Skin
Illustration © Blamb, Agency: Shutterstock.com

You know a little bit about the skin already because you studied it when we discussed tissues. Now we want you to learn about it in more depth. Skin is composed of two layers—the epidermis and the dermis.

Epidermis—The outer portion of the skin, formed by epithelial tissue that is attached to the dermis

Dermis—Dense irregular connective tissue that forms the deep layer of the skin

The epidermis is composed of stratified squamous epithelial tissue, while the dermis is composed of dense irregular connective tissue. At one time or another, you have certainly had a blister. A blister is a partial separation between the dermis and the epidermis. There also may be a layer below the dermis, which is called the hypodermis. It is not actually a part of your skin, but it is composed of loose connective tissue that binds the skin to underlying tissues.

Hypodermis—Loose connective tissue underneath the dermis that connects the dermis to muscle or bone

You probably know that leather is made from the skin of animals. A tanner makes leather from the animal's dermis. The dermis has two layers, but they are hard to specifically point out, because the two layers merge in a continuous fashion. As shown in figure 3.1, the upper part of the dermis (the part where the bumps are) is the papillary (pap' ih lar ee) layer. The bumps themselves are called dermal papillae (pa pil' ee). A papilla (singular of papillae) is a bump. These bumps increase the number of blood vessels exposed to the epidermis. The epidermis, which is epithelial tissue, does not have its own blood supply, so the papillae in the dermis bring the blood vessels close to the epidermis, giving it a healthy supply of blood.

Everyone knows what fingerprints are. They are formed from ridges on the epidermis. The ridges are (not surprisingly) called epidermal ridges. All of your skin has epidermal ridges, but the fingerprints formed by the epidermal ridges on the fingers are special. Interestingly, fingerprints are better identification for a person than DNA. Identical twins have the same DNA sequences, but they do not have identical fingerprints. That's because the formation of the epidermal ridges depends on the environment, and even though identical twins develop in the same womb, their slightly different positions and blood supply in that womb lead to slightly different environments, which makes for different epidermal ridges. So, even two identical twins can be uniquely identified using their fingerprints.

While law-enforcement officials use fingerprints for identification, you use them for something else. They increase the friction between your skin and the things you touch. This helps you to grasp things. The reason the epidermal ridges on your fingers are so pronounced is that your fingers are designed to grasp things, so they need deeper epidermal ridges than many other parts of your skin. If you look at the palms of your hands, you will see pronounced epidermal ridges there as well. Once again, that is because your hand is designed to grasp things. Your feet also have deep epidermal ridges, to increase the friction between them and the ground.

Now, do you know where those epidermal ridges come from? They actually come from the *dermis*. You see, the epidermal ridges are really just lines of dermal papillae. In other words, all of those tiny bumps in the dermis line up to make little ridges. Since the epidermis lies on top of the dermis, those ridges show through the epidermis. Think about a child trying to hastily clean his room. He throws all the toys that are on the floor onto his bed, and then he throws a blanket over them. Will that fool anyone? Of course not. The blanket simply lies on top of the toys, showing all of the ridges and bumps in the pile of toys. In the same way, the epidermis lies tightly over the dermis, showing all the bumps and ridges in the dermis. That makes the epidermal ridges.

Beneath the papillary layer of the dermis, we find the reticular (ruh tik' you lar) layer. Reticular is a good word for you to learn. Reti is Latin for "net." Remember the endoplasmic reticulum in the cell? It is a network of tubes in the cell. Well, the reticular layer of the dermis is the network of collagen fibers that runs beneath the papillary layer. Remember that the dermis is composed of dense irregular connective tissue. This network of fibers gives the dermis strength in all directions, allowing your skin to stretch without tearing. By the way, the smooth side of leather is the papillary layer (the papillae are microscopic). The rough, "stringy' side of leather is the reticular side, and the loose "strings" are fibers that are continuous with those in the hypodermis.

Now, remember that the collagen fibers in dense irregular connective tissue are not lined up in parallel bundles like they are in dense *regular* connective tissue. Nevertheless, the collagen fibers in the dermis are lined up to a certain extent, so they tend to lie in one direction more than another. This forms lines of cleavage in the skin, as illustrated in figure 3.2.

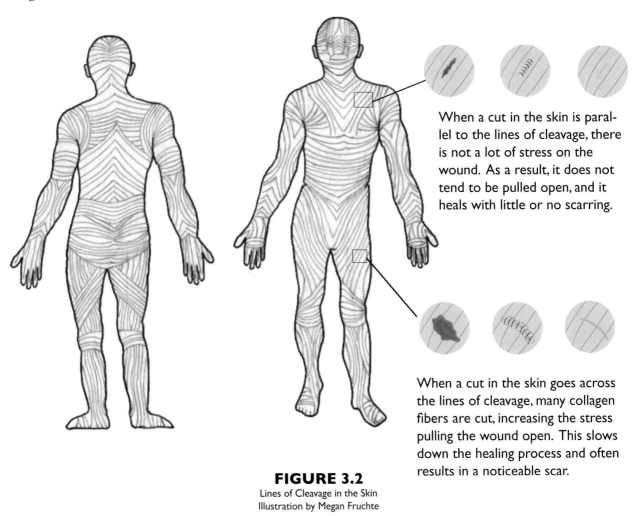

When a cut in the skin is parallel to the lines of cleavage, there is not a lot of stress on the wound. As a result, it does not tend to be pulled open, and it heals with little or no scarring.

When a cut in the skin goes across the lines of cleavage, many collagen fibers are cut, increasing the stress pulling the wound open. This slows down the healing process and often results in a noticeable scar.

FIGURE 3.2
Lines of Cleavage in the Skin
Illustration by Megan Fruchte

These lines of cleavage, often called lines of tension, are very important because they essentially point out the overall direction of the collagen fibers in the dermis. Since the collagen fibers tend to shrink and pull, there is tension along those lines. If you are cut *across* the lines of cleavage, the cut gets pulled apart. As a result, when the cut finally heals, it often scars. If you get cut so that the cut runs *parallel* to the lines of cleavage, there is little stress on the cut, and it doesn't open up as much. Thus, the cut heals with little scarring. Surgeons, especially plastic surgeons, are very careful to try to cut along the lines of cleavage rather than across them, in order to minimize scarring.

Now that you have seen the basic structure of the skin, let's look at it in a little more detail in figure 3.3.

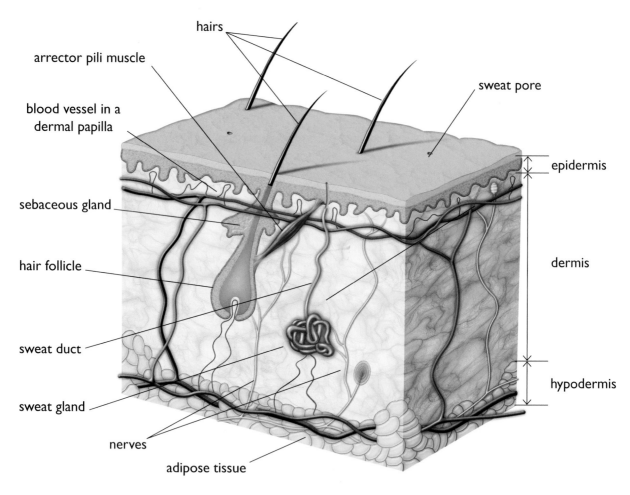

FIGURE 3.3

A More Detailed View of the Skin with a Portion of the Hypodermis

Illustration © Andrea Danti, Agency: Shutterstock.com

To orient yourself again, notice that the epidermis and dermis are labeled on the right side of the figure. We have included a bit of the hypodermis in this picture, just so you have an idea of where it is. Remember, however, that the hypodermis is not part of the skin.

This figure includes a bit more detail and a few additional structures compared with figure 3.1. First, notice the nerves shown in the figure. In reality, there would be many more neurons in that amount of skin. However, for illustrative purposes, we have included just a few. You are going to study neurons in more detail in an upcoming module, but nevertheless, they send signals to and receive signals from the brain and the spinal cord.

Consider the neurons in the figure. Look at the ones that touch the hair follicle. What do those neurons do? Well, have you ever noticed that, if you touch the hair on your skin, you can feel it? Hair is keratinized tissue, so its cells are dead. Therefore, your hair does not feel anything. That's good when it comes to haircuts! Instead, you feel it when your hair is touched or windblown because neurons in the dermis surround the hair follicle and sense that the hair is being moved. These neurons ultimately send a signal to the brain, and your brain interprets it as a feeling that your hair is being moved. Some neurons interact with your hairs so you get sensation from them; others are imbedded in the skin so that the skin itself can provide sensation: heat, cold, light, touch, pressure, pain, tickle, and itch. We call these sensory neurons, because they take messages from sensory receptors to the brain. For example, around the hair follicle are hair follicle receptors. They are just one of many kinds of receptors in your skin, designed to provide you with many sensations.

Human skin is highly sensitive because of its many sensory receptors. Let's look at the hair follicle. We will study the hair in more detail in the next section. However, we want to tell you about one of its most important functions now, and it has to do with skin damage. Consider burns. There are three degrees of burns that you can get. The least damaging is called a first-degree burn. If you get a first-degree burn, you have killed many cells in the epidermis. That is not very bad, though, because those skin cells will be replaced quickly through mitosis. A sunburn is an example of a first-degree burn.

If you get a second-degree burn, however, the epidermis is completely destroyed, and some cells in the dermis have been damaged. When that happens, there is a problem, because there are no more epidermal cells to undergo mitosis in that region of the skin. The burn has killed them all. Nevertheless, the epidermis will be replaced because the hair follicles are made of epithelial tissue. When you look at the figure, notice that the cells surrounding the hair follicle look the same as the epidermal cells. That's because they are. The cells around the hair follicle are really an extension of the epidermis into the dermis. Thus, even if the surface epidermal cells are completely destroyed, they will be replaced by mitosis of the hair follicle cells! In other words, the hair follicle is made of epithelial tissue that dips down from the epidermis. So do the epithelial cells that form the sweat glands and ducts. This provides a storehouse of cells for healthy regeneration of the epidermis in case the entire epidermis in a region of the skin is destroyed. First- and second-degree burns are also classified together as partial-thickness burns.

A third-degree burn is a burn that has completely destroyed *both* the dermis and the epidermis. It is also called a full-thickness burn. In that situation, the only thing that can help is a skin graft. This is a medical procedure in which portions of the dermis and epidermis from one part of a person's body are transplanted onto the damaged area of that same person.

The arrector (uh rek' tor) pili are smooth muscle cells that are associated with the hair. When these muscle cells contract, they change the position of the hair. Normally, the hair lies at an angle relative to the surface of the skin. When the arrector pili muscles contract, they move the hair follicle, causing the hair to "stand on end." When the hair follicle moves, it causes a little bump to form on the skin. We call those bumps goose bumps, and we usually get them in response to cold temperatures or fear. When the hair stands on end, warmer air is trapped against the surface of the skin. This helps us retain heat. So, goose bumps do serve a purpose!

The hypodermis, also called the subcutaneous (sub kyou tay' nee us) layer, is not part of the skin, but it is shown in figure 3.3. It is made of loose connective tissue and adipose tissue. The loose connective tissue connects the skin to the muscle or bone below, and the adipose tissue provides protective padding and insulation. The amount of adipose tissue in the hypodermis varies, depending on the part of the body. In the eyelids, for example, there is no adipose tissue. In the midsection of the body, there may be quite a bit of adipose tissue in the hypodermis. There is always loose connective tissue in the hypodermis, as the skin must be attached to something.

Have you ever heard of a subcutaneous injection? The nurse or doctor makes a "tent" by lightly pinching the skin, and the needle is injected into the hypodermis. Why would you want to inject something into the hypodermis? There are many blood vessels there (see figure 3.3), and the blood will pick up quite rapidly whatever has been injected into the hypodermis. Such needles are called hypodermic needles.

While we are on the subject of blood vessels, remember when we mentioned the dermal papillae? Notice the blood vessel loops in the figure. Those are what we were talking about. Those loops of blood vessels increase the surface area of the epidermis that is exposed to blood. This increases the transfer of oxygen and nutrients up into the epidermis, which has a deep layer of living cells that are constantly undergoing mitosis.

ON YOUR OWN

3.1 A master criminal finds a doctor who has developed a procedure to remove the dermal papillae in a person's hands. Why would a criminal be so interested in this procedure?

3.2 The above criminal undergoes the unscrupulous doctor's procedure and finds that he has constant skin problems in his hands. Why?

3.3 In a fencing accident, a man receives two similarly-sized, deep cuts on the skin in the region of his abdomen. The first is horizontal along the skin, while the other is vertical. Which cut is more likely to leave the most noticeable scar?

Finally, notice that there are sweat glands and sebaceous (suh bay' shus) glands in the skin, as well. The sweat produced by the sweat glands travels up the sweat ducts and spills out onto the skin through the sweat pores. Sweat cools the skin by evaporation. The sebaceous glands produce oil that softens the skin, protects it from drying, and provides some protection from bacteria. We will discuss both of these glands in more detail in another section of this module.

A CLOSER LOOK AT THE EPIDERMIS

Although you have looked at the epidermis already, let's now examine it in more detail. It is made of stratified squamous epithelial tissue, which means it has layers. Figure 3.4 is a photomicrograph of skin tissue. Notice that in this photo, you can see that the epidermis has distinct layers.

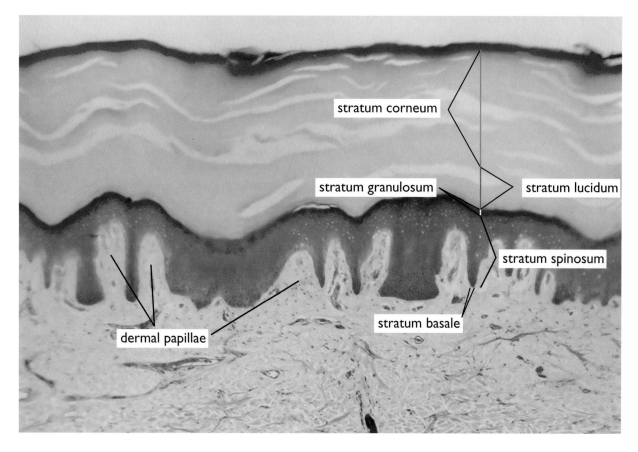

stratum corneum

stratum granulosum

stratum lucidum

stratum spinosum

stratum basale

dermal papillae

FIGURE 3.4
The Layers of the Epidermis (Thick Skin) (400x Magnification)
Photo © Jubal Harshaw, Agency: Shutterstock.com

Starting with the deepest layer and working outward, we find the stratum basale (ba sal' ee). This layer is one cell thick and is composed of cells that are constantly undergoing mitosis. As the cells in this layer reproduce, they are pushed up into the next layer, the stratum spinosum (spih noh' sum). This layer is several cells thick and also undergoes mitosis. In these two layers, especially near the stratum basale, there are interesting cells called melanocytes (mel an' oh sites), which produce a class of pigments known as melanin. The two main types of melanin found in skin and hair are eumelanin (yoo mel' uh nin), which is dark, and pheomelanin (fee oh' mel uh nin), which has a red tint. Now, melanocytes are cells with long extensions called processes. These cells make melanin and package it into vesicles via Golgi apparatuses. The vesicles then move outward into the processes of the cells and, remarkably, the stratum basale cells and the stratum spinosum cells engage in phagocytosis, engulfing the melanin-laden processes. In other words, the cells in these two layers just chew off a chunk of the process of a melanocyte and take in the vesicles full of the pigment! This causes the stratum basale and stratum spinosum cells to develop color. Isn't that amazing?

As you might have guessed, the melanin produced by the melanocytes and "eaten" by the stratum basale and stratum spinosum cells influences the color of your skin.

Oddly enough, no matter what your skin color, you have about as many melanocytes per square inch of skin as the next person. However, the ability of your melanocytes to make melanin can be very different depending on many factors, including genetics, hormones, and the sunlight to which you are exposed. So, even though most people have the same *number of melanocytes*, there are many different skin colors among them because some people's melanocytes make much more melanin than other people's melanocytes.

Besides influencing the color of the skin, melanin protects the skin against ultraviolet radiation from the sun, which is the main cause of skin cancer in humans. Have you ever heard of melanoma (mel' uh noh' muh)? It is the most dangerous form of skin cancer. A malignant melanoma results from the uncontrolled mitosis of melanocytes. There are other types of skin cancer, as well. A basal cell carcinoma (car' si noh' muh) of the skin, for example, results from the uncontrolled mitosis of cells in the stratum basale layer of the skin. This type of cancer is considered curable if it is surgically removed. Finally, stratum spinosum cells cause what's called squamous cell carcinoma. This cancer is considered a little more dangerous than basal cell carcinoma, but it can also be controlled by surgery. Severe sunburns increase the risk of all three types of skin cancer. However, gradual exposure to the sun, while avoiding sunburn, has the very healthy effect of enabling the skin to begin production of vitamin D.

Now, let's move up a little and look at the third layer of the epidermis: the stratum granulosum (gran you loh' sum). Here we have a progressive change in the skin cells. In this layer, the skin cells begin to die. These cells produce large amounts of a protein called keratin (kair' uh tin). The cells in the two deepest layers produce keratin as well, but the cells in the stratum granulosum produce much, much more. Keratin is an incredibly important protein, as it gives your skin its waterproofing capabilities. Without keratin, water would soak into your skin when you take a bath and would evaporate out of your skin when you are dry. However, with keratin, the skin repels water from the outside and keeps the water inside your body from evaporating. When a person suffers severe burns over a large part of the body, loss of fluid from the loss of the skin is a major, life-threatening problem.

The next layer, the stratum lucidum (loo' sih duhm), is found mostly in the thick skin of the palms and soles. Once cells are pushed up into this layer, they are dead.

The most superficial layer of the skin is the stratum corneum (kor' nee uhm). This part of the skin is composed of 25 to 30 layers of dead keratinized cells. These cells, which are pushed up from below, eventually flake off the skin from the top, a process known as desquamation (des kwa may' shun).

You see, then, the epidermis is composed of several layers, and the characteristics of the cells in those layers change. As the cells travel from the stratum basale to the stratum corneum, they slowly begin to die through the process of keratinization. The cells in the stratum basale and stratum spinosum are still living and can reproduce via mitosis. However, the cells die in the stratum granulosum. When they reach the stratum corneum, they flake off and must be replaced by new cells, which have, once again, traveled up from the stratum basale. This process happens continuously throughout the entire integumentary system. You replace your skin every few months.

In human anatomy and physiology, we make a distinction between thin skin and thick skin. In thick skin, all epidermal layers are present, and the stratum corneum has several layers of keratinized cells. Thick skin is found mostly where your body is exposed to pressure or friction. Thus, the palms of the hands, the soles of the feet, and the finger-tips all have thick skin. Thin skin has no stratum lucidum, and each of the other layers has fewer cells than what you find in thick skin. The concept of thin versus thick skin involves only the epidermis, not the dermis.

Experiment 3.1
A Closer Look at the Skin

Supplies:

- Microscope
- Prepared slide: human skin (not the one with follicles or hairs)

Purpose: To examine the dermis and epidermis in more detail

Procedure:

1. Place the prepared slide under the microscope at 40x magnification. Look for a wavy pattern of dark tissue near the top of the sample. That is the epidermis. Center on the epidermis and increase magnification to 100x.
2. Focus, center the epidermis, and increase magnification to 400x.
3. Focus again, and, using Figure 3.4 as a guide, try to identify each layer of the epidermis. Please realize that the tissue sample on your slide might not be from thick skin, so you may not have the stratum lucidum. Also, the layers might not the same thickness as what you see in the figure.
4. Notice the change in cell size and shape in the different regions.
5. Notice also the dermal papillae and how their size varies.
6. Now begin to scan the slide. Note how the thickness of the layers changes across this tissue sample. You may wish to use a lower power to do this.
7. Draw at least two fields of the scope where the thickness varies greatly.
8. Put everything away.

COLORING BOOK
EXERCISE 3.1

You can review the five layers of the epidermis in your coloring book on page 39. Color and label a-f.

ON YOUR OWN

3.4 Cancer results from the abnormal, uncontrolled mitosis of a group of cells. In what layers of the epidermis is it possible to get cancer? Why is it impossible to get cancer in the other layers of the epidermis?

HAIR AND NAILS

Now that we have discussed the epidermis, let's look at two derivatives of epidermal cells: hair and nails. We'll start with hair. Probably one of the first things you learned about mammals is that they all have hair. That is one of their distinguishing characteristics. Human beings have hair over almost all of the body. So, what is hair, anyway?

Well, let's start with figure 3.5.

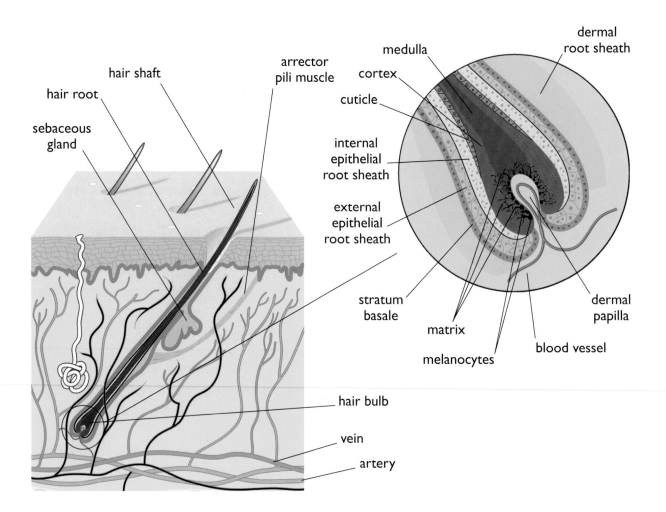

FIGURE 3.5
A Closer View of Hair
Illustration © Blamb, Agency: Shutterstock.com

A hair is divided into two sections: the shaft and the root. The shaft is the part above the surface of the skin, and the root is the part within the skin. The base of the root is called the hair bulb. Most of the root and shaft are made up of dead keratinized cells that are arranged in three concentric layers: the medulla, the cortex, and the cuticle. Because hair is made of closely packed epithelial cells, it is an epithelial tissue.

In order to understand the differences between the three layers of hair, you need to know that there are actually two kinds of keratin: hard keratin and soft keratin. Hard keratin contains more sulfur than soft keratin. This increased sulfur increases the strength of the keratin, making it harder. That is why hair feels different from skin. Skin is composed entirely of cells that have soft keratin, while many of the cells in hair have hard keratin. This is also the reason that hair smells so bad when you burn it. During the combustion of hair, the sulfur in the keratin combines with hydrogen to form hydrogen sulfide, the same gas that gives rotten eggs their terrible smell!

As shown in figure 3.6, the medulla is the innermost layer of hair, and it contains two or three layers of dead cells that hold soft keratin. Fine hair often has no medulla, but coarse hair usually does. The cortex, on the other hand, makes up most of the hair, and it contains several layers of cells that hold hard keratin. Finally, the cuticle is a single layer of dead cells containing hard keratin. The cuticle is structured so that the cells overlap with one another, much like shingles on a roof.

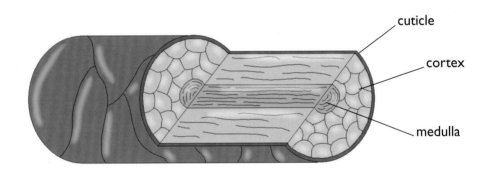

FIGURE 3.6
The Three Layers of the Hair Shaft and Root
Illustration by Megan Fruchte

The hair follicle is the tiny pocket out of which the hair grows. It is made mostly of epithelial tissue. The epithelial tissue that forms the hair follicle has two regions: the internal epithelial root sheath and the external epithelial root sheath. The internal root sheath firmly attaches the hair root to the follicle. If a hair is pulled out, the white tissue attached to the hair is the internal epithelial root sheath. The external epithelial root sheath is covered with the dermal root sheath.

Inside the hair bulb, right on top of a dermal papilla, is the matrix. This matrix is not related to the matrix you learned about in the previous module. This matrix is a mass of undifferentiated cells, which means that the cells have not specialized yet. As new cells are formed by mitosis within the matrix, the cells will differentiate or specialize, becoming part of one of the regions of the hair. As that happens, the cells keratinize, forming either hard or soft keratin depending on whether the cell becomes part of the medulla, cortex, or cuticle.

Have you ever heard of electrolysis? This is a procedure that eliminates hair growth. It does so by killing the matrix cells. In this procedure, a thin needle with a current is inserted into the hair follicle, and the energy from the electricity kills the matrix cells. Without the matrix, there is no mitosis of cells to make hair, and no hair will grow there again. Laser hair removal works in a similar way, but it uses heat from a laser to destroy the matrix.

Hair is interesting because in some places on the body, such as your eyebrows, it doesn't grow very long. In other places of the body, such as your head, it grows very long. What is the difference? Any hair will grow, on average, about one-half inch a month. If it continues to grow for an entire year, it will grow to be about 6 inches long. However, suppose it stopped growing after only two weeks. If that happened, the hair would be only a quarter of an inch long. It turns out that hair follicles have time periods in which the cells of the matrix undergo mitosis rapidly and as a result, the hair grows. Those times are called growth stages. There are also times when the cells in the matrix rest and do not undergo mitosis. Those times are called rest stages.

During the growth stage, cells are being reproduced, they differentiate, and then they keratinize. That causes the hair to grow. During the rest stage, the hair follicle shrinks and tightens, holding the hair in place. Once the rest stage is over, the old hair is actually pushed out of the follicle by a new hair. Have you ever noticed hair coming out in your hairbrush or in the shower? Even though you seem to lose a lot of hair, you do not go bald. Why? The hair you are losing has fallen out *because* it is being replaced by new hair. So, at least when you are young, hair loss does not mean you are going bald. It usually means that you are just growing new hair.

Now, back to the question of why some hair stays short while other hair grows long. It turns out that different hair follicles in the body have different growth and rest stages. For example, a hair follicle on your head might have a growth stage that lasts three years, letting your hair grow to approximately 18 inches long. After that, the follicle has a rest stage of about one year. However, while that follicle rests, other follicles are still in the growth stage. At any given time, about 90% of the hair follicles on your head are in the growth stage. Thus, while some of the hair on your head is growing, there are other hairs that are just staying the same length, because those follicles are in their rest stage. In addition, you lose about 100 hairs a day on your head, since that is approximately the number of hair follicles that have gone from their rest stage to their growth stage. Compare the length of the growth stage for a follicle on your head with one on your eyelash. A hair follicle for your eyelash has a growth stage of about 30 days and a rest stage of about 100 days. As a result, eyelash hair grows to less than half an inch or so. The differences in hair length at different places on your body, then, are determined by the differences in the growth and rest stages of the hair follicles.

Notice one more thing in figure 3.5. Right on the base of the hair bulb, in the matrix, you will see melanocytes, the cells that produce melanin and fill their processes with it. The matrix cells engage in phagocytosis to take in the melanin from the processes of the melanocytes. This is how hair gets its color. Remember from our discussion of skin color that there are two types of melanin: eumelanin (which is dark) and pheomelanin (which is red). Also remember that the color is determined, not by the number of melanocytes, but by how much the cells take in. Dark hair is made of cells that have taken in a lot of eumelanin and not much pheomelanin. Red hair is made of cells that have taken in a lot of pheomelanin and not much eumelanin. Blonde hair can have either of the melanin pigments, but in small amounts. If the pigment in blonde hair is mostly pheomelanin, the hair is "golden blonde," while blonde hair with mostly eumelanin is "ash blonde." If the cells take in no melanin at all, the hair is white. When most people get old, their hair turns gray or white because the melanocytes in the matrix produce less melanin, which means the hair cells cannot absorb much melanin.

Although you might not realize it, nails are a lot like hair. Figure 3.7 demonstrates this. The nail that you see, like the hair shaft, is just the portion of the nail that lies above the surface of the skin. There is also a nail root that lies under the skin. At the bottom of the nail root is the nail matrix. Like the hair matrix found at the bottom of the hair root, the matrix is where undifferentiated cells are undergoing mitosis. The cells then differentiate and keratinize with hard keratin, allowing the nail to grow. Unlike the hair matrix, the nail matrix does not have a rest stage. As a result, nails grow constantly. They do not grow as quickly as hair, but they do not stop growing.

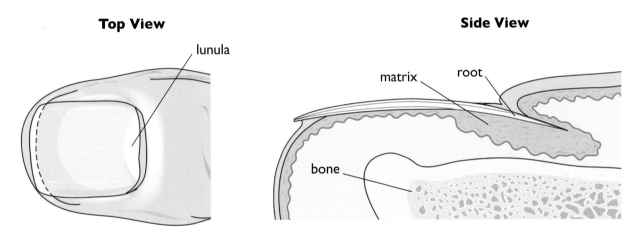

FIGURE 3.7
A Fingernail
Illustration © Blamb, Agency: Shutterstock.com

Although the nail matrix is found at the base of the nail root, it does extend out of the skin a bit. If you look at your thumbnail, you will see a little white crescent at the base of the nail. This is called the lunula (loon' you luh), and it is the upper portion of the nail matrix. It is thicker than the rest of the nail, which makes it harder to see the pink tissue below. This makes the lunula look white. All fingernails have a lunula, but it is easiest to see in the thumb. Remember, just like in hair, the nail can always regrow as long as the matrix is alive. Thus, if you hit your thumb with a hammer and damage the nail, it will regrow, as long as you did not kill the matrix cells.

It is important to have nails. They offer protection to the ends of the digits, but that is not their only use. Because they are so hard, they reinforce the fingertips. This makes grasping things much easier. Consider grabbing a screw between your thumb and forefinger and then trying to turn it. Since the thumb and forefinger each have a nail, there are two hard surfaces against which the skin at the end of the fingers can push. This helps you maintain a firm grasp on the screw. Also, nails can be used for scratching, which can relieve skin irritation.

Experiment 3.2
A Closer Look at Follicles

Supplies:

- Microscope
- Prepared slide: human skin with follicles or hair

Purpose: To examine the details of the hair follicle

Procedure:

1. Place the prepared slide under the microscope at 40x magnification and focus. Once again, look for the wavy, dark tissue that marks the epidermis. You should see several hair follicles.

2. Scan the slide to find a follicle with a well-defined bulb. A well-defined bulb has a reasonably circular shape and at least some white in the middle. If you can see a hair sticking out of the follicle, that would be ideal.

3. Center the bulb, increase magnification to 100x, and focus. At this point, you should start being able to see the structure of the hair follicle. You should see individual cells, and the divisions between the hair (medulla, cortex, and cuticle) and the follicle (internal epithelial root sheath, external epithelial root sheath, and dermal root sheath) should be noticeable. Spend a little time observing at this magnification before going on to the next step.

4. Center the bulb, increase magnification to 400x, and focus again. Now you should be able to see some real detail.

5. Begin by looking at the bottom of the bulb. This is the matrix. You can tell it is the matrix by the density of cells in that region. The cells are simply denser than in other parts of the follicle.

6. Look at the follicle just above the bulb, and try to identify the regions of the hair follicle. Notice the tissue of the dermis below the follicle. Do you see a thin line of tissue like it surrounding the outer layer of the follicle? That is the dermal sheath. The internal and external epithelial root sheaths will be essentially the same color, so you might have a hard time distinguishing them. However, the external sheath is wider, and the internal sheath has smaller cells. The hair should be distinct from the follicle. Most likely, the tissue of the hair will be darker. That will be one way to tell where the internal epithelial root sheath is. You can look at the hair, and the layer of tissue right outside of the hair is the internal epithelial root sheath.

7. Draw the bulb and the portion of the follicle you see in this field of the scope. Label what you can identify.

8. Now look at a hair shaft. Hopefully, the follicle you were examining will have one. If not, find another follicle with a hair shaft.

9. It will be very difficult to separate the medulla from the cortex. However, you can easily see the cuticle by adjusting the focus. If you focus in on the cells at the center of the hair shaft (the medulla and cortex), and then de-focus one way and then the other (remember, you only use fine focus at high magnification), you should see a fine, yellow outline around the hair. Notice the darker lines in that yellow outline. Do you see how they overlap like shingles? That's the cuticle of the hair. Draw it.

10. Put everything away.

COLORING BOOK EXERCISE 3.2

A review of skin, hair, and nails can be found on pages 39-41 to color.

ON YOUR OWN

3.5 A hair cell contains soft keratin. From what region of the hair was it taken?

3.6 Where can the hair cells with no keratin be found?

3.7 A hair follicle is empty, but the matrix is not dead. Has the hair follicle just entered its growth stage or rest stage?

SKIN GLANDS

There are two basic kinds of glands in the skin: the sebaceous glands and the sweat glands. You can see both of these glands back in figure 3.3. There are actually two kinds of sweat glands. The most widespread sweat glands in the skin are merocrine glands, which are found over most of the skin. Recall that merocrine glands secrete substances without any cellular material in the secretion. When you "work up a good sweat," your merocrine sweat glands are producing sweat and releasing it onto the surface of your skin.

Now remember, sweat has a function. It cools you off because, once it hits the surface of the skin, it starts to evaporate. In evaporation, the energetic, "hot" molecules become water vapor, leaving the skin cooler. If you live in a humid climate, you may think that sweating is ineffective since it will not evaporate into the humid air, which is already full of water vapor. That's true. But if the humidity is not overly high, sweating is effective enough to lower your body temperature even below the environmental temperature!

There are also apocrine sweat glands in the body. They are found in the armpit and also in the pubic region. Now, it turns out that these are not really apocrine glands at all. When they were first discovered, scientists thought they were apocrine glands. However, we now know that this is not true. They are, in fact, merocrine glands. Nevertheless, since they were originally called apocrine sweat glands, we still call them that, even though they do not secrete like apocrine glands. What are the differences between these glands and the merocrine sweat glands? Well, the first is very obvious. The secretions of the apocrine sweat glands produce a strong odor. That's why as you entered puberty you began using under-arm deodorant. It helps control the smell of the apocrine sweat glands that are found there.

There are also anatomical differences between the merocrine sweat glands and the apocrine sweat glands. First, the apocrine sweat glands are found deeper in the skin. They are typically in or near the hypodermis. Merocrine sweat glands, however, are found only in the dermis. Also, apocrine sweat glands do not empty their secretions directly onto the skin. Instead, they usually empty into the hair follicle, and the secretions empty out onto the skin at the point where the hair emerges from the skin.

The other skin glands that we will discuss are the sebaceous glands. Sebaceous glands are holocrine glands; that is, they secrete the entire epithelial cell. As you can see from figures 3.3 and 3.5, they are located such that they open into a hair follicle. This is not true of all sebaceous glands, but it is true of the vast majority of them. These glands secrete oil, called sebum, which softens and conditions the hair and the skin. If you have ever experienced dry, chapped skin, you know how painful it can be. Sebum keeps that from becoming an everyday occurrence. It also helps protect the body from harmful organisms because it makes it harder for bacteria to attach to the skin.

These glands are absolutely necessary for healthy skin, but they can also be a nuisance for young people, because sebaceous glands are prone to acne when they become very active during adolescence. Since they are holocrine glands, their secretions contain a lot of nourishing substances that were originally a part of the epithelial cells that formed the secretions. As a result, bacteria can live on the secretions of the sebaceous glands. A particular bacterium, *Propionibacterium acnes* is part of what causes acne, but scientists still are not sure exactly how acne forms. It seems that something happens in the hair follicle, which causes too many cells to form in the epidermis of the hair follicle. This leads to many keratinized cells falling off the epidermis. These cells can stick together, plugging up the hair follicle. As sebum builds up beneath the blockage, a whitehead is formed. The pressure eventually causes the hair follicle to rupture, and bacteria cause

ON YOUR OWN

3.8 Do the secretions of the apocrine sweat gland contain cellular material?

3.9 A medical researcher comes up with a way of shutting down the activity of the sebaceous gland. Although teenagers everywhere rejoice, other researchers publish articles against this discovery. Why would teenagers everywhere rejoice at such a discovery? Assuming that the procedure itself is safe, why would other medical researchers oppose the technique?

inflammation of the surrounding tissue, which forms the red bump associated with acne. In any case, good hygiene and a good diet containing healthy food and limited junk food are good for your skin generally, and they may also help to reduce acne.

THE SKELETAL SYSTEM

After spending some time on the body's covering, the integumentary system, it only seems natural to spend some time on the body's framework, the skeletal system. You can think of it as "skin and bones!" Before we deal with the anatomy of the skeletal system in detail (module 4), however, we want to discuss the five functions of the skeletal system. Probably the most obvious is *support*. Bone is well designed for bearing the weight of the body; cartilage provides firm but flexible support for structures such as the ears and nose, and ligaments bind the bones together.

The second function is *protection*. Since bone is hard, it protects the organs it surrounds. The skull protects the brain, and the rib cage protects the heart and lungs. Probably most fascinating and marvelous is the way that bone protects the spinal cord. The spinal cord is like a "ponytail" on the brain, and it is encircled by your vertebral column. The spinal cord is just as delicate as the brain, but to give us flexibility, it must be able to move as you bend and twist. Our vertebral column is perfectly designed to give us flexibility of motion, while at the same time protecting the spinal cord.

Of course, this brings us to a third and major function of the skeletal system: *movement.* In order to move, the skeleton is formed from many bones that form joints.

think about this

Shakespeare wrote, "The good (men do) is oft interred with their bones," and he was correct. We can tell a lot from examining old bone. Whether a person was male or female can be determined by examining a skeleton's pelvic bones. The size of a bone helps scientists estimate the age of the person at the time of death. The density of the bone can help determine the occupation of the person; someone who lifted heavy items regularly would have had denser bones than a person whose occupation required little weight bearing-activity. A habitual horseback rider would leave clues behind in his leg and pelvis bones. Even the type of diet the person ate can be determined by examining teeth. It's amazing how our bones record our life's history!

The fourth function, *storage*, might not be as obvious as the previous ones. Your skeletal system actually stores many materials for your body's use. For example, it stores minerals such as calcium, phosphorus, and magnesium. Should the concentration of those ions drop in the blood, they will be released from the bone. Also, the skeletal system stores fat. It is nice when your skeletal system stores fat, because the fat is stored in hollow areas inside the bones. That means the adipose tissue stored in your skeletal system does not affect your waistline! The adipose tissue stored in your bones is called yellow bone marrow. In general, adult long bones of the arms, legs, hands, and feet contain yellow bone marrow.

The last function of the skeletal system is hemopoiesis (he' moh poy ee' sis). Hemo refers to hemoglobin, which is found in red blood cells. Poiesis relates to the manufacture of a substance. Thus, we arrive at the definition.

Hemopoiesis—The process of manufacturing blood cells

Surprisingly enough, hemopoiesis is a function of the skeletal system. Inside some bones there is red bone marrow rather than yellow bone marrow. That red bone marrow produces the red blood cells that end up in the bloodstream. Even though the name does not suggest it, red bone marrow also produces white blood cells. The function of lipid storage, then, is accomplished by the yellow bone marrow in the long bones of the arms, legs, hands, and feet. The function of hemopoiesis is accomplished by red bone marrow, which is in the bones of the skull and vertebral column as well as in a few others. We see again that blood is a connective tissue, since its cells are produced by bone, which is a connective tissue.

With the functions of the skeletal system out of the way, let's study its gross anatomy in figure 3.8.

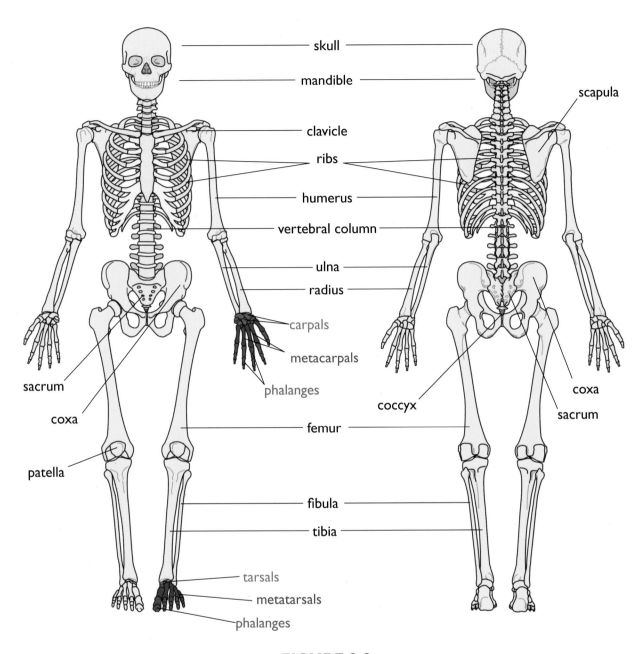

FIGURE 3.8
The Skeletal System
Illustrations © Lippincott, Williams, and Wilkins

GROSS ANATOMY OF BONE

Bones can be classified into five basic categories: long bones, short bones, flat bones, irregular bones, and sesamoid (ses' uh moyd) bones. Figure 3.9 illustrates these different kinds of bones.

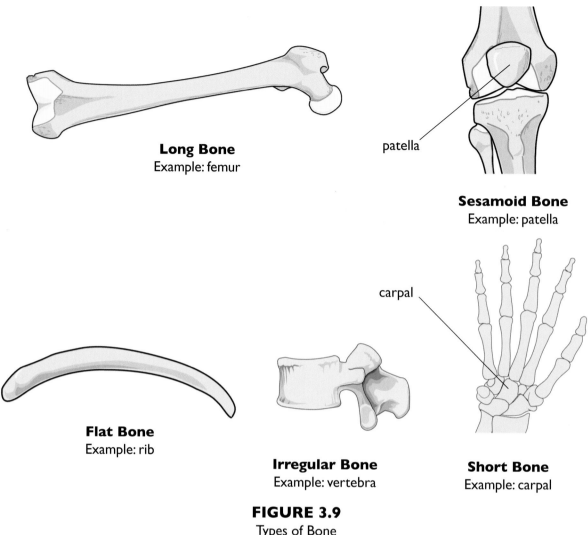

Long Bone
Example: femur

patella

Sesamoid Bone
Example: patella

carpal

Flat Bone
Example: rib

Irregular Bone
Example: vertebra

Short Bone
Example: carpal

FIGURE 3.9
Types of Bone
Illustrations © Lippincott, Williams, and Wilkins

If a bone is longer than it is wide, but not flat, it is called a long bone. The long bone drawn in the figure is the femur. If a bone is about as wide as it is long, it is a short bone. Carpals are considered short bones. Flat bones may be long, but they are thin and usually curved. The rib in the figure is a typical flat bone. The patella and other small, round bones that develop inside tendons are called sesamoid bones. Finally, if a bone does not fit into one of these categories, it is considered an irregular bone. The vertebra pictured in the figure is an excellent example of an irregular bone.

Perhaps the most interesting type of bone to examine first is the long bone. It has three major components: the diaphysis (dye af' ih sus), the epiphysis (eh pif' ih sus), and the epiphyseal (ep ih fiz' ee uhl) plate or line. The diaphysis is the shaft of the bone. It is composed primarily of compact bone.

Compact bone—Dense bone matrix organized into microscopic tubes of bone called osteons

We will see the histology of compact bone in the next module. For now, just understand that compact bone tissue is dense.

The epiphysis is found at the end of the bone. It is made mostly of cancellous (kan' sih lus) bone, also called spongy bone.

Cancellous bone—Networks of bone with many marrow-filled spaces surrounding the bone matrix

Cancellous bone has a lattice-like appearance (see figure 3.10). The spaces within the lattice contain red or yellow bone marrow. Between the diaphysis and the epiphysis lies the epiphyseal plate or epiphyseal line. This plate is made of hyaline cartilage when a person is young. The growth of the bone's length comes from the epiphyseal plate. When a person is fully grown, the hyaline cartilage is replaced by bone, and that bone is the epiphyseal line.

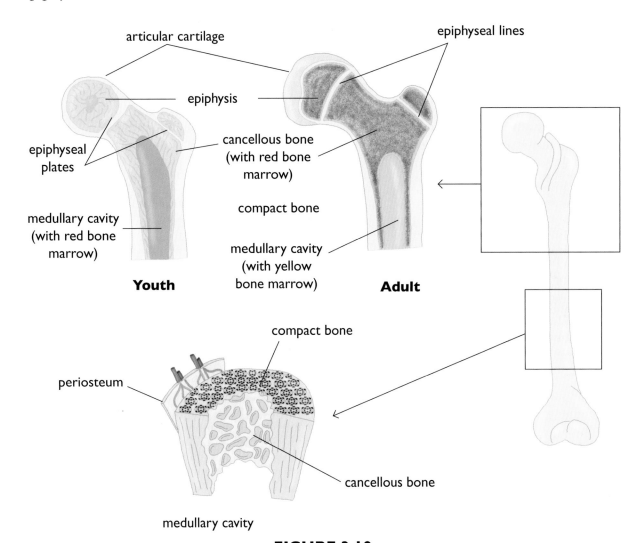

FIGURE 3.10
The Anatomy of a Long Bone
Illustration by Megan Fruchte

Notice in the upper part of figure 3.10 that the bone changes significantly from youth to adulthood. When a person is young, the cancellous bone is very resilient, and the epiphyseal plates are present with hyaline cartilage. The epiphyseal plates allow the bone to grow. Once a person has matured, however, the cancellous bone is less resilient. Also, there is no need for the bone to grow anymore. As a result, the epiphyseal plates are converted to bone. Since the bone-formation process is called ossification (os' ih fih kay' shun), we could say that the epiphyseal plate has ossified into the epiphyseal line.

Ossification—Bone formation

Another difference between a young bone and a mature bone can be seen in the articular cartilage.

Articular cartilage—Hyaline cartilage that covers the ends of a bone in a joint.

Another important difference between the long bones of a young person and the long bones of an adult is the bone marrow. In a young person, the cavity that runs down the center of the diaphysis, the medullary (med' you lar ree) cavity, usually contains red bone marrow, where red blood cells are produced. As a person matures, however, the red bone marrow in the long bones is replaced by yellow bone marrow, which stores lipids. In an adult, the long bones of the limbs typically contain yellow bone marrow (except near their attachments to the trunk), and the red bone marrow is contained in the cancellous bone of the rest of the skeleton.

Now, look for a moment at the details of the diaphysis, as illustrated in figure 3.10. The entire bone is covered with a sheath called the periosteum (pehr ee os' tee uhm). This sheath is composed of two layers. The outer layer is dense irregular connective tissue that contains blood vessels and nerves. The inner layer is a single layer of bone cells. You will study this in more detail in the next module.

We concentrated on the anatomy of a long bone because it contains the most features. The other bones are considered "simpler" than long bones. For example, a flat bone typically has no diaphysis or epiphysis. Instead, it can be thought of as a "cancellous bone sandwich." By this we mean that a flat bone is composed of three layers: an inner layer of cancellous bone covered on each side by a layer of compact bone. The cancellous bone contains red bone marrow in youth, but more yellow marrow as the person matures. Short and irregular bones have no diaphyses (plural of diaphysis), but some have epiphyses. It is important to note that although a bone might not have a diaphysis, it can still contain bone marrow.

AN OVERVIEW OF THE SKELETAL SYSTEM

Now that you have learned the gross anatomy of bones, it is time to take a tour of the skeletal system. We want to start with some general points and then look at portions of the skeleton in detail. First, there are 206 separate bones in the average adult's skeleton. Children actually have more bones than adults because, as children mature, some of the separate bones in the body fuse together to become one bone. We want you to learn all of these bones, but don't worry—you do not actually have to memorize 206 different bones. That is because many bones in the body come in pairs. For example, there are two parietal bones in the skull. Also, other bones come in groups. The vertebral column, for example, contains 26 bones, but there are only five different *groups* of bones. In the end, you will need to learn about 40 different names of bones. Now that's not so bad, is it?

The first thing you need to know is that the skeleton can be divided into two major sections: an axial skeleton and an appendicular (ah pen dihk' you luhr) skeleton.

> **ON YOUR OWN**
>
> **3.10** In an adult, which of the five functions of the skeletal system does the humerus perform? Hint: The head of each humerus, the part forming the shoulder, contains red bone marrow. The shaft, or long part, contains yellow bone marrow.
>
> **3.11** Using Figure 3.8, classify the following bones as long, short, irregular, or flat.
>
> (a) metatarsals; (b) tarsals; (c) coxa; (d) radius.
>
> **3.12** If the epiphysis of a long bone contains epiphyseal plates, can the person still grow taller?

Axial skeleton—The portion of the skeleton that supports and protects the head, neck, and trunk

Appendicular skeleton—The portion of the skeleton that attaches to the axial skeleton and has the limbs attached to it

As you can see from figure 3.11, the vertebral column, ribs, and skull make up the axial skeleton. The pectoral girdle *along with* the upper limbs that attach to it and the pelvic girdle along with the lower limbs that attach to it make up the appendicular skeleton.

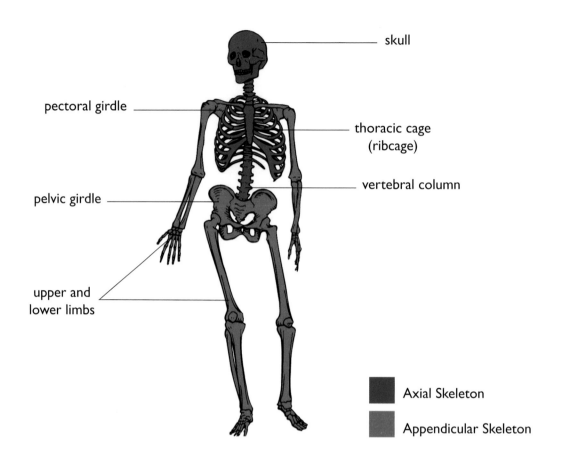

skull

pectoral girdle

thoracic cage (ribcage)

vertebral column

pelvic girdle

upper and lower limbs

Axial Skeleton

Appendicular Skeleton

FIGURE 3.11
Axial and Appendicular Skeleton
Illustration © Denis Barbulat, Agency: Shutterstock.com

There is one technical note we must make before we end this section. In the language we use every day, we refer to our upper limbs as *arms*. That is fine for everyday use, but in anatomy, we must be more precise. In anatomy, the term *arm* refers only to the portion of each upper limb defined by the humerus. In the same way, the term *leg* refers only to the portion of each lower limb containing the tibia and fibula. Thus, when we talk about everything from the shoulder to the hand, we say *upper limb*, not arm. In the same way, when we talk about everything from the hip to the feet, we say *lower limb*, not leg. *Arm* means "upper arm". *Forearm* is used in a precise way in anatomy. We say *thigh* and *leg* for the lower limb above and below the knee.

DETAILS OF THE APPENDICULAR SKELETON: THE LIMBS

In general, the appendicular skeleton is easier to discuss than the axial skeleton, so we will begin with that. Let's start with the pelvic girdle, the pectoral girdle, the lower limbs, and the upper limbs. Please note that we will show you a few more bones in the figures than those we are requiring you to know.

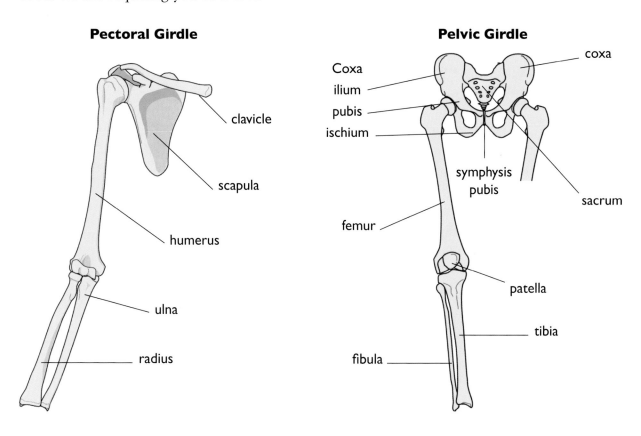

Pectoral Girdle

clavicle

scapula

humerus

ulna

radius

Pelvic Girdle

Coxa

ilium

pubis

ischium

symphysis pubis

femur

coxa

sacrum

patella

tibia

fibula

FIGURE 3.12
The Pectoral Girdle, Upper Limbs, Pelvic Girdle, and Lower Limbs
Illustrations © Lippincott, Williams, and Wilkins

Remember, the appendicular skeleton is composed of the limbs and the girdles that attach the limbs to the axial skeleton. The pectoral (pek' tor uhl) girdle attaches the upper limbs to the axial skeleton. It is an incomplete ring composed of two pairs of bones: the clavicle and the scapula. The clavicle is commonly called the collarbone, and the scapula is commonly called the shoulder blade. The arm attaches to the pectoral girdle. It is made up of only one bone, the humerus. The forearm consists of two bones: the radius and the ulna. The ulna is on the same side of the forearm as the little finger, while the radius is on the same side of the forearm as the thumb. The ulna is slightly longer than the radius.

The lower limbs are somewhat similar to the upper limbs. They attach to the axial skeleton at the pelvic girdle, which is a complete ring made of three bones: two coxae (plural of coxa) and the sacrum. Each coxa is made up of three bones fused into one: the ilium (il' ee uhm), the pubis, and the ischium (ih' she uhm). During childhood, these bones are separate but, as a child grows, the bones fuse into a single bone called the coxa, which is commonly called the hip bone. The two coxae (joined at the symphysis [sim' fih sis] pubis) and the sacrum join together to form a strong arch that supports the upper body.

What we commonly call the leg is actually composed of the thigh and the leg. The thigh is made of one bone, the femur, which attaches to the pelvic girdle at the hip. The leg, composed of the tibia and fibula, joins to the thigh at the knee, where the femur and tibia join. The patella is a sesamoid bone. It develops almost like a calcified "callous" within the tendon that joins the thigh muscle to the tibia. It acts like a lever, reducing the force that the muscles must exert in order to move the leg.

DETAILS OF THE APPENDICULAR SKELETON: THE HANDS AND FEET

There are many similarities between the hands and feet, so it only makes sense to discuss them together. Believe it or not, over *half* of the bones in the body are contained in the wrists, hands, ankles, and feet. There are 27 bones in each hand and wrist, and 26 in each ankle and foot. That makes a total of 106 bones! Obviously, we will not require you to know them all.

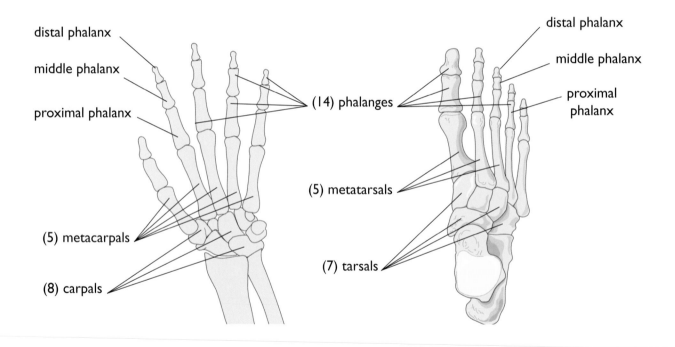

FIGURE 3.13
Hands and Feet
Illustrations © Lippincott, Williams, and Wilkins

The wrist is made up of eight short bones called carpals. These carpals are arranged in two rows of four bones each. If you have ever heard of carpal tunnel syndrome, it refers to a situation in which a ligament that passes across the carpals pinches a nerve that runs below it. The hand, which attaches to the wrist, is formed from five metacarpals and five digits. Each digit (except the thumb) is composed of three phalanges (fuh lan' jeez): the proximal phalanx (singular of phalanges), the middle phalanx, and the distal phalanx. The thumb has only a proximal and a distal phalanx. In anatomy, the term proximal simply means "nearest," while the word distal means "distant." Nearest to what? To the attachment of the limb to the trunk. More distant from what? From the attachment of the limb to the trunk.

In the same way, the ankle is composed of seven short bones called tarsals. The ankle attaches to the foot, which is composed of five metatarsals and five digits. As is the case with the digits of the hands, each digit (except for the great toe) is composed of three phalanges: a proximal phalanx, a middle phalanx, and a distal phalanx. Like the thumb, the great toe has only a proximal and a distal phalanx.

COLORING BOOK EXERCISE 3.3

To finish your study of the appendicular skeleton, follow the instructions on pages 63 and 79 of your coloring book.

To review the bones you have just studied, try to find them on your own body. Can you feel your humerus? Can you distinguish between your radius and your ulna? Can you feel where your carpals end and your metacarpals begin? What about your phalanges? Can you distinguish them from your metacarpals? Try doing the same thing for the bones of your lower limbs. This approach to learning anatomy is called surface anatomy.

DETAILS OF THE AXIAL SKELETON: THE SKULL

Now that we have covered the appendicular skeleton, it is time to take a good look at the axial skeleton. Starting our tour of the axial skeletal system at the top, let's discuss the skull. The skull, although it might appear to be just one bone, is actually composed of 28 different bones. If you hold a skull in your hand, you would find that only one of those bones (the mandible or jawbone) is easy to separate from the skull. It takes considerable effort to separate the rest of the bones in the skull. The skull's main job, of course, is to support and protect the brain. It also supports and protects the eyes, ears, and nose. Figure 3.14 gives you three views of the skull.

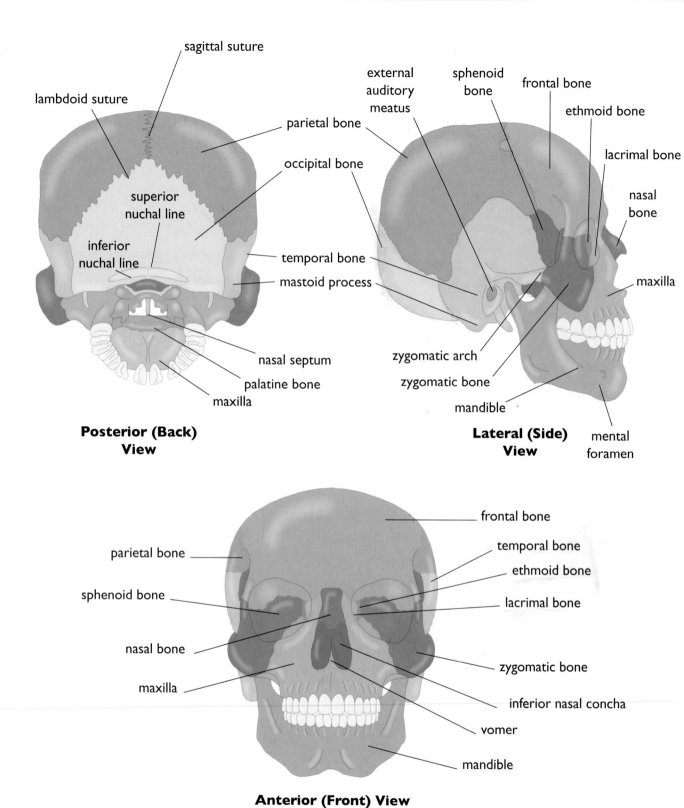

Posterior (Back) View

Lateral (Side) View

Anterior (Front) View

FIGURE 3.14
The Skull
Illustration by Megan Fruchte

So that you can see the bones of the skull in a more ordered way, table 3.1 summarizes the groups of bones shown in the figure, as well as one group of bones not shown.

Bones of the Cranial Vault	Number	Bones of the Face	Number
Parietal	2	Maxilla	2
Temporal	2	Zygomatic	2
Frontal	1	Palatine	2
Sphenoid	1	Lacrimal	2
Occipital	1	Inferior nasal concha	2
Ethmoid	1	Mandible	1
Auditory ossicles (not in figure)	6	Vomer	1

TABLE 3.1
The 26 Bones of the Skull

Let's start our discussion of skull bones by looking at the posterior view of the skull. As you can see from the figure, a posterior view is a view from behind. Looking at the back of the skull, then, you can easily see three bones: the parietal bone (there are two of them), the occipital (ock sip' ih tuhl) bone, and the temporal bone (there are two of them as well). Note the joints between the bones, which are called sutures.

Suture—An immovable joint between flat bones of the skull

Although the sutures are labeled for completeness, you need not worry about recognizing them. Concentrate on the bones of the figure, which are all labeled in boldface type. You can also see the two palatine bones in this view.

In order to orient you properly for all three views of the skull, we have labeled a few other structures. Notice first the mastoid process. This is important anatomically because muscles involved in the movement of the head attach here.

Process—A projection on a bone

The mastoid process, then, is a projection on the temporal bone. You can see the mastoid process more clearly in the lateral view of the skull. You can feel it on your own skull behind your ear lobe.

Notice also the superior nuchal line and the inferior nuchal line. Neck muscles attach to the skull along these lines. Now, the superior nuchal line is not "better" than the inferior nuchal line. In anatomy, the terms inferior and superior are terms that help us orient ourselves. Superior simply means "above" and inferior means "below." Thus, the superior nuchal lines are *above* the inferior nuchal lines.

Let's now look at the lateral view of the skull. In anatomy, "lateral" simply means "away from the middle." A lateral view of the skull is a view from the side. In this view, we can once again see the parietal bone (one of two), the single occipital bone, and one of the two temporal bones. In addition, we can see the single frontal bone, the single sphenoid (sfee' noyd) bone, and one of the two lacrimal (lak' rih muhl) bones. Notice as well the nasal bone (one of two). The external structure of the nose is mostly made of cartilage, so it is not included in the skeleton. That's why the nose appears to be "missing" from the skull.

The two zygomatic bones are commonly known as the cheekbones. A process from these bones joins a process from the temporal bones to form the zygomatic arch, which forms a bridge across each side of the skull. Each bone is attached to one of the two maxillae (plural), which contain the upper (superior) set of teeth. The single mandible is inferior to the maxillae and holds the lower (inferior) set of teeth. When you open your mouth to chew or speak, the mandible is what actually moves. It is the only bone in the skull that has movable joints. The last bone you can see from this view is the single ethmoid bone, located between the eyes.

Once again, there are some features pointed out in the figure that you do not need to be able to identify, but are nevertheless interesting to discuss. The external auditory meatus (mee ay' tus) is the passageway through which sound waves travel in order to reach the eardrum. That leads us to another vocabulary word.

Meatus—A passageway

A meatus is not the only opening you will find in bone. The mental foramen (for ay' men) [plural: foramina] is a hole through which the mental nerve passes.

Foramen—A hole

The mastoid process is also shown here, to help orient you in comparison to the side view.

Finally, if you look at the anterior view of the skull, you will see many of the bones we have already mentioned: the frontal bone, the parietal bones, the sphenoid bone, the lacrimal bones, the nasal bones, the temporal bones, the maxillae, and the mandible. The only new bone to look at from this view is the vomer. This single bone, along with a plate from the ethmoid bone, forms the bony part of the nasal septum, which divides the nasal cavity in two. Several of the bones associated with the nasal cavity have hollowed-out regions in them. Such a hollow region is covered with a thin membrane of pseudostratified epithelium and is called a sinus (sigh' nus).

Sinus—A hollowed out space in a bone

The sinuses in the bones associated with the nasal cavity are called the paranasal sinuses. These sinuses reduce the weight of the skull and actually affect the sound of your voice. Consider, for example, the difference in a person's voice when he or she is healthy as compared with when he or she has congested sinuses, like during a cold. That gives you an idea of how much the paranasal sinuses affect your voice.

Probably the most striking features of the skull are its orbits, which are commonly called the eye sockets. The orbits, of course, house and protect the eyes. They are formed by the junction of seven of the bones that have already been pointed out. A part of the frontal bone forms a portion of each orbit's roof. The sphenoid bone forms the other portion of the roof as well as part of the lateral wall. The rest of the lateral wall is formed by the zygomatic bone. The inside wall (called the medial wall) of the orbit is formed by the lacrimal, ethmoid, and maxilla bones, while the inferior (lower) part of the orbit is formed by the maxilla.

DETAILS OF THE AXIAL SKELETON: THE VERTEBRAL COLUMN

The vertebral column protects the spinal cord. As we mentioned already, you can think of the spinal cord as a "ponytail" that hangs off of the brain. It brings the

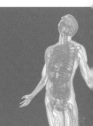

COLORING BOOK EXERCISE 3.4

On pages 43-49 of the coloring book, you will find several views of the skull to color for review.

control capability of the brain down to the upper and lower limbs. It is a critical part of the nervous system. If the spinal cord gets injured, the brain can lose control of entire sections of the body. As a result, God has protected the spinal cord by placing it within the vertebral column.

Even though the vertebral column must provide strong protection for the spinal cord, it also must allow us to bend and twist at the waist. Thus, the vertebral column must be solid and strong, but it also must be flexible. This is, perhaps, one of the most obvious examples of God's incredible design ingenuity.

How can the vertebral column both be flexible and at the same time provide excellent protection for the spinal cord? Well, let's first look at its overall plan. The vertebral column can be divided into five sections: Seven cervical vertebrae (ver' tuh bray), twelve thoracic (thor as' ik) vertebrae, five lumbar vertebrae, a sacrum, and a coccyx (kok' six). These are illustrated in figure 3.15.

Although protection of the spinal cord is the most important function of the vertebral column, there are other functions it performs. The cervical vertebrae support the head and neck, while the lumbar vertebrae support the upper body, torso, and lower back. The sacrum is a critical part of the weight-bearing arch that also involves the hip bones (coxae). The vertebral column also allows spinal nerves to exit the spinal cord, and it permits motion of the head and trunk.

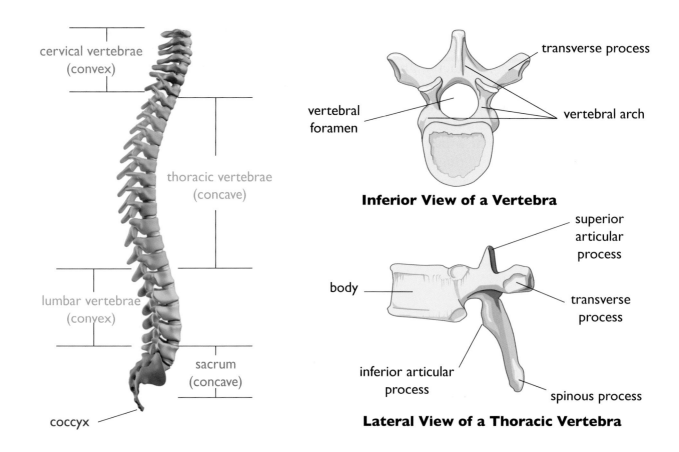

cervical vertebrae (convex)

thoracic vertebrae (concave)

lumbar vertebrae (convex)

sacrum (concave)

coccyx

transverse process

vertebral foramen

vertebral arch

Inferior View of a Vertebra

superior articular process

body

transverse process

inferior articular process

spinous process

Lateral View of a Thoracic Vertebra

FIGURE 3.15
The Vertebral Column
Illustrations on right ©Lippincott, Williams, and Wilkins

The curvatures of the spinal cord are quite interesting. In figure 3.15, we have noted that the cervical and lumbar vertebrae are arranged in a convex curve, while the thoracic vertebrae and the sacrum are arranged in a concave curve. Of course, the definition of whether a curve is convex or concave depends on the orientation from which you look. Our definitions are based on an anterior view of the spinal cord, which means a view from the front of the body. The purpose of this shape is to provide a cushioning effect against the impact of walking or running. In other words, the vertebral column can compress or expand, depending on the stresses that it experiences. This is just another of the incredible design features that we see in the body. Interestingly, the spinal cord does not start out in this "S" curve. When a baby is born, the entire spinal cord is curved in a concave fashion, so that the baby curves into its mother's arms. At around two months of age, the baby learns to lift up its head, and the convex curvature of the cervical vertebrae develops. At around six months, the child learns to sit up, and thus develops the convex curvature of the lumbar vertebrae.

Another ingenious design feature of the spinal cord rests in the shape of the vertebrae. Look at the inferior view of the vertebra in figure 3.15. The body of the vertebra bears the weight. The vertebrae stack on top of each other so that their bodies rest upon one another. Intervertebral disks of tough fibrocartilage snugly join the bodies of the vertebrae and keep them from rubbing against one another. This is shown in figure 3.16.

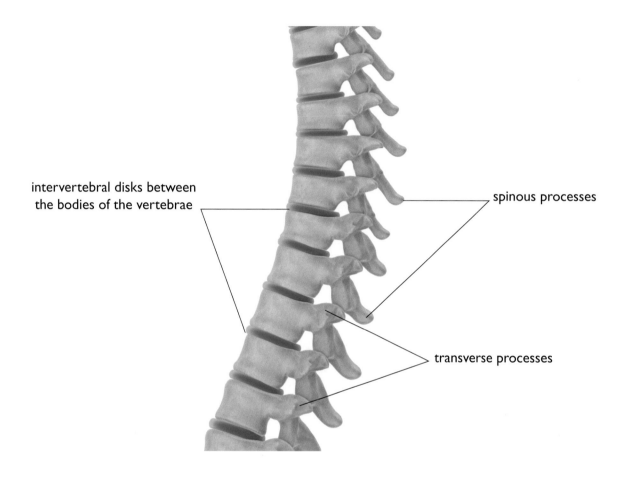

intervertebral disks between the bodies of the vertebrae

spinous processes

transverse processes

FIGURE 3.16
Lateral View of Vertebral Column
Illustration © Sebastian Kaulitzki, Agency: Shutterstock.com

The vertebral arch, along with the body, forms the vertebral foramen. The foramina of all of the vertebrae form a canal through which the spinal cord travels. Think about the design here. The spinal cord is surrounded by bone because the vertebrae stack on top of one another. Thus, the spinal cord is safe within its canal of bone. However, the canal itself does not bear weight. The weight is borne by the bodies of the vertebrae, which are anterior to the spinal cord!

Not only does the canal not have to bear weight, it can also move! To accomplish movement, there are processes that extend from of each vertebra. There is a transverse process that extends to the sides of each vertebra and a spinous process that extends posteriorly and inferiorly, pointing downward. You can feel the spinous processes of the vertebrae by running your fingers down the middle of your back. Those bumps are the spinous processes. Many small muscles attach to these processes, and these muscles control a large part of the movement of the vertebral column.

Each vertebra also has a superior articular process and an inferior articular process. When the vertebrae stack on top of one another, the superior articular process of one vertebra overlaps with the inferior articular process of the vertebra directly above it. This adds to the rigidity of the vertebral column, but at the same time, these two processes can move relative to one another, giving the vertebral column greater ability to move.

Now think about this incredible system for a minute. You have several individual pieces that stack one on top of one another. Since the vertebral column is made of individual pieces, it can bend rather easily. If that were the end of the story, however, it would not offer any support to the body, because a bunch of pieces stacked together can topple very easily. Thus, the intervertebral disks made of fibrocartilage hold the pieces together, as well as cushion them, so that they do not rub against each other.

That's not quite enough. Even with the intervertebral disks, the vertebral column would be *too* flexible, and the spinal cord could be stretched to the point that it would be harmed. Thus, the inferior and superior articular processes overlap, allowing for increased rigidity, but, at the same time, the motion of one vertebra relative to another.

**COLORING BOOK
EXERCISE 3.5**

To help you remember the details of the vertebral column, follow the directions on page 53 of the coloring book.

All told, then, the vertebral column provides a safe canal through which the spinal cord can travel, but it is so well designed that it allows for great flexibility of the back. In addition, this mobile canal is strong enough to support the head, upper limbs, and thoracic cage all at the same time. That is truly amazing!

DETAILS OF THE AXIAL SKELETON: THE THORACIC CAGE

The thoracic cage, commonly called the rib cage, protects the heart and lungs. It is an essential part of the breathing process, which we will discuss in a later module. The thoracic cavity is one of three cavities in the trunk of the body, and it is defined as the space enclosed by the thoracic cage.

The thoracic cage has twelve pairs of ribs. The superior seven pairs of ribs are called true ribs because they are attached directly to the sternum via costal cartilages, which are made of hyaline cartilage. The inferior five pairs of ribs are called false ribs, because the first three pairs do not attach directly to the sternum, and the last two pairs do not attach to the sternum at all. The first three pairs of false ribs have costal cartilages that attach to a shared cartilage, which is then attached to the sternum. Thus, these three pairs of false ribs are attached to the sternum, but not directly. The two most inferior pairs of false ribs, which are also called floating ribs, are quite small and do not attach to the sternum at all. The sternum, commonly called the breastbone, is divided into three parts: the manubrium (mah new' bree uhm), the body, and the xiphoid (zif' oyd) process.

You can see all of these bones in figure 3.17. Please note that to give you some orientation, this figure contains some bones that are not a part of the thoracic cage. They are labeled in blue to indicate that they are for orientation only.

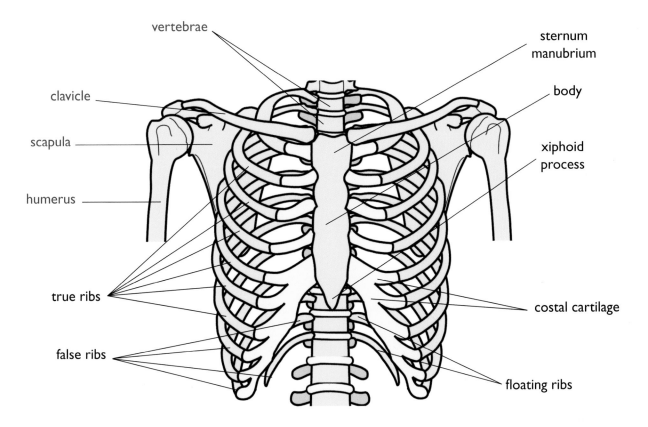

FIGURE 3.17
The Thoracic Cage
Illustration © Lippincott, Williams, and Wilkins

think about this

Have you ever heard someone say that men have one less rib in their thoracic cages than women? That is of course a myth. Some people mistakenly assume this must be so because of Genesis 2:21 where God removed a rib from Adam to make Eve. Remarkably, Adam probably was not missing a rib for very long. As long as the periosteum of the rib is left on the thoracic cage, the rib will actually regenerate! The rib periosteum (the connective wrapping around a bone) has more ability to regenerate bone than any other periosteum in the body. Surgeons make use of this fact all of the time. Often, for reconstructive surgery, surgeons need to take bone from one part of the skeleton and use it somewhere else. They usually take the bone they need from the ribs knowing that the ribs will regenerate quickly!

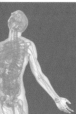

**COLORING BOOK
EXERCISE 3.6**

In order to become more familiar with the thoracic cage, follow the directions on page 61 of your coloring book.

We hope you have enjoyed your tour of the skeletal system. Obviously, you have a lot of bones to learn, but between the coloring book and some good, old-fashioned memory work, you should be able to identify all of the bones. It is important for many reasons to know the bones, not the least of which is that as you learn about other organs in the body, you will often be given the names of bones as a reference, so that you know where those organs are.

ANSWERS TO THE "ON YOUR OWN" QUESTIONS

3.1   Without dermal papillae, there would be no fingerprints. That would be ideal for a criminal!

3.2   Without dermal papillae, the skin will not get enough nutrients. Remember, the blood vessels loop through the dermal papillae, increasing the amount of blood flow to the basement membrane of the skin. Without these loops, the skin would not get enough nutrients.

3.3   According to figure 3.2, the lines of cleavage in the skin run horizontally in the region of the abdomen. The horizontal cut, then, runs along the lines of cleavage, while the vertical cut runs across them. Thus, the vertical cut will be more likely to leave a scar.

3.4   Only the cells in the stratum basale and the stratum spinosum can undergo mitosis. Since the cells in the other layers are dead or dying, they cannot undergo mitosis and therefore cannot form cancers. The skin cancer called melanoma results from the uncontrolled mitosis of melanocytes, which are in both of these layers. Basal cell carcinoma is a cancer that results from uncontrolled mitosis of the cells in the stratum basale. The third kind of skin cancer, squamous cell carcinoma, comes from the uncontrolled mitosis of cells in the stratum spinosum.

3.5   Only the medulla contains cells with soft keratin.

3.6   Hair cells will contain some form of keratin when they differentiate. If the cell contains no keratin, it has not differentiated yet, so it must be in the matrix.

3.7   If the hair follicle is empty, the hair is gone. However, since the matrix is not dead, hair will still grow. Thus, this hair follicle must have just entered the growth stage. Remember, a hair follicle loses its hair at the end of the rest stage so that it can grow another one.

3.8   The apocrine sweat glands are not really apocrine glands. They were once thought to be, and that is how they got their name. However, we now know that they are just merocrine glands, so they do not secrete cellular material. Someone really ought to change the name!

3.9   Teenagers everywhere would rejoice because without the oil from the sebaceous gland, there would be no acne. Other researchers would not approve such a procedure because you need that oil for healthy skin. It keeps the skin from painfully cracking, and it also makes it harder for harmful bacteria to attach to your skin.

3.10 The humerus supports the arm, forming its framework. It also is a place of lipid storage, since the limbs of an adult contain yellow bone marrow. The humerus itself does not really protect anything. Because of its joints at the shoulder and elbow, it contributes to the movement of the body. Also, it contains red bone marrow near the shoulder, so it is a site of hemopoiesis.

3.11 a. Looking at figure 3.8, the metatarsals are clearly longer than they are wide. Thus, even though they are small bones, they are classified as long bones.

b. Looking at Figure 3.8, the tarsals are about as long as they are wide. Thus, they are short bones.

c. The coxa does not fit into the long or short category, so it is an irregular bone.

d. The radius is longer than it is wide, so it is a long bone.

3.12 Epiphyseal plates exist when the bone is growing. When these plates of cartilage ossify, becoming bone, they are called epiphyseal lines, and the bone stops growing longer. Since the epiphyseal plates have not ossified in this case, this is not a mature bone, so the person still can grow taller.

STUDY GUIDE FOR MODULE 3

1. Define the following terms:
    a. Epidermis
    b. Dermis
    c. Hypodermis
    d. Hemopoiesis
    e. Compact bone
    f. Cancellous bone
    g. Ossification
    h. Articular cartilage
    i. Axial skeleton
    j. Appendicular skeleton
    k. Suture
    l. Process
    m. Meatus
    n. Foramen
    o. Sinus

2. What are the two layers of the skin? Which layer contains keratinized cells? Which layer contains papillae?

3. How do the dermal papillae help the epidermal cells?

4. Why do some cuts heal quickly with little scarring while other cuts of similar size and depth heal more slowly with more scarring?

5. How does the hair follicle or sweat gland help heal bad burns?

6. What kind of tissue is always present in the hypodermis? What kind of tissue is often, but not always, present in the hypodermis?

7. What is the function of sebaceous glands?

8. What is the function of sweat glands?

9. List the five layers of the epidermis, starting at the bottom and working up to the top.

10. In what layers of the epidermis are the cells still alive?

11. What are melanocytes, and what do they do to the skin?

12. What are the three sections of the hair? Which section(s) contain(s) cells with soft keratin? Which contain cells with hard keratin?

13. What is the hair matrix?

14. Identify the structures pointed out in the skin cross section below:

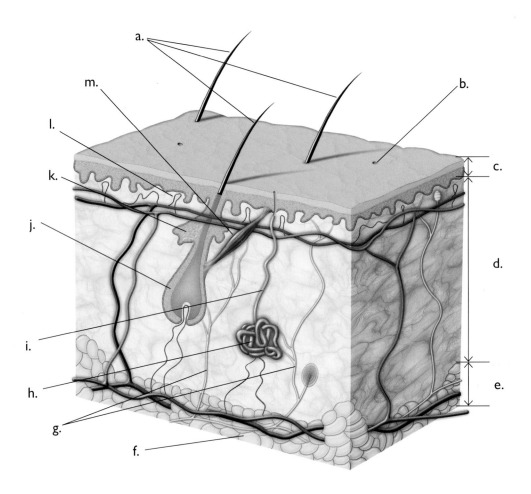

15. Classify sweat glands as apocrine, merocrine, or holocrine.

16. Classify sebaceous glands as apocrine, merocrine, or holocrine.

17. Classify the following bones as long, short, flat, irregular, or sesamoid.
    a. ribs
    b. metatarsals
    c. carpals
    d. patella
    e. coxa

18. Where is the bone marrow found in a long bone?

19. What are the five functions of the skeletal system?

20. Label the bones or other structures in the figure below:

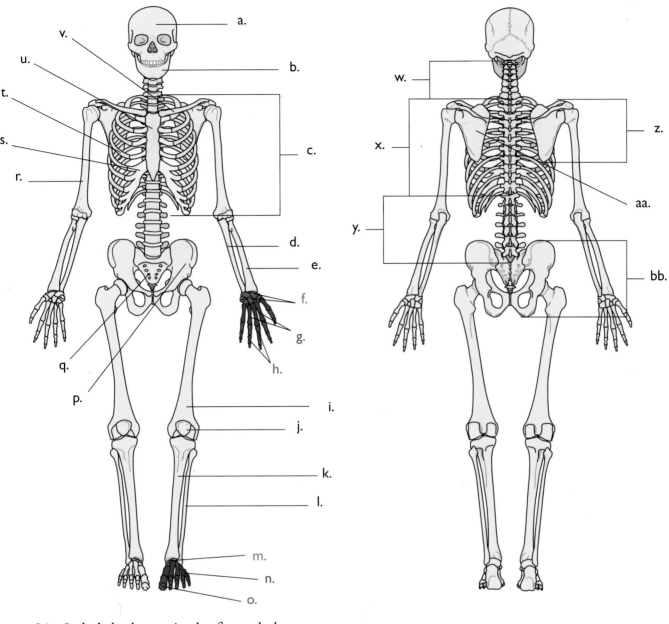

21. Label the bones in the figure below:

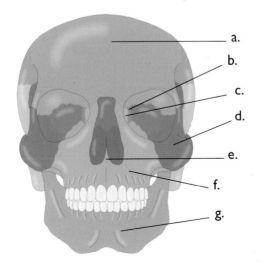

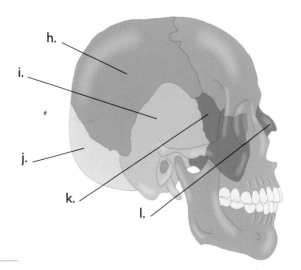

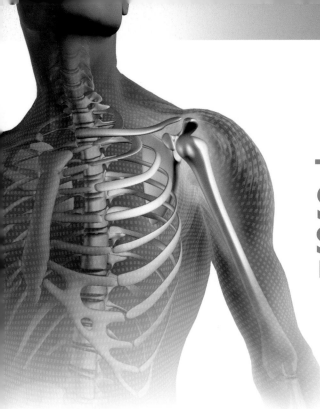

THE
SKELETAL
SYSTEM
HISTOLOGY AND MOVEMENT

We are not yet finished with the skeletal system. The human body is a complex and incredible design. You will see that much of the material that you study in this course builds on previous knowledge, so we have chosen to present the systems in a logical manner that allows you to build on material you have already learned.

heart of the matter

Each of us has a skeletal frame existing inside of us that gives us a quiet and dependable strength. It bears our stresses and offers protection. Although made up of rigid bone, this frame does not burden us, but rather frees us to move about.

Bone is classified as a connective tissue. The function of connective tissues (whether they are bone, connective tissue proper, or cartilage) depends on the composition of the tissue. The structure of connective tissue is determined mostly by its extracellular material, which is called the matrix. Yes, there are cells in connective tissue. They produce extracellular material, and the way the tissue functions depends mostly on the composition of the matrix that results. That is, the bone matrix will determine the function of bone.

Before we look at the extracellular material in bone, however, let's look at the cells that produce that extracellular material. When we discuss cells, the term *blast* means "immature cell" while the term *cyte* means "mature cell." Furthermore, the term *osteo* refers to "bone." With this knowledge, it is easy to understand the difference between osteoblasts (os' tee oh blasts) and osteocytes (os' tee oh sites).

Osteoblast—A bone-forming cell

Osteocyte—A mature bone cell surrounded by bone matrix

Osteoblasts are the cells that produce bone matrix. Once the matrix is fully formed, the cells are surrounded, and at that point, they are considered osteocytes. Just as is the case in cartilage, the osteocytes are housed in a microscopic space within the matrix, which is called a lacuna. An osteocyte in a lacuna is shown in figure 4.1.

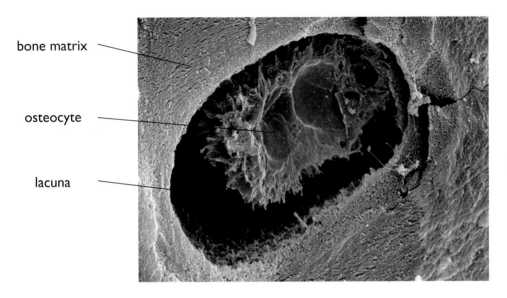

bone matrix

osteocyte

lacuna

NOTE: This is a scanning electron microscope image, and the colors were artificially added.

FIGURE 4.1
An Osteocyte in a Lacuna (4,000x magnification)
Photo © 2010 Steve Gschmeissner/Science Photo Library

There is actually one other major type of bone cell. An osteoclast (os' tee oh klast) is a cell that breaks down bone. You can remember this because the term clast means "to break."

Osteoclast—A large, multinucleated cell that breaks down bone

You might find it odd that there is a type of cell dedicated to breaking down bone. Nevertheless, such cells are essential for your good health. You see, your bones deteriorate on their own. In order to have healthy bones throughout your life, your body actually has to break down bone and then build it back up again. Also, when the body needs minerals that are stored in bone, the osteoclasts break down the bone tissue, releasing those minerals.

Bone contains these three basic types of bone cells, but the bone matrix gives bone its characteristics. First of all, bone matrix contains protein in the form of collagen fibers. In fact, about 30% of your bone is collagen. Where does this protein come from? The osteoblasts secrete it as they build the bone matrix. What is the function of collagen in bone? It gives the tissue flexibility and tensile strength. Remember, tensile strength is the kind of strength a rope has. You can pull on a rope, and it holds together firmly. Compare this to the strength of a tree branch. If you needed to pull someone out of a deep hole, you might be able to use either a rope or a tree branch. However, what do you risk when you use a tree branch? You risk the tree branch breaking. The tree branch has tensile strength, but it is much more brittle and can easily break in two. A rope also has tensile strength, but its flexibility keeps it from breaking. Why? The rope is made of fibers. In a similar way, your bones have tensile strength and some flexibility because of the collagen fibers that make up the bone matrix.

Of course, that can't be the end of the story. After all, your bones are not nearly as flexible as rope. It is a good thing that they aren't, or you would not be able to stand! In addition to collagen, bone matrix contains calcium salts (also called calcium minerals, bone salts, or bone minerals). Now remember from chemistry that the term *salt* refers to an ionic compound. Calcium salts are ionic compounds that contain calcium ions (Ca^{2+}). In addition, the term "mineral" refers to inorganic crystalline compounds. Ionic compounds form crystals as solids. Regardless of what you call them, the calcium salts in bone matrix are mostly $Ca_{10}(PO_4)_6(OH)_2$. The chemical name for this ionic compound is hydroxyapatite (high drok' see ap' uh tight). It is important to note that unlike the other components of connective tissue matrices (plural of matrix), the cells *do not* produce the calcium salts that are found in bone matrix. Instead, the blood brings the calcium salts into the bone matrix.

We are all accustomed to thinking of bone being calcium, and yet, if you calculate the composition of hydroxyapatite by mass, you will find that it is about 40% calcium and about 20% phosphorous. Thus, phosphorous is also a major element in bone tissue. We hear plenty of people telling us to drink milk and take calcium supplements because calcium will build strong bones. Why don't these same people talk about getting more phosphorous in our diet? The reason is simple. Most people get plenty of phosphorus in their diets. That is, most individuals get all of the phosphorous they need for healthy bones. However, some do not get enough calcium from their diets. Nevertheless, do not make the mistake of thinking that bones are made of just calcium. Calcium is certainly there, but other elements are important as well!

Hydroxyapatite gives bone its hardness, and it also gives bone its compressive strength. Compressive strength is the kind of strength that holds weight. For example, a rope standing on its end will not hold anything up, but a metal rod standing on its end will. That is because the rod has compressive strength. Concrete also has compressive strength. Bone, then, is an ingenious mixture of two substances, each of which provides something different. The collagen provides tensile strength with some flexibility, while the calcium salts provide compressive strength so that the bones can bear weight. To get some idea of how these two substances work together to give bone its properties, perform the following experiment.

science and creation

To call bone an "ingenious mixture" of materials is probably an understatement. Indeed, right now, bone's amazing blend of flexibility, tensile strength, and compressive strength is beyond the reach of human technology. Antoni Tomsia is a scientist who works for Lawrence Berkeley National Laboratory in California. His team is trying to produce "artificial" bone tissue, but they cannot produce anything close to the bone tissue your body makes. He says, "[We] want a strong, light, and porous material, which is almost a contradiction in terms, but nature does it... Bone is made from calcium phosphate and collagen, which are both extremely weak. But nature mixes them together at room temperature and without toxic chemicals to create something that is very tough — this fascinates us."

Experiment 4.1
Calcium Salts in Bone

Supplies:

- An uncooked chicken bone (preferably a wishbone or wing bone)
- A jar with a lid
- Vinegar (preferably white vinegar)

Purpose: Bone tissue is made of an ingenious mixture of collagen and calcium salts. In this experiment, you will see what bone tissue would be like if it did not have the calcium salts.

Procedure:

1. Clean the bone of all meat and tendons. Make it as bare as possible.

2. Allow the bone to dry overnight.

3. The next day, test the bone by trying to gently bend it. Do not use so much force that you break it! Notice that the bone bends a bit but is still mostly rigid.

4. Next, fill the jar with enough vinegar so that the bone will be fully immersed.

5. Put the bone in the jar and close it.

6. Every day, pull the bone out of the vinegar and test it as you did in step 3.

7. Note the difference that you observe.

8. Put the bone back into the vinegar and close the jar again.

9. Continue this process for 7 days or more.

10. When you are finally finished, clean up your experiment.

As time goes on, you will find that the bone gets more and more flexible. Why? Vinegar is an acid—dilute acetic acid. Notice one of the ions in hydroxyapatite—the hydroxide ion. That ion acts as a base. Thus, the acetic acid in the vinegar reacts with the hydroxide ion in hydroxyapatite. This destroys the calcium salt, and the Ca^{2+} ions dissolve into the solution. In the end, the bone matrix loses its calcium salt and, therefore, loses its compressive strength. The result is a bone that has the consistency of rubber! Have you heard of the disease called rickets? It is the result of low calcium levels in the body. This leads to a lack of hydroxyapatite in the bones, and as a result, the bones are more rubbery than normal bones. This causes the bones to bend as weight is put on them. Think for a minute about the "rubbery" bone that is left without its calcium salts. The bone has not disappeared into the vinegar. In fact, it is still shaped like a bone. What remains is mostly collagen, showing us that bone actually is about 30% collagen. It turns out that vitamin D is essential for the body to absorb calcium out of the intestines and into the blood, so the classic cause of rickets is a lack of vitamin D.

Now, imagine what would happen if you were to perform another experiment in which the collagen of the bone matrix was destroyed, but the calcium salts were left intact. What would you have then? You would have a very *brittle* bone. It would be hard, but with no flexibility, it would easily crack like a piece of chalk (which is calcium carbonate).

ON YOUR OWN

4.1 One type of bone cell secretes acid. Is it an osteoblast, osteocyte, or osteoclast?

CANCELLOUS AND COMPACT BONE HISTOLOGY

In discussing bone histology, we separate cancellous (spongy) bone tissue from compact bone tissue, as they appear different under a microscope. Let's start with cancellous bone, which is illustrated in figure 4.2.

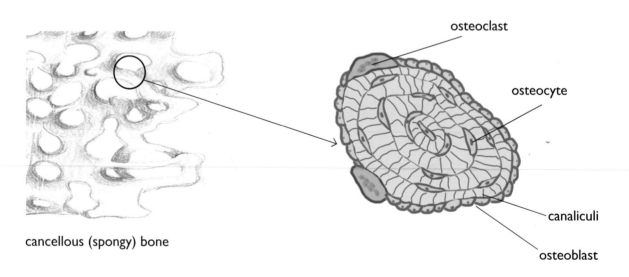

cancellous (spongy) bone

osteoclast

osteocyte

canaliculi

osteoblast

FIGURE 4.2
Cancellous Bone Tissue
Illustrations by Amanda Bitting (left)/Rachael Yunis (right)

Notice from the left side of the figure that cancellous bone does, indeed, look like a sponge. The little "beams" of bone that form the latticework you see in the drawing are called trabeculae (truh bek' you lay). The spaces in between these bones contain bone marrow and blood vessels. Now, if you were to look at one of the trabeculae under the microscope, you would see something like the drawing on the right side of the figure. Notice the three kinds of cells. The osteocytes are the ones on the inside of the bone. They are mature bone cells, having already surrounded themselves in extracellular material. Although surrounded by extracellular material, they do have a hollow living space (a lacuna), just like cartilage cells. The osteoblasts are on the edge of the bone. That should make sense, because osteoblasts form new bone tissue. So, they cannot be surrounded by the bone matrix. Finally, osteoclasts are large cells with several nuclei, and they break down the bone. Do not be misled by the spongy appearance; cancellous bone is hard and bears much of your body's weight. Just like the wooden framework of a house is not solid but bears weight, so does cancellous bone.

Now, let's compare figure 4.3 to a drawing of what compact bone would look like under a microscope.

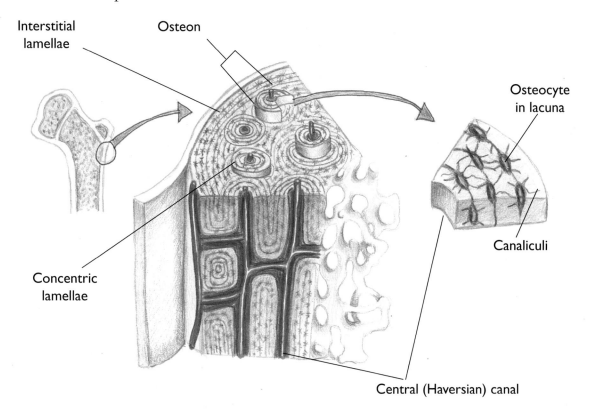

Interstitial lamellae

Osteon

Osteocyte in lacuna

Canaliculi

Concentric lamellae

Central (Haversian) canal

FIGURE 4.3
Compact Bone Tissue
Illustration by Amanda Bitting

Notice that the compact bone tissue is arranged in tightly-packed cylinders called osteons (os' tee onz). These structures used to be called Haversian systems, but the term has been changed to osteons over the course of time. In the middle of the osteon is a hollow tube called a central canal, which is still sometimes called the Haversian canal. Blood vessels run through that tube. Unlike cartilage, bone has a plentiful blood supply. You can see that in the figure. An osteon is composed of concentric lamellae (luh mel' lee), which are tubes of bone tissue that surround the blood vessels that run through the central canal. In between the osteons, there may be layers of tissue that do not form complete cylinders. This bony tissue is called interstitial lamellae, and it can be thought of as the "packing material" between the osteons.

The osteocytes in bone tissue have surrounded themselves with bone matrix and are trapped in their lacunae. Osteocytes are shaped like spiders, because they have microscopic "legs," called processes, extending from the main cell body. These processes allow the osteocytes to communicate with one another. This can happen because the process of one cell actually touches the process of another cell. This links the cells to one another. Those processes run through channels in the bone called canaliculi (kan uh lik' you lie), which is Latin for "tiny canals." Please note that the cancellous bone tissue also has canaliculi, as shown in figure 4.2.

Now let's see what these kinds of bone tissue actually look like under the microscope.

Experiment 4.2
Cancellous and Compact Bone Histology

Supplies:

- Microscope
- Prepared slide: bone marrow, red
- Prepared slide: dried human bone tissue

Purpose: To examine the details of bone tissue

Procedure:

1. Place the prepared slide of bone marrow under the microscope at 40x magnification. Look at the pattern made by the pink tissue. What does that look like? It looks like the cross section of a sponge, doesn't it? That is cancellous bone. The pink tissue is the tissue of the trabeculae, and the white spaces are the spaces between the trabeculae.

2. Increase magnification to 100x and focus. Notice now that the large white spaces in between the pink tissue contain tiny red dots. Those are cells in the bone marrow. The spaces in cancellous bone often contain red bone marrow. (They may also contain yellow bone marrow.)

3. Center the tissue of a trabecula (singular of trabeculae) and increase magnification to 400x. Focus again.

4. Now you really should be able to see the structure of the bone. Notice the little white circles in the trabeculae. Many of the circles contain a darker, purplish blob. The blob is an osteocyte, and the white circle is the lacuna in which the osteocyte is trapped. This, then, tells you that the pink tissue is really the matrix of the cancellous bone. Once again, the tiny red dots in the huge white spaces are cells in the red bone marrow.

5. Draw the section of the slide that you are examining. Be sure to label the lacunae, the osteocytes, the matrix, and the bone marrow cells, if they exist in the field you are examining.

6. Return your microscope to 40x magnification and replace the prepared slide of bone marrow with the prepared slide of human bone tissue. This slide contains compact bone. It might also contain some cancellous bone, but the compact bone is what we want to focus on.

7. Increase the magnification and focus. Can you see the cylinders made of concentric tissue layers? Those are the osteons.

8. Center an osteon, increase to 400x, and focus.

9. The lacunae in which the osteocytes are housed should be easy to spot. They are the black ovals with all of the hair-like extensions. Those extensions are the canaliculi. In addition, you should be able to see the tissue in between the osteons. Those are the interstitial lamellae.

10. Draw what you see, labeling an osteon, the central canal, the concentric lamellae, the interstitial lamellae, the lacunae, and the canaliculi.

11. Put everything away.

BONE GROWTH AND BONE REMODELING

Although you might not think of it, the bones in your body are constantly changing. To some extent, that is easy to understand. After all, when you are growing, your bones must grow with you. How is that accomplished?

ON YOUR OWN

4.2 You examine a sample of bone tissue under the microscope. It is composed of osteons. Is this compact bone tissue or cancellous bone tissue?

4.3 A bone cell is at the edge of a sample of bone tissue, and it is not surrounded by bone matrix. It has only one nucleus. Is this an osteocyte, osteoblast, or an osteoclast?

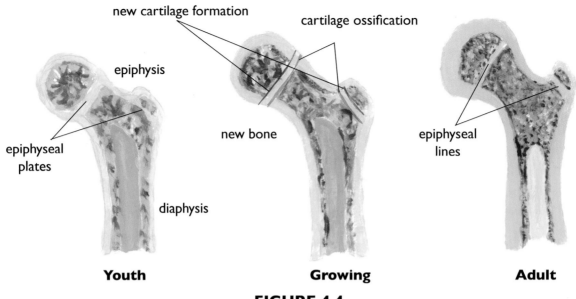

FIGURE 4.4
Long Bone Growth
Illustration by Amanda Bitting

When you are young, your long bones have epiphyseal plates that separate the diaphysis from the epiphysis. Those plates are made of hyaline cartilage. The cartilage cells (chondrocytes) near the epiphysis undergo mitosis, forming new cartilage. The area of new cartilage formation is shown in blue in the middle of the figure. You would think that this would make the thickness of the epiphyseal plate grow, right? Wrong!

You see, the older chondrocytes (mature cartilage cells) near the diaphysis enlarge, increasing the size of their lacunae. At the same time, calcium salts begin to accumulate in this older cartilage. As the calcium salts accumulate, the chondrocytes die, leaving behind holes which were once their lacunae. At this point, the cartilage is known as calcified cartilage. Once the chondrocytes are dead, blood vessels grow into the lacunae. Remember, cartilage has no blood vessels, but bone does. These blood vessels bring in osteoblasts and osteoclasts. The osteoblasts begin laying bone matrix on top of the calcified cartilage, forming new cancellous bone. This process is called ossification, and the result is to turn cartilage into bone. The area in which ossification occurs is shown as a red line in the middle figure.

What is the net result of all of this, then? The epiphyseal plates stay the same thickness as you grow—usually less than a millimeter in thickness. The cartilage near the diaphysis is ossified as quickly as the new cartilage near the epiphysis is formed. However, what does change is the length of the diaphysis. Since new bone is forming on the end of the diaphysis, the diaphysis grows, which increases the length of the bone! When you reach maturity, your bones no longer need to grow in length. Gradually, because of hormonal changes, the cartilage in the epiphyseal plate is overrun by the ossification process, and the epiphyseal plate is replaced with a bony marking called an epiphyseal line.

Although we did not show it in the figure, the epiphysis of a bone can grow in exactly the same way. The chondrocytes in the articular cartilage can undergo mitosis, forming new cartilage near the edge of the bone. The innermost cartilage then ossifies, forming new bone in the epiphysis. The only real difference between this process and the growth of the diaphysis is that the articular cartilage never completely ossifies. Even after the bone is fully grown, there is still articular cartilage at the end, which enables the bone to move smoothly in a joint.

That is all pretty incredible, isn't it? Cartilage grows at just the right speed, allowing the bone to grow without increasing the thickness of the epiphyseal plate. Of course, that is not the end of the story. Bone not only has to grow in length, but it also must grow in diameter as well. That is actually a relatively simple task, at least in comparison to the growth in length. Bones grow in diameter when osteoblasts lay new bone matrix on the surface of a bone. This is called appositional bone growth.

At the same time, osteoclasts remove bone from the medullary cavity, increasing the cavity size, as well. So you can see that the osteoclasts are necessary to growth. As it turns out, engineers long ago discovered that a hollow tube such as the diaphysis of a long bone could bear almost as much weight as a solid rod of the same diameter! Osteoclasts enlarge the medullary cavity as we grow, and the hollow area even stores energy in the form of fat (yellow marrow). An efficient use of the body's building materials!

Believe it or not, that is still not the end of the story. Bone is not static. It is broken down by osteoclasts because it is wearing out, and then it is rebuilt. That is called bone remodeling. Now, why would your body need to do this? First, while you are growing, your bones are growing, too. However, all new bone tissue is formed as cancellous bone tissue. Here is an analogy to explain this. Do you sew, or have you observed someone who sews? Often, in order to hold the cloth together quickly, the seamstress makes large, in-and-out stitches that are intended to be temporary. Once those stitches are holding the cloth together, she then uses the sewing machine to make the complex tight stitches that do the job exactly right. The first stitches (called basting stitches) are removed then, as they have served their purpose—a quick and easy, temporary fix.

Cancellous bone, like the basting stitches, is faster for the cells to produce, as it is less orderly than compact bone. So, it is laid first, making a quick fix that gets the job started. It can be replaced, a bit at a time, with the dense, orderly osteons of compact bone. This is not always necessary, though, and some bone is not replaced. You can see that in the cancellous bones within the epiphyses of long bones. However, any bone that is formed — whether you had a break in your bone, you are replacing old bone, or you are a child growing — is formed first as cancellous bone. So, any compact bone in your body is the result of bone remodeling.

A second reason for bone remodeling shows an amazing structural-functional relation. Although you probably have never thought about it, your bones increase or decrease their mass as needed! For example, bones that bear weight must be firm. If you walk around, exercise, and exert yourself, your bones will be stressed and will respond by increasing their mass to become more firm. On the other hand, if you are bed-ridden or very inactive, that stimulation is not there. As a result, bone will gradually be removed by osteoclasts as it deteriorates. In addition, if you gain weight, your bones will have more weight to bear and will therefore increase their mass to be able to do their job. If, on the other hand, you lose a lot of weight, your bones need not bear as much weight as they were used to bearing, and they will gradually lose mass.

The "stress" that we just mentioned is a compressive force on your bones. At the cellular level, you can think of it this way: Osteoblasts do not like to be "squashed" by your running, jumping, or other weight-bearing activities. They respond by secreting a protective shell around themselves so they can live in peace. That shell is more bone! Of course, nutrients such as protein, calcium, phosphorus, and others must be available to build strong bones. Osteoblasts that are not stressed have no stimulation to lay more bone, but the osteoclasts still actively remove old, deteriorating bone.

Yet another reason your body must remodel its bones is to reshape them. Orthodontics is a good example of reshaping bone. You might say your teeth are being straightened, but in reality your maxilla and mandible are being encouraged to remodel due to the gentle stress of the wire bands. When a tooth is pulled in one direction, its ligaments stress the bone, and more bone is laid there. On the opposite side of the tooth, there is compression on the tooth's ligament, and the bone is gradually removed by osteoclasts. The result is that the tooth moves into the newly remodeled socket, figure 4.5. By the way, bone remodeling also explains why you must wear retainers after orthodontics. The ligaments, which hold tooth to bone, have long memories, the orthodontists like to say. They have been stretched, and want to pull back to their original position. Without regular use of a retainer, they will gradually remodel the bone toward the original!

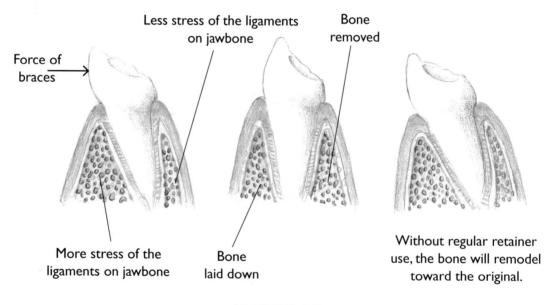

Less stress of the ligaments on jawbone

Bone removed

Force of braces

More stress of the ligaments on jawbone

Bone laid down

Without regular retainer use, the bone will remodel toward the original.

FIGURE 4.5
How Braces Work
Illustration by Amanda Bitting

How is this bone remodeling accomplished? It is done through the work of osteoblasts and osteoclasts. Don't forget, osteoblasts lay new bone, and that happens throughout life. The osteoclasts, on the other hand, break down bone tissue. Osteoclasts are big, multinucleate cells, which means that they have more than one nucleus. Osteoclasts secrete an acid that dissolves bone salts. Remember, the hydroxide ion is present in hydroxyapatite, and since it is a base, it will react with acid. That will cause the other ions in hydroxyapatite, including the calcium ion, to dissolve. In addition to acid, osteoclasts secrete proteolytic (pro tee' oh lih' tik) enzymes, which are enzymes that digest protein. What protein in particular do these enzymes digest? Collagen, of course!

The best way to describe how this all works is to give you an example. Let's discuss how a bone heals itself when it breaks. Figure 4.6 provides a quick overview of the process, which we will then explain in detail.

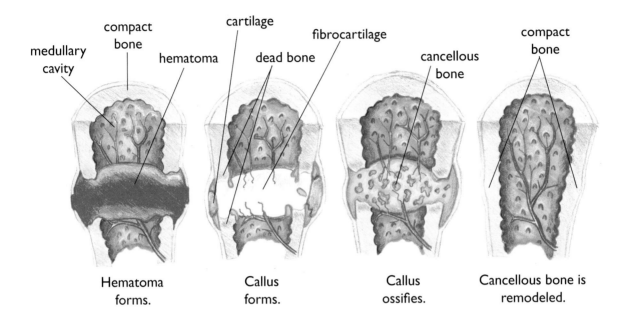

FIGURE 4.6
Bone Repair
Illustration by Amanda Bitting

When a bone is broken, the blood vessels in the bone and the periosteum are damaged. As a result, blood flows out of the vessels and into the surrounding tissues. This forms a hematoma (hee muh toh' muh).

Hematoma—A mass of blood that is confined to an organ in some limited space

The hematoma will eventually form a clot, which stops the bleeding. Because the blood vessels in the bone have been broken, many osteocytes near the break do not get the oxygen and nutrients that they need, and bone tissue surrounding the break dies. After the hematoma forms a clot, a callus (kal' us) forms.

Callus—A mass of connective tissue that connects the ends of a broken bone

Typically, a distinction is made between the callus that forms between the breaks in the bone (the internal callus) and the callus that forms around the outside of the bone (the external callus). While the internal callus will eventually form the new bone tissue, the external callus is formed of cartilage that is faster to produce than bone. It will stabilize the bone while it is being healed. Have you ever had to glue two pieces of wood together but the pieces would not stay in place while the glue dried? You might have taped the wood pieces in place, knowing that the tape would hold the pieces together until the glue could dry. Tape could not be used as a permanent solution, but it was a quick way of holding the wood together until the glue could form the real connection between the two pieces of wood. The external callus is like the tape in that situation. It holds the bone together while the slow process of forming bone tissue takes place. In modern medicine, we often use a cast in order to hold the bones together even more securely than the external callus.

As the internal and external calluses form, blood vessels grow into the internal callus, and fibroblasts start producing collagen. Chondroblasts then form cartilage within the fibers of collagen. Meanwhile, phagocytic cells (white blood cells that enter the tissues and engulf foreign or dead cells) begin breaking down the blood clot and cleaning away the debris. At the same time, osteoclasts break down dead bone tissue. Finally, osteoblasts start laying down new bone tissue. As time goes on, the cartilage in the internal and external callus is ossified, forming new cancellous bone tissue.

Of course, that is not the end of the story, because cancellous bone is not the proper replacement for the original compact bone. The break would never heal completely, unless the compact bone tissue that was originally in the bone can be replaced by more compact bone tissue. At this point, then, bone remodeling begins to occur. Osteoclasts gradually break down the cancellous bone in the external callus. Now that the bone tissue has formed, there is no need for an external callus anymore. Remember, when the glue between the two pieces of wood we discussed above dries, the tape is removed. In the same way, osteoclasts begin removing the external callus, which is no longer needed. At the same time, the cancellous bone is remodeled into compact bone. If the break occurred in the diaphysis of a long bone, the cancellous bone in the middle is removed by osteoclasts so that the medullary cavity is re-formed.

At the end of the healing process, then, the bone is as good as new. It is generally a little thicker than the surrounding bone because the external callus is not fully removed. The whole process can take quite some time, but the longest part is the remodeling that takes place at the end. The process in which the cancellous bone is remodeled into compact bone and the external callus is removed can take more than a year to complete, depending on which bone was broken and where the break occurred. If you have ever broken a bone, you may remember how long the "bump" lasted, even though the bone healed a long while ago.

If you have ever had a broken arm or leg, it was probably put into a cast or brace. Thankfully, however, you did not have to wear the brace for a year! That's because you need not wait for the entire process to finish before removing it. You really just have to wait until the bone is healed enough so that the two broken pieces will stay together. That is usually when the cancellous bone has been formed but has not yet been remodeled.

Now think about this entire process for a moment. Why doesn't your body simply repair the bone break right away with new bone tissue? Why go through the whole process of starting with cartilage, forming an external callus, forming cancellous bone,

and then remodeling the cancellous bone with compact bone? Why not just replace compact bone with compact bone to begin with? That takes an enormous amount of time. During that time, the bone would be weak and probably useless. Instead, then, your body forms a quick repair with cartilage, because cartilage grows much faster than bone. Since this quick repair is not as strong as bone, an external callus is formed to reinforce the repair. That way, the bone is functional in a matter of weeks, not months. After that, the slow process of compact bone formation can begin.

ON YOUR OWN

4.4   A medical researcher shows you an epiphyseal plate that has been removed from an immature bone. The researcher wants to know which side of the plate was closest to the diaphysis and which was closest to the epiphysis. If you had a microscope how could you tell?

4.5   When someone breaks an arm, the doctor often puts a cast on the arm. You can think of a cast as an "extra external callus." Why?

BONE HOMEOSTASIS

The skeletal system maintains homeostasis in the body in a number of ways. This involves the use of hormones. In this course, we will not wait to discuss hormones when we get to the endocrine system, which produces them. We want to discuss the individual hormones that affect each system, as we deal with that system. Since we are talking about the skeletal system now, we need to discuss the hormones that affect bones. When we finally get to the endocrine system, you will already have a good working knowledge of the major hormones in the body, and we will be able to talk about how hormones affect cells and how receptors respond to hormones.

In the anterior side (front) of your neck, at the base, there is a soft butterfly-shaped gland that you probably can't feel if it is normal in size. It's your thyroid gland. Chances are you've heard of it before. Embedded in the four edges of the thyroid gland are four small parathyroid glands. Even though you probably have not heard of these four, they are essential for life. If they were removed or stopped functioning, without medical treatment you would die within a few days. These parathyroid glands secrete what is called parathyroid hormone, abbreviated PTH. This hormone regulates the concentration of calcium ions in the blood. The thyroid gland itself secretes several hormones, one of which is called calcitonin (kal sih toh' nin). This hormone is also involved in regulating the concentration of calcium in the blood, but it is not essential for life.

The concentration of blood calcium affects many processes in the body. When blood calcium levels drop, for example, the neurons become overactive and overstimulate the muscles. As a result, the muscles can't relax. This can become so severe that a person's fingers may stay clenched. If the condition persists, the muscle that controls breathing (the diaphragm) cannot relax, and the person can asphyxiate (die from an inability to breathe). Calcium ions in the blood also affect blood clotting, neuron-to-neuron communication, and heart muscle contraction. So, you can see that PTH, which regulates blood calcium, truly is essential for life.

In order to keep this from happening, the body has a negative feedback system, as illustrated in figure 4.7.

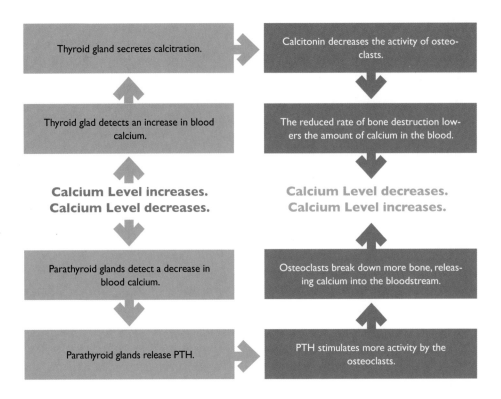

FIGURE 4.7
Calcium Regulation by PTH

As shown in the figure, when the level of calcium in the blood decreases, the parathyroid glands detect the decrease, and that causes them to release PTH. This hormone causes osteoclasts to increase their activity. This means more bone will be broken down. Is that good? In this case, yes, it is. Remember, one of the functions of the skeletal system is to store calcium. So, when PTH is released, it is telling your body to make a withdrawal from your "calcium bank." The PTH signals the osteoclasts to break down some bone, releasing calcium from the bone into the blood. That raises blood calcium levels.

That is probably the main way in which your body keeps the calcium level in the blood from dropping. However, your body was designed very intricately and precisely. As a result, there are several other ways that your body counteracts a decrease in blood calcium. This makes your body the marvel of efficiency that it is. As you will learn later, the kidneys cleanse the blood and control the levels of many chemicals in the blood. One way they do this is by removing excess chemicals from the blood and releasing them into the urine. PTH stimulates the kidneys to decrease the amount of calcium in the urine, which increases the amount left in the blood. Also, PTH stimulates the production of vitamin D, and vitamin D in turn increases the amount of calcium that your body can absorb from the food that you eat. This one hormone stimulates several separate mechanisms by which calcium levels in the bloodstream can be increased!

As you learned in the first module, each variable in the body has a set range in which it can operate. If the value of a variable is too low or too high, the body will suffer negative consequences. This is true of blood calcium, as well. Low blood calcium levels are a problem, but high blood calcium levels are also a problem. So, there is another negative-feedback system that counteracts increases in blood calcium levels. This is controlled by the thyroid gland's hormone, calcitonin.

When the thyroid detects an increase in blood calcium level, it secretes calcitonin. This hormone decreases the activity of osteoclasts. As a result, bone continues to be formed by the osteoblasts, an ongoing process of bone remodeling, but it is not destroyed as quickly. This causes the blood to lose calcium, as calcium is moved from the blood to the bone. As a result, the blood calcium level decreases, and homeostasis—a state of healthy balance—is achieved. This, then, can be viewed as making a deposit into the "calcium bank." Since the blood contains too much calcium at the moment, it is stored in the skeletal system for later use.

As we mentioned, however, God has designed the body so incredibly well that there is often more than one way in which variables are controlled. Such is the case with calcium levels in the

science and creation

We want to pause a moment and point out something from science history. Evolutionists have routinely predicted that there should be many **vestigial organs** in nature because as a species evolves, it might not need the function of one or more of its organs. Darwin not only expected many vestigial organs in nature, he actually likened them to the "silent letters" that appear in many English words. The letters serve no purpose, but they provide clues regarding the word's origin. In the same way, vestigial organs would serve no purpose in an organism, but they would give clues regarding the path by which the organism evolved.

Why do we bring this up now? Because, in 1893, a very famous anatomist named Robert Wiedersheim published a book in which he listed all the vestigial organs in the human body. In total, he said there were 86 vestigial organs, and both the thyroid and parathyroid glands made his list! He gave what was considered at the time very strong evidence that they served no useful function. We know better now. Indeed, without the actions of your thyroid and parathyroid glands, you would become sick and die within a short while.

The point we want to make is threefold. First, even world-renowned experts in their field can be drastically wrong about issues in their field, as Wiedersheim's pronouncement that the thyroid and parathyroid glands are vestigial clearly shows. Second, scientific knowledge continues to change. As a result, things we think we know for certain might very well be demonstrated to be incorrect a few years down the road, including some of the things you read in this book! Finally, when you hear scientists discuss what they consider to be solid evidence for evolution, remember that over time, many supposedly conclusive evidences for evolution have been shown to be drastically wrong.

blood. Although the thyroid can produce calcitonin, which decreases osteoclast activity in order to reduce calcium levels, the parathyroids can also reduce calcium levels by simply making less PTH. If PTH levels increase, osteoclast activity increases. However, if PTH levels decrease, osteoclast activity will decrease, as well. If you compare the effect of calcitonin increase or PTH decrease on lowering calcium in the blood, the decrease of PTH levels is probably the more important one. How is it that the parathyroids, whose hormone raises blood calcium, are considered essential to life, but the thyroid's calcitonin, which lowers blood calcium, is not? The kidneys can always excrete excess calcium, lowering the blood levels of this ion. So, we see yet another way that our body maintains homeostasis.

Returning to the subject of hormones, there are other hormones that control the skeletal system. One of those is growth hormone, abbreviated GH. This hormone is secreted by the anterior pituitary gland. The pituitary gland is found at the base of the brain and is actually composed of two glands that are quite different. As the name implies, the anterior pituitary is the part in front. It secretes several hormones including GH. GH, as the name also implies, stimulates tissue growth. It stimulates other tissues besides bone tissue, but bone is a major target tissue. GH, as you might imagine, stimulates osteoblast activity. If osteoblast activity is increased, bone tissue will grow.

If too little GH is released by the anterior pituitary gland during childhood, bone tissue will not grow very quickly, and the child will not grow well. Untreated, this leads to dwarfism, a condition in which a person is much shorter than the average human. If too much GH is released from the anterior pituitary gland, bones will grow too rapidly, resulting in giantism, a condition in which someone is significantly taller than the average human. If the GH levels rise in an adult, the epiphyseal plates are already ossified, and the bones cannot grow longer. However, they will grow thicker. This will cause the brow to look thick and the hands and feet to get abnormally large. This is all caused by the abnormal thickening of the bones.

Human growth hormone is one of the hormones that we can artificially synthesize. The body is a significantly better chemistry lab than human science's greatest laboratories. It can produce many, many more chemicals than human science can. However, human growth hormone is one of the few chemicals that human science can manufacture almost as well as the human body can. This hormone can be injected into children who suffer from low GH levels, allowing them to grow normally if their epiphyseal plates have not yet ossified.

The sex hormones estrogen and testosterone also stimulate osteoblastic activity. They are secreted from the sex organs (testes in males and ovaries in females). Women also get estrogen from body fat. Have you ever noticed that children usually have a spurt of growth during puberty? That is because their sex organs begin releasing sex hormones. Since these hormones stimulate osteoblastic activity, it causes rapid bone growth. Interestingly, however, these same hormones also cause the epiphyseal plates in long bones to ossify. This, of course, stops growth. So, the sex hormones initially cause a rapid growth spurt, but eventually lead to the cessation of growth. As one enters puberty, then, one grows rapidly, but the same hormones that cause that rapid growth sooner or later cause you to stop growing altogether!

ON YOUR OWN

4.6 A person's parathyroid gland actively starts increasing its secretion of PTH. Was the person's blood calcium level too low or too high?

4.7 Several health care organizations stress that puberty is a very important time to make sure children are getting plenty of calcium in their diet. Indeed, some studies indicate that adequate calcium intake during puberty is essential for long-term health of the skeleton. Why?

NUTRITION FOR BONE HEALTH

Everyone, it seems, knows that calcium is necessary for bone growth and maintenance, and you have just learned that phosphorus also is essential to form bone. You also know that protein is needed in order to form collagen. So, you already are well aware of three nutrients essential for bone growth. Milk is an excellent source of all three.

However, many other nutrients contribute to bone health. Vitamin D is essential to absorb calcium. Magnesium is the third most common mineral in bone, after calcium and phosphorus. It enables the calcium to be used properly in bone formation. Vitamin C is essential to form collagen.

This is not a complete list, either. Other vitamins and minerals are required to form the enzymes that bone cells use in making or breaking down bone. A number of vitamins and minerals are needed to release energy within bone cells. Recent research shows that vitamin K helps maintain strong bones, and as time goes on, you will likely hear about other nutrients that enable bone to grow and to remain strong throughout life.

THE THREE MAJOR TYPES OF JOINTS IN THE SKELETON

There is one more part of the skeletal system that we need to discuss: joints. Joints allow the skeletal system to move. They are places where different bones are joined. There are three basic kinds of joints: fibrous joints, cartilaginous joints, and synovial (sih noh' vee uhl) joints. Examples of the first two types of joints are shown in figure 4.8.

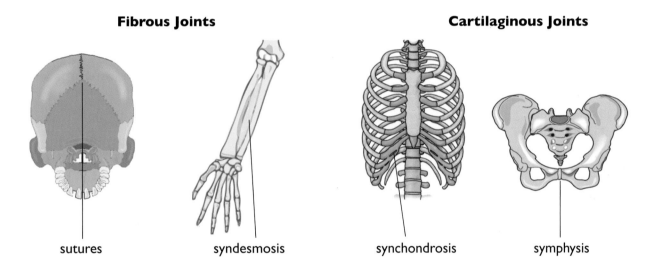

Fibrous Joints   **Cartilaginous Joints**

sutures   syndesmosis   synchondrosis   symphysis

FIGURE 4.8
Examples of the Major Types of Fibrous and Cartilaginous Joints
Cartilaginous joint illustrations © Shutterstock.com/ Blamb

A fibrous joint consists of two bones that are joined together with fibrous connective tissue. These joints are either immovable or slightly movable. A fibrous joint can be further classified as a suture or a syndesmosis (sin' dez moh' sis). A suture is completely immovable. When you studied the bones of the skull (fig. 3.14), you saw tight junctions between bones called sutures. Sutures are found only in the skull. A syndesmosis is a fibrous connection between two bones that are farther apart from each other compared with the tight fit of bones in a suture. One of the best examples of a syndesmosis is in the forearm. The radius and ulna are connected by fibrous connective tissue. This forms a slightly moveable joint. So, unlike sutures, syndesmoses are slightly moveable.

Cartilaginous joints are the points at which bones are united with fibrocartilage or hyaline cartilage. These joints are also either immovable or slightly moveable, and can be further classified as a synchondrosis (sin' kon droh' sis) or a symphysis (sim' fih sis). Synchondroses (plural of synchondrosis) consist of joints made by hyaline cartilage. The epiphyseal plates in youthful bone are examples of synchondroses, as are the strips of cartilage that attach the ribs to the sternum. On the other hand, a symphysis consists of bones joined by fibrocartilage. The symphysis pubis, which joins the two coxal bones, is an example of such a joint, as are the intervertebral disks between the bones of the vertebral column.

The third type of joint is the synovial joint. We will concentrate on this type of joint, because it is the one that allows for free movement of the skeleton. There are six different kinds of synovial joints, which we will discuss in a moment. First, however, let's look at the general characteristics of a synovial joint.

Synovial joints are joints that contain synovial fluid. They are significantly more complex than the other types of joints, mostly because they are so incredibly efficient at allowing smooth, painless, low-friction movement. A typical synovial joint is shown in figure 4.9.

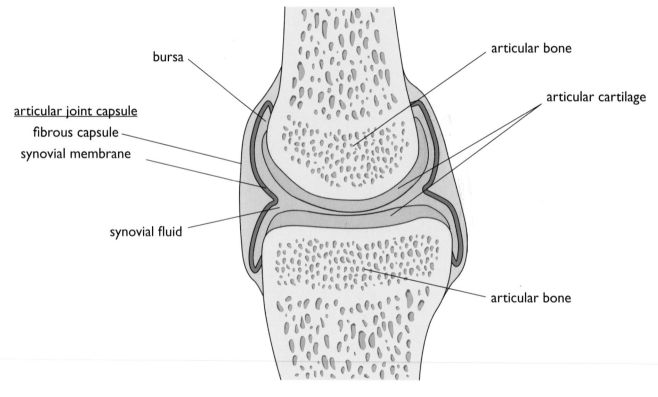

FIGURE 4.9
A Synovial Joint
Illustration by Lippincott, Williams, and Wilkins

In a synovial joint, the ends of the bones are covered with articular cartilage, made of hyaline cartilage. Hyaline cartilage has some of the characteristics of hard plastic. What is the purpose of the articular cartilage? It helps the bones move smoothly inside the joint. If the bones in a synovial joint rubbed against one another as they moved, it would cause severe damage to the bone tissue, as well as pain and inflammation. The articular cartilage in a synovial joint, however, provides a smooth "hard plastic" coating for the bones so that they can rub against one another without damage.

Although the articular cartilage allows the bones to move without damaging each other, there is another aspect of bone movement that must be considered. If you take two pieces of hard plastic and rub them up against one another, what happens? The surfaces eventually get hot, right? That is because of friction. When two surfaces rub against each other, there is always friction. Friction does two things. First, it reduces the efficiency of motion. Think about it. The bones in a joint must move. It takes a certain amount of energy to make that happen. The more friction there is, the more energy it takes to make the motion happen. That reduces the efficiency of the motion. Second, as we just pointed out, friction causes heat. Too much heat can be deadly to tissue.

The synovial joints in the body are designed to reduce friction in a most ingenious way. A synovial joint is surrounded by an articular capsule, which is also called a joint capsule. You can think of the articular capsule as a tough but thin sac that surrounds the joint. The capsule is made of two layers. The outer layer is called the fibrous capsule. It is made of dense irregular connective tissue, and it is actually an extension of the outer layer of the periosteum. This fibrous capsule holds the bones in the joint together. Depending on the individual joint, the fibrous capsule can be thick and form ligaments, which are strands of dense regular connective tissue that add more stability to the joints, holding the bones together with more strength than the fibrous capsule alone.

If the joint cavity filled with synovial fluid extends well beyond the joint, it is usually called a bursa. A bursa provides a fluid-filled cushion between parts that would otherwise rub against one another. For example, tendons would rub against bone or other tendons in many joints if it were not for a bursa. You may have heard the term bursitis (ber sigh' tis). This malady is an inflammation of a bursa that can cause pain and restrict joint movement.

The inner layer of the articular capsule is called the synovial membrane. This membrane is a collection of connective tissue cells that produce synovial fluid, a truly wondrous substance! This liquid is made from blood plasma and chemicals secreted by the cells in the synovial membrane. These chemicals include proteins, fats, and polysaccharides. Probably the most important chemical in the mix is a polysaccharide called hyaluronic (hi' uh loo ron' ik) acid. This acid makes synovial fluid very slippery, much like egg white. In fact, the *ovial* in synovial means "egg-like."

The slippery nature of synovial fluid *lubricates* the joint, reducing friction between the articular cartilage of the two bones. Now think about that for a moment. A synovial joint *produces its own lubricant*. This lubricant significantly reduces friction, allowing the bones of the joint to move efficiently without an overwhelming amount of heat being produced. Interestingly, however, that's not the only function of synovial fluid. It also supports the chondrocytes in the articular cartilage of the joint by supplying them with oxygen and nutrients

think about this

Take a moment from your studies to contemplate the amazing facts that you have learned about bones. Throughout history, the skeleton has been used as a symbol of death, but you now know that it represents life! It is strong and yet light and efficient. It is constantly growing and responding to your body's needs. It has joints and lubricates itself to permit movement. Perhaps most amazing of all, when it is broken, it heals itself! There are no man-made machines that can claim these feats.

while relieving them of carbon dioxide and metabolic wastes. In addition, it acts as a shock absorber for the joint. Isn't that incredible?

There are six major types of synovial joints found in the human body. They are summarized in figure 4.10.

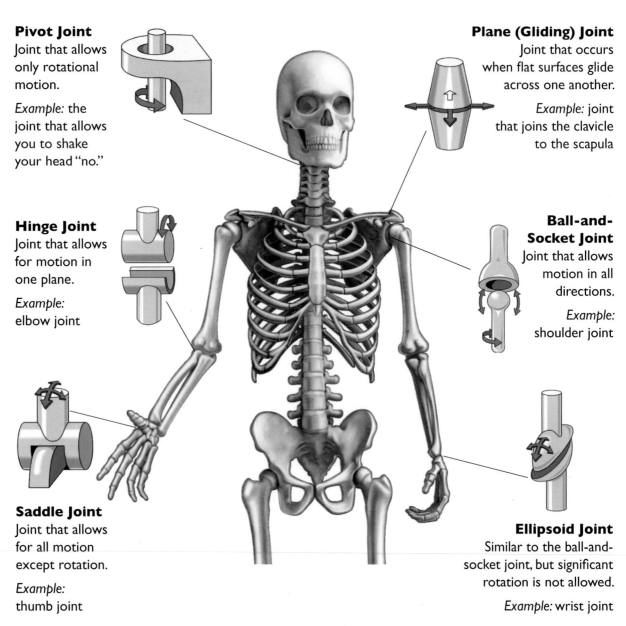

Pivot Joint
Joint that allows only rotational motion.

Example: the joint that allows you to shake your head "no."

Hinge Joint
Joint that allows for motion in one plane.

Example: elbow joint

Saddle Joint
Joint that allows for all motion except rotation.

Example: thumb joint

Plane (Gliding) Joint
Joint that occurs when flat surfaces glide across one another.

Example: joint that joins the clavicle to the scapula

Ball-and-Socket Joint
Joint that allows motion in all directions.

Example: shoulder joint

Ellipsoid Joint
Similar to the ball-and-socket joint, but significant rotation is not allowed.

Example: wrist joint

FIGURE 4.10
The Six Major Types of Synovial Joints
Skeleton Illustration : Andrea Danti Agency: Shutterstock.com
Joint Illustrations by Lippincott, Williams, and Wilkins

The first type of joint, the ball-and-socket joint, provides for the highest range of motion. This joint consists of a rounded head (the ball) on the end of one bone resting in a rounded depression (socket) on the end of the other bone. This kind of joint is designed for movement in all directions. The hip and shoulder joints are both examples of ball-and-socket joints. Think of all the different ways in which you can move your arm at the shoulder. You can twirl it around, move it up and down, and swing it back and forth. That is the excellent range of motion provided by the ball-and-socket joint. The hip joint is more deeply set, so it does not have quite the range of motion of the shoulder joint, except possibly in young gymnasts, who never fail to amaze us!

The hinge joint does not offer such a wide range of motion. These joints are composed of a cylinder at the end of one bone, resting in a cylindrical depression at the end of the other bone. They provide for motion in only one plane. Think of the hinge on a door. The door can swing in or out on the hinge, but that's it. It can't swing in any other direction. The same is true for hinge joints. Your elbows and knees are hinge joints. The elbow is a true bony hinge, but the bones of the knee joint are quite flat. However, strong ligaments around the knee ensure that only hinge motion can occur. These ligaments, as you may know if you are a sports fan, can be damaged by sudden twisting motions and may require surgery for repair. To get an idea of how different the range of motion is between a ball-and-socket joint and a hinge joint, compare the many ways you can move your arm at the shoulder to the single way you can move your forearm at the elbow.

Saddle joints are composed of two saddle-shaped bones that are oriented perpendicular to one another. These joints provide a larger range of motion than the hinge joint, but they do not allow for rotation. So, they provide less freedom of motion than a ball-and-socket joint, but more freedom of motion than a hinge joint. The joint that joins your thumb's metacarpal to the carpal in your wrist, called the *carpometacarpal joint*, is a saddle joint.

Ellipsoid joints are similar to ball-and-socket joints. However, as their name implies, they are elliptically shaped instead of spherically shaped, as is the case in ball-and-socket joints. Because the joint is not spherically-shaped, the range of motion is more limited than it is in the ball and socket joints. Only a slight amount of rotation is allowed, making the range of motion very similar to that of a saddle joint. Some joints in your wrists are examples of ellipsoid joints.

Pivot joints are formed when a process from one bone is surrounded by a ring of another bone. This interesting type of joint allows only for partial rotational motion. For example, the second cervical vertebra (called the axis) has a long process (called the dens) that pokes through the foramen of the first cervical vertebra (called the atlas). This forms a pivot joint that allows you to rotate your head in the motion commonly used to mean *no*.

Finally, plane joints (also called gliding joints) consist of two flat surfaces of about equal size that slide against one another. Typically, there is very little motion in this type of joint. A process from the scapula rubs against a process in the clavicle to make a gliding joint. Another example of a plane joint comes from the vertebral column. A vertebra has a superior articular process which forms a synovial joint with an inferior articular process of another vertebra. This joint is a gliding joint.

You might be wondering why there are so many different kinds of joints in the body. After all, for the maximum amount of motion possible, why aren't all joints just ball-and-socket joints? That way, you could move your skeleton any way you wanted it to move. Well, the answer is that each joint is designed to do a specific job. Some joints (like the shoulder joint) do need to provide a wide range of motion, and these are the ball-and-socket joints. However, ball-and-socket joints are generally less stable than other joints, so the wide range of motion comes at a cost.

Compare this to an elbow or knee joint. These are hinge joints. They offer a limited range of motion but, as a result, are much more stable. So, each joint is designed specifically to meet a need. Some joints offer a wide range of motion, but they cannot hold much weight or be subjected to much stress, because they are not as stable. Other joints offer a limited range of motion, but they can bear much weight and stress because they are quite stable. The wide range of synovial joints in our bodies is a testament to the design ingenuity of the Creator. He designed each kind of joint to do the exact job it needs to do in the body.

COLORING BOOK EXERCISE 4.1

To review what you have learned about joints, follow the directions on pages 91-93 of your human anatomy coloring book.

ON YOUR OWN

4.8 One of the specific joint types discussed in this section actually forms a joint that may exist only during childhood. In adults, many of these joints are gone. To which joint type do we refer? Hint: It is *not* a synovial joint.

4.9 Leaving out pivot joints, list the other synovial joints in terms of *increasing* range of motion.

4.10 A synovial joint lacks synovial fluid. What part, most likely, is damaged?

MOTION AND TERMS OF MOVEMENT

We soon will explore the muscle system when we get to the next module. Muscles, of course, allow us to move our skeleton at the joints. In order to properly discuss muscles, we need to introduce some specific terminology when it comes to motion. However, before we can do that, we must first define some points of reference. After all, to be aware of motion, you must first have a reference point. If a person moves from the couch to the refrigerator, you know that the person moved because you have a point of reference: the couch. Since the person's position relative to the couch is changing, you know that the person is moving. In human anatomy, we also have a reference point. It is called the anatomical position.

Anatomical position—The position acquired when one stands erect with the feet facing forward, the upper limbs hanging at the sides, and the palms facing forward with the thumbs to the outside

Now imagine yourself standing like that. That is a reference point. From there, we can develop certain terms for direction, as illustrated in figure 4.11.

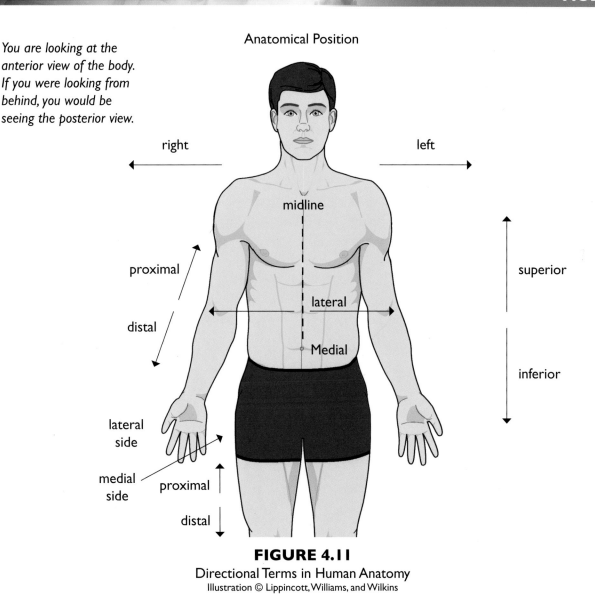

Anatomical Position

You are looking at the anterior view of the body. If you were looking from behind, you would be seeing the posterior view.

FIGURE 4.11
Directional Terms in Human Anatomy
Illustration © Lippincott, Williams, and Wilkins

As you have already learned, superior means above, and inferior means below. Please note that these two terms are only used in reference to the head, neck, and trunk. When discussing the limbs, we use the terms proximal (nearest to the attachment to the trunk) and distal (distant from the attachment on the trunk). In addition, anterior means front, and posterior means back. In the anatomical position, then, your chest is superior to your waist, and your back is posterior to your chest. Your humerus is proximal to the radius and ulna, which are distal to the humerus.

In addition to these directional terms, we can add some terms that relate to positions within the body as well. The midline is the imaginary line that runs down the center of the body, separating your right and left sides. If you imagine a plane that runs through the body at the midline, that plane is called the midsagittal (mid saj' ih tuhl) plane, and it divides the body into two equal left and right halves. If a part of the body is located away from the midsagittal plane, we say it is lateral. If a part of the body is close to the midsagittal plane, we say it is medial.

With these points of reference and directions, we can finally define the terms of movement that we need for joints. When we discuss movement, the terminology refers to the *body part* that moves. The joint allows that movement, of course. The terms summarized in figure 4.12 refer to the motion of a limb or other body part.

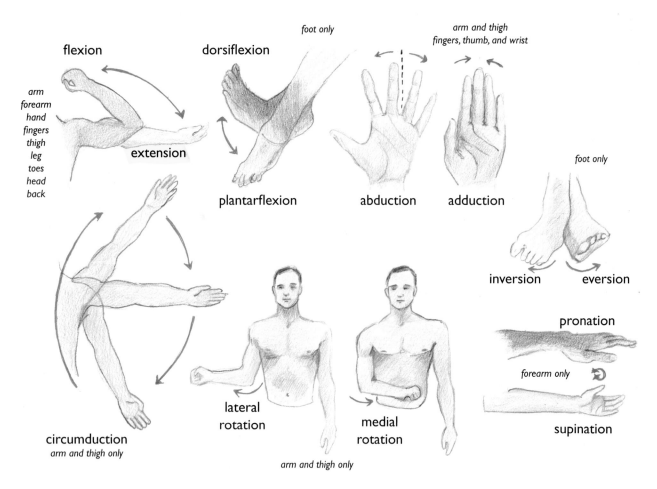

FIGURE 4.12
Terms of Movement
Illustration by Amanda Bitting

The term to start with is extension. As shown in the upper left portion of the figure, extension means to straighten a body part. The limbs, hands, fingers, toes, head, and back can be extended. *In the anatomical position, all body parts are extended.*

The opposite of extension is flexion. In flexion, you decrease the angle between the bones of the joint. When you are in the fetal position, meaning curled up like you are trying to stay warm in a cold bed, most of your body parts are flexed. Look once again at the upper left drawing in figure 4.12. In flexion, the angle between the humerus and the radius (or ulna) decreases. Your fingers, wrists, elbows, shoulders, vertebral column, thighs, legs, and toes can flex.

As you can see from the drawing, the ankles have special terms for their motion. When you move your ankle so that you can stand on tiptoes, you are performing plantarflexion. When you move your ankle so that the angle between your foot and leg decreases, you are performing the opposite, dorsiflexion. Stand on your heels with your toes off the floor to perform dorsiflexion of the foot.

The next drawing to the right illustrates abduction. In this motion, *body parts move away from the midline.* In the drawing that is in the figure, the midline refers to the imaginary line that runs down the middle of the hand. As the fingers spread, they are moving away from the midline of the hand. The opposite of this is adduction (illustrated in the next drawing), where the limbs or fingers move toward the midline.

Midline, however, usually refers to the imaginary line down the center of the body. Imagine that you are standing in the anatomical position and you suddenly raise your right arm and point out to the right. At that point, you are moving your arm away from the midline, so you are performing abduction. When you let your arm drop to the side again, you are performing adduction. The thighs also can abduct, as when you spread your legs in a jumping jack. When you bring them back together to the anatomical position, they are adducting.

The next terms are easy. When you turn your foot inward, you are performing inversion of the foot. When you turn your foot outward, it is eversion of the foot. Only the foot performs this motion. Circumduction is a circular motion that is performed by ball-and-socket joints. As shown in the figure, when you move your arm in a circle, you are performing circumduction of the arm. Although the hip joint is a ball-and-socket joint, it is too deep to allow for complete circumduction of the thigh.

Rotation occurs when a joint turns a bone on its axis. As shown in the figure, there are two kinds of rotation. If the rotation is toward the midline, it is medial rotation. If the rotation is away from the midline, it is lateral rotation. The shoulder and hip joints allow for medial and lateral rotation of the arm and thigh. In fact, when a baby is born, the birth attendant usually medially and laterally rotates the baby's thighs to make sure that the birthing process has not dislocated the hip joints.

The last two terms, pronation (pro nay' shun) and supination (sue' pih nay' shun) refer only to the unique rotation of the forearm. If you rotate your forearm so that the palm faces anteriorly, you have performed supination of the forearm. If you rotate your forearm so that the palm faces posteriorly, you have performed pronation. One way to think about this is to make a "soup bowl" with your hands. In this position, your forearms are supinated. In the anatomical position, the forearms are supinated.

ON YOUR OWN

4.11 When you shake your head *no*, what kind of motion is the head performing?

4.12 When you bend at the waist to pick something up off of the ground, what motion is your vertebral column performing?

4.13 A ballet dancer stands in the anatomical position and then lifts his right thigh sideways, so that it is pointing to the right. What motion did the thigh perform?

4.14 A student stands in the anatomical position and then turns his hands so that the palms face posteriorly rather than anteriorly. What motion did the forearms perform?

4.15 A student stands in the anatomical position and then rotates his feet so that the toes on his left foot point to the toes on his right foot and vice-versa. What motion did the feet perform?

ANSWERS TO THE "ON YOUR OWN" QUESTIONS

4.1   If the cell secretes acid, it must be an osteoclast. Remember, osteoclasts break down bone tissue. What happened in experiment 4.1? An acid broke down the calcium mineral part of the bone tissue. So, acid destroys bone tissue.

4.2   Only compact bone tissue is composed of osteons.

4.3   It is not an osteoclast, since it has only one nucleus. It cannot be an osteocyte, as an osteocyte (or bone-laying cell) is only mature once it is *surrounded* by bone matrix. So, this is
an osteoblast.

4.4   Look for the side that is partially ossified. Remember, the epiphyseal plate ossifies on the side nearest the diaphysis.

4.5   The main job of the external callus is to hold the bone pieces together so that they can heal properly. That is also what a cast does. As a result, the cast is just helping the external callus do its job.

4.6   Remember, PTH stimulates osteoclast activity. This breaks down bone tissue, which releases calcium into the blood. So, the person's calcium level must have been too low.

4.7   The sex hormones stimulate osteoblast activity, and they are very active during puberty. Since osteoblasts' activity increases during puberty, the body needs extra calcium. This is because osteoblasts make new bone, and the formation of bone requires calcium.

4.8   A synchondrosis is a joint that is made of hyaline cartilage. One of the examples is an epiphyseal plate. These plates ossify as the bone matures, eliminating the cartilage. So, what was once a joint is now just part of a bone. That means some synchondroses exist only in children and not in adults. Other synchondroses, such as the cartilage that attaches the ribs to the sternum, exist in both children and adults because those cartilages do not ossify.

4.9   The gliding joints usually have the least movement, as mentioned in the text. Ball-and-socket joints have the most, and saddle and ellipsoid joints are just a little less move able. The saddle joints have all of the motion of ball-and-socket (and ellipsoid) joints except rotation, and hinge joints allow motion only in one plane. Thus, the order is as follows: **(1)** gliding joints, **(2)** hinge joints, **(3)** ellipsoid joints, **(4)** saddle joints, **and (5)** ball-and socket-joints.

4.10   The joint's synovial membrane must be damaged, because the cells in that membrane produce the synovial fluid. This can happen in rheumatoid arthritis, a disease in which the body makes abnormal antibodies that attack the synovial membranes.

4.11   This is rotation. Your head is rotating around the neck. When you rotate your head so that your face turns sideways, that is lateral (away from the midline) rotation. When you move your head back so that you face forward, that is medial (toward the midline) rotation. In this case, lateral rotation can be "left lateral rotation" or "right lateral rotation."

4.12   When you bend at the waist, you are decreasing the angle between your vertebral column and your pelvic girdle. This, then, is flexion of the vertebral column.

4.13   Lifting the right leg sideways so that it points to the right moves the leg away from the midline. That is abduction of the thigh.

4.14   This is pronation. Look at last drawing in figure 4.10. If the elbow is extended, the portion labeled "supination" would correspond to the anatomical position. Turning the palms the other way, then, is pronation. These terms are used as if you are in anatomical position, whether you really are in it or not.

4.15   This is inversion, as the feet are being turned inward in order for the toes to point to the opposite foot.

STUDY GUIDE FOR MODULE 4

1. Define the following terms:
   a. Osteoblast
   b. Osteocyte
   c. Osteoclast
   d. Hematoma
   e. Callus
   f. Anatomical position

2. What are the two principal agents in bone matrix, and how do they each affect the properties of bone tissue?

3. A bone cell is completely surrounded by bone matrix. What kind of bone cell is it?

4. A bone cell has more than one nucleus. What kind of bone cell is it?

5. Looking at bone tissue under a microscope, you see no osteons. Is this compact or cancellous bone tissue?

6. What kind of bone tissue contains trabeculae? What do you often find in the spaces between trabeculae?

7. What is the term for the layers of bone tissue that form an osteon? What is the term for the layers of bone between osteons?

8. What are canaliculi?

9. There are at least six reasons bone must be continually remodeled. Can you list at least five of them?

10. Bone growth occurs when new cartilage is added to the bone's epiphyseal plate. Why doesn't the epiphyseal plate get thicker as the bone grows?

11. The epiphyseal plate separates the diaphysis from the epiphysis. On which side of the plate does the tissue ossify?

12. If a long bone has no epiphyseal plates because they have become epiphyseal lines, is there *any* way that a bone can grow?

13. What is appositional bone growth?

14. The following are processes that occur when bone is repaired. Order them according to the sequence in which they occur.
    a. The external callus is removed by osteoclasts, and cancellous bone is remodeled as needed.
    b. A hematoma forms.
    c. The callus is ossified.
    d. The callus forms.

15. What is the purpose of the external callus? What is the purpose of the internal callus?

16. Which gland secretes calcitonin? Which glands secrete PTH?

17. What is the effect of calcitonin on bone cells? What is the effect of PTH on bone cells?

18. A person's medical tests show a large increase in the calcitonin levels of the body. What does that tell you about the calcium level in the person's blood?

19. Which gland secretes growth hormone, and what effect does this hormone have on bone tissue?

20. What effect do the sex hormones have on bone growth?

21. What are the three major types of joints in the body, and which type is associated with most of the movement in the skeleton?

22. Label the parts of the following synovial joint illustration.

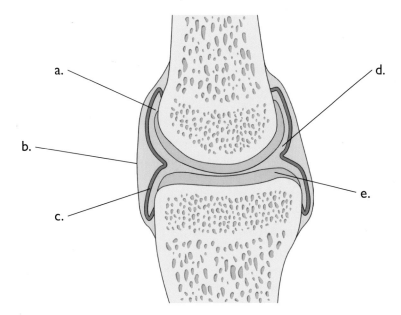

23. What is the purpose of the articular cartilage in a synovial joint?

24. What is the purpose of the synovial fluid in a synovial joint?

25. What produces synovial fluid?

26. List the six major types of synovial joints in order of *decreasing* range of motion. Assume that pivot joints offer slightly more motion than hinge joints.

27. Name the kind of motion exhibited in the following actions:
    a. A ballet dancer stands on tiptoe.
    b. A person is doing push-ups. His elbows are bent so that his body is close to the ground. He then lifts his body up by straightening his arms at the elbow.
    c. A gymnast who is already standing on just one leg begins to twirl the lower limb that is in the air in circles.
    d. A person is holding his palms up and then turns his hands so that the palms point down.
    e. A person holds his arms down at his sides and then lifts them both up so that they are horizontal to the ground, pointing out to each side.

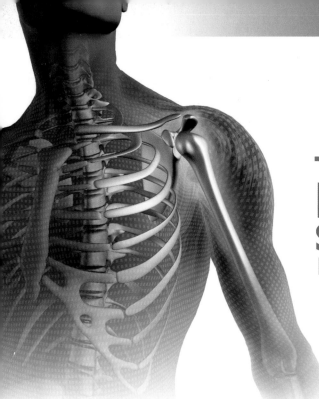

THE MUSCULAR SYSTEM
HISTOLOGY AND PHYSIOLOGY

Have you ever "made a muscle?" You know what we mean—you flex your forearm, and deliberately tighten your biceps muscle. The muscle hardens and bulges more if you have been working out in the last few weeks, but noticeably even if it is not in the best of shape. The wonderful mysteries of how muscle contracts will soon be explained: why your muscles bulge when you contract them; why you have to decide to contract them; why muscles get bigger when you exercise them; why muscles fatigue; why you often breathe heavily after using your muscles vigorously, even though you are now resting; why you start a free throw in basketball with arms and legs somewhat flexed; and why warming up and cooling down are important to your muscles' best efforts. We are on an adventure of exploration of muscle that has many, many practical applications!

heart of the matter

Movement, something you do all day and take for granted, is only possible with the action of your muscles. They comprise more of your weight than your bones and use up much of the energy you produce from the foods you ingest. Without them, your bones would collapse into a heap, and your movement would cease. Your muscles were designed to help you accomplish many different functions. You can lift heavy objects, take a stroll or jog about your neighborhood, and even turn the page of a book—all without much thought on how to make it happen. You don't even have control over some very important muscles, such as those in your heart. You wake up, go about your day, and eventually go back to sleep with these muscles working. Try today to recognize all of the movement with which you have been blessed.

Your muscular system performs three major tasks. The first task is the most obvious: The muscle system provides movement for your body. Muscles move your skeleton, your tongue, and your diaphragm. Muscles push food through your digestive tract, urine from your urinary bladder, and blood through your heart and blood vessels. Muscles constrict and dilate the pupils of your eyes. As we continue through the organ systems of the body, in almost all cases, muscle will somehow contribute to structure and function. Muscle also enables you to maintain posture, even though you are not moving. For example, you can stand still in the anatomical position and not move, but without muscle activity, you would collapse like a rag doll. Finally, the muscular system is involved in heat production for the body. On a cold day, you stay warmer if you do some exercise instead of just standing around. If you are really cold, your body contracts its muscles, making you shiver. It may feel unpleasant if you get cold enough to shiver, but shivering is a highly effective way of generating heat if you have to stand in one place.

There are actually three kinds of muscle tissue: skeletal muscle, cardiac muscle, and smooth muscle. Figure 5.1 shows how these different types of muscle tissue appear under the microscope.

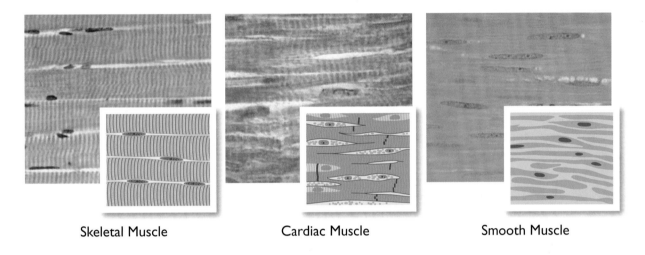

| Skeletal Muscle | Cardiac Muscle | Smooth Muscle |

FIGURE 5.1
The Three Types of Muscle Tissue
Skeletal Muscle Photo © Phototake/Eric Grave | Smooth and Cardiac Muscle Photos © Phototake/North Carloina Biological Supply
Small Insert Photos © LifeArt

Skeletal muscle tissue is usually described as striated, which refers to the distinct, orderly, striped pattern you see in figure 5.1. It makes up the voluntary muscles, which are muscles that you can control consciously, including all the muscles that move the bone, the tongue, and the diaphragm. Sometimes, these muscles are controlled automatically by the nervous system, but you are able to exercise at least limited conscious control over them. For example, the diaphragm is a skeletal muscle involved in breathing. It is operated automatically by the nervous system so you don't have to think about breathing. However, if you choose to, you can override that automatic control and hold your breath for a minute or so. The long and thin cells that make up skeletal muscle tissue are multinucleated, which means that they have many nuclei. Cardiac muscle is found only in the heart. This tissue is also striated, but each cell usually has only one nucleus. This tissue is involuntary, which means that you cannot exercise conscious control over it. The third type of muscle tissue, smooth muscle, is also involuntary. It is called smooth because the cells are nonstriated, or not striped. Smooth muscle cells are small and have only one nucleus. This is the kind of muscle that enables your internal organs, such as the digestive, urinary, and reproductive organs, to do their job. In this module, we will focus on skeletal muscle.

Muscle tissue can do its job because it is incredibly well engineered. It has been designed with four major functional characteristics. First, it has contractility (kon trak til' ih tee). This means that it can contract (shorten) forcefully. Much of this module will explain how it does so. Second, it has excitability. As you will learn, muscle responds to a stimulus—most often stimulation by the nervous system—with its own cellular signal called an *action potential*. Cells that can produce such signals are called excitable cells. The action potential is absolutely essential to the muscle cells' ability to contract, because it signals the muscle cell to do so. Action potentials produced by neurons also allow the nervous system to control skeletal muscles. Muscle tissue also has extensibility (eks ten' sih bil' ih tee), which means that it can passively stretch out. As you learn about the ways in which muscles control the skeleton, you will find that they contract, and then relax. That is what produces movement. When muscles relax, they can be pulled out to their normal length if another muscle or gravity pulls on them. That's extensibility. Finally, muscles have elasticity. This means that when the muscles are extended, they tend to recoil back to a shorter length. If a muscle's tendon is accidentally cut, the muscle would automatically shorten somewhat, even without actively contracting. That shortening is evidence of the somewhat elastic nature of muscle tissue.

SKELETAL MUSCLE STRUCTURE

The best way to introduce you to skeletal muscle is to examine its structure. Figure 5.2 illustrates the structure of a skeletal muscle on three different levels.

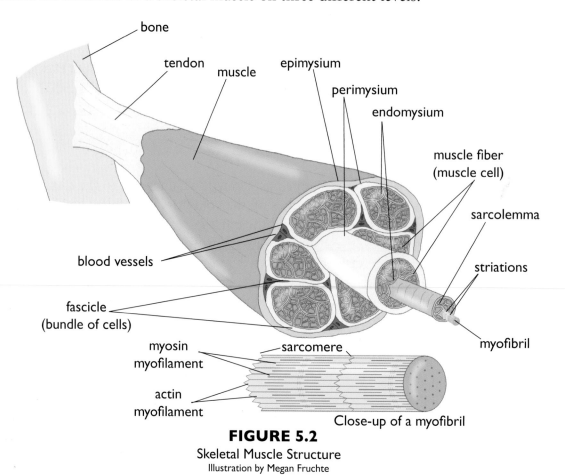

FIGURE 5.2
Skeletal Muscle Structure
Illustration by Megan Fruchte

Let's start at the upper left side of the figure. Notice that the muscle is attached to the bone by a tendon. That is important. Skeletal muscles do not connect directly to bone. They are connected to bone by a tendon, which is a strap of dense regular connective tissue.

The belly of the muscle is composed of the actual muscle cells. This illustration is showing you only a part of the muscle's belly. The whole muscle is divided into bundles of cells called fascicles (fa' sik uhls). Each individual muscle cell is called a fiber because it is very long and thin. When you read the term muscle fiber, you need to think muscle cell. Each cell is wrapped in a thin collagen layer called the endomysium (en' doh mis' e uhm). Each fascicle is further wrapped in a collagen layer called a perimysium (pehr' ih mis' e uhm). Those fascicles are wrapped together in another layer of collagen, called the epimysium (ep ih mis' e uhm). The epimysium is really what differentiates one muscle from another. Each muscle has its own epimysium, which wraps together several fascicles. The epimysium is also known as the fascia (fash' ee uh), but this term is generally used in a much broader sense to refer to sheets of tissue that lie underneath the skin. When that tissue wraps a muscle, it is called the epimysium.

Each individual muscle fiber is harnessed strongly and securely to the bone that it is designed to move. How is it secured? Well, the collagen fibers that make up the endomysium extend past the end of the muscle belly. They straighten out, forming the dense regular connective tissue of the tendon. Remember that bone has collagen. The collagen in the dense regular connective tissue of the tendon continues into the bone and actually becomes a part of the bone. In the end, then, each muscle fiber is tightly harnessed to the bone that it moves because the collagen in the tendon is continuous with the collagen in the bone.

Muscle tissue contains many nerves and blood vessels. The blood vessels, shown in the figure, are easy to understand. When muscles are active, they are high users of nutrients and oxygen. It makes sense, then, that there are plenty of blood vessels in muscle tissue to supply nutrients and oxygen. What you might not realize, however, is that nerves are also critical for muscle activity. A skeletal muscle will not contract without nerves to stimulate it. Think of a person whose spinal cord is accidentally severed at the level of the waist. That person will not be able to move his or her legs. There is nothing wrong with the *muscles* in the legs. Without nerve stimulus, however, the skeletal muscles will not contract.

Now let's talk about a muscle fiber, which is the same thing as a muscle cell. Skeletal muscle fibers are multinucleate. The nuclei are located just under the sarcolemma, which is the plasma membrane of the muscle fiber. Why does it have a different name? Well, muscle fibers are rather specialized, so there are special names for some of their components. The prefix *sarco* means literally "flesh" or "meat." When you eat meat, you are actually eating an animal's muscles. So, the prefix *sarco* is often added to muscle structures. In the same way, the sarcoplasmic reticulum is just the endoplasmic reticulum of a muscle fiber.

The sarcolemma has tiny tubes, called T-tubules, extending into the sarcoplasmic reticulum. These T-tubules form pits in the sarcolemma. What does a T-tubule do? It allows the action potential, which is a special signal, to get down to the sarcoplasmic reticulum. Later on, we will see what the action potential is and how works. The T-tubule makes it possible for the action potential to get to where it needs to be in order to stimulate muscle movement.

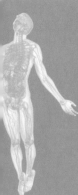

ON YOUR OWN

5.1 A medical researcher shows you a sample of muscle tissue. He asks you to tell him whether the sample is the complete muscle or just a part of a muscle. How can you tell?

5.2 A cellular term you will see later in this module is *sarcoplasm*. Given what you have learned in this section and what you already know about the general layout of a cell, what is sarcoplasm?

The sarcoplasmic reticulum surrounds regions that are packed with many myofibrils (my oh fye' brilz). These myofibrils are thread-like structures that are only a few micrometers in diameter. They are long, though, extending from one end of the cell to the other. They are structured in repeating units, and that causes the striations, "stripes." Each unit of a myofibril contains two basic types of filaments called actin myofilaments (my' oh fil' uh ments) and myosin myofilaments. We will discuss these in much more detail in the next section. For now, it is important to know that these thread-like myofibrils are the organelles within muscle fibers that actually do the contracting. Relative to other cells in your body, muscle fibers contain many mitochondria because they expend a great deal of energy.

Experiment 5.1
Skeletal Muscle Histology

Supplies:

- Microscope
- Prepared slide: human striated muscle

Purpose: Skeletal muscle tissue is easy to identify under a microscope. This laboratory exercise will allow you to see the main features of skeletal muscle tissue.

Procedure:

1. Place the prepared slide on the microscope stage and focus at 40x magnification.

2. Center some tissue and increase to 100x magnification. Focus again.

3. At this magnification, the structure of skeletal muscle should be apparent. The strands of color are the muscle fibers. The dark spots are the cell nuclei. Each strand is one cell. Observe how long they are. Compare that in your mind to what you saw when looking at epithelial cells.

4. Center some tissue and increase to 400x magnification. Focus again.

5. There are several things to notice at this magnification. First, look at the nuclei. Notice that there are several per strand. That is because skeletal muscle fibers are multinucleate.

6. Next, notice the placement of the nuclei. They are not near the middle of the cell, as is the case with the other tissues you have studied. Instead, the nuclei run along the edge of the cell.

7. Finally, notice the tiny, dark bands that repeat over and over again through the cell. Those are the striations. You will learn in the next section that those striations are the result of the orderly arrangement of certain proteins in the muscle fiber. The striations are one of the most important features in identifying skeletal muscle.

8. Draw what you see in the field, labeling the individual cells, the nuclei, and the striations.

9. Put everything away.

HOW A MUSCLE FIBER CONTRACTS

In the introduction to this module, we noted that muscle tissue has contractility. In fact, that is how a muscle causes movement; it contracts. In the next module, we will show you how that produces bodily movement. For right now, however, let's look at how an individual muscle fiber actually shortens or contracts. The description we are going to give you is called the sliding-filament model, and it is really quite incredible! Remember, the myofibrils are the contractile units of skeletal muscle. If you understand the myofibril, you will understand the contraction of the muscle fiber, and then you can understand the contraction of the whole muscle.

First, remember that the strands of a muscle fiber have striations. Those striations are caused by the fact that the myofibrils are composed of repeating units. The repeating units of the myofibrils are called sarcomeres (sar' koh meres), and those sarcomeres are attached end-to-end, forming the myofibril.

Sarcomere—The repeating unit of a myofibril

Figure 5.3 is a simplified drawing of the internal structure of one sarcomere. Since the entire myofibril is made up of repeating sarcomeres, you need only understand one sarcomere to understand the whole thing.

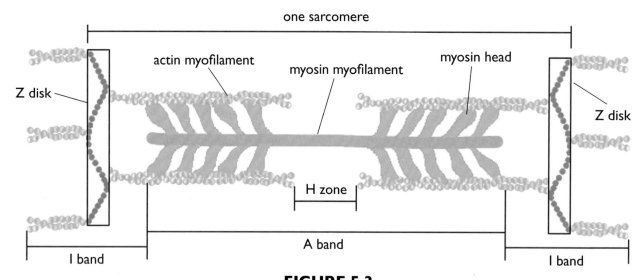

FIGURE 5.3
One Sarcomere in a Myofibril
Illustration by Megan Fruchte

The structure of a sarcomere is the first thing that you must learn. As you know, muscle (meat) is a high-protein food. In this figure, you see two of those proteins. One is myosin, which forms the myosin myofilament. The prefix *myo* means "muscle," and *sin* means "protein." Thus, *myosin* is "muscle protein." The myosin myofilament is the thicker of the two myofilaments. The thinner myofilament is made of the protein actin. Notice how these two myofilaments interact. The heads on the myosin myofilament can attach to the actin myofilament. There are certain active sites on the actin, and the combination of a myosin head with the active site of an actin myofilament is called a cross bridge. The cross bridges are really the basis of muscle contraction. In brief, the head of the myosin can grasp the actin at its active site and pull on it, shortening the sarcomere. This happens at the same time to all of the sarcomeres in the muscle fiber, so that the entire muscle fiber contracts. You can think of it as analogous to a rowing team who synchronize their oar movements perfectly to get the strongest movement of their boat.

Now remember, skeletal muscle fibers are striated. They are striated because of the sarcomeres. Why do the sarcomeres show striation? Well, myosin is thicker than actin. As a result, myosin appears darker than actin under a microscope. Thus, the thick, dark stripes you saw in

think about this

If skeletal muscles fibers do not undergo mitosis after babyhood, why does a muscle get obviously bigger if you work out with it? The answer lies with the contractile organelles, the myofibrils. Exercise stimulates them to produce more actin and myosin. They divide lengthwise, forming more myofibrils and thicker muscle fibers, but not more muscle fibers.

experiment 5.1 indicate the presence of myosin, and the lighter areas show where the actin is. The thick, dark stripes are called the A bands, while the lighter areas are called the I bands. Now look at figure 5.3 again. See what the A band and I band look like.

What about the thin, purple wavy line? That wavy line represents the Z disks. Z disks are also made out of protein. They serve to anchor the actin myofilaments. In a practical sense, they mark the boundaries of the sarcomere. Each sarcomere is located between two Z disks. Finally, the H zone, as labeled in the figure, is the area within the A band in which no actin is present.

Let's make this clear before we continue, because the terminology is very important. When we discuss how the muscle contracts, we will be using this terminology. The Z disks separate one sarcomere from another. The actin myo-filaments are connected to those Z disks. One group of actin myofilaments stretches from the Z disk on the left, and another group stretches from the Z disk on the right. These two sets of actin myofilaments are separated from one another by the H zone, which contains only myosin.

The myosin myofilaments are located between actin myofilaments. The heads of the myosin myofilaments can bind to the actin myofilaments, forming a cross bridge. A single myosin myofilament forms cross bridges with actin myofilaments from both Z disks because it has many heads. The myosin myofilament defines the A band; that is, the A band is the exact length of the myosin myofilaments. The portions of the sarcomere with actin myofilaments and *no* myosin myofilaments are called the I bands.

Please realize that the contractile organelle of muscle, the myofibril, is composed of many sarcomeres attached end-to-end to each other. Now let's learn how the muscle contracts. First, we'll show you what happens to the sarcomere when it contracts, and then we'll give you the molecular details of how this happens. Now remember, you already know the basic mechanism. The heads of the myosin myofilament attach to active sites on the actin myofilament and pull on the actin. This causes the Z disks to be drawn together. Figure 5.4 illustrates how this works.

think about this

Why do you flex your arms and legs a certain way before a free throw in basketball? Why does a sprinter crouch before the breakaway start? Why not just stand upright to begin a strong muscular contraction? These questions involving the posture of the whole organism can be answered at the molecular level. When a resting muscle is stretched out passively, the actin and myosin cannot overlap well to make cross bridges. A weak contraction results. If the muscle is too short to begin (imagine trying to use your biceps to pick up something heavy with your arms bent like a chicken wing), the actin and myosin are already so overlapped that cross bridges still cannot form. When the limb is semi-flexed—knees and elbows bent somewhat—the actin and myosin are somewhat overlapped. When a contraction begins, they can form plenty of cross bridges, and they have room to shorten. That's why coach says to "bend those knees, but not too much!" Coach is helping your actin and myosin to overlap enough to give the best jump!

BEFORE CONTRACTION:

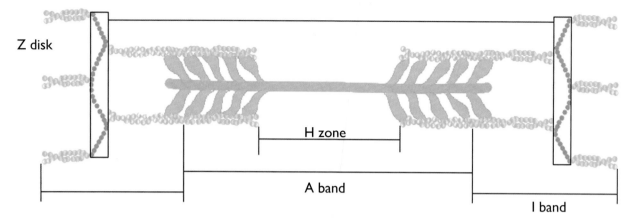

Z disk

H zone

A band

I band

AFTER CONTRACTION:

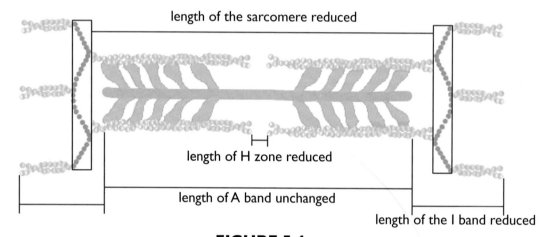

length of the sarcomere reduced

length of H zone reduced

length of A band unchanged

length of the I band reduced

FIGURE 5.4

Contraction of a Sarcomere

Illustration by Megan Fruchte

Notice what happens when a sarcomere contracts. All the heads of the myosin myofilaments "grab" the actin myofilament and bend. This pulls the Z disks toward the center of the sarcomere. Since this happens simultaneously on each end of the myosin myofilament, each Z disk gets pulled toward the center, shortening the length of the sarcomere. Since the sarcomere's length shortens, there is less space between the actin myofilament from one Z disk and the corresponding actin myofilament from the other. Since the actin myofilaments have been pulled into the center of the sarcomere, there is more overlap between the myosin myofilament and the actin myofilament. This overlap of actin and myosin explains why a whole muscle bulges out when you contract it, the way you can "pop out" your biceps. The whole muscle is shorter, but now thicker, as actin and myosin are more overlapped. As a result, the H zone is reduced, and the I bands, the areas in which only actin (but no myosin) is found, shorten as well.

Notice that although the length of the sarcomere, the length of the H zone, and the length of the I bands are all shorter, there are three things that remain the same. The lengths of the actin myofilaments are not changed. Neither is the length of the myosin myofilament. As a result, the length of the A band, which is the length of the myosin, is not changed. Thus, although the sarcomere itself contracts, the myofilaments that do the work *do not* contract. Now remember, this happens *simultaneously* throughout many muscle fibers all at once. Isn't that amazing?

We promised to give you a little more detail on how the myosin myofilaments "grab on" to the actin myofilaments. The process starts with the formation of a cross bridge, as illustrated in figure 5.5.

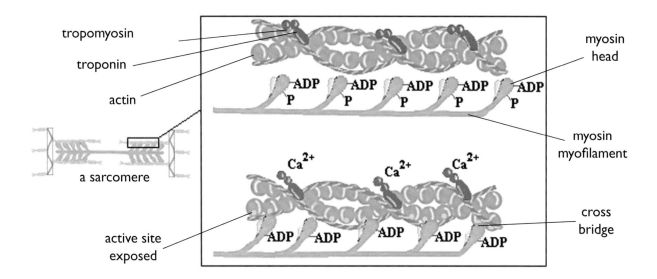

FIGURE 5.5
The Formation of Cross Bridges
Illustration by Megan Whitaker

The actin myofilament contains two other proteins besides actin: troponin (troh' poh nin) and tropomyosin (troh' poh my' oh sin). As illustrated in the figure, the tropomyosin winds around the strand formed by the actin molecules. The troponin lie across the tropomyosin. When you decide to contract a muscle, neurons send a signal, which ultimately causes the sarcoplasm reticulum to release calcium ions (Ca^{2+}) into the myofibrils. The Ca^{2+} then bind to the troponin, causing it to change the way it sits on the tropomyosin, as shown in the lower portion of the figure. This causes the tropomyosin to roll slightly back from the actin, resulting in the exposure of active sites along the actin myofilament. These active sites immediately attract the heads of the myosin myofilament and bind to them, creating a cross bridge.

Now we realize that this is very technical, so please stay with us here. The important thing to understand is that the release of Ca^{2+} from the sarcoplasmic reticulum causes the molecules that make up the actin myofilament to change position. This exposes sites on the actin that attract the heads of the myosin myofilament, causing them to bind to the actin myofilament. What causes the release of Ca^{2+}? We will cover that in the next section, but for now, realize that it is the action of *neurons* that initiate their release. Without those neurons, the skeletal muscles would not contract and would, therefore, be useless.

There is still one thing in the figure that we have not discussed. What are the ADPs and Ps in the figure? As a review, cells store the energy produced in cellular respiration by taking ADP (adenosine diphosphate) molecules and binding them with phosphate (P) molecules to form ATP (adenosine triphosphate). As you will soon see, in the last stages of the muscle contraction process, an ATP molecule binds to the head of the myosin myofilament and breaks down into ADP and P. What does that do? It releases energy. That is ATP's job. It stores energy for the cell. When the cell needs energy, it breaks ATP into ADP and P. Where does the energy go? In this case, it "powers up" the head of the myosin myofilament, so that the head has the energy to do what it does next.

In order for the myosin head to bind to actin and move, it needs energy. It gets that energy from the only place any part of the cell can get energy: the breakdown of ATP. The ADP molecules that are bound to the head of the myosin myofilament in the top portion of the figure are just remnants from that process. Phosphate molecules are also being released. This must happen in order for the myosin head to bind to the actin. Once the cross bridges are formed, then, the myosin heads have only ADP bound to them.

What do we have so far, then? We have myosin heads bound to active sites on the actin myofilament. Each head has energy because an ATP molecule has broken apart on the head. A remnant of that process, ADP, is still attached to the myosin head at this point. Figure 5.6 illustrates what happens next.

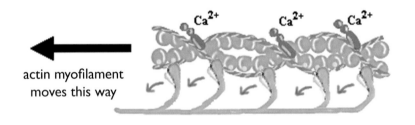

myosin head pulling on actin myofilament

actin myofilament moves this way

FIGURE 5.6
The Power Stroke
Illustration by Megan Whitaker

The myosin heads now use the energy that has been released there by the ATP to pull the actin myofilament. This causes the ADP still bound to the myosin head to fall off. That ADP, along with the P, which was dropped off in the earlier step, will eventually be recycled into ATP via cellular respiration. The overall effect of this step is that the actin myofilament moves one step toward the center of the sarcomere. This shortens the length of the sarcomere, causing contraction. This step of the process is called the power stroke.

The process still is not over, however. Once the myosin heads have finished pulling the actin myofilament just one step towards the center of the sarcomere, they have expended all of the energy that one ATP provided them. What happens next? Well, the heads now have neither ADP nor P bound to them, so ATP comes in and binds to them, as shown in figure 5.7.

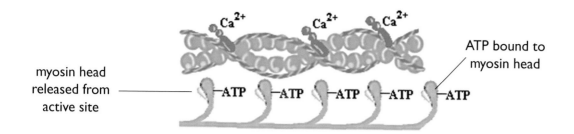

myosin head released from active site

Ca^{2+} Ca^{2+} Ca^{2+}

ATP bound to myosin head

ATP ATP ATP ATP ATP

FIGURE 5.7
ATP Binding to the Myosin Heads
Illustration by Megan Whitaker

When the ATP binds to the myosin head, it releases the bond between the actin active site and the myosin head. That is, the cross bridge is broken. Another one can now form to continue the movement. It is as if we have explained exactly one stroke of the oar by one oarsman on a crew team. He's rowing very fast, and all his teammates are doing the same rapid stroke at the same time, again and again. Yet, if we evaluate just one stroke, we can understand the whole movement.

You should be able to guess what happens next. In order to supply the myosin head with the energy it needs to repeat the process, the ATP breaks down into ADP and P. This "pumps" the myosin head back up, readying it to repeat the procedure. This is called the return stroke.

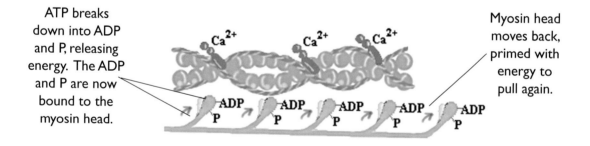

ATP breaks down into ADP and P, releasing energy. The ADP and P are now bound to the myosin head.

Ca^{2+} Ca^{2+} Ca^{2+}

Myosin head moves back, primed with energy to pull again.

ADP P ADP P ADP P ADP P ADP P

FIGURE 5.8
The Return Stroke
Illustration by Megan Whitaker

So, now the myosin myofilament is ready to start the whole process again. What determines whether or not it will? After all, the muscle cannot contract forever. The contraction must stop eventually. What determines when it stops contracting? Well, the myosin heads will continue to grab and pull as long as the active sites on the actin are exposed and there is ATP to give the energy needed. Since ATP is *usually* available in a cell, the main control rests on the exposure of the active sites. When you want your muscle to stop contracting, you send neural signals, which ultimately cause the sarcoplasmic reticulum to actively transport the Ca^{2+} away from the myofibrils. This removes the Ca^{2+} from the troponin, which causes tropomyosin to roll, *hiding* the active sites from the myosin myofilament. The muscle contraction stops. We know that this was a lot of detailed information, so we have combined this process into figure 5.9.

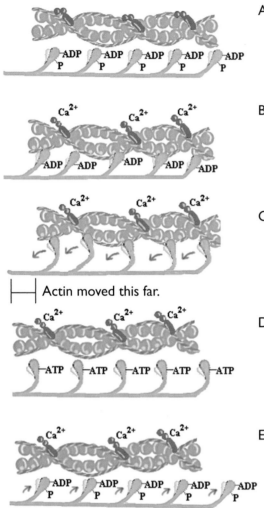

A. At rest, before contraction, the active sites on the actin myofilament are not exposed. Thus, the heads of the myosin myofilament are primed and ready, but they can't bind actin. The contraction can't happen.

B. To start a contraction, Ca^{2+} bind to the troponin, causing tropomyosin to move away from the actin myofilament. This exposes the active sites to which the myosin heads can bind. Phosphate is ejected when the myosin heads bind to the active sites.

C. Power Stroke: The myosin heads then bend, pulling the actin myofilament toward the center of the sarcomere. This causes the ADP to be ejected.

D. ATP molecules bind to the myosin heads, causing them to break their bond with actin's active sites. As a result of the power stroke from the heads in step (C), the actin myofilament has moved.

E. Return Stroke: ATP molecules break down into ADP and P, which stay bound to the myosin heads. This releases energy, and the myosin heads are now powered up like a set mousetrap, ready to start the process all over again.

FIGURE 5.9
One Cycle of Sarcomere Contraction
Illustration by Megan Whitaker

THE NEUROMUSCULAR JUNCTION IN A SKELETAL MUSCLE

It is critical to understand that skeletal muscle will not move without a neuron to stimulate it. Skeletal muscles are controlled by nerves (bundles of neurons), which contain motor neurons (nur' onz), cells specifically designed to carry signals called action potentials from the brain and spinal cord to the skeletal muscles at a high rate of speed.

Neuron—The functional unit of the nervous system, a nerve cell

A motor neuron, then, is a specialized nerve cell that is designed to control skeletal muscles. You will learn about neurons in detail in a later module. For now, just know that each neuron has a very long process that extends far away from the main body of the cell. The neuron's process is called an axon, and its purpose is to carry signals away from the main cell body. An axon may be two or three feet long as are, for example, axons from the spinal cord to your calf muscle.

When the axon of a motor neuron reaches the perimysium surrounding several muscle fibers, it branches repeatedly, each branch connecting with one muscle fiber, forming a neuromuscular (nur' oh mus' ku lur) junction. Such a junction is illustrated in figure 5.10.

In a neuromuscular junction, the motor neuron does not actually touch the muscle. Instead, there is an extremely tiny gap between the end of the axon and the muscle fiber. This gap is called a synaptic (sih nap' tik) cleft. The neuromuscular junction itself is one type of synapse. Neurons communicate with other cells across a junction called a synapse.

Synapse—The interface between a neuron and another cell

Examine figure 5.10 to learn the anatomy of the neuromuscular junction. On the left-hand side of the figure, you see a muscle fiber. It has several myofibrils and mitochondria in it. Also, you can see the various branches of the sarcoplasmic reticulum. None of this is new; you have learned about these structures

think about this

The incredibly detailed process of muscle contraction happens over and over again, countless millions of times every time a muscle contracts! It is started by signals from neurons, which eventually cause Ca^{2+} to travel from the sarcoplasmic reticulum to the actin myofilament, where they bind to the troponin molecules on the filament. Neurons also signal the process that ends with Ca^{2+} moving back into the sarcoplasmic reticulum, allowing the contraction to stop. In between, all of the steps illustrated in figure 5.9 happen over and over again, making the muscle contract. Now think about the design here. It is truly astounding! If you think you are impressed now, however, wait until you read the next section!

ON YOUR OWN

5.3 Several steps happen in order for a sarcomere to contract. Arrange the following steps in the order in which they actually happen to initiate this process:

a. ATP binds to the myosin heads, breaking the cross bridges and making them release the active sites on the actin.

b. Ca^{2+} binds to troponin, causing tropomyosin to move and expose the active sites on the actin, and allowing the myosin heads to grab onto the actin.

c. The return stroke.

d. The power stroke.

5.4 ATP molecules are bound to the myosin heads in a sarcomere and are breaking down. Is this the return stroke or the power stroke?

5.5 Suppose you were looking at the Ca^{2+} concentration in the sarcoplasmic reticulum of a muscle fiber. If the Ca^{2+} concentration within the sarcoplasmic reticulum suddenly increased dramatically, is the muscle starting its contraction or has it finished contracting?

already. The new information in this part of the figure is the motor neuron. It branches, almost connecting to the muscle fiber. If we magnify the place where it closely approaches the muscle fiber, we get the drawing on the right-hand side of the figure.

In this drawing, we see the very end of the neuron, called the presynaptic (pree' sih nap' tik) terminal. Remember, the interface between a neuron and another cell is called a synapse. So, you will see part of the word synapse in several of the structures we want to discuss because they all relate to this interface. As we already mentioned, the space between the end of the presynaptic terminal and the muscle fiber is called the synaptic cleft, and the membrane of the muscle fiber in this region is called the postsynaptic membrane.

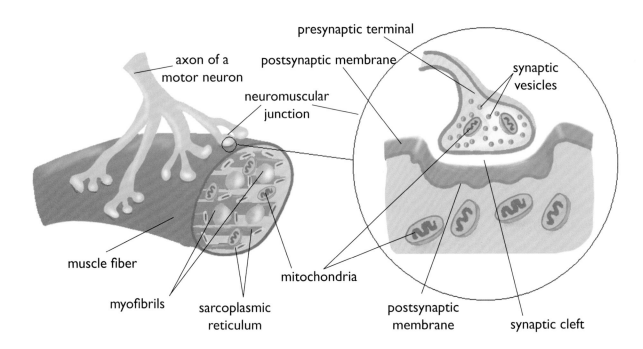

FIGURE 5.10
Neuromuscular Junction
Illustration by Megan Whitaker

Inside the presynaptic terminal are several organelles. There are mitochondria, which produce energy for the neuron, and there are synaptic vesicles. What do the synaptic vesicles do? Recall that vesicles are sac-like organelles that hold substances for the cell. The synaptic vesicles of neurons that stimulate muscle fibers hold an important chemical called acetylcholine (uh see' tuhl koe' lean), which is abbreviated ACh. Acetylcholine is one of many different chemicals called neurotransmitters.

Neurotransmitter—A chemical released by a neuron, which diffuses across the synaptic cleft, enabling the neuron to communicate with another cell.

Do you understand what a neurotransmitter does? Note from figure 5.10 that the presynaptic terminal does not actually touch the muscle fiber. Nevertheless, the neuron must send a signal to the cell in order to control it. To accomplish this, the neuron releases neurotransmitter from its presynaptic terminal. The neurotransmitter then diffuses across the gap (the synaptic cleft), and binds to the muscle fiber on the other side. The chemical interaction stimulates the muscle fiber.

What does this particular neurotransmitter do? Well, when ACh binds to the postsynaptic membrane of a muscle fiber, it initiates a series of signals that ultimately cause the muscle fiber to contract. Thus, it stimulates the process we discussed in the previous section. The motor neuron, then, controls the muscle fiber by releasing ACh into the synaptic cleft. When the ACh binds to the muscle fiber, it forms a signal, and that signal starts further processes, which will signal the muscle fiber to contract.

That is not the end of the story, however. If ACh makes a signal that stimulates the muscle to contract, something must happen to the ACh, or the muscle would just keep on contracting until it ran out of ATP. If that were the case, then a muscle fiber could contract until it ran out of ATP, and then that would be it. That would not be very useful, would it? So, there must be something that gets rid of the ACh so that the muscle stops contracting. That something is an enzyme called acetylcholinesterase (as' ee til ko lin es' ter ayse), and it is abbreviated ACh-ase. The *ase* on the end of a chemical word usually means that it is an enzyme that acts on the chemical. ACh-ase inactivates ACh so that the muscle can relax. Interestingly, sprayed insecticides used to kill flying insects do so by destroying their acetylcholinesterase. The result is that the ACh in their bodies cannot be inactivated, and their muscles just wildly contract. In other words, the insects drop and buzz themselves to death!

We want to get into this in just a little more detail, but first let's review what you have learned so far. The motor neurons that control skeletal muscles have axons that branch in several places. These branches eventually end in a synapse between the neuron and the muscle fiber. The end of the neuron (the presynaptic terminal) is separated from the membrane of the muscle fiber (the postsynaptic membrane) by the synaptic cleft. In order to communicate with the muscle, then, the presynaptic terminal releases the neurotransmitter ACh, which it has stored in synaptic vesicles. The ACh diffuses across the synaptic cleft, binding to the postsynaptic membrane. This initiates a signal, which ultimately causes the muscle fiber to contract. If there is no ACh, the muscle relaxes. Thus, the motor neuron controls the muscle fiber by either secreting ACh in order to stimulate contraction, or not secreting any ACh, which results in the muscle relaxing. If ACh is secreted, it is quickly inactivated by ACh-ase so that the muscle does not continually contract.

think about this

As you've been reading about muscle contractions, have you been sitting perfectly still? Did you write down any notes? Did you have an itch that needed to be scratched? Perhaps you took a "mental break" and walked into the kitchen to get a snack. At the very least, you needed to turn the pages of your textbook. Every movement you made while reading this section was caused by the mechanisms you've been studying! It can almost be overwhelming to think of the intricate details of how you were designed. It's easy to take for granted the every day action of putting on your socks or tying your shoes, but now you are aware of the millions of processes that must occur to make that happen. Keep in mind too that something that seems simple, like tying your shoes, actually involves many other organ systems! For example your brain coordinates your finger movements, registers the direction of gravity, monitors your body's balance, and maintains homeostasis. Your eyes register your progress; your skin measures the pressure of your fingers on the shoelaces, and so forth.

That is the big picture. Now let's fill in the some details. This whole process starts with an action potential, a neural signal which rapidly travels down the axon of a motor neuron. We do not want to get too detailed about what this is because we will cover it in a later module. For now, think of it as an electrical message. That electrical message comes down the motor neuron, signaling synaptic vesicles to release ACh.

The ACh diffuses across the synaptic cleft to the postsynaptic membrane of the muscle fiber. There, the ACh chemically interacts with the special proteins called receptors in the membrane of the cell, initiating a *second* action potential in the *muscle* fiber membrane. It is the same type of message, but this one is carried on the muscle fiber membrane rather than along the axon of the neuron. So, it is often called a muscle action potential. The muscle action potential then travels along the cell membrane (sarcoplasm) until it hits a T-tubule. Now remember what a T-tubule is. In figure 5.2, we showed you a drawing of a muscle fiber. The T-tubules are the pits in the sarcolemma that lead to the sarcoplasmic reticulum. The action potential traveling along the sarcolemma signals the sarcoplasmic reticulum through one of those T-tubules.

What happens next? Well, we need to set up the scene first, to make the order of events clear. As you already know, Ca^{2+} are important in muscle contraction. In order for the muscle to contract, Ca^{2+} must attach to the troponin in the actin myofilament, causing tropomyosin to move and exposing active sites for the myosin heads to bind. That is how cross bridges are formed. As we mentioned previously, those Ca^{2+} are stored in the sarcoplasmic reticulum.

How did those Ca^{2+} get into the sarcoplasmic reticulum? The concentration of Ca^{2+} inside the sarcoplasmic reticulum is much greater than it is outside of the sarcoplasmic reticulum. So, the membrane of the sarcoplasmic reticulum must use *active transport* to bring in the Ca^{2+}. As a result, the sarcoplasmic reticulum expends ATP energy as it gathers Ca^{2+} into itself.

When the muscle action potential travels from the muscle fiber membrane (sarcolemma), down the T-tubule, and to the sarcoplasmic reticulum, it causes the Ca^{2+} that has been concentrated inside to be released. This allows the Ca^{2+} to diffuse out of the sarcoplasmic reticulum and into the myofibrils, where they attach to the troponin on the actin myofilaments. This causes the troponin and the tropomyosin to rearrange, exposing active sites on the actin myofilament. This, then, initiates the contraction sequence that you have already learned. As long as the motor neuron stimulates the muscle fiber, Ca^{2+}

ON YOUR OWN

5.6 Several steps happen in order for a muscle fiber to begin contracting. Arrange the following steps in the order in which they actually happen to initiate this process:

a. Calcium ions are released from the sarcoplasmic reticulum.
b. An action potential travels down the axon of a motor neuron.
c. ACh binds to the muscle fiber's postsynaptic membrane to initiate a muscle action potential.
d. The muscle action potential travels down a T-tubule.
e. ACh is released from the synaptic vesicles of the presynaptic terminal.
f. ACh diffuses across the synaptic cleft.
g. Calcium ions bind to the troponin in an actin myofilament.

5.7 When the sarcoplasmic reticulum releases Ca^{2+} in response to the action potential, do the ions move through the membrane of the sarcoplasmic reticulum via osmosis or diffusion? Is this active or passive transport?

will be available to bind to troponin, and using ATP, the cross bridges will form, move, break, and reform. This happens multiple millions of times so that the muscle moves by its cross bridges like a rowing team moves a boat by rowing in sync.

That is a lot of work, isn't it? All of these detailed processes take place for the purpose of causing a muscle fiber to contract. Believe it or not, however, we are not done yet! After all, we now know how the muscle contracts, but that is only half of the job. At some point, the muscle must relax again. We need to learn how that happens, as well. Thankfully, muscle relaxation is not any more difficult than muscle contraction. If you understand contraction, you will understand relaxation, which is covered in the next section.

HOW A MUSCLE FIBER RELAXES

For a muscle to relax, the action potentials traveling down the neuron must stop. After all, as long as action potentials travel down a motor neuron, ACh is released, which ultimately causes Ca^{2+} to bind to troponin. Once the action potentials along the motor neuron stop, ACh is no longer released from the neuron's presynaptic terminal. So, no more ACh diffuses across the synaptic cleft. Nevertheless, there is still ACh interacting with the cell membrane. That ACh must be broken down by acetylcholinesterase.

Once the ACh is broken down, there is no longer a stimulus to cause a muscle action potential, so the muscle action potentials stop. If you think about it, *not* having a signal is a signal. Once the muscle action potential stops, the diffusion of Ca^{2+} out of the sarcoplasmic reticulum stops. In addition, the sarcoplasmic reticulum goes back to its standard mode of operation, which is to actively transport Ca^{2+} back inside itself.

The active transport of Ca^{2+} into the sarcoplasmic reticulum removes those ions from the troponin that are on the actin myofilaments. So, the troponin and tropomyosin rearrange again, but this time they rearrange so that the active sites on the actin are hidden. As a result, the myosin heads have nothing to grab onto, and no cross bridges can form.

Not to be morbid, but do you know what rigor mortis (rig' er more' tis) is? It is short-term stiffening that occurs after death. When a dead body becomes stiff, we say that rigor mortis has set in. Why? In order for Ca^{2+} to be gathered into the sarcoplasmic reticulum, active transport must occur. That transport takes energy. After death, the cells no longer produce ATP, so active transport stops. As a result, Ca^{2+} leak into the muscle fibers, causing cross bridges to form. However, since there is no longer a supply of ATP, the complete muscle contraction process cannot take place. Remember, once the power stroke occurs, ATP must come in and bind to the myosin heads to make them *release* the active sites to which they are currently bound. Without ATP, that can't happen, so the cross bridges just stay formed. As a result, the muscle can neither contract nor relax. It is simply stuck. That makes the body rigid. The muscles will remain stiff until the muscle tissue degenerates.

Have you ever used your muscles so much that they just stiffened up on you for a while? Think about losing a hard arm wrestling game, or pulling with all your might at tug-of-war until your fingers were stiff. That is *physiological contracture*, which can be explained as a sort of living version of rigor mortis. You exerted the muscles so much that you used up the available ATP, and your muscles did not have enough ATP to contract or to break the cross bridges and remove the Ca^{2+}. This happens even faster if your fingers are cold, because there is less blood flow to bring in nutrients and oxygen.

ON YOUR OWN

5.8 Suppose someone is working out and is pushing himself well beyond his limit. In fact, he gets so fatigued that he runs out of energy, and his muscle fibers can no longer produce ATP. What will happen in his sarcomeres?

Let's get back to normal muscle activity. It is important to understand that when the Ca^{2+} are actively transported away and the cross bridges are broken, the muscle is still shortened. It cannot lengthen itself. However, no further tension is exerted. The sarcomeres are all reduced in length, but there is nothing holding them in that position. As a result, they can be stretched passively back out again. Thus, a relaxed muscle does not automatically stretch back out. However, since it has no cross bridges, it easily can be stretched out by gravity or by the action of an antagonist muscle, a muscle which performs the opposite action of the muscle in question.

MOTOR UNITS

Based on our discussion so far, it is obvious that the motor neurons that control a muscle are critically important. Without them, there would be no muscle contraction. So, it is worth studying the motor neurons a little longer. First, let's introduce a new term, motor unit.

Motor unit—One motor neuron and all the muscle fibers it innervates

If you are not familiar with the verb innervate, don't worry. It is just a technical term for "control." If a neuron innervates a cell, it means that a branch from the neuron's axon closely approaches the cell at a synapse. So, the neuron controls, or innervates, the cell, somewhat the way an electric wire controls a light bulb through its electrical current.

Now remember, the axon of a neuron may branch many, many times, and those branches can innervate many different muscle fibers. Figure 5.11 illustrates how this happens.

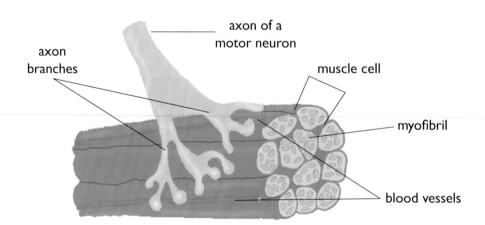

axon of a motor neuron

axon branches

muscle cell

myofibril

blood vessels

FIGURE 5.11
A Small Motor Unit
Illustration by Megan Whitaker

In some motor neurons, the axon branches just a few times. In other motor neurons, the axon branches hundreds of times. How much it branches makes a big difference. A small motor unit is exactly one neuron that might branch ten times and therefore inner-vate ten different muscle fibers. A large motor unit is one neuron that might branch one thousand times, innervating one thousand muscle fibers. Why is there such a big differ-ence between motor units? Well, the amount of branching in a motor unit affects how finely the whole muscle is controlled.

Think about it. If a single neuron branches a thousand times and controls a thousand different fibers, how fine will the control be over the muscle? A single neuron can send only one action potential at a time. When the action potential comes down the axon, it will divide equally among the branches. So, every muscle fiber innervated by this axon will get exactly the same signal and, as a result, will do exactly the same thing at the same time. If one of the muscle fibers contracts, they all will. If one of them relaxes, then they all will. That is what one motor neuron does. It controls a group of muscle fibers, each of which does exactly the same thing. The one motor neuron and all the muscle fibers it innervates form the motor unit.

So, within a muscle, there would be no individual control over the muscle fibers that are controlled by the same motor neuron, meaning they are part of the same motor unit. This reduces the precision with which the muscle can be controlled. However, that is not a problem in certain muscles. Big muscles, especially, tend to be controlled this way because they tend to have movements that are powerful, but not precise. For example, your biceps muscle contracts to flex your forearm. You need a lot of strength there, but not a lot of precision in the movement. The biceps, then, have relatively few neurons that branch many times and innervate all the muscle fibers there. So, it contains *large* motor units, which is okay, because this muscle does not require preci-sion in its motion.

Where would you think the body has the smallest motor units? Large motor units result in coarse muscle control, but small motor units enable fine muscle control. So, you would expect to find small motor units wherever the body must exert fine control over the muscles. For example, there are small motor units in the muscles of your eyes. Think about how you can scan across this page with your eyes. That is very delicate movement. Small motor units may be one neuron innervating just five or ten muscle fibers. That gives precise control.

ON YOUR OWN

5.9 Two muscle fibers lie side by side. They contract and relax at different times, however. Are these two fibers a part of the same motor unit?

MULTIPLE MOTOR UNIT SUMMATION

As was illustrated in figure 5.2, a whole muscle is formed by several or many muscle fibers. Those muscle cells might all be controlled by a few motor neurons or a large number of motor neurons, depending on the individual muscle involved. It is important to understand that each *individual* muscle fiber (muscle cell) within that muscle contracts *maximally* in response to an action potential. Therefore, there is no control over how much an individual muscle fiber contracts. It either contracts maximally, or it does not contract at all. There is no partial contraction in a given muscle *fiber*. This is called the all-or-none law of skeletal muscle contraction.

All-or-none law of skeletal muscle contraction—An individual muscle fiber contracts maximally in response to an action potential.

Now think of what this means in terms of a motor unit. A single motor neuron produces a single action potential that travels equally to all muscle fibers in its unit. In a given motor unit, then, all of the muscle fibers will contract *exactly the same with every action potential produced by the motor neuron.*

Now, on the face of it, this seems to make no sense. After all, you know that you can contract your biceps muscle a little, and your forearm will flex a little. However, if you contract it a lot, your forearm will flex a lot. How, then, can you have that much control over your forearm flexing if all of the muscle fibers in a motor unit respond in an all-or-nothing way? Well, *whole muscle can perform in a much more graded fashion because it is comprised of many motor units.* Although each individual motor unit will act according to the all-or-none law, the motor units can combine to give a weak or strong motion to the whole muscle.

How does this work? In module 7, we will study action potentials in more detail. For right now, we just want to give you some basics. In order for an action potential to be carried on an axon, the neuron must be *stimulated* to produce the action potential. You stimulate motor neurons by consciously or automatically willing a movement to occur. For example, just make a fist with one hand. How did you do that? A particular conscious area of your brain initiated action potentials in motor neurons. These motor neurons stimulated others, which stimulated the motor neurons to the muscles that flex your fingers. Those muscles contracted, and you made a fist! When that stimulus occurs, action potentials can be generated to run down the axon of the neuron. Now, suppose a motor neuron receives a stimulus. It is possible that the stimulus is simply too small for the motor neuron to respond. If that is the case, the stimulus is called a subthreshold stimulus.

Subthreshold stimulus—A stimulus too small to create an action potential in a neuron

If a subthreshold stimulus is applied to a motor neuron, no muscle contraction takes place, because no action potentials stimulate the muscle fiber.

As the strength of the stimulus increases, however, it will eventually trigger *one* action potential in a motor neuron. That is called a threshold stimulus.

Threshold stimulus—A stimulus strong enough to create one action potential in a neuron

When a motor neuron generates one action potential, that action potential travels down the axon of the motor neuron, which triggers action potentials on all of the muscle fibers it innervates. That triggers contraction of all of the muscle fibers in that motor unit.

This is the all-or-none law in action. One action potential causes complete contraction of one motor unit.

If you need to contract the muscle more, your nervous system needs to send more action potentials down the axons of more motor neurons. As the stimulus increases, more action potentials are produced by more motor neurons. This results in more motor units being activated, causing more muscle fibers to contract, which in turn results in more muscle contraction. These stimuli are called submaximal stimuli.

> **Submaximal stimuli**—Stimuli of increasing strength that create more action potentials along more neurons

As the stimulus increases, the stimulus strength eventually reaches a point at which it creates an action potential in every motor neuron of the nerve to the particular skeletal muscle, such as the biceps. At that point, all muscle fibers contract, because all motor units are activated. This is called a maximal stimulus.

> **Maximal stimulus**—A stimulus that is strong enough to create action potentials on all motor neurons to a particular muscle.

Once the maximal stimulus is applied, no further muscle contraction can occur in that muscle. If more stimulus is given, it is called a supramaximal stimulus, but it produces no further effect. All motor units have already been activated, and all the muscle fibers are already responding maximally.

Do you see what is happening here? A muscle is composed of several, or many, motor units. The motor neurons innervating those units are all wrapped together in a single nerve. When a stimulus occurs, action potentials travel down the axons of the motor neurons. When action potentials travel down the axon of a single motor neuron, the muscle fibers in that unit all contract, according to the all-or-none law. As the original stimulus gets larger and larger, action potentials are generated on more and more of the motor neurons in the nerve, activating more and more motor units. This causes more muscle fibers in the muscle to contract, so the whole muscle contracts more.

When the muscle fibers in a motor unit contract, we say that the motor unit has been recruited. The muscle fibers in a recruited motor unit all contract maximally. If only a few motor units are recruited, the whole muscle (for example, the biceps) contracts with only a small amount of force. If many motor units are recruited, the whole muscle contracts with greater force. This is called multiple motor unit summation, and it allows the individual muscle fibers to contract in an all-or-none way, while the whole muscle contracts with differing amounts of force, depending on how many motor neurons and motor units are activated. Truly amazing, isn't it?

ON YOUR OWN

5.10 A muscle contracts, but only a small percentage of its motor units have been recruited. What kind of stimulus (threshold, submaximal, maximal, or supramaximal) is being applied?

MUSCLE TONE

Suppose you had to pick up and carry a three-year-old child. Which would be easier: to pick up and carry the child when he is asleep or when he is awake? It is easier to pick him up when he is awake, right? Why? The answer lies in a discussion of muscle tone. When you try to pick up a child who is asleep, the child just sags. That is because when a person is asleep, he has less muscle tone than when he is awake.

> **Muscle tone**—The state of partial contraction in a muscle, even when the muscle is not being used

Now remember, an individual *muscle fiber* cannot be partially contracted. The all-or-nothing law states that it is either fully contracted or not contracted at all. However, a *whole muscle* can be partially contracted, as it is when only some of its motor units are recruited.

Even though a person has less muscle tone when he or she is asleep, muscle tone normally never disappears totally, even while the person sleeps. Why not? The motor units within a muscle take turns contracting and relaxing so that some motor units are always recruited in the muscle. Consequently, muscle tone goes down when we sleep, but it does not disappear. One way to lose muscle tone entirely would be to accidentally sever the nerve that controls the muscle. At that point, you will have living cells in the muscle, but they will not contract because they will not receive any action potentials. If this happens, the muscle cells will continue to live, but they will shrink due to the lack of use. This is called atrophy.

ENERGY IN SKELETAL MUSCLE FIBERS

Obviously, the motion of muscles requires quite a bit of energy. To review, energy is stored in the cell in the form of adenosine triphosphate, or ATP. When the cell releases energy from its nutrients through cellular respiration, it takes adenosine diphosphate (ADP) and adds another phosphate group (P) to make ATP. When the cell needs energy, the ATP breaks back down into ADP and P, with a release of energy.

In order to learn how skeletal muscle fibers get the energy that they need, we need to look at how muscle fibers produce ATP. There are three basic ways that ATP is generated in a skeletal muscle. The first is through aerobic respiration. In short, aerobic respiration is a multistep process in which glucose reacts with oxygen, and the energy released from that process is used to drive the reaction of ADP and P into ATP. Aerobic respiration produces 36 molecules of ATP for every molecule of glucose burned. This is a lot of ATP, and the glucose burns clean, producing only carbon dioxide and water as waste products. The problem is that aerobic respiration is a relatively time-consuming process that depends on a steady supply of both fuel (glucose or other food molecule) and oxygen. A muscle fiber cannot rely on aerobic respiration when it needs a lot of energy quickly. Typically, muscle fibers rely on aerobic respiration during periods of rest, when energy demands are low. If warm-up occurs, meaning blood vessels to the muscles have opened up to bring in plenty of fuel and oxygen, aerobic respiration is also used. In endurance-type activities such as long-distance running, aerobic respiration is the most efficient means of energy production.

However, muscles often need short bursts of high energy. Compare sprinting to long-distance running. In long-distance running, you run at an even pace for a long time. In sprinting, you run as fast as you possibly can for a short time. In that kind of exercise, your muscles need energy very quickly. Since aerobic exercise requires oxygen, the speed at which it can produce ATP is dependent on how quickly oxygen can get into the muscle fibers from the blood. In sudden vigorous exercise, oxygen simply cannot get to the muscle fibers quickly enough to support the amount of aerobic respiration needed. Something else must be done.

If the muscle fibers have had enough rest time in between periods of high energy consumption, they create an energy reserve. They do this by using aerobic respiration to produce a chemical called creatine (kree' uh teen) phosphate. Creatine phosphate is a high-energy molecule stored in skeletal muscle. In the presence of ADP, the following reaction occurs:

creatine phosphate + ADP = creatine + ATP

Do you see what happens in this reaction? The creatine phosphate donates its phosphate to the ADP, making ATP. What is this good for? Well, this reaction occurs very quickly. It is a quick means by which active muscle fibers can convert ADP back to ATP.

Suppose a muscle fiber has made a lot of ATP via aerobic respiration. In fact, suppose it can't make any more ATP. If it were not for creatine phosphate, then there would be no more energy that it could store up. However, when it can no longer make ATP, a muscle fiber will make creatine phosphate. Now remember, when ATP gets broken down in order for the cell to use its energy, the products are ADP and P. Those must be transformed *back* into ATP in order for the cell to get more energy. Suppose the cell does not have the time, the oxygen, or the fuel for aerobic respiration to produce more ATP. What can it do? Well, if it has creatine phosphate stored up, it can use that creatine phosphate to make ATP. This reaction is much faster than aerobic respiration, so it allows the cell to make a new supply of ATP quickly. As you can see by the reaction above, it does not require oxygen, so the muscle fiber need not wait for oxygen to be delivered by the blood.

Creatine phosphate, then, can be thought of as a super energy reserve. Muscle fibers produce it so that when ATP starts getting broken down much more quickly than aerobic respiration can replace it, the fibers can use the creatine phosphate to replenish the ATP quickly. There is only one drawback. A muscle fiber has only enough creatine phosphate to sustain itself for 10 to 15 seconds of vigorous contractions. This is a great energy reserve for sudden vigorous exercise, without relying on warm-up to bring in more oxygen and glucose-rich blood, but it is only a short-term solution.

Well, what happens if a muscle fiber suddenly begins contracting vigorously over a long period of time? After 10 to 15 seconds, the creatine phosphate runs out, and the muscle fiber is still using ATP much more quickly than it can be replaced by aerobic respiration. Does the cell just stop contracting, then? No, of course not! Our bodies are designed much better than that. The cell has a third means by which it can produce ATP. It can use anaerobic respiration.

Anaerobic respiration is actually the first step in aerobic respiration, which is a multistep process. The first step, called glycolysis (gly-call' luh-sus), involves a glucose molecule being broken down into two pyruvic (pie-rue' vic) acid molecules, generating four ATPs. This step actually requires two ATPs in order for it to get started, however, so the net gain for the cell is only two ATPs. Since oxygen is absent, the pyruvic acid molecules produced in anaerobic respiration are converted into *lactic acid*, which then diffuses out of the muscle fibers and into the blood.

Now, think about it. When a cell has the time to go completely through aerobic respiration, it can produce 36 ATPs from one glucose molecule. When it can only undergo anaerobic respiration, it can only produce two ATPs from one glucose molecule. This is incredibly inefficient, but it is *fast*. So, when the cell needs ATP quickly, it must resort to anaerobic respiration. During short periods of intense exercise before warm-up increases the blood supply to the active muscle, the combination of creatine phosphate and anaerobic respiration can provide up to a 3-minute supply of ATP. Eventually, however, the muscle cannot sustain the intense exercise. At some point, the creatine phosphate and the glucose supply of the muscle fiber run out. At that point, there is just no way to produce ATP quickly enough. In addition, if too much anaerobic respiration takes place, the lactic acid does not have time to diffuse into the blood. As a result, it builds up in the muscle fiber. This is bad, because lactic acid is deleterious to muscle tissue, causing muscle fatigue and otherwise gumming up the cellular machinery.

Think about what happens after you have finished a round of intense exercise. After you are done exercising vigorously, you can't just sit down and go about your business, can you? Instead, you have a period of time in which you are breathing almost as hard as you were when you were exercising, even though you are not exercising anymore. You have to breathe like that to make up for the oxygen debt that your muscles have experienced as a result of this intense exercise.

What is the oxygen debt? It is as if we did not get enough oxygen while we were exercising vigorously, and, therefore, we have to "pay it back" by breathing more when we are at rest. Why do we have to "pay it back?" There are two main reasons. First, when you exercise vigorously, you use up ATP and creatine phosphate. These have to be restored via aerobic respiration. Your muscle fibers need extra oxygen to replace the ATP and the creatine phosphate that were used up.

The second reason is a result of anaerobic respiration. Remember, one of the by-products of anaerobic respiration is lactic acid. As we mentioned above, lactic acid is harmful to muscle tissue, and needs to be eliminated from the muscle fiber. One way that happens is for it to diffuse into the blood, where it is picked up by the liver and recycled back into glucose. This requires energy.

WARM-UP AND COOL-DOWN

Warm-up refers to gradually using a muscle more and more just before you are ready to engage it in vigorous activity. Think of what happens as a baseball pitcher warms up: He starts with easy lobs of the ball, gradually increasing until he is "throwing bullets." Now he is ready for the pitcher's mound and his best effort.

What is the value of warm-up? It enables each muscle fiber to do its best by *increasing the muscle temperature*, which increases all chemical reactions in the muscle fiber—production and break down of ATP, cross bridge formation and breaking, and even the movement of calcium ions out of the sarcoplasmic reticulum. Warm-up's effect on *calcium availability to the sarcomeres* is a significant benefit to muscle contraction. Warm-up also causes a number of changes that *increase the blood flow to the muscle* so that oxygen, glucose, and other fuel molecules, such as fatty acids, are delivered much more quickly.

Long-distance runners who say they got their "second wind" are referring to improved aerobic respiration due to warm-up effects. Warm-up has the additional effect of preventing injuries to connective tissue, which also benefits from the increased warmth and blood supply.

Cool-down seems to be less understood than warm-up, and it is easy for amateur athletes to forget it. The term cool-down refers to mild exercise for a period of time immediately after the end of vigorous exercise. It has the big advantage of maintaining the blood flow to the muscle after the stressful exercise is over. That blood flow helps wash the lactic acid away from the muscles and into the blood. People who keep horses learn that cool-down for a horse is essential, since lactic acid not washed out can cause deadly problems in these big, muscular animals.

SUMMING UP

In this module, you have studied the basic details of *skeletal muscle* structure and function. Realize that the skeletal muscle system is even more complex than we have explained here. Also remember that there are *smooth muscles* throughout your body, mostly working your body's organs, and *cardiac muscle,* which pumps your heart. We will discuss those muscles in later modules. The point is that what we have shown you is but a glimpse of the wonder involved in the muscular system of the body.

ANSWERS TO THE "ON YOUR OWN" QUESTIONS

5.1 To tell whether or not it is a whole muscle or just part of one, look for several fascicles, each wrapped in its own perimysium. Then, look for a wrapping around all of those fascicles. If there is a wrapping around all of the fascicles, it is the epimysium, which indicates it is a complete muscle. If an epimysium is present, it is a complete muscle.

5.2 Remember, sarco means "meat," which refers to muscle. All cells have *cytoplasm*. Sarcoplasm, then, is the cytoplasm of a muscle fiber.

5.3 The proper order is:
   b. Ca2+ binds to troponin, causing tropomyosin to move and expose the active sites on the actin, and allowing the myosin heads to grab onto the actin.
   d. The power stroke.
   a. ATP binds to the myosin heads, breaking the cross bridge and making them release the active sites on the actin.
   c. The return stroke.

5.4 This is the return stroke. The ATPs bind to the myosin heads so that they break the cross bridge and release the active sites. Then the ATP breaks down, giving the myosin heads the energy they need to spring back into their original "power up" positions.

5.5 The sarcoplasmic reticulum releases Ca^{2+} in order to start the contraction process. Therefore, if the muscle were beginning to contract, the calcium ion concentration in the sarcoplasmic reticulum would *decrease*. In order for contraction to stop, the calcium ions need to leave the sarcomere and go back into the sarcoplasmic reticulum. This will *increase* the calcium ion concentration in the sarcoplasmic reticulum. So, the muscle in this question has finished contracting.

5.6 The proper order is:
   b. An action potential travels down the axon of a motor neuron.
   e. ACh is released from the synaptic vesicles of the presynaptic terminal.
   f. ACh diffuses across the synaptic cleft.
   c. ACh binds to the muscle fiber presynaptic membrane to initiate a muscle action potential.
   d. The muscle action potential travels down a T-tubule.
   a. Ca2+ are released from the sarcoplasmic reticulum.
   g. Ca2+ bind to the troponin in an actin myofilament.

5.7 There is a large concentration of Ca^{2+} *inside* the sarcoplasmic reticulum. That is why the sarcoplasmic reticulum must use active transport to bring them in. If the Ca^{2+} move out of the sarcoplasmic reticulum, that would be a solute (the Ca^{2+}) moving from an area of higher concentration to lower concentration. That's the way diffusion happens. Also, diffusion happens by random molecular motion, so this would cost no cellular energy. Osmosis refers only to the diffusion of *water* through a semipermeable membrane. So, this is diffusion, and it is passive transport.

5.8 This is a physiological contracture, which is like temporary rigor mortis. If the muscle fibers run out of ATP, there is no ATP to bind to the myosin heads. So, the myosin heads remain bound to the active sites. This makes it so that the muscle cannot contract (the contraction process can't continue), but it is also unable to relax (the myosin heads need ATP to release the active sites for the muscle to relax). So, the muscle would temporarily stiffen, much like rigor mortis. This can also happen to musicians whose fingers just get too tired to play.

5.9 They are not a part of the same motor unit. The fibers in a motor unit all work exactly the same because they all receive the same signal.

5.10 If only a small percentage of the motor units have been recruited, the muscle's nerve has not reached maximal stimulus. However, it has passed threshold stimulus because that causes just one motor unit to be recruited. Thus, this is submaximal stimulus.

5.11 If the cells have a lot of lactic acid in them, they have been undergoing anaerobic respiration. That means the cells must need ATP faster than aerobic respiration can produce them. Since creatine phosphate is used as a storehouse of energy to make ATPs quickly, that must be used up as well, or the cell would not be depending on anaerobic respiration. Therefore, there must be little or no creatine phosphate in the cells.

5.12 The person is breathing heavily. Remember, one of the reasons we breathe heavily is to make up the oxygen debt caused by anaerobic respiration. We need that oxygen to help recycle lactic acid back into glucose. If there is still a lot of lactic acid in the cells, the person has not "paid back" the oxygen debt and is, most likely, still breathing heavily.

STUDY GUIDE FOR MODULE 5

1. Define the following:
   a. Sarcomere
   b. Neuron
   c. Synapse
   d. Neurotransmitter
   e. Motor unit
   f. All-or-none law of skeletal muscle contraction
   g. Subthreshold stimulus
   h. Threshold stimulus
   i. Submaximal stimulus
   j. Maximal stimulus
   k. Muscle tone

2. What are the four major functional characteristics of muscle tissue?

3. What are the three types of muscle tissue?

4.   Label the following structures of a whole muscle:

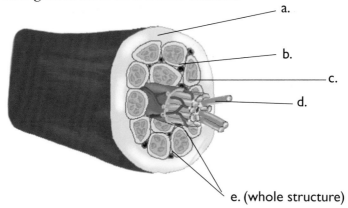

a.
b.
c.
d.
e. (whole structure)

5. In terms of their nuclei, skeletal muscle fibers are different from most cells in two ways. What are those ways?

6. Label the parts of the sarcomere below:

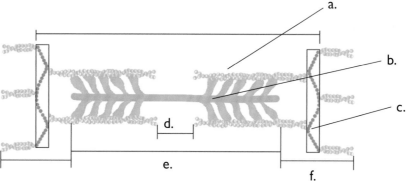

a.
b.
c.
d.
e.
f.

7.   When a muscle fiber contracts, what happens to:
     a. The distance between the Z disks?
     c. The length of the I bands?
     d. The length of the H zone?
     e. The length of the myosin myofilament?
     f. The length of the actin myofilament?

8.   The following steps occur for muscle contraction. Put them in the proper order:
     a. The muscle action potential travels down a T-tubule.
     b. ACh is released from the presynaptic terminal.
     c. ATP binds to the myosin heads, making them release the active sites on the actin.
     d. Ca^{2+} binds to troponin, causing tropomyosin to move and exposing the active sites on the actin, allowing the myosin heads to bind the actin.
     e. ACh travels across the synaptic cleft.
     f. The return stroke.
     g. Ca^{2+} are released from the sarcoplasmic reticulum.
     h. The power stroke.
     i. An action potential travels down the axon of a motor neuron.
     j. ACh interacts with the muscle fiber membrane to create a muscle action potential.

9.   The concentration of Ca^{2+} in the sarcoplasmic reticulum is decreasing. Is the muscle fiber starting to contract or has it finished contracting?

10. The myosin heads of a sarcomere have just received a boost of energy. Is the power stroke or the return stroke about to happen?

11. A myosin head has ADP attached to it but not an individual phosphate. Which is going to happen next: the return stroke or the power stroke?

12. Label the parts of the neuromuscular junction:

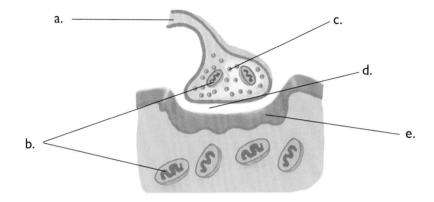

13. If you could look at several muscle fibers while they are in action, how could you determine which fibers are a part of the same motor unit?

14. What is the function of acetylcholinesterase? If it were not for acetylcholinesterase, what would happen to a muscle fiber?

15. There are two major roles that ATP plays in muscle contraction and relaxation. The first involves the sarcoplasmic reticulum, while the second involves the myosin head. What are those two roles?

16. A muscle is stiff. It can neither contract nor relax. What is wrong in the sarcomere? What causes this?

17. When a muscle fiber relaxes, does it automatically stretch back to its resting size?

18. A motor unit has just been recruited. What has just happened?

19. All of the motor units in a muscle have been recruited. If more stimulus is applied, what is that called?

20. A muscle is expending energy faster than it can be replaced by aerobic respiration. There is also no creatine phosphate left. What can the muscle fiber do?

21. What will build up in the cell described in question 20?

22. When we breathe hard after we are finished exercising, what two things is the increased oxygen supply doing for the muscle fibers?

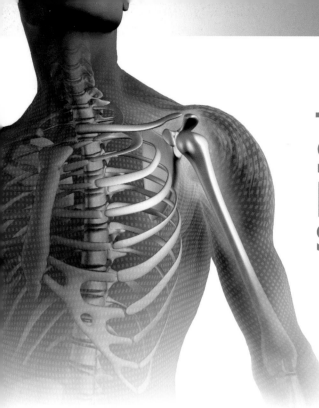

THE SKELETAL MUSCLE SYSTEM

Do you remember how you learned to read? You probably started out by recognizing the shapes of the letters of the alphabet and learning their names. Next, you most likely learned the sound associated with each letter. Once you knew your letters and their sounds, you could put them together to form words, and, even better, once you could form words, you could then understand sentences! This textbook on anatomy and physiology is fairly analogous to that example.

In the previous module, you learned

heart of the matter

Your muscles work along with many other structures in your body to allow you freedom of movement. Although you will study muscle movement in this module, it is essential that you keep your whole body in the back of your mind. Much like puzzle pieces that come together to create the bigger picture, the study of anatomy and physiology is also accomplished in smaller pieces that build on one another. Each individual piece has a special purpose that, when put together with the functional pieces of others, can accomplish far greater things.

about the structure and physiology of skeletal muscle. In this module, you will see how individual skeletal muscles—there are about 640 of them—come together to form the human skeletal muscle system. Keep in mind that there are two other kinds of muscle tissue: smooth muscle and cardiac muscle. We will deal with those later, when we discuss their relevant organ systems.

Before we start showing you the muscles with which we want you to become familiar, we need to go over some general terms and principles.

Skeletal muscles attach to bone via tendons. Typically, a muscle attaches to one bone that moves significantly and another that stays relatively stationary. We can define the parts of a muscle based on these bones.

The place that the tendon attaches to the relatively stationary bone is called the origin of the muscle, while the point at which the tendon attaches to the moving bone is called the insertion. It is actually easy to learn which is which. *In the limbs, the origins are usually more proximal (closer to the trunk) and the insertions are more distal (farther from the trunk). In the trunk of the body, the origins are usually more medial (nearer to the midline), and the insertions are more lateral (farther from the midline).* There are a few exceptions to these rules, but they are both extremely useful guides to follow.

Origin—The point at which a muscle's tendon attaches to the more stationary bone

Insertion—The point at which a muscle's tendon attaches to the more moveable bone

The muscle belly is the largest part of the muscle, and it is where the muscle fibers are found, between the origin and insertion.

Belly—The largest part of the muscle, which actually contains the muscle cells

The most important thing to remember about muscle action is that muscles almost never work individually, even though we study them that way. They generally work in groups of two or more. Consider, for example, the motion depicted in figure 6.1 where two muscles, the biceps brachii (bray' kee eye) and the triceps brachii, work together to flex and extend the forearm. Before we start explaining the way these muscles work together, remember from the previous module that a relaxed muscle can be lengthened passively without much effort, since the myosin heads have released the actin myofilaments, but a muscle cannot lengthen itself.

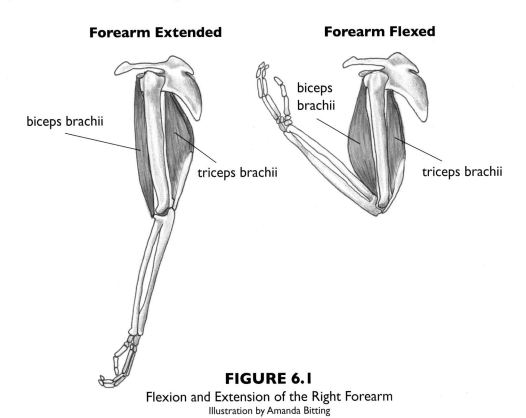

Forearm Extended   **Forearm Flexed**

biceps brachii

triceps brachii

biceps brachii

triceps brachii

FIGURE 6.1
Flexion and Extension of the Right Forearm
Illustration by Amanda Bitting

The drawing on the right in figure 6.1 illustrates how these two muscles flex the forearm. To flex the forearm, the radius and ulna must be pulled toward the humerus. To do this, the biceps brachii (often referred to as just the biceps) contracts. However, that is not enough. Look at how the triceps brachii (often called just the triceps) is attached to the ulna. If the radius and ulna are going to move toward the humerus, the triceps must be relaxed. Otherwise, it would fight the motion caused by the contraction of the biceps. Now remember, muscles do not lengthen themselves. They can only contract, which means to shorten. However, if the triceps relaxes, the contraction of the biceps will pull on the radius and ulna. As long as the triceps is relaxed, the force provided by the biceps will passively lengthen the triceps. Thus, to flex the forearm, the biceps contracts, providing the power, and the triceps relaxes so that it can be passively lengthened.

In the drawing on the left in figure 6.1, we show how these same two muscles can extend (straighten) the forearm. To do that the triceps contracts. This pulls the radius and ulna away from the humerus, straightening the forearm. However, for this to happen smoothly, the biceps cannot be contracted. Otherwise, it would oppose the motion of the radius and ulna. Thus, the biceps relaxes and is passively stretched out by the movement of the radius and ulna.

This is typical of how skeletal muscles work. They work as partners that are opposite one another. When the first partner contracts, the second relaxes, and movement in one direction is caused. Movement in the other direction is caused when the two partners switch jobs, and the first relaxes while the second contracts. In reality, this is an oversimplification. Muscles tend to work in large groups, depending on the joints involved. In other words, there may be a group of muscles that creates movement in one direction and then another group of muscles that create the opposite movement. The movement requires the synchronization of all of these muscles.

When muscles work together to create the same movement, they are called synergists (sin' er jists). If one muscle is more important than the others in creating that movement, it is called the prime mover or (agonist). When a muscle works opposite of another muscle, it is called an antagonist. The triceps brachii, then, is the antagonist of the biceps brachii, and the biceps brachii is the antagonist of the triceps brachii.

The last general principle you need to understand is that muscles tend to work as levers in the body. Remember, a muscle can only contract. It cannot lengthen on its own. Thus, muscles *pull*; they cannot push. A muscle, then, creates a pull on a lever made out of bone. A lever consists of a rigid bar that rotates around a fixed point called the fulcrum. When a force (the effort) is applied, a weight (the resistance) is moved. There are actually three types of levers, each of which has a different arrangement of the fulcrum, effort, and resistance. You find those three lever types in the human body, as well, as figure 6.2 shows.

First-Class Lever
In a first-class lever, the fulcrum is between the effort and the resistance.

Second-Class Lever
In a second-class lever, the resistance is between the effort and the fulcrum.

Third-Class Lever
In a third-class lever, the effort is between the fulcrum and the resistance.

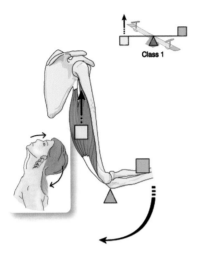
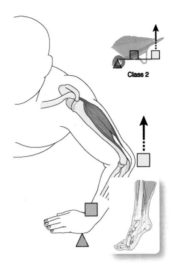
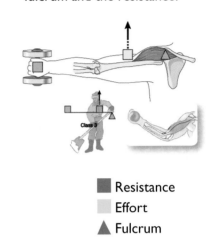

■ Resistance
□ Effort
▲ Fulcrum

FIGURE 6.2
Lever Types in the Muscle System
Arm and muscle illustrations by LifeArt | Insets by Megan Whitaker

The best example of a first-class lever is a seesaw. A child sits on one end and another child sits on the other end. The fulcrum is in the middle. One child's weight is the effort, which lifts the other child (the resistance) up. So, the fulcrum is between the effort and resistance. The posterior neck muscles which tilt your head up are an example of such a lever in your body. The muscles pull down on the back of the head. The joint between your skull and your first cervical vertebra is the fulcrum, and your head is the resistance. Since the resistance is near the fulcrum, only a small effort is needed to pull a large resistance.

A common example of a second-class lever is the wheelbarrow. In this kind of lever, the resistance is between the fulcrum and the effort. In your foot, your calf muscles pull on your heel. The ball of your foot acts as the fulcrum. Using this second-class lever, your calf muscles can lift the entire weight of your body, but only a short distance. When you stand on your tiptoes, then, you are using this second-class lever so that one set of muscles lifts your entire body.

The third-class lever is actually the most common lever in the body. In a third-class lever, the effort is between the fulcrum and the resistance. Depending on how you use a shovel, it can act as such a lever. When you hold the handle of the shovel still and lift the contents of the shovel with your other hand, you are using the shovel as a third-class lever. One of the many examples of such a lever in your body is your forearm. When the biceps brachii pulls on your radius, your elbow acts as the fulcrum, and the items in your hand (the resistance) are lifted. This kind of lever actually requires a much greater force to be used as the effort, but the resistance can be lifted much farther than it can in the other two types of levers.

ON YOUR OWN

6.1 For the arm muscles illustrated in figure 6.2, where are the origins and where are the insertions?

6.2 When you kick a ball with your leg straight and your knee locked, your rectus femoris muscle on the anterior (front) of the thigh contracts. Its origin is on the pelvic girdle, and its insertion is on the tibia. This flexes the thigh at the hip. What kind of lever system is this?

AN OVERVIEW OF THE SKELETAL MUSCLE SYSTEM

You are not required to memorize the names and positions of all 640 skeletal muscles in the body! Instead, we will present some of the major muscles, starting with the superficial skeletal muscles illustrated in figure 6.3. These are the muscles on the surface of the skeletal muscle system. There are deeper muscles, but if you were to peel back a person's skin, the superficial muscles would be the first ones you would see.

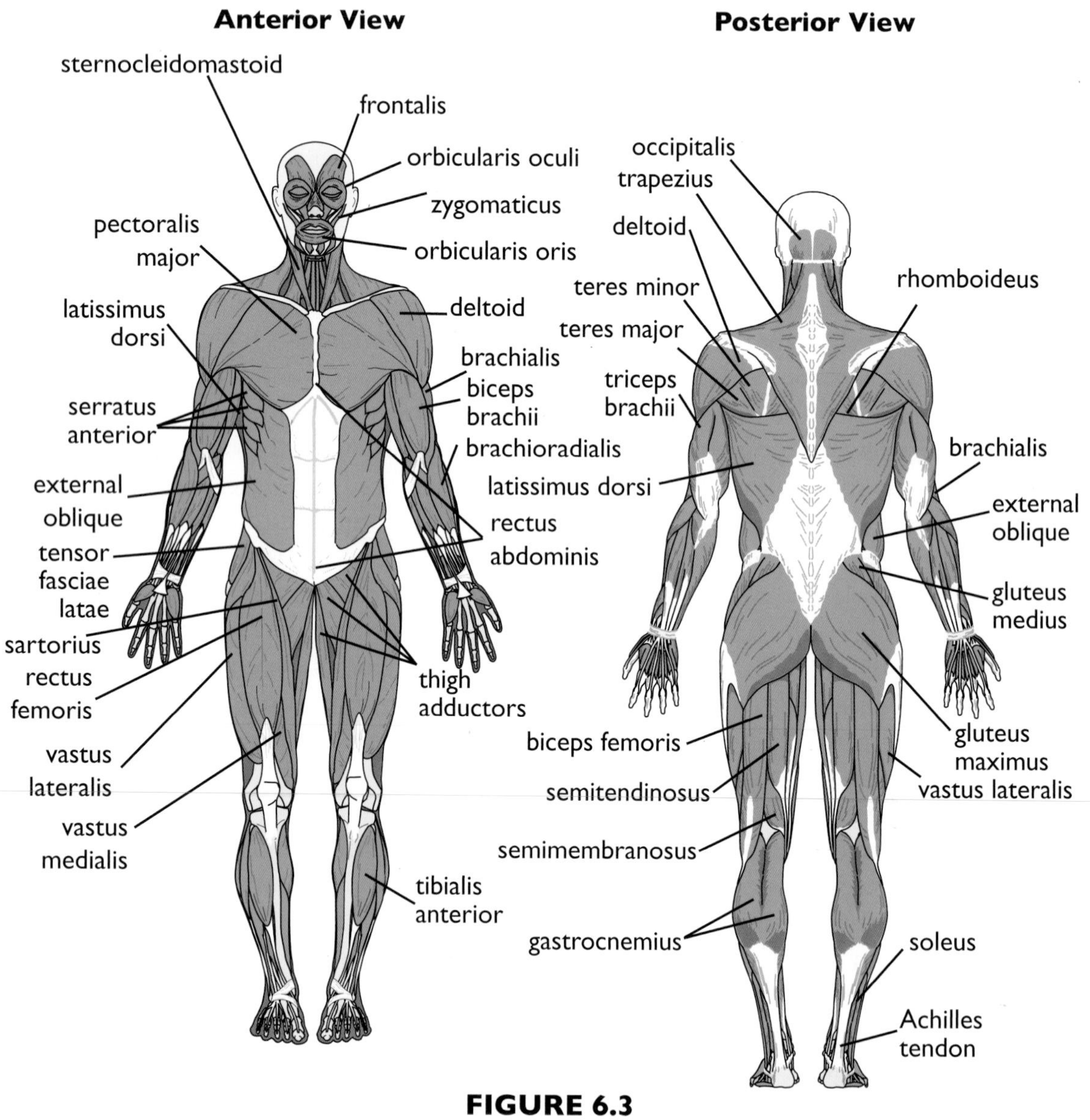

Anterior View

sternocleidomastoid
frontalis
orbicularis oculi
zygomaticus
orbicularis oris
pectoralis major
deltoid
latissimus dorsi
brachialis
biceps brachii
serratus anterior
brachioradialis
latissimus dorsi
external oblique
rectus abdominis
tensor fasciae latae
sartorius
rectus femoris
thigh adductors
vastus lateralis
vastus medialis
tibialis anterior

Posterior View

occipitalis
trapezius
deltoid
teres minor
teres major
triceps brachii
rhomboideus
brachialis
external oblique
gluteus medius
biceps femoris
semitendinosus
semimembranosus
gastrocnemius
gluteus maximus
vastus lateralis
soleus
Achilles tendon

FIGURE 6.3
The Superficial Skeletal Muscles
Illustration by LifeArt

As figure 6.3 shows, the names of the muscles are based on Latin. If you learn a few general principles about how muscles are named, you will find it easier to learn these names. In general, skeletal muscles are named according to one or more of the following seven criteria:

1. Muscle size
2. Muscle shape
3. Location of the muscle
4. Orientation of the muscle's fascicles
5. Muscle origin and insertion
6. Number of heads (origins) on the muscle
7. Muscle function

Unfortunately, there are no set rules. Some muscles are named based on shape alone, while others are named based on location alone. Still others are named for both their location and size. The best way for you to see how this works is to give you a few examples.

Look, for example, at the *brachialis* muscle in the top right of Figure 6.3. This muscle is on the arm. The term *brachium* is Latin for "upper arm." The brachialis is named solely for the location of the muscle. Of course, location alone does not work very well, since you can see from the figure that there are several muscles in the arm. Therefore, some muscle names mix naming methods. For example, notice the *biceps brachii* pointed out in the anterior view of figure 6.3. This muscle has two heads or origins. That's why it is given the name *biceps*, which is Latin for "two heads." To point out that this muscle is on the arm, it is called the biceps brachii. *Brachii* is Latin for "of the arm." The bone over which the muscle is located can also be used in the name. For example, the *tibialis anterior* muscle illustrated in the anterior view of figure 6.3 is located over the tibia on the anterior side.

Muscle names also can blend location and size. For example, notice the gluteus maximus labeled in the posterior view of figure 6.3. The first part of its name refers to the fact that it is on the buttock, because *gluteus* refers to the buttock. The second part of the name indicates that it is the largest gluteus muscle. There is another buttock muscle, the gluteus minimus (not shown because it is deeper), which is the smallest buttock muscle. Finally, there is the gluteus medius, which is between the other two in size. The terms *longus* and *brevis* are also used to indicate long and short, respectively.

Muscle shape can be used as a sole criterion for naming. The *deltoid* muscle (pointed out in both views of figure 6.3) gets its name from the fact that it is triangular, and the Greek letter delta is a triangle. The *trapezius* muscle is shaped like a trapezoid. A *quadratus* muscle is rectangular, while a "rhomboid" muscle is in the shape of a rhombus.

The orientation of a muscle's fascicles (bundles of muscle fibers) can play a role in naming as well. Notice the *rectus abdominis* muscle in the anterior view of figure 6.3. The term *rectus* means straight. Thus, the fascicles of this muscle run straight down the abdomen. The *external oblique* muscle pointed out in both views of figure 6.3 gets its name from the fact that the muscle fascicles lie oblique (neither perpendicular nor parallel) to the body's longitudinal axis.

Some muscles are named according to their origin and insertion. The *brachioradialis* muscle illustrated in the anterior view of figure 6.3 has its origin in the arm on the humerus and its insertion on the radius. The *sternocleidomastoid* muscle in the anterior view of figure 6.3 has its origin on the sternum and clavicle and its insertion in the mastoid process of the temporal bone. *Cleido-* refers to clavicle. Both are related to the Latin word for key, referring in this case to the shape of the clavicle.

Finally, some muscles are named based on their action. The *masseter* muscle shown in the anterior view of figure 6.3 is a muscle involved in mastication (chewing). The thigh *adductors* shown in the anterior view of figure 6.3 adduct the thighs; that is, bring them together in the anatomical position.

COLORING BOOK EXERCISE 6.1

An introduction to the skeletal muscle system as well as an anterior muscle view and posterior muscle view can be found in your coloring book on pages 331-335.

ON YOUR OWN

6.3 Where is the biceps femoris located? What can you say about this muscle without even looking it up?

6.4 There is a muscle in the arm called the supinator. What does this muscle do?

6.5 There is a muscle in the forearm called the flexor digitorum superficialis. What does this muscle do? Where is it located in relation to the other such muscles?

MAJOR MUSCLES OF THE HEAD AND FACE

The major muscles of the head and face are illustrated in figure 6.4. In the top part of the figure, you can see several of the muscles involved in facial expression and head movement. For example, the sternocleidomastoid (ster' noh klee' doh mas' toyd) muscle is the prime mover of a group of muscles (including the posterior triangle, an array of muscles), which rotate and flex the head. Now remember, you have to be familiar with the terms of motion (rotation, flexion, etc.) discussed in module 4 to be able to understand this module.

The sternocleidomastoid muscles are found on both sides of the neck. If the muscle on just one side of the neck contracts, the head rotates so that the chin moves over towards the *opposite* side. If the muscles on both sides contract together, the head is flexed, bringing the chin closer to the chest. Try turning your head to the right. Can you feel the left sternocleidomastoid muscle contract? Try lying down flat on your back. Without moving your back, raise your head. Can you feel both muscles contract?

The *muscles of facial expression* are unusual in that they insert into the skin or connective tissue of the face and thereby earn their name. The frontalis (frun tay' lis) and occipitalis (ok sip ih tay' lis) muscles are often considered two bellies of a single muscle, called the occipitofrontalis (ok' sip ih toh frun' tay lis) muscle. The frontalis elevates the eyebrows and wrinkles the forehead. The orbicularis (or bik' you lay' ris) oculi (ok' you lie) circles the orbit and is used to close the eye, as in winking. Another circular muscle, the orbicularis oris (or' is), surrounds the lips and is used to purse them. It is often nicknamed the "kissing muscle."

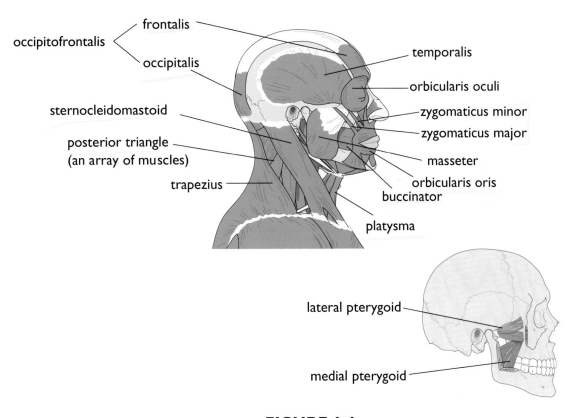

FIGURE 6.4
The Major Muscles of the Head: Lateral View
Illustration by LifeArt

The buccinator (buk' sih nay' tor), or cheek muscle, compresses the cheek, making rapid changes in the volume of the oral cavity. For example, when you fill your mouth with water and squirt it out, you are using the buccinator.

The zygomaticus (zye' goh mat' ih kus) major elevates and draws the corner of the mouth laterally. The zygomaticus minor elevates the upper lip. When you smile, then, you use these two "smiling" muscles. On the other hand, the platysma (pluh tiz' muh) pulls the corners of the mouth down into a frown. Now you can understand the wrinkles that form in the skin of the face as people age. They are part of the dermis, and they form at right angles to the contraction of the muscles. The fascicles of frontalis, on the forehead, run vertically to lift the eyebrows, so the wrinkles in the forehead are horizontal. The crow's feet at the lateral corners of the eye are radial in orientation, roughly at right angles to the circular contraction of orbicularis oris. When you smile, the creases along each side of your mouth are at right angles to zygomaticus major. Puckering the lips often, as smokers do, results in radiating creases in the upper lip, at right angles to the orbicularis oris. Try all these movements in a mirror. You may be too young to have permanent wrinkles, but you can make temporary ones. Do not do it too much; as Mom said when you were younger, "Your face will freeze that way!" She meant the wrinkles would become permanent!

The other muscles in the figure represent some of the major muscles that control mastication.

Mastication—The process of chewing

The temporalis (tem' puh ra' lis) muscle's fascicles converge on the mandible, enabling the temporalis to elevate the mandible powerfully. It also can be used to retract the mandible (to pull the jaw backward). The masseter (mas' seh ter) also powerfully elevates the mandible, and it can be used to protract the mandible (to push the lower jaw forward), as well. The lateral pterygoid (ter' ih goyd) depresses (lowers) the mandible. It is used to open the mouth. The medial pterygoid elevates the mandible (along with the masseter and temporalis) in order to close the mouth. These muscles all work together to make the motions that enable you to grind your food with your teeth. They are also used as you move your mouth in speech.

COLORING BOOK EXERCISE 6.2

The facial muscles discussed can be found in your coloring book's flashcard section. Take the time to color these muscles and learn their actions.

MAJOR MUSCLES OF THE ANTERIOR CHEST AND ABDOMINAL WALL

Figure 6.5 illustrates the major muscles that you find within the anterior chest and abdominal wall.

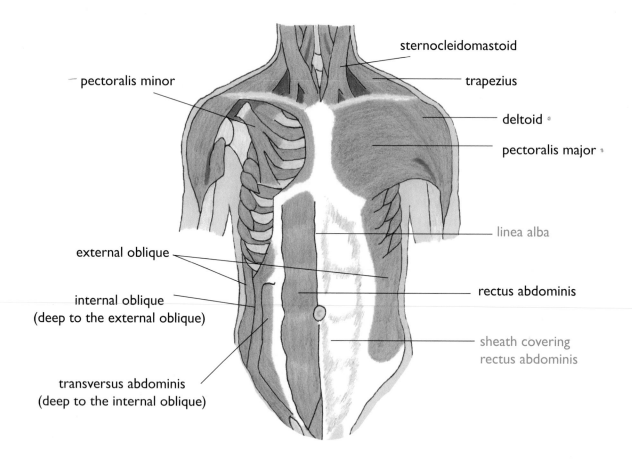

FIGURE 6.5
Major Muscles of the Chest and Abdominal Wall: Anterior View
Illustration by Megan Whitaker

To help orient you in terms of what you have already seen, the sternocleidomastoid muscle is labeled in this figure. The deltoid muscle packs three different groups of fascicles into one muscle. The anterior muscle fascicles in the deltoid flex the arm. This means that the arm is raised up, as you would do if you pointed straight ahead. The lateral fascicles abduct the arm, bringing them straight out away from the body. Finally, the posterior fascicles extend the arm, which brings it from a flexed position back to the anatomical position. Gravity does this when you are upright, explaining why weight-lifting machines in a gym require you to use a pulley system to pull a weight by extending your arm.

The pectoralis (pek' tor al is) major muscle acts on the arm. It adducts, flexes, and medially rotates the arm. Adduction brings the outstretched arm back to anatomical position. Flexion, as mentioned before, puts the arm in a pointing-straight-ahead position, and medial rotation twists the arm toward the trunk. If you try these movements, you will see why the "pecs" are so important in swimming. The pectoralis minor, on the other hand, does not act on the arm. Instead, it elevates the ribs, as in taking a deep breath, and depresses the scapula, as in pulling down on something above your head. It is located deep to the pectoralis major.

The other muscles in figure 6.5 are the major muscles of the abdominal wall. They flex and rotate the vertebral column. They can also compress the abdomen. This is useful in urination, vomiting, defecation, and childbirth because these muscles can powerfully compress the contents of the abdomen. If you are a relatively muscular person with little body fat, you can see a thin line that runs down the center of the abdominal wall. It starts near the end of the sternum and runs through the navel to the pubis. This is called the linea (lin' ee uh) alba (al' buh), or "white line." It is not a muscle, and that is why it is labeled in blue ink. Instead, this is a band of connective tissue that binds all of the abdominal muscles.

On either side of the linea alba, you will find the rectus (rek' tus) abdominis (ab dom' ih nus). This straight muscle is covered with a sheath of connective tissue, as pointed out in the figure. Once again, the sheath is not a muscle, so it is labeled in blue. On the left side of the figure, the sheath has been removed to reveal the rectus abdominis. Since the fascicles run vertically, this muscle flexes the vertebral column. You can try this motion by lying down and doing a sit-up. Lateral to the rectus abdominis is the broad external oblique muscle. It flexes the vertebral column, but can also rotate it. The internal oblique does the same job, but it lies deep to the external oblique. Beneath the internal oblique, you will find the transversus abdominis. This muscle does not act on the vertebral column. Its main job is to compress the abdomen.

THE MAJOR MUSCLES OF THE SHOULDER, BACK, AND ARM

Looking at the muscles from a posterior point of view (figure 6.6), we see some of the major muscles of the shoulder and upper arm. The trapezius (truh pee' zee us) muscle extends up the neck to the shoulder and down the thoracic vertebrae. This muscle extends the head. It is sometimes called the shoulder-shrugging muscle, as it can also elevate, depress, and retract the scapula. To retract the scapula means to pull it back.

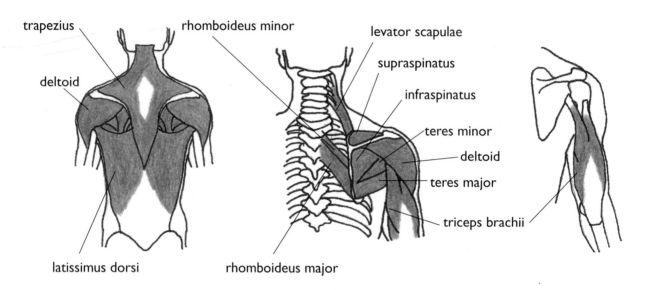

FIGURE 6.6
Muscles of the Shoulder and Arm: Posterior View
Illustration by Megan Whitaker

The latissimus (luh tis' ih mus) dorsi (dor' sigh) works opposite the deltoid to adduct the arm. In other words, it brings an arm that is pointing sideways from the trunk back to anatomical position. It also medially rotates and extends the arm. When you row a boat or use exercise equipment to pull downward powerfully, you are working your "lats." It is a medial rotator of the arm, not a lateral rotator, as you might think, because it originates in the vertebral column, but its insertion is on the *inside* of the humerus, not on the outside.

The teres (tee' reez) major works with the latissimus dorsi to adduct, extend, and medially rotate the arm. Like the latissimus dorsi, it inserts on the inside of the humerus. The rhomboideus (rom boy' dee us) major and rhomboideus minor work with the levator scapulae (luh vay' tor skap' you lee), the trapezius, the serratus anterior, and the pectoralis minor to move the scapula. This provides for a wide range of motion, and it also helps to stabilize the scapula, which is quite movable. The triceps brachii, as we discussed previously, works to extend the forearm at the elbow.

As you learned in module 4, the shoulder joint is a ball-and-socket joint. To provide maximum range of motion, the socket is rather shallow. In addition, because ligaments reduce the range of motion in a joint, the ball of the humerus is held into the socket of the scapula by muscle tension during shoulder movements. The four muscles that cause this tension are the supraspinatus (soo pruh spy nay' tus), infraspinatus (in fruh spy nay' tus), teres minor, and subscapularis (sub' skap you luh' ris). The first three of these muscles are illustrated in figure 6.6. The last one is shown in figure 6.7.

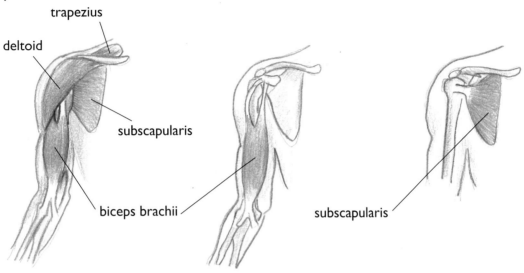

trapezius

deltoid

subscapularis

biceps brachii

subscapularis

FIGURE 6.7
Muscles of the Shoulder and Arm: Anterior View
Illustration by Amanda Bitting

These four muscles provide joint security and are often called the rotator cuff muscles, the rotocuff, or the musculotendinous cuff. A rotator cuff injury (pulling or tearing one or more of these muscles) is quite common in many sports, and is often a serious injury.

MAJOR MUSCLES OF THE FOREARM

Figure 6.8 illustrates the major muscles of the anterior forearm. The top portion of the illustration shows the muscles of the anterior forearm, while the lower part of the drawing eliminates certain muscles so that other muscles can be seen in their entirety.

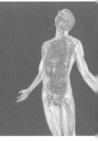

COLORING BOOK EXERCISE 6.4

The shoulder, back, and arm muscles discussed can be found in your coloring book flashcard section. Take the time to color these muscles and learn their actions.

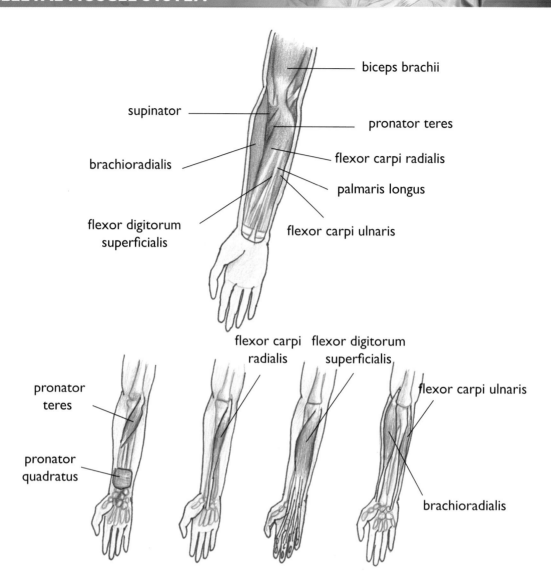

FIGURE 6.8
Muscles of the Right Forearm: Anterior View
Illustration by Amanda Bitting

As you have already learned, the biceps brachii flexes the forearm at the elbow. When you flex your forearm to show your muscle, the muscle that you see bulging is the biceps brachii. The brachioradialis (bray' kee oh ray' dee ay' lis) aids the biceps brachii in flexing the forearm.

Pronator teres pronates the forearm at the elbow, turning the forearm to a palms-down movement. The pronator quadratus (kwah drat' us) aids the pronator teres in this function.

The supinator, as its name implies, supinates the forearm, which turns the palm upward. The biceps brachii, because of its point of insertion at the radius, aids the supinator in this function. This actually leads to an interesting effect. Have you ever noticed that if you are left-handed, you seem to have a talent for opening tight jar lids? Or if you are right-handed, you switch to your left hand if you can't open a tight jar lid? This is because on the standard jar lid, you *supinate* your *left forearm* to open the lid, or you *pronate* your *right forearm*. Well, since the biceps brachii powerfully aids the supinator, supination is a stronger action than pronation. Thus, if you use your left hand, you can use a more powerful force to open a standard jar lid. This is such a strong effect that even right-handed people can have more success opening a jar lid with their left hand!

The flexor carpi (kar' pie) radialis flexes and abducts the hand, and the flexor carpi ulnaris (uhl nay' ris) also flexes the hand. Rather than abducting the hand, however, the flexor carpi ulnaris acts as the antagonist of the flexor carpi radialis, adducting the hand. If you put your hands in anatomical position, you are adducting the wrist when you bring your little fingers toward your trunk. When you cock your thumb outward (like you are hitchhiking), you are abducting your hand. There is an easy way to remember this: We say, "Don't abduct your hand, or you might get abducted!" The palmaris longus also flexes the hand. Because it is between the two flexor carpi muscles and inserts straight into the middle of the palm, it can only flex the hand, not abduct or adduct it. The flexor digitorum (dij' ih tor' uhm) superficialis (soo' per fish' ee ay' lis) flexes both the wrist and the four fingers (not the thumb) to which it inserts. There is a deeper muscle called the flexor digitorum profundus (pro fun' dis), which is not shown. As its name indicates, it aids the flexor digitorum superficialis in its function.

On the posterior side of the forearm, we find mostly the extensor muscles, (figure 6.9). They are antagonists to the flexor muscles on the anterior side, which we have just discussed. The extensor carpi radialis longus and the shorter extensor carpi radialis brevis extend and abduct the hand. While the extensor carpi ulnaris extends the hand with the two muscles above, it is also an antagonist to those same muscles because it adducts the hand. Notice that the hand adductors are on the medial side, while the hand abductors are on the lateral side. This should make sense to you, given the movement they create. The extensor digitorum is the antagonist of the flexor digitorum superficialis, as it extends the hand and the four fingers (not the thumb).

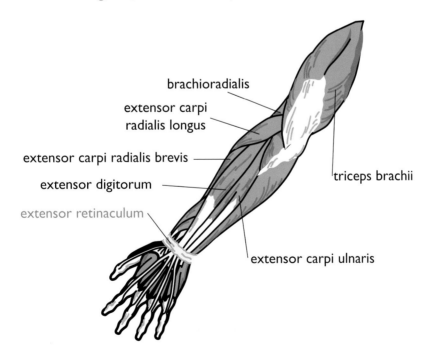

FIGURE 6.9
Major Muscles of the Left Forearm: Posterior View
Illustration by LifeArt

One important structure illustrated in figure 6.9 is the extensor retinaculum (ret i nak' you luhm). It is not a muscle, and that is why it is labeled in blue. Instead, it is like a bracelet of dense regular connective tissue that winds around the wrist, covering the extensor tendons. This holds the tendons down as the muscles work. If it were not for the extensor retinaculum, the extensor tendons would bow outward when the extensors contracted. There is a similar structure on the anterior wrist, called the flexor retinaculum. It will be discussed in more detail in the next section.

COLORING BOOK EXERCISE 6.5

The forearm muscles discussed can be found in your coloring book's flashcard section. Take the time to color these muscles and learn their actions.

ON YOUR OWN

6.6 We discussed two muscles that flex the forearm. List them. List the antagonist we discussed as well.

6.7 There are two supinators of the forearm. List them. List their two antagonists.

MUSCLES OF THE HAND

The hand is a strong, yet delicate instrument. Why? It gets its strength from the fact that it is "cable operated" by powerful muscles in the forearm. The "cables" are long, thin tendons that run from the muscle in the forearm to the hand. You can see some of these tendons by looking at the posterior side of your hand and then making a "cat's claw." The ridges you see rising underneath the skin are tendons from the muscles in the forearm. Because these muscles (some of which we have already discussed) are in the forearm, but cause movement in the hands, they are called the extrinsic hand muscles.

Extrinsic hand muscles— Muscles in the forearm that create movement in the hands

The term extrinsic refers to the fact that the muscles control hand movements, but are outside the hand. That is where the hands get their strength. Where do the hands get their ability to move delicately enough to play the piano or thread a needle? That delicate movement comes mostly from tiny intrinsic hand muscles.

think about this

Take a moment to piece together the information you have learned thus far, and apply it to the hand. You grasp your pencil in your fingers. Your fat cells change the shape of your finger in response to the pressure, and fit its shape. Your grip is strong enough to hold the pencil, but not too strong so that you snap it in half. Additionally, you can use your hands to button a shirt, play a piano, chop an onion, and even support you when you go rock climbing. You were created with the ability to manipulate delicate objects, as well as handle large, heavy ones. "Simple" tasks such as typing on a keyboard, brushing your teeth, or tying your shoes can be done without much thought. Your body is a continuous creation! It is never static, but rather each movement has the potential to create something new.

Intrinsic hand muscles—Muscles in the hand that produce movement in the hand

There are several intrinsic hand muscles, but we will not cover them by name. Just realize that they do exist.

MAJOR MUSCLES OF THE THIGH

Many of the muscles in the hip have origins on the coxa and insertions on the femur. We will show you three views of the thigh so that you can see the major muscles. Two of those views (lateral and posterior) are shown in figure 6.10. The lower views show deeper muscles.

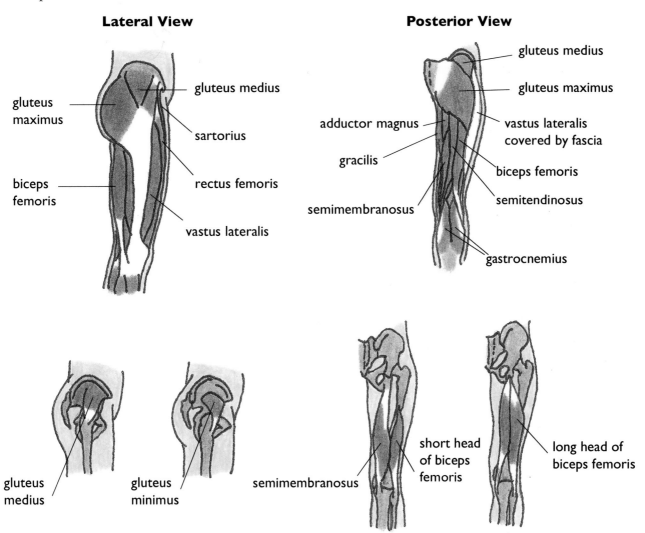

Lateral View

gluteus maximus

biceps femoris

gluteus medius

sartorius

rectus femoris

vastus lateralis

Posterior View

gluteus medius

gluteus maximus

adductor magnus

gracilis

semimembranosus

vastus lateralis covered by fascia

biceps femoris

semitendinosus

gastrocnemius

gluteus medius

gluteus minimus

semimembranosus

short head of biceps femoris

long head of biceps femoris

FIGURE 6.10
Muscles of the Right Thigh: Lateral and Posterior Views
Illustration by Megan Whitaker

Many of the lateral muscles can be seen in the posterior view, as well. The most prominent, of course, is the gluteus (gloo' tee us) maximus (mak' sih mus). It extends, abducts, and laterally rotates the thigh. Because it powerfully extends the thigh, it is a very important muscle for running. The gluteus medius (me' dee us) runs deep to the gluteus maximus. This is one of the most common parts of the body into which a health practitioner will inject medicine if an intramuscular injection is necessary. Why? The gluteus medius is far from the sciatic nerve, a major nerve in the buttocks that can be injured by the injection needle. The gluteus medius abducts and medially rotates the thigh. Deep to the gluteus medius is the gluteus minimus (min' ih mus). It also abducts and medially rotates the thigh.

Looking now at the posterior view in figure 6.10, you can see the biceps femoris (fem' oh ris), the semimembranosus (seh' me mem bruh noh' sus), and the semitendinosus (seh' me ten dih noh' sus). These three muscles are known collectively as the hamstring muscle group. Their main jobs are to flex the leg and extend the thigh. They flex the leg if other muscles stabilize the thigh, preventing it from moving.

To discuss the other muscles in the figure, it is best to show you the anterior view of the thigh, as seen in figure 6.11.

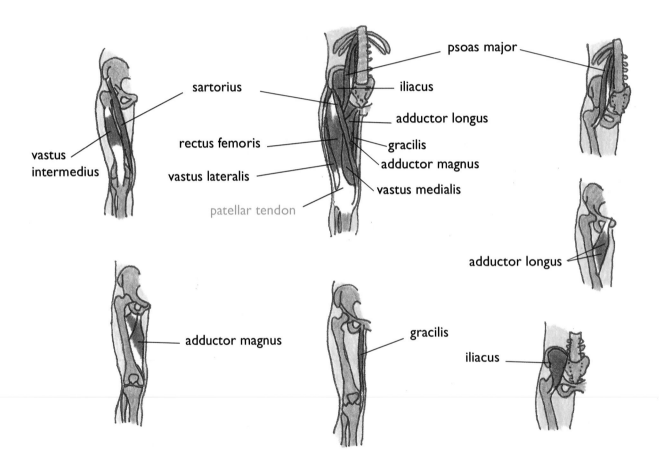

FIGURE 6.11
Muscles of the Right Thigh: Anterior View
Illustration by Megan Whitaker

The iliacus (il ee' uh kus) and the psoas (so' as) major flex the thigh. They have the same insertion on the femur and work toward the same motion, so they are often considered one muscle, the iliopsoas (il' ee oh so' as). When you do sit-ups, these muscles do most of the work. They are unusual in that they originate in the posterior abdominal wall, on the lumbar vertebrae and ilium. They insert into a process on the proximal end of the femur. In people who sit for long periods of time, these muscles do little work. As a result of the constant sitting motion, they tend to shorten. This causes backaches when the person stands. The "fencer's position" (one lower limb forward, the other one extended) is used to stretch the iliopsoas passively. This can help relieve such backache, if it is done regularly.

The rectus femoris, the vastus (vah' stus) lateralis, the vastus intermedius, and the vastus medialis are together called the quadriceps femoris. They are grouped together in this way because their insertions are all on a process of the tibia, the bump that you can feel on the tibia below the patella. The quadriceps femoris extends the leg. In addition, the rectus femoris flexes the thigh.

The sartorius (sar tor' ee us) is the longest muscle in the body. It flexes and laterally rotates the thigh, and also flexes the leg. When you sit on the floor cross-legged, you are using all three actions of your sartorius muscle.

The adductor longus and the adductor magnus work together to (you guessed it) adduct the thigh. These are the muscles that will ache after a horseback ride, unless you ride regularly. They also work together to laterally rotate the thigh. They are antagonists when it comes to flexion and extension, however. The former flexes the thigh while the latter extends it. The gracilis (gras' il is) adducts the thigh and flexes the leg.

MAJOR MUSCLES OF THE LEG

We now move on to the muscles of the leg. Figure 6.12 shows you the posterior and lateral views. The gastrocnemius (gas trok nee' me us) and soleus muscles form the bulge on the posterior side of the leg that is commonly called the calf. They both plantarflex the foot (which is the motion of standing on your tiptoes), and the gastrocnemius also flexes the leg. They insert into the calcaneus (heel bone) via the calcaneal (kal kay' nee uhl) tendon. This is also called the Achilles tendon, and is often the site of injury in athletes. Why is it called the Achilles tendon? This is a reference to the Greek legend of Achilles, a hero whose mother dipped him into the river Styx to make him invincible. However, she had to hold onto him when she dipped him into the river, so she held onto his heel. So, his heel was not covered in the water, and that was his only vulnerable spot.

COLORING BOOK EXERCISE 6.6

The thigh muscles discussed can be found in your coloring book's flashcard section. Take the time to color these muscles and learn their actions.

ON YOUR OWN

6.8 List all of the muscles that are involved in flexing the thigh. List their antagonists.

6.9 List all of the muscles that are involved in abducting the thigh. List their antagonists.

6.10 List all of the muscles that are involved in medially rotating the thigh. List their antagonists.

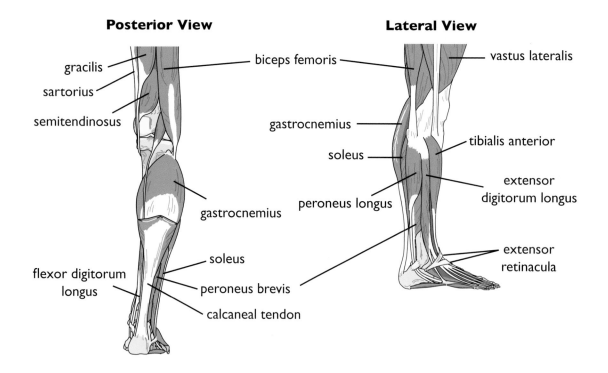

Posterior View

- gracilis
- sartorius
- semitendinosus
- biceps femoris
- gastrocnemius
- flexor digitorum longus
- soleus
- peroneus brevis
- calcaneal tendon

Lateral View

- vastus lateralis
- gastrocnemius
- soleus
- peroneus longus
- tibialis anterior
- extensor digitorum longus
- extensor retinacula

FIGURE 6.12
Muscles of the Leg: Posterior and Lateral Views
Illustration by LifeArt

The tibialis anterior works to dorsiflex (lift the forefoot up) and invert the foot (turn the foot inward). The peroneus (per oh' nee us) longus (also called the fibularis longus) and peroneus brevis (also called the fibularis brevis) muscles evert the foot. These peroneus muscles are especially active when you are walking on your toes, because they also plantarflex the foot. The flexor digitorum longus flexes the four lateral toes (not the big toe). You use this muscle, for example, when you curl your toes. The extensor digitorum longus is the antagonist, as it extends the four lateral toes. Notice the extensor retinacula (plural of retinaculum) in the figure. These structures perform the same task as the retinacula in the wrist; they keep the tendons from bowing when the muscles are contracted.

Figure 6.13 illustrates the major muscles of the leg in the anterior view. We have already discussed many of the muscles that you see in this figure. The extensor hallucis (hal' uh sis) longus dorsiflexes and inverts the foot, as well as extends the big toe. The peroneus tertius (also called fibularis tertius) has essentially the same origin as the peroneus muscles discussed above, but it is really just a part of the extensor digitorum longus.

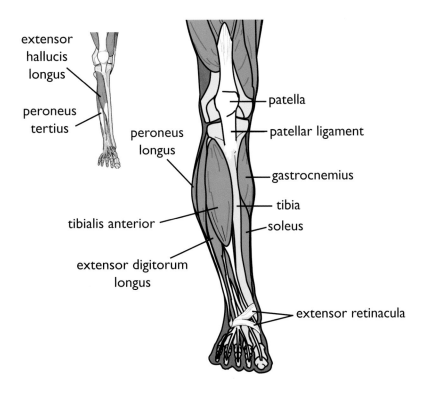

extensor
hallucis
longus

peroneus
tertius

peroneus
longus

patella

patellar ligament

gastrocnemius

tibia

tibialis anterior

soleus

extensor digitorum
longus

extensor retinacula

FIGURE 6.13
Muscles of the Leg: Anterior View
Illustration by LifeArt

The other structures of note in figure 6.13 are not muscles at all. The patella, as you learned in module 3, is a sesamoid bone; that is, a bone that grows like a calcified callus within a tendon where the tendon rubs over a bone. The patella is located in the tendon of the knee joint, and it acts like a lever, reducing the force that the muscles must exert in order to move the femur. Extending from the patella is the patellar ligament. When testing your reflexes, a health-care practitioner will strike this ligament with a hammer, stimulating your quadriceps femoris to contract reflexively in response to the sudden stretch that the hammer tap caused.

COLORING BOOK
EXERCISE 6.7
The leg muscles discussed can be found in your coloring book's flashcard section. Take the time to color these muscles and learn their actions.

THE MUSCLES OF THE FOOT
In the previous section, you learned some of the extrinsic muscles that move the foot or the toes. As was the case with the hands, we will not go into any detail on the intrinsic muscles of the foot.

SUMMING UP

The structures and functions of the skeletal muscle system are incredible! Even so, we did not completely cover the skeletal muscle system, as we did not (thankfully!) discuss all 640 skeletal muscles in the body. However, we have discussed enough so that you can get a deep appreciation for how the skeletal muscle system is put together. It is truly remarkable, isn't it?

Take a moment to try to imagine all that happens at the starting line when a race is about to begin. The runners get into position; their hearts beat in anticipation; their ears listen for the starting gun. Multiple systems keep the runner balanced and poised for the moment, ready to leap into action. The signal is given, and the runners are off! Now, think about what you have learned in previous modules as well as this one. Try to comprehend the signals given by the nervous system to make the movement happen, the homeostasis of the organ systems needed to keep the runners' bodies in balance, and the molecular events that power up the muscles and move the runners along the track with graceful strides! All of this happens without much thought of the design that makes it all possible. Never forget that your Creator made you to "run a good race."

ANSWERS TO THE "ON YOUR OWN" QUESTIONS

6.1 The origin is the bone that is relatively stationary, and on the limbs it is usually proximal (near the trunk). When the forearm flexes, the shoulder stays stationary. The shoulder is also nearer the trunk than the opposite end at the elbow. So, the origin is at the shoulder, and the insertion is at the elbow. When anatomists discuss the origin and insertion of muscles, they actually get much more specific than that, but we are not going to approach that level of detail in this course.

6.2 When you kick a ball with your knee locked, your hip is the part that does not move. That is the fulcrum. Since the insertion of the muscle is on the tibia, the muscle will pull on that point when it is contracted. So, that is the effort. The resistance is the ball that you are kicking, which is at your feet. The effort, then, is between the fulcrum and the resistance, making it a third-class lever. Of course, you could have just guessed that, since third-class levers are the most common ones in the body!

6.3 Remember, the location is often part of the name. Femoris refers to "femur," which is the bone of the thigh. So, this muscle is on the thigh. Without even looking it up, you know that it has two heads because of biceps.

6.4 You should recognize supination as a movement term from module 4. This muscle supinates a structure. This muscle supinates the forearm, which means it turns the hands palms up.

6.5 From the first part of the name *flexor digitorum*, it should be obvious that this muscle flexes digits (fingers). You use this muscle when you make a fist. From the *superficialis* part of the name, you can conclude that it is closer to the surface than other such muscles.

6.6 The two flexors we discussed are the biceps brachii and brachioradialis. An antagonist works against the movement of another muscle. The antagonist will be the muscle that extends the forearm. The extensor we discussed is the triceps brachii.

6.7 The supinators are the biceps brachii and the supinator. Antagonists produce the opposite movement, so those are the pronators. The pronators are the pronator teres and the pronator quadratus.

6.8 The thigh flexors are the tensor fasciae latae (Figure 6.3), rectus femoris, sartorius, iliopsoas, and adductor longus. The antagonists are the extensors: gluteus maximus, semitendinosus, semimembranosus, biceps femoris, and adductor magnus.

6.9 The thigh abductors are gluteus maximus, gluteus medius, gluteus minimus, and tensor fasciae latae. Their antagonists are the adductors: adductor longus, adductor magnus, and gracilis.

6.10 The muscles that medially rotate the thigh are tensor fasciae latae, gluteus medius, and gluteus minimus. The antagonists are those that laterally rotate the thigh: gluteus maximus, adductor longus, and adductor magnus.

STUDY GUIDE FOR MODULE 6

1. Define the following terms:
   - a. Origin
   - b. Insertion
   - c. Belly
   - d. Mastication
   - e. Extrinsic hand muscles
   - f. Intrinsic hand muscles

2. Several muscles work together to laterally rotate the thigh. What do we call an entire group of muscles that work together?

3. One of the jobs of the flexor digitorum superficialis is to flex the wrist. When working in this fashion, does this muscle form a first-class lever, a second-class lever, or a third-class lever?

4. Identify the muscles in the figure:

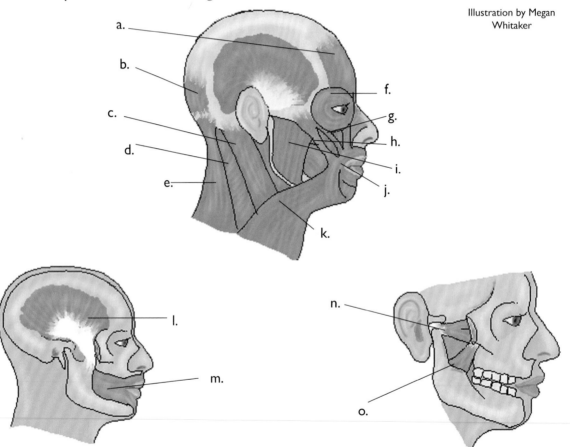

Illustration by Megan Whitaker

5. Of the muscles labeled above, which are involved in mastication?

6. Name the "kissing muscle."

7. Identify the structures in the following figure:

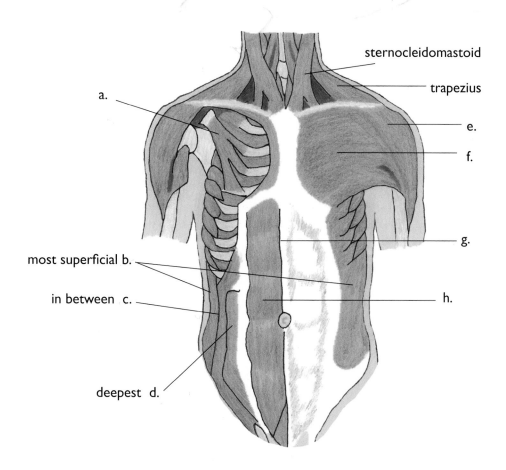

sternocleidomastoid

trapezius

a.

e.

f.

g.

most superficial b.

in between c.

h.

deepest d.

8. Which structure above is not a muscle? What is it?

9. Which of the muscles in the figure above act on the arm?

10. Which of the muscles in the figure above move the vertebral column?

11. Identify the muscles in the figure below:

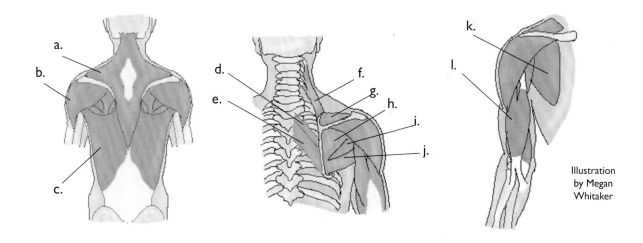

a.

b.

c.

d.

e.

f.

g.

h.

i.

j.

k.

l.

Illustration
by Megan
Whitaker

12. Identify the structures in the following figure:

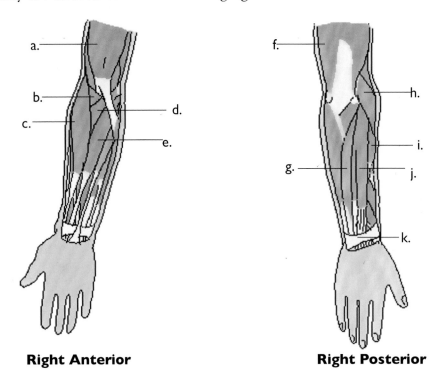

Right Anterior   **Right Posterior**

13. Which of the structures in the figure above is not a muscle? What is its job?

14. What is the difference between extrinsic hand muscles and intrinsic hand muscles?

15. Label the muscles in the figure below:

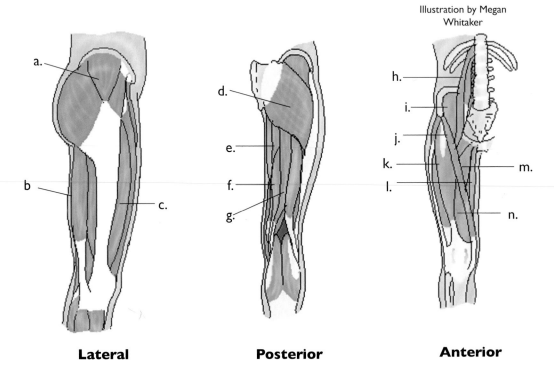

Illustration by Megan Whitaker

Lateral   **Posterior**   **Anterior**

16. List all of the muscles that are involved in flexing the thigh. List their antagonists.

17. List all of the muscles that are involved in abducting the thigh. List their antagonists.

18. There are two muscles that flex the forearm. List them. List their antagonist.

19. There are two supinators of the forearm at the elbow. List them. List their two antagonists.

20. Label the structures in the figure below:

Illustration by Megan Whitaker

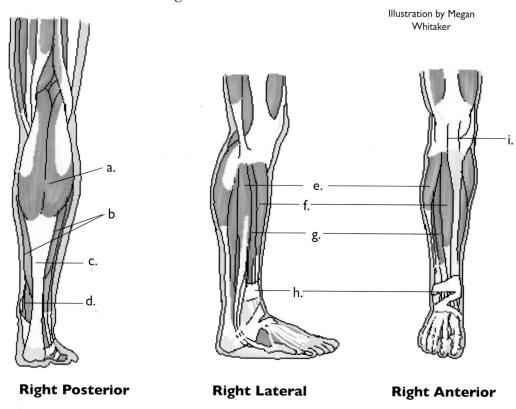

Right Posterior   **Right Lateral**   **Right Anterior**

21. Which of the structures in the figure above are not muscles?

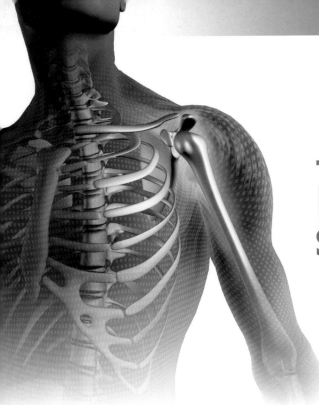

THE NERVOUS SYSTEM

We are going to ask you to stop and think for a moment about all that you have learned up to this point. We can present the details to you, but it is important for you to appreciate, not only the design of the human body, but also the Designer. Let's go back for a moment to you as a *single cell*. That one cell contained your entire DNA code, information needed to form all complex structures, such as your skin, your skeleton, your muscles, and your nerves, and we are only on module 7!

In this module, you are going to learn more detail about the system that connects them all—your nervous system. It is here that communication and cooperation between systems are at their finest. Just as complex corporations function at different levels of operation, so, too, does your nervous system.

heart of the matter

Your central nervous system (brain and spinal cord) and your peripheral nervous system (all other parts of the nervous system) were created to be a complex and elaborate communication network. Your nervous system receives and interprets stimuli signals, and then responds with its own messenger signals. All of these signals are responsible for coordinating the actions of your muscles, registering and interpreting your senses, as well as creating your speech, memories, thoughts, and emotions. Your nervous system is capable of gauging your intentions, consulting relevant cells, considering signals from other messaging systems (hormones), evaluating energy availability, and interpreting other information, such as weariness or pain. Then, in a split second, it responds with its decision. It seamlessly connects who you are with your surroundings, and it does so with beautiful harmony. It is always on guard and always ready to respond.

Accidently touch a hot pot on the stove, and your hand will immediately jerk away without any time for you to realize what has just happened. That is a reflex. Run down the driveway to greet your friend, and your heart rate will automatically speed up. That is a subconscious response from your brain stem. The interpretation of your feelings, the storage of your memories, and your created consciousness occurs in your brain.

Put all of these together, and you have something truly amazing. Your nervous system ensures your sense of survival. Go back to the hot pot. Imagine now that you are in a burning building (hopefully this will never happen) and the only means of escape is for you to turn a scorching-hot doorknob. Your nervous system will inform your cells that they are being asked to go beyond the call of duty. Your reflex to pull away will be suppressed, and the goal of escape will override the pain of grasping the doorknob. Sometimes your brain overrules, sometimes it delegates; but it always makes certain that your well-being is assured.

Let's take a closer look at your amazing nervous system and define some terms, starting with figure 7.1.

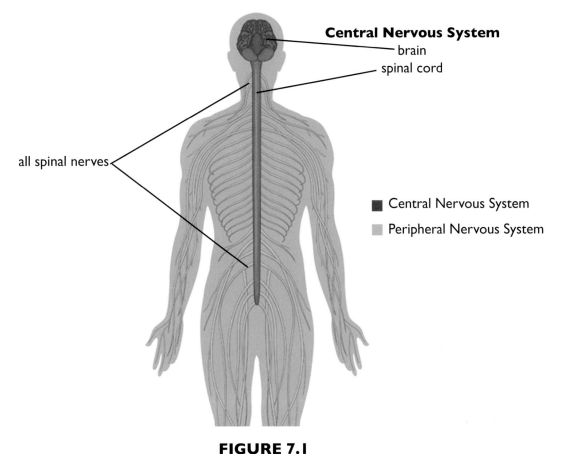

FIGURE 7.1
The Nervous System
Illustration by Matthew Cole

The central nervous system (CNS) is composed of the brain and the spinal cord. They are encased in bone for their protection. The brain is located in the cranial vault of the skull, and the spinal cord is encased in the vertebral canal, which is formed by the vertebral bones. The peripheral nervous system (PNS) is comprised of all the parts of the nervous system that are not the central nervous system. The PNS consists of nerves and ganglia (gan' glee uh).

Nerves—Bundles of neuron axons and their coverings, which are found outside the CNS

Ganglia—Collections of neuron cell bodies that are found outside the CNS

There are two basic kinds of nerves, both of which are part of the PNS: spinal nerves and cranial nerves.

Spinal nerves—Nerves that originate from the spinal cord

Cranial nerves—Nerves that originate from the brain

There are 12 pairs of cranial nerves in the human body and 31 pairs of spinal nerves. Thus, there are a total of 43 pairs of nerves that make up the PNS.

The PNS is subdivided in its structure and function as shown in figure 7.2. We can separate the *neurons* of the PNS (not the nerves) into two divisions: the afferent division and the efferent division.

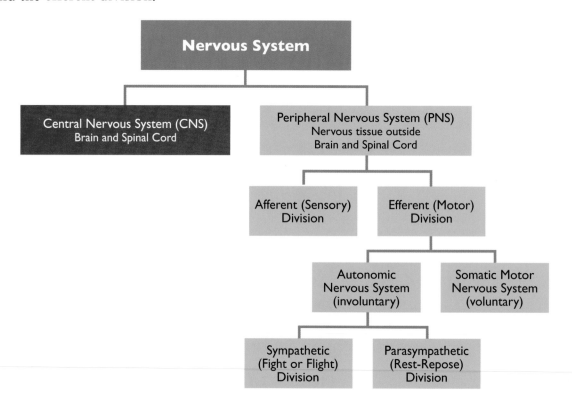

FIGURE 7.2
The Nervous System

Afferent neurons—Neurons that transmit action potentials from the sensory organs to the CNS

Efferent neurons—Neurons that transmit action potentials from CNS to the effector organs

Now remember from module 5 that an action potential is an electrical signal that travels along a neuron. The afferent division of the PNS, also called the sensory division, carries signals from the sensory organs, such as the skin, eyes, ears, nose, and tongue toward the CNS. This allows the CNS to process the information collected by the sensory organs. The afferent division also carries sensory messages from the internal organs to the CNS, which is why you can feel a stomachache or a full bladder.

The efferent division of the PNS, also called the motor division, carries signals from the CNS to effector organs, which are the muscles and glands. The efferent division of the PNS can be divided further into two parts: the somatic motor nervous system (SMNS) and the autonomic nervous system (ANS). These differ in both their anatomy and in their function.

Somatic motor nervous system—PNS neurons that transmit action potentials from the CNS to skeletal muscles

Autonomic nervous system—PNS neurons that transmit action potentials from the CNS to smooth muscles, cardiac muscles, and glands

As you can see, the SMNS division controls the voluntary skeletal muscles, while the ANS division controls the involuntary muscles and glands. In other words, we can exercise control over the muscles governed by the SMNS, but the muscles and glands under ANS control work without a conscious effort on our part.

In an effort to be even more specific, the ANS can be divided further anatomically and functionally into two divisions: the sympathetic division and the parasympathetic division.

Sympathetic division—Division of the ANS that generally prepares the body for increased energy expenditure

Parasympathetic division—Division of the ANS that regulates resting and nutrition-related functions such as digestion, defecation, and urination

The sympathetic division of the ANS increases the rate and strength of your heartbeat and raises your blood pressure. It stimulates your liver to release glucose into your blood, producing quick energy for the fight-or-flight response that you experience when you are excited, frightened or angry. In fact, the sympathetic division of the ANS is often referred to as the fight-or-flight division.

The parasympathetic system of the ANS, on the other hand, slows your heart rate and therefore lowers your blood pressure. In addition, it takes care of nutrition-related activities such as causing

COLORING BOOK EXERCISE 7.1

To review the information on the central nervous system and peripheral nervous system, color the section on page 103 of your coloring book.

ON YOUR OWN

7.1 When you flex your forearm, which division of the PNS (efferent or afferent) is being used? You can be even more specific than that. What would be the most specific way to describe the part of the PNS that is being used?

7.2 When you touch a hot stove, you immediately pull your hand away to avoid being seriously burned. Which system of the PNS (efferent or afferent) is utilized first in this situation?

the smooth muscles in your stomach to contract while you are digesting a meal. The parasympathetic division also causes some glands, such as the salivary glands and lacrimal (tear) glands, to secrete. Its nicknames summarize its functions: The parasympathetic division of the ANS is often called the *rest-repose* or "housekeeping" division.

THE NERVOUS SYSTEM AT THE CELLULAR LEVEL

There are only two basic types of cells that make up the nervous system: neurons and neuroglia. In this course, we will concentrate on the neurons. Now remember, we have already talked a little bit about neurons. When discussing muscles, we told you how motor neurons (part of the SMNS) transmit action potentials to skeletal muscle cells. Now let's look at a neuron in a little more detail.

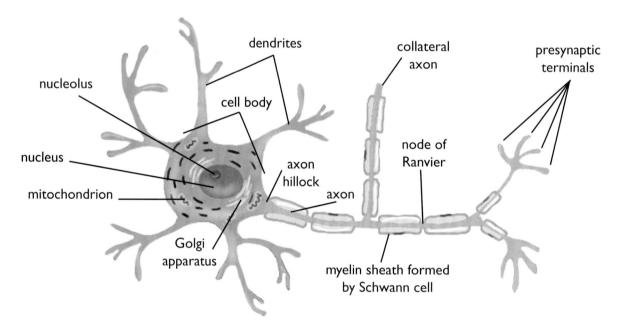

FIGURE 7.3
A Neuron of the PNS
Illustration by Megan Whitaker

A neuron consists of three basic units: the cell body, axons, and dendrites (den' drytz). The cell body, sometimes called the soma (soh' muh), houses the cell nucleus. It also houses many mitochondria because neurons use much energy in the form of ATP. Consequently, they need plenty of oxygen. In fact, after four to eight minutes without oxygen, most neurons die. In addition, the cell body has Golgi apparatuses because neurons secrete neurotransmitters. Neurons make their neurotransmitters in the cell body in the Golgi apparatuses and then send the neurotransmitters all the way down the axon, where they are secreted from the synaptic vesicles in the presynaptic terminals.

There are two types of processes that extend beyond the cell body: dendrites and axons. Dendrites are usually shorter, and their job is to bring messages *into* the cell body. Signals travel down the dendrites *toward* the cell body. The axon, on the other hand, sends action potentials away from the cell body. The action potential begins on the axon hillock, the area that marks the end of the cell body and the beginning of the axon. Once an action potential begins there, it will be conducted all the way down to the far end of the axon without a decrease in its strength.   How long are axons? Well, that depends. They might be microscopically short or they might be more than a meter long. For example, the cell body for the motor neuron that stimulates your toes to flex is located in your lower back. So, the axon starts at your lower back and ends in your lower leg. Its length depends on how tall you are. Axons can be very long!

think about this Interestingly enough, your neurons can no longer undergo mitosis. After infancy, these cells cannot be replenished. As a result, the neurons that you have right now are all that you will ever have! In fact, what you have now is more than you will ever have in the future, because you will lose neurons over time. Does that worry you? Well, if you are doing things that destroy neurons (excessive alcohol intake, use of illicit drugs, and so forth), you should be worried. However, if you are not doing those things, there is no cause for alarm. Why? Well, look how many we have. It is estimated that the human body has 1×10^{11} (100 billion) neurons. No one really knows, but some have estimated that under normal conditions, humans lose 7,000 neurons each day. Please understand that this number is an estimate with several underlying assumptions, which cannot be verified. However, let's just assume for the sake of argument that it is correct. That sounds like a lot; doesn't it?

Even though it sounds like a lot, it really is not. If you lose 7,000 neurons every day that means you lose $7,000 \times 365.25 = 2,556,750$ neurons each year. To keep the proper number of significant figures, that is 3,000,000 every year. Let's suppose that you live to be 100 years old. This means that over the course of your life, you will lose $3,000,000 \times 100 = 300,000,000$ neurons. Once again, that sounds like a lot, right? However, when you compare that number with the number of neurons you actually have, it is hardly anything! Remember, you have roughly 1×10^{11} neurons. If you lose 300,000,000 over the course of your life, you will have only lost 0.3 % of your total neurons! So, as long as you do not do things that actively destroy neurons, you do not have to worry about the fact that your neurons cannot be replaced!

Axons are often wrapped in a myelin (my' uh lin) sheath, which is a fatty wrapping that speeds up the conduction of the action potential down the axon. These myelin sheaths are produced by specialized cells (neuroglia), which have extensions that surround portions of the axon. If the neuron is in the PNS, these neuroglia are called Schwann cells. If the neuron is in the CNS, the cells are called oligodendrocytes (oh lig' oh den' droh sites). We will discuss these neuroglia cells more in a later section. Notice in figure 7.3 that there are gaps in the myelin sheath. These gaps are called nodes of Ranvier (ron' vee aye), and they will also be discussed in more detail later. Some axons split into collateral axons. Axons end by branching into presynaptic terminals, which are also called terminal boutons (byou tonz'), or just axon terminals.

Although the neuron presented in figure 7.3 is representative of a typical PNS neuron, there are structural differences among these cells. These differences can be seen in figure 7.4.

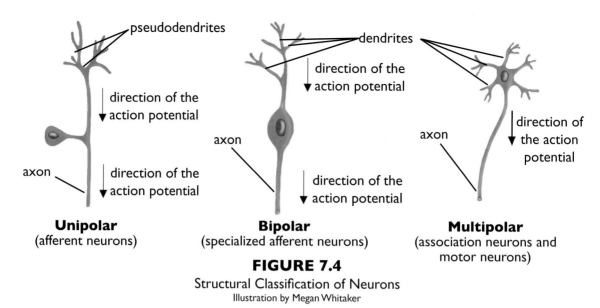

Unipolar
(afferent neurons)

Bipolar
(specialized afferent neurons)

Multipolar
(association neurons and motor neurons)

FIGURE 7.4
Structural Classification of Neurons
Illustration by Megan Whitaker

You can classify neurons based on how many processes they have. What is a process? It is a generic term that means extension. In the case of neurons, it means both dendrites and axons. Instead of saying how many dendrites and axons, we say how many processes. The first neuron in the figure is unipolar. It is called unipolar because it has only one process, and the cell body is suspended from that process. As you have already learned, the part of the process that carries signals away from the cell body is the axon. However, the part of the process that carries signals towards the cell body cannot really be called a dendrite. That is because although it does what a dendrite does (sends signals towards the cell body), it sends action potentials the way an axon does. You will learn how this happens in a later section. Afferent neurons are usually unipolar. Remember, the afferent division of the PNS is the sensory division, so afferent neurons are neurons that carry signals from the sensory receptors to the CNS.

The center neuron in figure 7.4 is bipolar. These neurons have two processes: one axon and one single dendrite split into many branches. Many specialized afferent neurons, such as the ones that send information from the eyes to the brain, are bipolar. By the way, this type of neuron has nothing to do with bipolar disorder, which is a mood disorder.

The right neuron in figure 7.4 is multipolar. This kind of neuron has many processes: several dendrites, but only one axon. No matter how many processes a neuron has, it will have *only one* axon. Multipolar neurons are usually either motor neurons or association neurons.

COLORING BOOK EXERCISE 7.2

To review the information on the structure of neurons and their shapes, color pages 105 and 109 a-f in your coloring book.

ON YOUR OWN

7.3 An axon has a myelin sheath produced by a Schwann cells. Is this neuron in the PNS or CNS?

Association neuron—A neuron that conducts action potentials from one neuron to another neuron within the CNS

Now remember, motor neurons are part of the efferent division of the PNS, since they send signals to effector cells such as muscle cells. Association neurons are within the CNS, and we will discuss them in more detail in a later module.

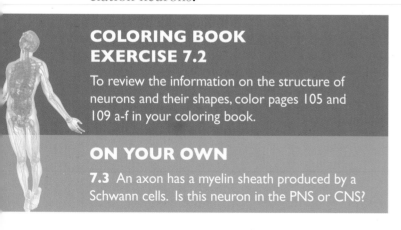

NEUROGLIA

As we mentioned previously, we will concentrate on neurons in this module. Nevertheless, we need to tell you some basic information about the other type of nervous system cells, *neuroglia* (also called glial cells). If you take that word apart, it means "neural glue." Neuroglia are like the "connective tissue" of the nervous system. Even though we will concentrate on neurons in this course, it is important to understand that the majority of nervous system tissue is actually made up of neuroglia. There are roughly nine neuroglia for every one neuron in the nervous system! Neuroglia, however, are smaller than most neurons. So, even though there are many more neuroglia than neurons in the brain, the neuroglia form only a little more than half of the human brain's mass.

Now remember, neurons do not undergo mitosis. However, you know that some people get brain tumors. A tumor is a site of uncontrolled mitosis. Where, then, do brain tumors come from? Most tumors come from the neuroglia. Neurons cannot undergo mitosis after infancy, but neuroglia can.

What do these neuroglia do? They perform a number of functions, depending on the type of neuroglia cell. Figure 7.5 illustrates several different neuroglia types. Let's start with oligodendrocytes and Schwann cells. Oligodendrocytes are found in the central nervous system, and they have two jobs. First, they bind neurons together. Notice in the figure that one oligodendrocyte binds together several axons. Second, they insulate the axons. In the PNS, Schwann cells are the cells that insulate axons. One distinction between these cells is where they are found (the former in the CNS and the latter in the PNS). The other distinction is that, while oligodendrocytes wrap around several axons, Schwann cells wrap around only a portion of *one* axon.

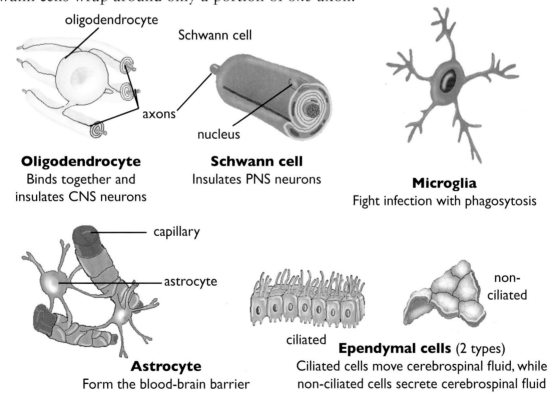

Oligodendrocyte
Binds together and insulates CNS neurons

Schwann cell
Insulates PNS neurons

Microglia
Fight infection with phagosytosis

Astrocyte
Form the blood-brain barrier

Ependymal cells (2 types)
Ciliated cells move cerebrospinal fluid, while non-ciliated cells secrete cerebrospinal fluid

FIGURE 7.5
The Six Types of Neuroglial Cells
Illustration by Megan Whitaker

Microglia (my kroh' glee uh) engage in phagocytosis to fight infections. They act almost as white blood cells do in the brain and spinal cord. How often do we get infections of the brain? Very, very rarely. These cells are a major reason why. Astrocytes (as' troh sightz) form the blood-brain barrier. There is actually a *barrier* between our blood and our brain. At first, that might surprise you, but we will explain to you why this elegantly designed system is *absolutely* necessary for your survival.

As you will learn in an upcoming module, your circulatory system is full of tiny blood vessels called capillaries. These blood vessels are porous so that they can let nutrients out into the surrounding tissue and absorb the waste products of the cells. This *cannot* be the case in the brain because many of the substances, which other parts of our bodies need, are toxic to neurons. Consequently, neurons must not be allowed to have direct contact with the blood. This is accomplished by astrocytes, which have processes that surround the capillaries, forming a tight barrier.

Of course, that is not the end of the story. After all, this situation protects neurons from the blood, but neurons are living cells! They must take in nutrients and discard waste products. This is accomplished by mutual cooperation between the astrocytes and specialized cells in the capillaries. Together, they mediate what can get out of the blood and into the surrounding tissue, and they also mediate what can be sent out of the tissue and into the blood.

COLORING BOOK EXERCISE 7.3

To review what you have learned about neuroglia, follow the directions on page 107 of the coloring book.

ON YOUR OWN

7.4 In studying a rat's brain, a scientist notices that the microglia are very active. What does this tell you about the rat's brain?

Experiment 7.1
Neurons and Neuroglia

Supplies:

- Microscope
- Prepared slide: human cerebrum

Purpose: Although a bit difficult, neurons can be distinguished from neuroglia with a microscope.

Procedure:

1. Place the prepared slide on the microscope stage and look at it on low magnification. Focus onto some of the pink tissue, and increase to medium magnification.

2. Refocus. Notice that there is a lot of pink tissue, but there are nearly circular regions of white that have a cell or two in the middle. Center on one of those white regions and increase to maximum magnification.

3. Refocus. The cells in the middle of these white regions are neurons. Slowly move the slide around and look at a few. Notice how different one neuron is from another. They vary dramatically in size. Also, the shape varies quite a bit. Notice that many of the neurons have processes. Typically, you can see only the beginning of the processes, so they tend to look like sharp points on the edge of the neurons. The vast majority of these neurons will be multipolar since this is brain tissue and most brain neurons are association neurons. Draw a few neurons.

4. Notice the pink tissue surrounding the neurons. Do you see how it looks as though it is made of fibers? Do you know what those fibers are? They are dendrites and axons. By looking at this slide, you should get a deep appreciation for how much interconnection there is between neurons!

5. Put everything away.

Even though the blood-brain barrier is incredibly designed, not all substances toxic to brain cells are held back by it. For example, certain drugs can pass through the blood-brain barrier and damage brain cells. People who use illegal drugs to get high do not realize that they are tampering with a system that God has designed to protect very sensitive neurons. As a result, most illegal drugs that affect the brain also kill brain cells. Alcohol also passes through the blood-brain barrier, and it is not good for brain tissue. Recent studies have indicated that teens who drink a substantial amount of alcohol have trouble with memory functions and learning.

Finally, we come to the ependymal (e pen' dih muhl) cells. There are actually two types of these neuroglia. The cells without cilia secrete cerebrospinal (ser ee' broh spy' nuhl) fluid. This fluid bathes brain and spinal cord tissue and provides a protective cushion around the CNS. The ciliated ependymal cells move this fluid around.

NERVE STRUCTURE

"You've got some nerve." Have you heard that expression? Well, we've all got more than just some nerve! We have *lots* of nerves. We defined the term earlier (nerves are bundles of axons and their sheaths, which extend from the CNS), but now it is time to discuss nerves in a bit more detail. Figure 7.6 illustrates the basic structure of a nerve.

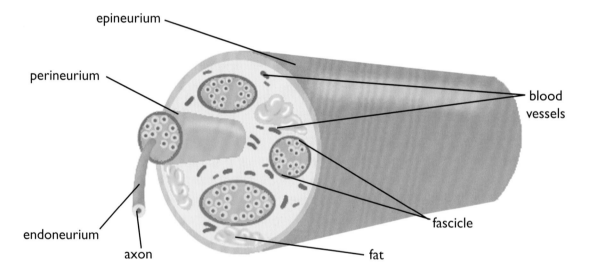

FIGURE 7.6
Nerve Structure
Illustration by Megan Whitaker

If you were to look at a nerve in the human body, it would look whitish. Nerves look white because they are wrapped in a connective tissue covering called the epineurium (ep ih new' ree uhm). If you take apart the name, it makes sense. *Epi* means "on the top," and *neurium* means "nerve." So, this is the collagen layer on the top of the nerve. This wrapping encloses several bundles of axons, and each bundle, called a fascicle, is wrapped together in what is called perineurium (pehr ih new' ree uhm). The perineurium is made of the same material as the epineurium; it just wraps smaller bundles. Each individual axon of the bundle is wrapped, not only in its Schwann cells, but also in an endoneurium (en doh new' ree uhm).

In the body, nerves usually travel along with blood vessels. Consequently, where you find a medium-sized artery and vein, you tend to find a medium-sized nerve. What do we mean by a "medium-sized nerve?" Well, a medium sized nerve will look a lot like a white shoestring in size and shape. There are much thicker nerves in the body, as well as much smaller nerves. However, a shoestring is a good approximation of a medium-sized nerve. The thickest nerve in the body is the sciatic (sigh at' ik) nerve, which passes through your buttocks and down your posterior thigh. It is about as thick as your little finger.

think about this

If some of this material is sounding a bit familiar, remember that in module 5, you learned that skeletal muscle fibers were wrapped in endomysium and bundled together in fascicles, which were wrapped in perimysium, and those fascicles were bundled together and wrapped in an epimysium. This is just one of many examples in which the Designer of the human body took the same basic design and applied it in different ways to produce an incredibly efficient organic machine.

We can classify the nerves in our body as sensory, motor, or mixed. And, to explain what that means, we will give you a short anecdote. One of us had a student who said that he had severed his ulnar nerve. The ulnar nerve runs along the ulna, and it is about as big as a shoestring. It innervates the area of your little finger and about half of your ring finger. His hand had gone through a window; the broken glass had severely lacerated (cut) him. The student said that the nerve had taken about three years to heal, but now he had 90% of the movement and feeling back. So, when the nerve was severed, he lost two things: movement and feeling. That shows that the ulnar nerve is a *mixed* nerve. It carries sensory axons as well as motor axons.

Now remember, each neuron is a one-way street. Sensory (afferent) neurons can only send incoming messages to the CNS. Motor (efferent) neurons can only send outgoing messages from the CNS to muscles or glands. However, a nerve is a bundle of *many* axons from *many* neurons, so a nerve can carry the axons of both kinds of neurons. If it does so, it is called a mixed nerve.

Most nerves in the body are mixed. There are a few that are purely sensory. For example, each eye has a big optic nerve for vision. It is not mixed. What do you think it is: sensory or motor? Well, the eye is a sensory organ, so the optic nerve is a sensory nerve. There are a few nerves, very few, that are purely motor nerves. Interestingly enough, they are mostly in the area of the eye, as well. There are many tiny muscles which control the movement of your eyes, and a few of the nerves that innervate the eye region carry signals only to those muscles, making them motor nerves.

One very interesting aspect of nerves is how they heal. First, you have to remember that neurons cannot undergo mitosis. If a neuron cell body dies, it cannot be replaced. However, suppose a nerve gets severed, such as what happened with the ulnar nerve of the student mentioned previously. That nerve healed. However, other kinds of damage to the nervous system cannot be healed. For example, if a person's spinal cord is severed, it cannot heal. Why can the ulnar nerve repair itself, while the spinal cord cannot?

Let's go straight to the bottom line. If Schwann cells cover an axon, the *axon* can regenerate. A couple of conditions must be met, however. First, its cell body must remain alive. Second, the two parts of the severed nerve need to be lined up fairly well. However, if Schwann cells do not cover the axon, no regeneration can take place. Think about the implications here. Only neurons from the PNS have Schwann cells covering their axons. The axons of neurons in the CNS are covered by oligodendrocytes. So, these axons cannot regenerate. (Scientists are, however, studying these facts and working hard to find a way to help neurons in the CNS regenerate.) That is why a severed spinal cord cannot heal in such a way as to restore function. It is part of the CNS, and its neurons have no Schwann cells. The ulnar nerve, however, is in the PNS, so its neurons have axons covered with Schwann cells. That nerve can heal.

What is so special about Schwann cells? What can they do that oligodendrocytes cannot? Well, when an axon in the PNS gets severed, the part still attached to the cell body begins branching, trying to "find" the other end. Schwann cells from the severed end aid this process because they form a tube-like path that helps guide the branching axon to its target. However, if the branching axon is not pointing in the general direction of the severed end, it will never find its target, even with the help of the Schwann cells. Therefore, not only does the axon have to have Schwann cells, it must also be relatively well aligned with the severed end. This is often the goal of neural surgery. When a nerve is severed, the surgeon aligns the two parts of the nerve, getting them as close as possible. This allows the branching axons to find their targets, healing the nerve and restoring function.

Why can't oligodendrocytes do the same thing, if CNS axons are severed? Think about it. The process of guiding the axon to its target takes many cells. The cells actually form a track that guides the axon so that it grows to its target. This is okay for Schwann cells because each axon usually has many Schwann cells devoted solely to that axon. This is not the case for oligodendrocytes, however. These cells each surround and insulate *several* axons. Rather than several cells for one axon, in the CNS, there is one oligodendrocyte for many axons. As a result, they cannot form a track to guide the branching axon. Instead, they inhibit axon regeneration.

ON YOUR OWN

7.5 Carpal tunnel syndrome is a problem resulting from pressure in the flexor retinaculum, which compresses the median nerve, a nerve that is about the thickness of a shoestring and is found in the wrist. When that nerve does not function properly, the grip gets weak and the hand easily goes numb. Is the median nerve a motor nerve, a sensory nerve, or a mixed nerve?

7.6 A group of axons bundled together is severed and does not heal. There are two possible reasons. What are they?

ACTION POTENTIALS I: THE RESTING POTENTIAL

Now that you know something about neurons and nerves, we want to spend some time discussing the signals that they carry. In module 5, you learned that the electrical signal carried by an axon in a neuron is called an action potential. We are going to discuss this action potential and then how it moves along the axon. Before we do that, however, we need to clarify a couple of definitions. First, we need to define the term excitability.

Excitability—The ability to undergo an action potential in response to a stimulus

There are two types of excitable cells in the body: muscle cells and neurons. You already learned that in response to neurotransmitters released at a synapse, a muscle cell will undergo an action potential that ultimately signals contraction in the muscle. Well, neurons also undergo action potentials in response to a stimulus. Now remember, neuroglia are completely different than neurons. Neurons are excitable cells. Neuroglia are not, which means that neuroglia cannot undergo action potentials. Only neurons do so.

Action potentials are electrical signals. In fact, movements of ions cause the electrical signal. It is really an *electrochemical* phenomenon. It is also a membrane effect. The action potential is a disturbance of the membrane. Because it is a surface phenomenon, there will be a difference in the electrical nature of the membrane, as compared with another part of the cell. We can measure this difference, which we call a potential difference.

Potential difference—A measure of the charge difference across the cell membrane

Now, please understand that in physics, the definition of potential difference is more precise. However, this will work for us. Potential difference is measured in volts. We will actually be measuring very small potential differences, so we will use millivolts (mV).

Now that we have those definitions, we can concentrate on the electrical properties of an axon. If you look at figure 7.7, you will see an illustration of an axon at rest. The term "at rest" simply means that there are no action potentials running down the axon at that point.

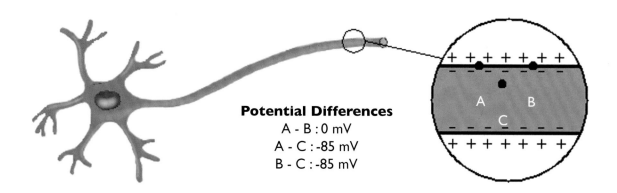

Potential Differences
A - B : 0 mV
A - C : -85 mV
B - C : -85 mV

FIGURE 7.7
The Resting Membrane Potential of an Axon
Illustration by Megan Whitaker

Look at what is shown in figure 7.7. The first thing to realize is that the axon is a part of a cell. So, it has an inside and an outside separated by a plasma membrane. The outside has a net positive charge while the inside, just below the membrane, has a net negative charge. The important thing here is not the charge on the inside or outside, but the *difference in charge* (potential difference) between the two. In the figure, for example, you see that there is *no potential difference* between points A and B. Why? Well, point A is on the outside, and point B is, as well. They both, then, are positively charged. While the axon is at rest, all parts of the outside surface have the same positive charge. So, there is no potential difference between any points on the outside surface because they all have the same amount of positive charge. However, there is a potential difference (-85 mV) between the surface and the inside of the cell (points A and C or points B and C). Why? The inside is negatively charged. So, there is a difference in charge between the outside surface of the cell and the inside of the cell. As a result, there is a potential difference, and we call that the resting potential of the axon. We call it a resting potential because it is there when the axon is not carrying any signal at that point. You need to remember that during the resting potential, *the inside of the neuron is negative.*

Before you learn about the cause of the resting potential, you need to realize that there are two kinds of rest. Think about a mousetrap that you might buy at the store. Before being set, the parts rest harmlessly. It is truly at rest. Now, imagine you pull on the spring-loaded wire, putting in some effort, and arrange the parts so that the trap is set. You can carefully place it where a hapless mouse might find it, but, meanwhile, it is at rest, right? Yes, but this kind of rest is energized and ready to spring. The resting potential of neurons is like that kind of rest. The neuron has expended energy to achieve that resting potential, and the axon is set and ready to undergo the action potential! If you understand the setting of the resting potential, you can move easily to understanding the action potential.

The potential difference of the resting potential arises because of a difference in charge between the surface of the membrane and the inside of the axon. We say that the membrane at rest is polarized. The term polarized simply means separated. The positive charges on the surface are separated from the negative charges inside. With the charges separated, the membrane is polarized.

The real question is, of course, why it is like that? Why is the membrane polarized?

Well, there are proteins trapped inside the cell, and they bear a negative charge. Why are proteins trapped inside? Why don't they just diffuse out and meet up with the positive charges to which they are attracted? The answer is that proteins are made within the cell, and are simply too big to get through the membrane. Remember from module 1 that only small molecules can diffuse through the membrane on their own. Large molecules must have a transport mechanism (such as exocytosis) to get through the membrane. If that mechanism is not there, a large molecule simply cannot get through the membrane. The negatively charged proteins are just too big and are trapped inside the cell.

That is only part of the reason that there is a potential difference across the plasma membrane. The rest of the reason is because of the action of two kinds of positive ions: sodium ions (Na^+) and potassium ions (K^+). The Na^+ are transported out of the cell through the membrane. That requires active transport because there are more Na^+ outside the cell than inside. The K^+, on the other hand, are transported *into* the cell. Once again, this requires active transport because there are more K^+ inside the axon than outside. This two-ion system is called the sodium-potassium exchange pump. Remember, the term pump is used to emphasize that this process takes energy. Just as you must expend energy to pump water out of a well, the cell must expend energy to pump Na^+ out of the cell and pump K^+ into the cell.

Now, think about this for a moment. The cell is pumping Na^+ out and K^+ in. Both of these ions are positive. It sounds like an even exchange doesn't it? Well, not quite. There are two factors to consider. First, the sodium-ion exchange pump takes three Na^+ out for every two K^+ it brings in. Consequently, there are more positive ions outside the cell (Na^+) than inside (K^+). Also, the K^+ tend to diffuse back out. The plasma membrane is 50-100 times more permeable to K^+ than to Na^+. If the Na^+ were to diffuse, it would go into the cell because diffusion takes substances from areas of high concentration to areas of low concentration. However, at rest the membrane is not very permeable to Na⁺. As a result, Na⁺ stay outside the cell, where the sodium-potassium exchange pump put them. However, since the membrane is reasonably permeable to K⁺, it can diffuse out of the cell. Remember, there are more K⁺ inside the cell than outside, so the K⁺ will diffuse out of the cell.

Let's make sure you understand what is going on with these ions. In summary, the cell membrane actively transports three Na⁺ out of the cell for every two K⁺ it actively transports into the cell. As a result, during the resting phase, more positive ions are found outside the cell than inside the cell. In addition, some of those K⁺ leak back out of the cell through diffusion. Since the Na⁺ cannot diffuse back in, this results in even more positive ions on the outside surface of the cell. This effect and the fact that there are negatively charged proteins trapped inside the cell work together to make the negative resting potential of an axon. We say that the resting potential is negative (-85 mV) because the inside of the cell is more negative than the outside of the cell.

Please do not get confused by terminology here. It is important to realize that even though this is a resting potential, it takes energy to maintain this, as we explained with the resting-mousetrap analogy. The sodium-potassium exchange pump actively transports Na⁺ one way and K⁺ the other. This requires the breakdown of ATP. So, even though the axon is resting, the neuron is still expending energy, and we can say it is charged up and ready for action!

ACTION POTENTIALS II: STIMULUS AND RESPONSE

Now that you know how the resting potential is maintained, you can understand the amazing signal called an action potential. The first thing you need to know is that an *action potential is an all-or-nothing event.* There are no big action potentials and little action potentials. You either get one or you don't. The next thing you need to know is that *to get an action potential, there must be a stimulus.* So, only excitable cells (muscle cells and neurons) can produce action potentials. Remember from module 5 that skeletal muscle cells undergo an action potential in response to the neurotransmitter acetylcholine. In the case of skeletal muscle cells, acetylcholine is the stimulus for the action potential.

There are many things that can stimulate an action potential. For example, acetyl-choline is not the only kind of neurotransmitter. There are many others which can act as a stimulus for an action potential. Now remember, neurotransmitters are released at a synapse. Although we have talked only about the synapse that exists between an axon and a muscle cell (the neuromuscular junction), neurons pass action potentials to other neurons across billions of synapses. Therefore, neurotransmitters are used to pass an action potential from one neuron to another.

In addition to neurotransmitters, a change in the environment can result in a stimulus. For example, movement can cause a stimulus. If you push your finger against something, there must be action potentials produced. After all, you *feel* what your finger touches. Signals (action potentials) must be getting sent to the brain. What stimulates these action potentials? In this example, the movement of receptor cells stimulates the action potential. Light can also be a stimulus for the right kind of cells. Light does not affect skin cells, but it does affect certain cells in your eye. Light

ON YOUR OWN

7.7 Suppose the membrane suddenly became very permeable to Na⁺. What would happen to the potential difference between the inside and outside of the axon?

entering the eye ultimately triggers action potentials on the optic nerve, which allow you to see. Another example is heat. How do you know whether something is hot or cold? Heat triggers action potentials on heat receptors. Chemicals can also trigger action potentials. How do you taste something? A chemical in the food triggers action potentials in the taste buds. Electric shock can also stimulate action potentials on muscles or neurons, but this is not a normal stimulus.

So, what is an action potential? It is an interruption of the resting potential. Look at the graph in figure 7.8.

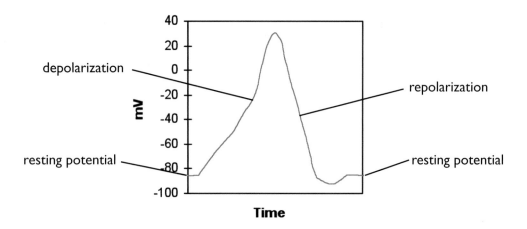

FIGURE 7.8
An Action Potential
Illustration by Megan Whitaker

In the graph, we are plotting the potential difference between the inside and outside of an axon versus time. The potential difference starts out at the resting potential of –85mV. Now, remember what the negative sign means. It means that relative to the outside of the cell, the inside is negative. Suddenly, a stimulus occurs. Perhaps the taste buds are exposed to food molecules, or perhaps a skin receptor gets exposed to heat. In any event, some stimulus occurs. What happens as a result? The potential difference changes. Notice what happens in the graph. As a result of the stimulus, the potential difference changes from –85 mV to +30 mV inside the axon.

How does this happen? Each excitable cell has the ability to react to the stimulus for which it is designed. The cells of the taste buds, for example, respond to specific chemicals. When the food molecules hits those cells, channel proteins (we discussed them in module 1) that were once closed, suddenly open. Those channel proteins are specific for Na^+, so Na^+ can travel across the plasma membrane. Now, think about what that means. Suddenly, the Na^+ can travel easily across the membrane. Which way do you think they will go? Well, there are many more Na^+ outside the cell than inside. As a result, the Na^+ will move from outside of the cell into the cell. What will that do? That will make the inside of the cell more positive. The potential difference will start to change. As the inside of the cell gets more positive, the potential difference will get less negative. In a matter of milliseconds, so many Na^+ will diffuse into the cell that the inside of the cell will be more positive than the outside of the cell. At that point, the potential difference actually becomes positive!

Let's review to make sure you really understand what is going on here. Remember, at rest, the axon has many Na⁺ outside of the cell. There are also many K⁺ inside the cell. Because the sodium-potassium exchange pump puts more Na⁺ outside of the cell than K⁺ inside, there are fewer K⁺ in the cell than Na⁺ outside of the cell. Also, since the cell membrane is more permeable to K⁺, some K⁺ diffuse out. In addition, there are negatively charged proteins inside the cell. As a result, at rest, the inside of the cell is more negative than the outside of the cell, giving a resting potential difference of −85 mV inside.

When a stimulus occurs in a neuron, channel proteins, which allow Na⁺ to travel through the membrane (Na⁺ channels), open up. As a result, Na⁺ can do something they were not able to do before: they can diffuse freely through the membrane. Since there are many Na⁺ outside the cell and few inside the cell, diffusion will cause the Na⁺ to move into the cell. Consequently, the inside of the cell starts to get more positive. Now remember, diffusion will make the Na⁺ concentration even out between the inside and the outside. That is what diffusion does. When that happens, there will be as many Na⁺ inside the cell as outside. However, there will still be many K⁺ inside the cell. At that point, then, the sum total of all the charges inside the cell will be *more positive* than the sum of the charges on the sodium ions outside the cell. At that point, then, the inside will be more positive than the outside, making a positive potential difference (+30 mV) inside the cell.

This process is called depolarization. Polarization means that there was a positive charge outside and a negative charge inside and that the charges were separated. Depolarization means no more separation. Technically, depolarization would mean that the potential difference becomes zero. The truth is, however, that so many Na⁺ get into the cell that the potential difference rises to +30 mV. Nevertheless, we can call this depolarization because the positive charges on Na⁺ that were being held outside were suddenly allowed inside.

Now we are halfway there. To review the depolarization phase, a stimulus causes Na⁺ channels to open, and Na⁺ move into the cell, turning the potential difference inside the cell from −85 mV to +30 mV. However, the signal is brief, so something has to happen to bring the axon back to its negative resting potential. How does that happen? We know what you are thinking. "Just get the Na⁺ back out, and it would be over with, right?" That sounds logical, and it could happen that way. However, to be efficient, the signal must be brief. The shorter the duration of the signal, the more efficient the signaling system. So, to maximize the efficiency of each neuron, God has designed a better means by which the resting potential can be restored.

In order to restore the resting potential, the Na⁺ channels close, and new channel proteins open. These proteins allow *K⁺* to travel through the plasma membrane (potassium channels). Now remember, there are still many more K⁺ inside the cell than outside. Of course, some have leaked out because the membrane is relatively permeable to potassium. Nevertheless, most of the K⁺ are still inside the cell. Well, when the potassium channels open, K⁺ rush out of the cell, according to the dictates of diffusion. This, of course, causes the inside of the cell to get *less positive* (the inside of the cell is losing positive ions). What happens to the potential difference? It gets lower and lower, eventually becoming negative. Think about it. The potential difference increased from −85 mV to +30 mV because positive ions (Na⁺) rushed into the cell. Then, as another set of positive ions (K⁺) rush out of the cell, the potential difference will go back to −85 mV. In fact, so many K⁺ rush out that the potential difference inside the cell actually becomes a little more negative than that.

The process of the potential difference going from +30 to below –85 mV is called **repolarization** because the charges are becoming separated again. Now, we still are not quite done yet. After all, we are not back to where we were to begin with, are we? Even though the axon is again negative inside, Na⁺ are inside and K⁺ are outside the axon. In order to get back to where we started, Na⁺ must be pumped out of the cell, and K⁺ must be pumped in. How does that happen? The sodium-potassium exchange pump starts working again! It pumps Na⁺ out of the cell and K⁺ back into the cell.

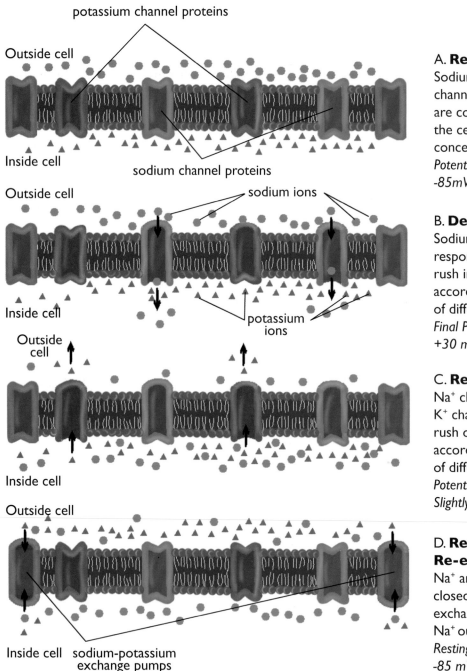

A. **Resting Potential**
Sodium and potassium channels are closed. Na⁺ are concentrated outside the cell; K⁺ are concentrated inside the cell.
Potential difference: -85mV

B. **Depolarization**
Sodium channels open in response to a stimulus. Na⁺ rush into the cell according to the dictates of diffusion.
Final Potential difference: +30 mV

C. **Repolarization**
Na⁺ channels close, and K⁺ channels open. K⁺ rush out of the cell according to the dictates of diffusion.
Potential difference: Slightly below -85 mV

D. **Resting Conditions Re-established**
Na⁺ and K⁺ channels are closed. Sodium-potassium exchange pump moves Na⁺ out and K⁺ in.
Resting potential difference: -85 mV

FIGURE 7.9
Resting Potential, Depolarization, and Repolarization of an Axon Membrane
Illustration by Megan Whitaker

We know that this is a tough concept, so we want to go over it one more time with an illustration. Figure 7.9 illustrates the steps in the process, along with an indication of what happens to the potential difference during that process.

To summarize, while the axon is resting, the sodium-potassium exchange pump has actively transported an excess of Na+ outside of the cell and an excess of K+ inside the cell. Also, there are negative proteins inside the cell. As a result, the resting potential inside the cell is –85 mV. During this time, the channel proteins, which conduct Na+ and K+ are all closed. Potassium ions can use other passages to get out of the membrane, but they are not as easy, so only some of the K+ "leaks" out of the cell. This is the situation illustrated in part A of figure 7.9.

When a stimulus occurs, the channel proteins that conduct Na+ open. As a result, Na+ rush into the cell. They do so because there is a higher concentration of Na+ outside the cell. Also, the inside of the cell is more negative than the outside of the cell, so the positive charge on the Na+ is attracted to the negative charge inside the cell. Eventually, so many Na+ have gotten into the cell that the inside of the cell becomes more positive than the outside of the cell, and the potential difference reaches about +30 mV. This part of the action process is called depolarization and is illustrated in part B of the figure.

After depolarization, the K+ channels open. This causes K+ to rush out of the cell. Once again, those ions do this for two reasons. First, the concentration of K+ is higher inside the cell, so diffusion acts to even out that concentration. Second, since the inside of the cell is now more positive than the outside of the cell, the positive K+ are repelled from the inside of the cell. This movement of the K+ restores the potential difference to something just slightly more negative than the original –85 mV. This phase of the action potential is called repolarization and is illustrated in part C of the figure.

After repolarization, all of the channels close, and the sodium-potassium exchange pump brings K+ back into the cell and sends Na+ back out of the cell, restoring the original situation (Part D of the figure shows the work in progress. Soon it will return to the picture we see in part A). This entire process happens within just a few milliseconds! Isn't that incredible? God has truly done a remarkable job with the design of the action potential!

ON YOUR OWN

7.8 If the K+ channels in an axon's membrane are fully open, is the potential difference becoming more positive or more negative?

7.9 At a given instant in time, an axon has a high concentration of Na+ inside the cell and a high concentration of K+ outside the cell. What will happen next?

ACTION POTENTIALS III: STIMULUS AND CONDUCTION

Now remember, an action potential is an all-or-nothing event. Either you get one or you do not. If a stimulus is strong enough to trigger the action potential, it is called a threshold stimulus. If the stimulus does not reach the threshold, it is called a subthreshold stimulus and will not produce an action potential. The best way to explain this is by analogy. Think about an ordinary toilet. When it is resting, it is not empty. It is charged up with water and ready to go. The tank is full, and when you pull down on the handle, the water rushes from the tank into the bowl, just like Na+ rushing into an axon during an action potential. The stimulus of pulling on the handle produces the action of a flush.

Have you ever pulled down the handle of a toilet but not gotten a flush? What happened? You heard a little whoosh, but the toilet did not really flush. That is a subthreshold stimulus. You pulled on the handle, but you did not pull hard enough to get the response. In the case of a neuron, when a subthreshold stimulus occurs, a small number of Na^+ enter the cell, but not enough to trigger the action potential. So, even though a few Na^+ get into the cell, the cell recovers by pumping them back out, restoring the resting potential. However, when those few Na^+ got into the cell, the potential difference did change slightly. That is called a local potential. A local potential is a small change in the potential difference that just dies out because the stimulus that produced it was subthreshold. It is called a local potential because it does not travel all the way down the axon. It happens in one spot, evens out, and goes no farther.

In order to produce an action potential, the stimulus must reach or pass the threshold. Think of the toilet again. If you pull down on the handle with just the right amount of force, the flush will begin. Once it begins, nothing you do to the handle will stop it, right? Once it starts, it goes to completion. Also, regardless of whether you pull down on the handle with all of your might or with just barely the force required, either way, the flush you get will be the same. The action potential is just like that. Once the threshold stimulus is reached, there is nothing that can be done to stop the action potential. It will complete the entire cycle, as shown in figure 7.9. Also, whether the stimulus is just at the, or way over the threshold, the size of the action potential is the same.

Now, wait a minute. When you put your finger in warm water, you get a nice, warm feeling. When you put it in hot water, it feels hot. How is that possible, if all stimuli above threshold produce the same action potential? After all, in both cases, the stimulus is heat. How can you feel differences in the intensity of the heat, if all stimuli at or above threshold produce the same action potential? Well, the intensity of the feeling depends not on the *size* of the action potential, but instead, it depends on the *frequency* of action potentials. Putting your finger in warm water produces a certain number of action potentials each second. Putting your finger in hot water produces the same action potentials, but it produces many, many more each second. That is how your CNS differentiates warm from hot. It is the same with other receptors. The frequency of action potentials tells the CNS the strength of the stimulus.

At this point, you should really be wondering about something: "How does an action potential travel down an axon?" After all, you now know what an action potential is. It is a brief change in the potential difference from negative to positive due to the movement of Na^+ and K^+ across the plasma membrane. However, you also know that action potentials travel from the axon hillock of a neuron down the entire axon, without dying out. How does that happen?

As it turns out, a single action potential affects only a small portion of the axon. However, the action potential has a really nice property: It provides a stimulus for the initiation of an action potential in the next part of the axon! Look at figure 7.10.

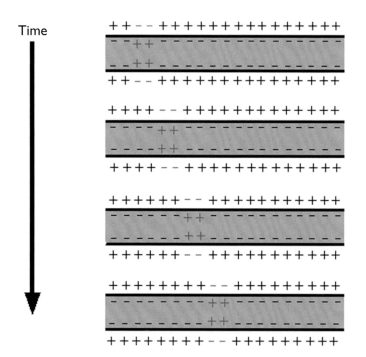

Time

Each of these pipes represents a portion of the axon at slightly different times. The lower you go, the more time has passed.

Notice that on the top pipe, the outside surface is mostly positive and the inside is mostly negative, except for a region near the left. There the charges are reversed. That is where the action potential is. The action potential moves to the right as time progresses.

FIGURE 7.10
Conduction of an Action Potential in an Unmyelinated Axon
Illustration by Megan Whitaker

Since the action potential stimulates another action potential farther down the axon, the action potential ends up traveling from the axon hillock (where the action potential begins) all the way to the other end of the axon. Note this is the way it happens in only one kind of axon (an unmyelinated axon). We will make this distinction clearer in a moment.

But, wait a minute. There is still a problem here, isn't there? After all, if an action potential can stimulate another action potential, why doesn't the signal travel both ways? After all, the action potential can stimulate an action potential *down* the axon, so why doesn't it also stimulate an action potential back *up* the axon as well? That does not happen because of the refractory period. The refractory period is the time when no action potential can be generated on the neuron because one is already in progress. The neuron is unresponsive because of an action potential already in progress.

Let's go back to the toilet analogy. What happens if the toilet is in full flush and you give it a good solid push on the handle? Nothing. Why? Because it is in a refractory stage. It will not respond because it cannot respond to a new flush in the middle of the current flush, which is its all phase of the all-or-none response to a threshold stimulus. A neuron is the same. While the action potential is being generated, a new stimulus will not produce another action potential. How can it, if the all-or-none action potential is in its all phase? During that time, we say it is in the absolute refractory period because, no matter how strong the stimulus, no additional action potential can occur. A toilet cannot be flushed again while it is in the middle of a flush, and a neuron cannot undergo another action potential at the same point where it is currently undergoing one.

However, have you noticed that once the flush is over and the toilet tank begins to fill, you can get a partial flush from the toilet? During that time, we might say that the toilet is in its relative refractory period. It is not really ready to flush again, but if you pull hard enough or long enough on the handle, you will get at least a partial flush. In the same way, neurons have a relative refractory period as well. During this time, the neuron is not really ready to undergo an action potential but, if the stimulus is strong enough, it can do so. Figure 7.11 shows the time frames for the absolute refractory period and the relative refractory period. Does this contradict the all-or-none law? Not at all. The all-or-none law assumes that the conditions are the same. In the relative refractory period, the conditions are not the same as during the resting period, so the resulting action potentials are not quite the same, either.

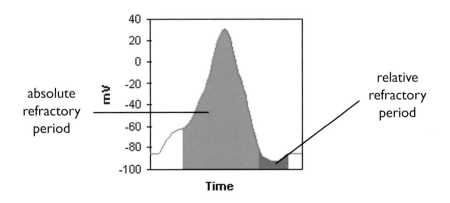

FIGURE 7.11

Absolute and Relative Refractory Periods

Illustration by Megan Whitaker

Now you can see why the action potential is guaranteed to travel in one direction only. The section of the axon nearer to the cell body has just finished undergoing its action potential. So, it is in a refractory period and cannot be stimulated into making another action potential. However, the portion of the axon that is farther away from the cell body has not undergone an action potential yet. It is charged up and ready to go. The action potential at a given region of the axon, then, cannot stimulate an action potential on the side of the axon nearer to the cell body, but it can stimulate an action potential on the portion of the axon farther away from the cell body. As a result, the action potential always travels *away* from its point of origin.

There are actually two ways that an action potential can be conducted down an axon. The first is shown in figure 7.10, and it represents how an action potential is conducted in an unmyelinated axon. What does that mean? Well, some axons are myelinated, but some are unmyelinated. The difference between the two types of axons is shown in figure 7.12.

Unmyelinated Axon
Schwann cells encompass several axons

Myelinated Axon
Schwann cells encompass only one axon

FIGURE 7.12
Myelinated and Unmyelinated Axons
Illustration by Megan Whitaker

When a Schwann cell thinly encases several axons, we say that the axons are unmyelinated. However, when many Schwann cells thickly encase one axon, that axon is myelinated. How does this affect the conduction of an action potential? Well, in an unmyelinated axon, the action potential must travel across the entire axon, each action potential stimulating the response of the next little section of the axon, as illustrated in figure 7.10. This is called continuous conduction. In myelinated axons, however, the signal actually hops down the axon, as shown in figure 7.13.

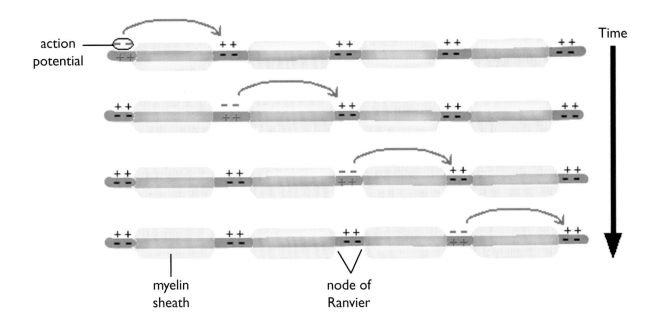

FIGURE 7.13
Conduction of an Action Potential in a Myelinated Axon
Illustration by Megan Whitaker

In a myelinated axon, the myelin sheaths act as insulation. In between these insulating coverings, there are tiny gaps called nodes of Ranvier. When an action potential occurs on one node, it stimulates a response on the next node over. So, the action potential need not travel over the portion of the axon that is myelinated. It leaps from one node to another. Since it need not travel through the portions of the axon that are covered with the Schwann cells, this kind of travel is *much* faster. This is called saltatory conduction because the Latin word *saltare* means "leap." Since the myelin sheaths make this kind of conduction possible, we say that the myelin sheath speeds up the travel of action potentials down the axon.

You certainly have experienced the fact that saltatory conduction is faster than continuous conduction. You probably just do not realize that you have. For example, have you ever cut yourself on something and gotten a sudden, sharp pain followed by a dull ache? That is the difference between saltatory conduction and continuous conduction. The myelinated axons in your body bring the sharp pain very rapidly to your CNS. The dull ache that follows comes more slowly because it is the result of signals from unmyelinated axons. So, the sharp pain comes first because it is traveling down the axons of your pain receptors using saltatory conduction. The dull ache gets to your CNS a split second later because those signals are traveling down different axons using continuous conduction.

The difference between myelinated and unmyelinated axons can also be seen in the development of infants. Have you ever wondered why a newborn calf can immediately get up and walk soon after birth, while a newborn baby can't even lift its head? Calves are born with a good portion of their axons myelinated. As a result, they can control their muscles well enough to start walking and even running immediately. Babies, however, have few myelinated axons when they are born. The myelin sheaths must develop as the baby develops. Now remember, the myelin sheaths allow the action potentials to travel quickly down the nerves. To control your skeletal muscles, you must send many action potentials down your motor neurons quickly. To control your skeletal muscles, your motor neurons need to be myelinated. Also, the faster signals can travel in the brain, the better you will be able to think.

When babies are born, then, they do not think well and cannot control their muscles properly because their neurons are not myelinated. As the baby begins to develop, myelination occurs, starting at the head and working down the body. It also works from the center of the body out to the edges. So, when the baby is born, the neurons in its brain are the first to begin myelination. This makes the baby smarter, you might say. As the myelination progresses to the peripheral nervous system, the child can begin to use his or her muscles more effectively.

When a baby is born, it cannot lift its head up or do anything but wave its arms aimlessly. One of the first developmental milestones is the point at which the baby can focus his or her eyes. At that point, myelination of the nerves that control the eye muscles has occurred. In a few more weeks, the baby is able to smile. Once again, myelination has occurred in the nerves that control the face muscles. In a little while longer, the baby can hold its head up. As the myelination proceeds out to the forearms and fingers, the baby starts getting really grabby! Then, after a while, the baby can sit up because the myelination proceeds on. And, about the time the baby is a year old, enough myelination has proceeded so that he or she can start walking.

Do you know which are the last nerves to get myelinated? If you think about it, you can probably guess. After all, what is the last real milestone in the development of a baby? Well, in our opinion, the last big developmental milestone is potty training. So, what are the last nerves to myelinate? The nerves that control the ring of skeletal muscle that closes off the bladder! That is why it takes so long to potty train a child. The nerves that control the bladder are the last to myelinate, so that is the last area that the child learns to control.

We just have one more point to make in this section. Although myelination strongly affects the speed at which an action potential travels down an axon, it is not the only factor. The width of the axon makes a difference as well. The axons of our neurons come in many different sizes. Some are large in diameter, and some are thinner in diameter. The larger diameter axons conduct action potentials faster because they offer less electrical resistance than the smaller diameter axons. Signals that need to travel quickly do so on wide-diameter, myelinated axons. Signals that travel more slowly do so on small-diameter, unmyelinated axons. Action potentials can travel as fast as 130 m/sec, or as slow as 2 m/sec.

SYNAPTIC TRANSMISSION

When we discussed muscles in module 5, we talked a bit about synapses (interfaces between neurons and other cells) and how signals are transmitted across them. We want to pick up that discussion now and continue it a bit. Consider the information in figure 7.14.

ON YOUR OWN

7.10 A perfectly healthy neuron does not respond to a stimulus. There are two possible reasons for this. What are they?

7.11 Suppose you are in a dimly lit room and then suddenly someone shines a bright light into your eyes. What changes occur in the action potentials being sent from your eyes to your brain?

7.12 Often, doctors ask you whether the pain you feel is a dull ache or a sharp pain. Thinking about what you have learned in this section of the module, what can your answer to that question tell the doctor?

MOD 7

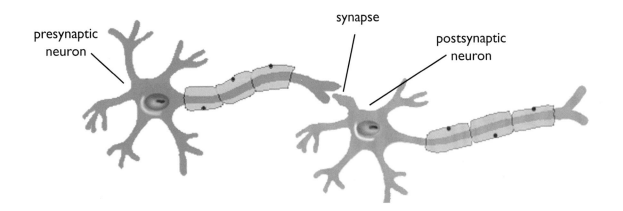

FIGURE 7.14
Two Neurons Forming a Synapse
Illustration by Megan Whitaker

The first neuron in line is called the presynaptic neuron because it carries signals to the synapse, which is the only place that a neuron can communicate with another cell. In module 5, we discussed synapses between neurons and muscle cells. However, our nervous system is also filled with multiple billions of synapses between two neurons. What is shown in figure 7.14 is a diagram of one neuron-to-neuron synapse. The second neuron in the figure is the postsynaptic neuron. Now remember, axons carry signals in one direction: from the axon hillock to the synapse. So, the action potential will be traveling from left to right in the figure. When the action potential reaches the end of the presynaptic neuron's axon, it signals the postsynaptic neuron. How? The axon terminal releases neurotransmitters that travel across the synapse. At the neuromuscular junction, we learned that the neurotransmitter stimulates an action potential on the membrane of the skeletal muscle cell.

If we have an action potential starting at the axon hillock of our first neuron, we know that that action potential will be conducted all the way to the end of the axon. So, whatever signal begins at the axon hillock will be expressed at the other end. If we have a very fast rate of action potentials beginning on the axon hillock of the presynaptic neuron, we will have the same rate of action potentials at the end of the axon. So, an axon will transmit information in the form of action potentials without change. This could present a problem, however. After all, there is an enormous amount of information that we must deal with. However, we need to focus on certain things. We need to eliminate the information that is not essential. In other words, we need a "gatekeeper" so that only important information gets to us, while the unimportant information is ignored.

Think about it. You are trying to concentrate on this book, we hope! However, in order to do so, you need to ignore other things. You can't be thinking about how hard the seat is, whether or not your shoes are too tight, the background noise of the furnace or air conditioner, the brightness of the lights, or the noises your little sister is making. That information would overwhelm and distract you. So, your nervous system has gatekeepers, which let through the information that we need and direct it in the right direction. These gatekeepers also keep out information that we do not need. What are these gatekeepers? They are the synapses that exist between neurons.

This demonstrates one big difference between a neuromuscular junction and the neuron-to-neuron synapse (often just called a synapse). In a neuromuscular junction involving skeletal muscle, an action potential is sent to a muscle membrane so that the muscle will contract. In a neuron-to-neuron synapse, the flow of information is *regulated* from one neuron to the next. In other words, a neuron-to-neuron synapse lets some information through, but it often limits the amount of information allowed through. In many cases, it may stop the information altogether. Synapses that stop information from passing to the next neuron are called inhibitory synapses, and these actually make up the majority of neuron-to-neuron synapses in the body.

Nevertheless, let's first look at an excitatory chemical synapse and see how it works. A chemical synapse simply means that a chemical, called a neurotransmitter, carries the signal across the space between the neurons (the synaptic cleft). The neuromuscular junction, which we discussed in module 5, is a chemical synapse. In a neuron-to-neuron synapse, the presynaptic neuron has synaptic vesicles, which release neurotransmitter. The postsynaptic neuron has receptor sites, which bind with the neurotransmitters.

When the receiver sites bind to the neurotransmitter, the postsynaptic neuron is excited. That is, Na$^+$ channels open and Na$^+$ diffuse in.

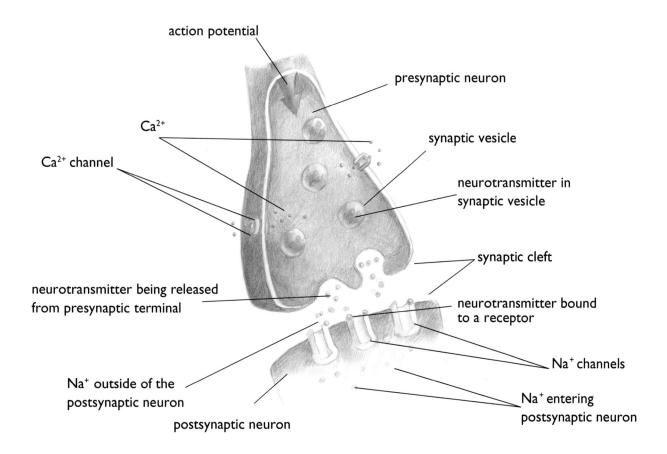

FIGURE 7.15
A Chemical Synapse
Illustration by Amanda Bitting

The synaptic cleft is so small that it can only be visualized with electron microscopy, but it is a real space. The presynaptic neuron and the postsynaptic neuron never actually touch one another. The synaptic cleft separates them.

Let's look at the events that send information from one neuron to another in an excitatory chemical synapse. First, we have an action potential on the axon of the presynaptic neuron. What does that action potential do when it reaches the presynaptic terminal? It actually causes Ca^{2+} channels to open. Like Na$^+$ and K$^+$ channels, Ca^{2+} channels are channel proteins that are specific for Ca^{2+}. Like Na$^+$, Ca^{2+} is more concentrated outside of the cell. Healthy cells do not want much Ca^{2+} inside, so they keep it outside. However, this action potential opens Ca^{2+} channels and allows Ca^{2+} to diffuse into the presynaptic terminal. Once it is inside the cell, the Ca^{2+} act as a signal molecule, causing the synaptic vesicles, which hold neurotransmitter, to release their neurotransmitter into the synaptic cleft. Once the neurotransmitter enters the synaptic cleft, it binds to a receptor on the postsynaptic neuron. When it does so, it opens Na$^+$ channels, which allow Na$^+$ to enter the postsynaptic neuron, exciting the postsynaptic neuron.

So far, we have not added much to what we discussed back in module 5. But, the neuromuscular junction is a bit more simple than a neuron-to-neuron synapse. How? First, there are two basic kinds of neuron-to-neuron chemical synapses-- excitatory synapses and inhibitory synapses. These synapses create two different responses - excitatory postsynaptic potentials (EPSPs) or inhibitory postsynaptic potentials (IPSPs). Let's continue to look at the excitatory synapses in more detail.

In an excitatory synapse, EPSPs occur. When this happens, the first neuron will *excite* the second neuron. This means that the signal from the presynaptic neuron will bring the *postsynaptic neuron* closer to undergoing an action potential. What do we mean when we say that the postsynaptic neuron will be closer to undergoing an action potential?

Remember, the synapse is a gatekeeper. It is a regulator. If the goal were simply to send the same number of action potentials from one neuron to the next, you would not need a synapse. An axon would do that just fine. An axon takes a signal and passes that same signal, unchanged, from the axon hillock to the end of the axon. However, the job of the neuron-to-neuron synapse is different. It must *regulate* the signal flow. How does it do that? It requires a *greater* signal in the presynaptic neuron in order to stimulate an action potential in the postsynaptic neuron. Now remember, action potentials work on the all-or-nothing principle. This means that the strength of the signal that travels down an axon depends not on the size of a single action potential, but on the *frequency* of action potentials. When we say greater signal, what we really mean is a *higher frequency* of action potentials.

In an excitatory chemical synapse, then, one action potential will *not* stimulate one action potential on the postsynaptic neuron. So, if just one action potential travels down the axon, the signal will not get through the synapse! Instead, several action potentials on the presynaptic neuron will be required in order to stimulate an action potential on the postsynaptic neuron. How does this work?

Think about it. Remember, to create an action potential, there must be a stimulus that reaches the threshold. Once that happens, an action potential is produced. What stimulates the signal on the postsynaptic neuron in a synapse? The neurotransmitter. When the neurotransmitter binds to a receptor in an excitatory synapse, Na^+ channels are opened and Na+ travel into the cell. This changes the potential difference from -85 mV to something less negative; let's say -80 mV. However, that potential difference is not at the threshold for creating an action potential. Look back at the graph in figure 7.8. The threshold is about -65 mV in that graph. So, the stimulus caused by one action potential on the presynaptic neuron is not sufficient to produce an action potential on the postsynaptic neuron.

However, suppose another action potential caused another release of neurotransmitter that caused more Na^+ channels to open. That would send even more Na^+ inside the cell, changing the potential difference even more, maybe to -75 mV. If another action potential caused even more neurotransmitter to be released, that would open even more Na^+ channels, making the potential difference something like -70 mV. Finally, if one more action potential caused the release of more neurotransmitter, that would open even more Na^+ channels, and the Na^+ diffusing in would change the potential difference to -65 mV. At that point, then, the stimulus on the postsynaptic membrane has reached threshold, and an action potential is produced on the postsynaptic neuron. The signal has crossed the synaptic cleft.

So, in order for an action potential to be produced on the postsynaptic neuron, there must be several action potentials, which release enough neurotransmitter so that many Na^+ channels open. This will allow many Na^+ to diffuse into the postsynaptic neuron, causing a threshold stimulus that will produce an action potential in the postsynaptic neuron. That is not too hard to understand, especially if you realize that the gatekeeper role of the synapse only allows significant information to pass. However, you need to realize that there are at least two different ways that this can happen.

First of all, the frequency of action potentials traveling down a *single* axon can be high. For example, in the discussion we just had, it took four action potentials in the presynaptic axon to release enough neurotransmitter to reach threshold and stimulate an action potential in the postsynaptic neuron. This could happen if the presynaptic axon had four action potentials running rapidly, one right after the other. As long as the action potentials were very close together, their individual subthreshold stimuli would add together so that a threshold stimulus was produced.

There is another way for this to happen, however. Suppose that four presynaptic neurons all have excitatory synapses with *the same* postsynaptic neuron. In other words, four different neurons all send their signals to the same receiving neuron. If these four axons all carry just one action potential all at the same time, they will all end up releasing neurotransmitter to the postsynaptic neuron at the same time. That will result in four subthreshold stimuli, which will add up to a threshold stimulus, producing an action potential on the postsynaptic neuron.

In an excitatory synapse, then, an action potential can be stimulated on the postsynaptic neuron in either of two ways. A single axon can carry several action potentials within a small amount of time. This is called temporal summation because the subthreshold stimuli are all produced by one presynaptic neuron in a small window of *time*. However, an action potential in the postsynaptic neuron can also be produced if many axons all carry an action potential to the same neuron all at once. This is called spatial summation because the subthreshold stimuli are all coming from different points in *space*.

Excitatory synapses, then, do not just transmit all action potentials. They *facilitate* the transmission of action potentials, but it takes several action potentials on the presynaptic side of the synapse to stimulate just one action potential on the other side. Can you see now why we call the synapse a gatekeeper? We do not want every last bit of information to travel across the synapse. We want it to regulate what goes into our nervous system. That way, the nervous system can process the important information and ignore the rest.

Now remember, we have been concentrating on excitatory synapses so far. However, there are also inhibitory synapses. In fact, the majority of synapses in the body are inhibitory. They specifically inhibit information from being transferred. They stop it. Why in the world would your body have these synapses? Think about it. What if all of the distractions you are experiencing right now (the brightness of the light, the little sounds that are going on around you, how tight your belt is, whether or not you are hungry, etc., etc.) all came to your brain at the same rate and the same time? You would overload on information! You just could not process it all. The inhibitory function of inhibitory synapses is very important because without it, we could not concentrate on anything!

What is the difference between the excitatory synapse and the inhibitory synapse? Well, anatomically, they look the same. However, the difference is in the kind of channels that an inhibitory synapse contains. Remember, in any chemical synapse, neurotransmitter is released and then binds to a receptor. In an excitatory synapse, that receptor opens Na^+ channels in the postsynaptic neuron, which causes the inside of the postsynaptic neuron to get more positive. In an inhibitory synapse, however, the neurotransmitter binds to receptors that open K^+ channels. What will that do?

Well, K^+ are more highly concentrated inside the neuron. When the K^+ channels open, K^+ will diffuse out of the cell, making the outside of the cell more positive and the inside more negative. What will happen to the potential difference between the outside of the cell and the inside? It will make the inside *more negative*. Remember, the resting potential is -85 mV. So, when neurotransmitter is released in an inhibitory synapse, the potential difference drops to something even more negative: -90 mV inside the postsynaptic neuron, for example.

Now think about what will happen as a result. In order to undergo an action potential, threshold must be reached in the potential difference. That threshold is something *less* negative than the resting potential. Let's use the number we used before: -65 mV. To get an action potential going, the potential difference must rise from -85mV to -65 mV. Instead, in an inhibitory synapse, it *drops* to -90 mV! *It goes even farther away from the threshold*. This is called hyperpolarization. Depolarization is a change that facilitates or stimulates the action potential. Hyperpolarization is the opposite: a change that takes the neuron farther away from producing an action potential. The effect of the inhibitory postsynaptic potentials (IPSPs), then, is to *decrease* the chance for an action potential!

It is important to realize that a synapse is either excitatory or inhibitory. It cannot be both. If the neurotransmitter-receptor interaction opens K^+ channels on the postsynaptic neuron, it is an inhibitory synapse. However, if its receptors open Na^+ channels, it is an excitatory synapse. Interestingly enough, however, that is about the only important difference between the two. In fact, each type of synapse can use the *same* neurotransmitter! Acetylcholine (ACh), for example, excites the neuromuscular junction. That is what we learned about in module 5. However, ACh also is secreted by parasympathetic neurons to the heart. In these synapses, ACh inhibits heart cardiac muscle fibers from contracting. So, ACh is used in the inhibitory synapses of the heart, as well as the excitatory synapses of the skeletal muscle system. What is the difference? The *receptors* in the neuromuscular junction of skeletal muscles are different from the receptors in the neuromuscular junction of the heart.

ON YOUR OWN

7.13 Below, there is a graph that shows the potential difference between the inside and outside of a postsynaptic neuron. The stimulus is the presence of a neurotransmitter.

Is the synapse inhibitory or excitatory? Which kinds of channels do the neurotransmitters open?

NEURON ARRANGEMENTS

The last subject we will discuss in this module is the way that neurons can be arranged in the nervous system. When we study the anatomy of the nervous system, the basic unit is the neuron. But, when we study the physiology of the nervous

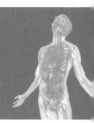

**COLORING BOOK
EXERCISE 7.4**
To review the anatomy of a synapse, follow the instructions on the bottom half of page 109 in the coloring book.

system, the basic unit really is comprised of groups of neurons, which are arranged for a particular function. Figure 7.16 illustrates simple examples of neural arrangements in the nervous system. Such arrangements are called neural circuits.

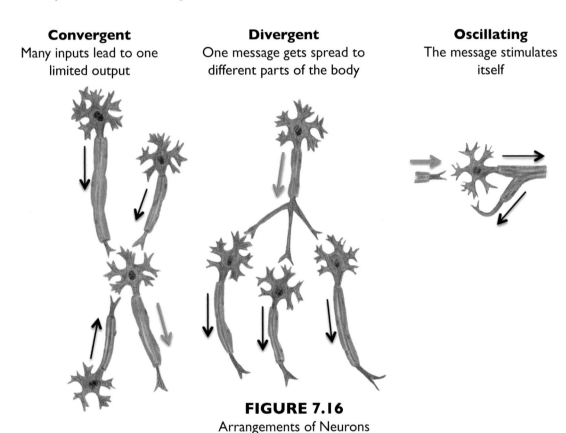

Convergent
Many inputs lead to one limited output

Divergent
One message gets spread to different parts of the body

Oscillating
The message stimulates itself

FIGURE 7.16
Arrangements of Neurons
Illustration by Taylor Sheehy

The first arrangement forms a converging circuit. It has several presynaptic neurons and one final postsynaptic neuron. As a result, the messages all go one way. Think about the neuron that is receiving the signals. It is a slave to the others. It is just receiving all of the inputs, and it will do whatever it is "told" to do. What is the function of a converging circuit? Well, consider your biceps brachii. Imagine just one motor unit in the biceps brachii. Is it contracting or relaxing? It depends on what you are choosing to do with the biceps. It depends on the automatic input as you stretch out your arm to grab the page. It also depends on input from your cerebellum that maintains a certain amount of muscle tone. There are many other neural inputs that help "decide" whether or not that one motor unit is to be contracted or relaxed. Ultimately, all of those inputs will determine the rate of firing of one final neuron: the one innervating that motor unit of the biceps brachii. So, many inputs are reduced to a limited output.

The second arrangement in figure 7.16 forms a diverging circuit. Here we have one input, but, because it diverges, it synapses with two different neurons. This kind of arrangement takes one input and creates many outputs. This is useful when one piece of information has to go several places. For example, suppose you touch something hot. You immediately pull your hand away before you even realize what you are doing. Why? Well, your skin receptors sense the burn and send out a signal. The signal then diverges to several neurons. Some neurons send signals on to the brain so that you will learn from this experience, but others send signals to the skeletal muscles in your arm so that you will pull your hand away quickly. This minimizes the time it takes for your hand to move. If the signal were not in a divergent circuit, you would have to wait until the signal traveled all the way to your brain. Then, you would have to wait for the brain to process the information and send a signal to the skeletal muscles. Finally, you would have to wait for that signal to travel to your skeletal muscles. By then, your skin would be fried! So, this diverging circuit allows for reflex actions to happen quickly, but at the same time, it allows for the processing of information in the brain.

The last arrangement is an oscillating circuit. In this kind of arrangement, a neuron sends a signal along but also sends it back to itself. What does that do? It allows the neuron to generate the signal again. This is called an after-discharge response, and it prolongs the effect of a stimulus. Eventually, the signal fades because the neuron is fatigued or because the signal is inhibited by other neurons. However, while the circuit is still working, a single stimulus can result in a long-lasting signal. Some theorize that this kind of circuit is what controls the cycle of staying awake and going to sleep. A single stimulus (the sound of the alarm clock, for example) can wake you up, and then the action potentials can be prolonged so that you stay awake until other neurons inhibit the signal, at which time you sleep again.

The breathing rhythm is also thought to be the result of oscillating circuits, which send a barrage of action potentials, which contract the inspiratory muscles. They then fade out, the muscle relaxes, and you exhale, and then the oscillating circuit repeats the pattern several times per minute. This is why breathing, though it involves skeletal muscle, is automatic (unless we choose to interrupt it by speaking or breath-holding).

We hope that you have begun to develop a deep appreciation for the extraordinary design of your nervous system. Neurons rapidly send signals called action potentials; but those are only the beginning. Your neurons are also capable of sending information to other neurons via synapses, which can regulate that information so as to discard the unimportant distractions and keep you focused on the task at hand. You are using that ability right now, as you learn about your amazing nervous system.

ANSWERS TO THE "ON YOUR OWN" QUESTIONS

7.1   This is the efferent division of the PNS, since signals are being sent to a muscle, which is an effector organ. You can be even more specific because the signal is being sent to skeletal muscles, so it is the somatic motor nervous system (SMNS).

7.2   Before you pull your hand away, you must *sense* that the stove is hot. So, the afferent division of the PNS works first, sending pain signals from the skin receptors to the CNS.

7.3   The neuron is in the PNS. The myelin sheaths of neurons in the CNS are formed by oligodendrocytes.

7.4   Microglia are specialized cells that fight infections in the nervous system. So, the rat's brain probably had an infection.

7.5   The median nerve must be a mixed nerve. If the grip gets weak, it must control muscles and, therefore, have some motor neurons in it. At the same time, however, the hand goes numb, indicating that the messages from the skin receptors are not getting to the CNS. So, it must have sensory axons as well.

7.6   Either the axons are in the CNS, or the two severed ends in the PNS, were not lined up well. Remember, CNS nerves cannot regenerate because they have oligodendrocytes instead of Schwann cells. However, just having Schwann cells, as in the PNS, is not enough. The broken ends must be reasonably well aligned so that the Schwann cells can lead the axon toward the muscle or sensory organ it innervates.

7.7   The potential difference would become less negative. After all, it is negative because the outside of the cell is positive and the inside is negative. If the membrane were permeable to Na^+, they would go inside the cell, since there are more of them outside than inside. That would make the inside *less negative*. So, there would be less difference between the inside and the outside. In fact, if enough Na^+ got into the cell, the potential difference could even become positive, indicating that the inside of the cell is more positive than the outside.

7.8   The potential difference is becoming more negative. If potassium channels are fully open in the repolarization phase of the action potential, the potential difference is decreasing from +30 mV to -85 mV.

7.9   There is a high concentration of K⁺ outside the cell and a high concentration of Na⁺ inside the cell when the repolarization is complete. The next step, then, is for the sodium-potassium exchange pump to move the K⁺ back into the cell and to move the Na⁺ back out so that the neuron is at its resting condition again.

7.10   The first possibility is that the stimulus is subthreshold. If the stimulus is not strong enough, an action potential will not be generated. The second possibility is that the neuron is in its absolute refractory period. During that time, even a strong stimulus cannot generate an action potential.

7.11   The change is the frequency of action potentials. Remember, an action potential is all-or-nothing. So, the *strength* of a nerve signal depends on the *frequency* of action potentials.

7.12   The answer to this question can help the doctor determine whether or not the nerve that the pain signal is traveling on is myelinated or unmyelinated. Sharp pains usually result from myelinated axons, while dull aches typically come from unmyelinated axons. This can help the doctor narrow down what the source of the pain is.

7.13   In this graph, the potential difference became more negative. So, it is moving away from the threshold. This means that the postsynaptic neuron is less likely to generate an action potential. So, the synapse is inhibitory. The only way to get movement away from threshold is to open K⁺ channels in order to get positive charge (K⁺) to diffuse out of the cell.

STUDY GUIDE FOR MODULE 7

1. Define the following terms:

   a. Nerves
   b. Ganglia
   c. Spinal nerves
   d. Cranial nerves
   e. Afferent neurons
   f. Efferent neurons
   g. Somatic motor nervous system

   h. Autonomic nervous system
   i. Sympathetic division
   j. Parasympathetic division
   k. Association neuron
   l. Excitability
   m. Potential difference

2. As you read this question, cells in your eyes are sending information to your brain which your brain uses to form an image of the words that you read. Is this information being sent along afferent or efferent nerves?

3. When you are digesting food, smooth muscles contract your stomach. Is this controlled by the afferent or efferent division of the PNS? You can be even more specific than that. What would be the most specific way to describe the nerves involved in this situation?

Illustration by Megan Whitaker

4. Identify the parts of the neuron below:

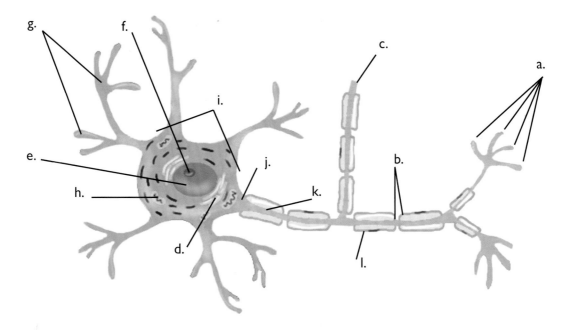

5. Name the six types of neuroglia and their functions.

MOD 7

6. Identify the structures in the nerve below:

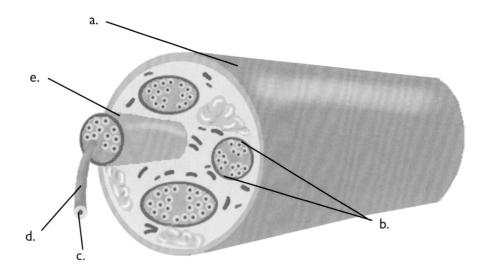

7. What are the differences between a sensory nerve, a motor nerve, and a mixed nerve? What is the most common kind of nerve in the body?

8. An axon is covered by an oligodendrocyte. Is it a part of the CNS or PNS? Will it regenerate a new axon, if severed?

9. An axon is covered by several Schwann cells. If it is severed, will it definitely heal? Why or why not?

10. At one point on the axon, there is a high concentration of K^+ outside the cell and a high concentration of Na^+ inside the cell. Is the neuron at rest?

11. At one point on the axon, there is a high concentration of Na^+ outside the cell and a high concentration of K^+ inside the cell. Is the entire neuron at rest?

12. A stimulus creates a change in the potential difference between the inside and outside of the cell so that the inside is less negative, but no action potential is created. What is this called?

13. The following steps occur during an action potential. Put them in the proper order.
    a. Na^+ gates open, and K^+ gates begin to open. Sodium ions rush into the cell according to the dictates of diffusion.
    b. Na^+ and K^+ gates are closed. Sodium-potassium exchange pump brings the system back to its original state.
    c. Na^+ and K^+ gates are closed. Na^+ are concentrated outside the cell; K^+ are concentrated inside the cell.
    d. Na^+ gates close, and potassium gates fully open. K^+ rush out of the cell according to the dictates of diffusion.

14. There is a specific name given to step a and a specific name given to step d. What are the names?

15. What keeps an action potential on an axon from stimulating another action potential that will travel back towards the cell body?

16. Why do myelinated axons carry action potentials faster than unmyelinated axons?

17. When you cut yourself, you feel an instant, sharp pain, followed a bit later by a dull ache. Why do you get these two different pains, and why do they come in that order?

18. If you press your finger lightly against an object, you feel a certain amount of pressure. Pressing harder against that same object causes you to feel more pressure. What is the difference between the action potentials in these two situations?

19. Identify the structures in the excitatory synapse below:

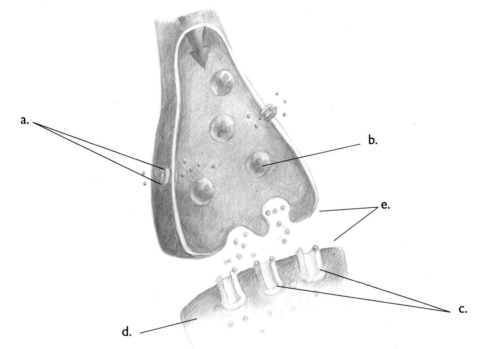

20. A neural signal needs to travel a long way through the body. It needs to have exactly the same properties at its destination as it did when it started. Should this signal be sent along one very long axon or a few shorter axons that are connected by synapses?

21. The potential difference in a postsynaptic neuron changes from -85 mV to -95 mV at the point of a synapse. What has happened? What can you say about the relative amounts of K^+ and Na^+ outside the membrane?

22. Twelve action potentials are traveling down an axon in a very short time period. They reach a synapse, and the postsynaptic neuron sends only two action potentials down its axon. Is this an excitatory synapse or an inhibitory synapse?

23. In the example above, is this temporal summation or spatial summation? How do you know?

24. We discussed three kinds of circuits which can be formed by neurons. Name the three circuits and what they are used for.

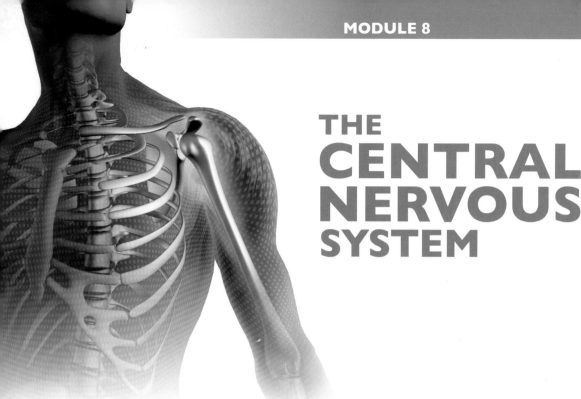

THE CENTRAL NERVOUS SYSTEM

Most textbooks will tell you that there are three main functions of your nervous system. First, your nervous system receives sensory input from its external and internal surroundings. Second, your nervous system processes and interprets this data. Third, your nervous system produces a response to the information. That is all technically correct, but we would like for you to see beyond the textbook for just one moment.

heart of the matter

Command Central, Mission Control, and your brain—all of these titles are equivalent to each other. It is here where data is processed, interpreted, and the most important decisions are made. The gray matter inside your skull is responsible for the functions of your body that are necessary for life, and it is here where your thoughts and emotions take form and make you uniquely you!

It's easy to break the human body down into its components and to study each in depth. In this module, you will study the central nervous system (CNS) in great detail, learning all about your brain and spinal cord. There will be so much information that we will save the peripheral nervous system (PNS) for module 9.

So, what else is there to learn? Perhaps while you are reading this module, you can try to appreciate the science without losing sight of the wonder of who you are! Technically, your nervous system may seem like a computer hooked up to a myriad of wires that receive and send information to accomplish a set goal, but you know better than that. Even though every person's nervous system is anatomically and physiologically similar, you are uniquely you. Try not to lose sight of that miraculous wonder.

THE BRAIN

Far and away, your brain is the most complex organ in your body. In fact, it is the most complex organ in all creation! Yet, it weighs only about 3 pounds. What gives it its immense complexity? It is its multiple millions of neurons, connected to one another in a vast, but orderly network. Figure 8.1 gives you a small idea of what all of this looks like.

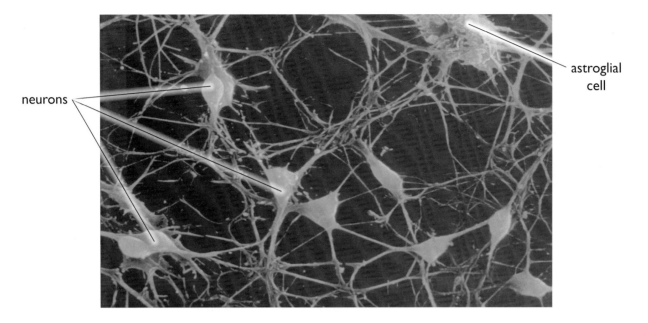

neurons

astroglial
cell

FIGURE 8.1
Association Neurons in a Culture
Image © Dr. Dennis Kunkel / Phototake

MOD 8

This photo is an electron micrograph of neurons (artificially colored, as electron microscopy produces black-and-white images) in a culture. A culture is an artificial situation in which biochemists grow cells for study. Notice how the neurons link to one another. This means that they are association neurons. That is what your brain is full of - association neurons linked to each other in a complex, orderly network. This culture is a simple representation of what a small part of that network looks like.

Of course, only a handful of neurons are shown in the figure. In the average adult brain, there are about 100 billion neurons. There are trillions and trillions of links between neurons. Indeed, there are more neuron-to-neuron links in one single human brain than there are electronic links in all of the computer systems in the world! In addition, the brain processes information significantly more quickly than does the most sophisticated computer. Neurologists, together with computer scientists, have estimated that the brain can perform in 100 computational steps what it would take the most sophisticated computer nearly one billion steps to accomplish!

We can define the brain, however inadequately, as a complex network of neurons. Think about what these neurons do. When they are at rest, they actively transport Na+ and K+ to maintain the resting potential. When they need to pass signals on to other neurons, they send action potentials rapidly down their axons. They also receive signals from large numbers of other neurons and process them. As you might expect, this takes energy. Your brain needs a steady supply of oxygen and glucose so that it can manufacture the enormous amount of ATP it needs. Even though the average adult's brain makes up only about 3% of the body's weight, it receives 20% of the body's blood supply!

If the blood supply is cut off from the neurons for just a few minutes, the lysosomes in the cell body burst, and the neurons are destroyed. Now remember, after babyhood neurons cannot undergo mitosis. Once you have lost a neuron, it is gone forever. This condition, called ischemia [is key' mee uh] (lack of blood), is very damaging to the brain. The brain needs its blood supply for both oxygen and glucose. In fact, glucose is normally the brain cells' only fuel, unlike other cells, which can use other nutrients to make ATP. If the glucose level in your blood drops enough, you have a condition called hypoglycemia (hi poh gly see' mee uh). When this happens, you cannot think clearly. Your brain fogs because the neurons simply cannot produce the ATP they need to send and receive signals.

Do you know someone who has had a stroke? A stroke is a medical condition that has profound effects on the brain. There are two basic types of strokes. In an ischemic (is keem' ik) stroke, a blood clot cuts off the blood supply to part of the brain. In a hemorrhagic (hem or adj' ik) stroke, a blood vessel in the brain bursts. Which do you think is the more deadly of the two? It is the second one. Hemorrhagic strokes more often are fatal. Why? When a blood vessel bursts, the blood supply to the neurons is interrupted. In addition, the neurons are bathed in blood chemicals that are toxic to them. This kills large numbers of neurons.

Ischemic strokes are damaging as well, and indeed, if an ischemic stroke goes on long enough, it can be deadly. However, in the last several years, treatment has been developed for ischemic strokes. There are drugs that have been developed specifically to deal with them. These drugs are designed to get rid of the blood clot and restore the blood supply to the brain. As a result, they are often nicknamed clot-busting drugs. These drugs must be administered within three hours of the symptoms of a stroke to be effective, however, because the brain cannot survive ischemia for long. A public awareness campaign is being conducted so that people know how to recognize when a person is having a stroke. Just like the symptoms of a heart attack, the symptoms of a stroke must be treated immediately. If someone has the symptoms of a stroke (loss of motor function or sensation, collapse - especially on just one side) you should get that person to a hospital immediately. The consequences of an untreated stroke are too severe to risk!

In addition to the glucose, your brain needs many other nutrients. It needs B vitamins and minerals so that its neurons' mitochondria can produce ATP efficiently. It also needs the right kind of fat. It needs fat (called essential fat) not just for the neurons, but even more for the supporting neuroglia. The neuroglia use these fats to make myelin. The brain, then, has

think about this

If you suspect a stroke, act F.A.S.T. and do this simple test:

F—FACE: Ask the person to smile. Does one side of the face droop?

A—ARMS: Ask the person to lift *both* arms. Does one arm drift downward?

S—SPEECH: Ask the person to repeat an easy phrase. Is their speech slurred or garbled?

T—TIME: If you observe *any* of these signs, call 9-1-1 immediately.

Stroke patients may not be eligible for treatments if they arrive at the hospital too late (generally three hours from the time of the stroke). Every minute counts, so remember to act F.A.S.T. at the first sign of symptoms!

very high nutritional needs, and your brain functions better when you feed it well. Fruits, vegetables, beans, grain, fish, meat, milk, and other whole foods are the best brain foods, since together they contain the nutrients that your brain needs.

ON YOUR OWN

8.1 If your blood glucose level drops, the other cells in your body can do something that will help your brain cells. What can these cells do to help the neurons in your brain?

BRAIN ANATOMY

Your brain is incredibly complex, and we could easily spend an entire course discussing nothing but your brain and its structure and function. In this course, however, we will just be hitting the highlights.

Before we discuss brain anatomy, let's begin with two vocabulary terms that you need to know: gray matter and white matter.

> **Gray matter**—Collections of neuron cell bodies and their associated neuroglia

> **White matter**—Bundles of parallel axons and their coverings

Figure 8.2 shows you two magnetic resonance images of the brain. Magnetic resonance imaging (MRI) is a useful tool that chemists originally developed to determine the arrangements of atoms in molecules. It was later adapted in conjunction with amazing computational technology to provide beautiful images of a living person's internal organs. These images have revolutionized medical diagnosis. Just as in figure 8.1, the colors you see in the image have been added. They are used in order to make the image easier to understand.

MOD 8

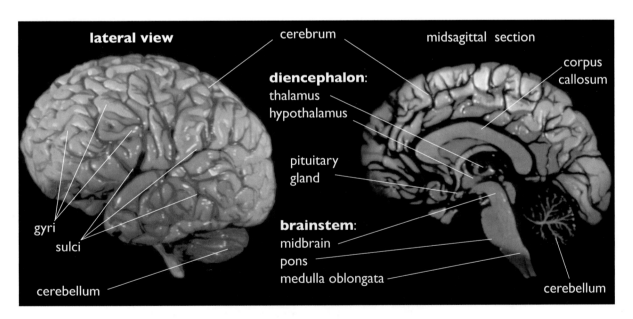

FIGURE 8.2
MRI Images of the Brain
Images © CNRI / Phototake

On the left-hand side of figure 8.2, you see the image of the brain's surface. You do not see much detail because the brain is mostly covered with the folded tissue of the cerebrum. The image on the right shows a slice down the center of the brain. This particular slice is called a midsagittal (mid sa' ji tal) section, because it splits the brain into equal left and right halves.

Looking at the image on the right side of the figure, you can see the most important structures in the brain. The brainstem can be separated into three sections: the medulla oblongata (ob' lon gah' tuh), the pons, and the midbrain. The medulla oblongata (often just called the medulla) is the site of decussation (dee kuss say' shun).

Decussation—The anatomical crossing over of neurons from left to right

This word comes from the Latin word *decussatus*, which means to form an X.

What is the point of decussation? Have you heard that the left side of the body is controlled by the right half of the brain and vice versa (or that only left-handers are in their "right" mind)? Well, it turns out that that is generally true. Most of this is the result of decussation, which takes place primarily in the medulla. The neurons anatomically crisscross at this point, sending signals from the right side of the brain to the left side of the body, and sending signals from the left side of the PNS to the right side of the brain. Now, not all crossing over occurs in the medulla. Some neurons cross over within the spinal cord. That is not the norm, however. Most of the decussation occurs at the medulla. Some neurons, especially those of the cranial nerves, do not decussate at all.

The medulla not only contains the point of decussation, but it also contains discrete groups of gray matter called nuclei. These nuclei act as control centers for the body's vital functions.

Vital functions—Those functions of the body necessary for life

What are the vital functions of the body? Well, one thing you can think of right away is the heart. If your heart stopped beating, you would die very quickly. The medulla contains nuclei that control the heart rate. Breathing is obviously a vital function. The medulla controls ventilation. The medulla also contains the vasomotor area, which controls the dilation or constriction of blood vessels throughout the body. This is a vital blood pressure control mechanism. In addition, nuclei in the medulla also control reflexes such as swallowing and vomiting.

Why can a sudden hard blow to the head be fatal? One reason is that swelling of the brain caused by a blow to the head can force the medulla to be pushed through the *foramen magnum*, which is the opening at the base of the skull through which the spinal cord and brain are connected. This damages the medulla, and since the medulla controls the body's vital functions, such damage can be instantly fatal.

Just superior to the medulla oblongata is the pons. The term pons means "bridge." This is a good description of one of its functions: it forms a bridge between the medulla and the upper brain stem. It also has several nuclei that relay messages between the cerebrum and the cerebellum. Interestingly enough, the pons also contains nuclei that are involved in ventilation. They work in conjunction with the nuclei of ventilation in the medulla, enabling the body to make the switch from breathing in (inspiration) to breathing out (expiration).

Just superior to the pons is the midbrain. The name describes its position well. It is in the middle, between lower and upper parts of the brain. It has four nuclei that form mounds on the surface of the midbrain. Two of those nuclei are involved in the sense of hearing. The other two are involved in the sense of sight. Reflexes that cause you to turn toward the source of a sudden sound or to look directly at something that catches your eye are controlled by these nuclei in the midbrain. In addition, of course, there are many nerve pathways that connect the brain stem to the upper parts of the brain.

Although the brainstem can be split into the three sections we mentioned above, there are some functions of the brain stem that are not isolated into one of these three regions. For example, there are several nuclei distributed throughout the brain stem called the reticular formation. These nuclei receive information from various afferent nerves, especially those of the face. These nuclei and their interconnections are called the reticular activating system, and this system plays a major role in determining the cycle of sleeping and waking.

Moving on up, we find the diencephalon (dye in sef' uh lon). If you take that word apart, you can better understand its meaning. The last part of the word comes from cephalic, which refers to the head. The di comes from dia, which can mean "in between." So, the diencephalon is the "between brain." It is the part between the brain stem and the cerebrum. The major components of the diencephalon are the thalamus (thal' uh mus) and the hypothalamus.

The thalamus is quite a large structure compared with what you see when you look at it on the midsagittal plane as is shown in figure 8.2. In the midsagittal plane, you see only the intermediate mass, which is a small cylinder that links the two sides of the thalamus. The best way to visualize the thalamus is to take your right hand and make a fist while sticking your thumb straight out to the left. Then, make a fist with your left hand so that it closes over the thumb that is sticking out. Your two fists now make a good model of the thalamus. It is situated deep in the back of the brain and is shaped like a miniature cerebrum.

The thalamus is a major relay station. Afferent axons synapse with other neurons in the thalamus. A large fraction of the incoming axons come from sensory neurons, especially those related to touch. Apparently, some crude interpretation of sensory information takes place in the thalamus, but it is not clear exactly what that interpretation is. It is also a relay station for motor neurons sending action potentials from the brain to the spinal cord and skeletal muscles. In addition to being a sensory relay station, the thalamus affects mood and body movements, especially those related to strong emotions, such as fear and anger.

The hypothalamus is a tiny area inferior to the thalamus. It is connected to the pituitary gland, which is below it. Through neural connections and its own hormones, the hypothalamus regulates the pituitary gland. The pituitary gland is often called the master endocrine gland because it secretes many hormones that affect such diverse functions as metabolism, reproduction, urination, and response to stress, yet it is completely controlled by the hypothalamus.

In addition to control of the pituitary gland, the hypothalamus is also involved in the functions of the autonomic nervous system, which controls smooth muscle, cardiac muscle, and glands. The hypothalamus has been compared to a thermostat in the way it controls body temperature. For example, investigators used a colony of Rhesus monkeys to study the primate hypothalamus. In each monkey, a device was implanted into the hypothalamus. The device could heat or cool the hypothalamus directly. The monkey could be made to shiver by just cooling the hypothalamus. Alternatively, the monkey could be made to pant (Rhesus monkeys do not sweat; they pant) just by heating up its hypothalamus. These responses would occur even though the room's temperature was maintained as normal. This research demonstrated that the hypothalamus directly sets body temperature.

The cerebrum is obviously the largest part of the human brain. It deals with what is often called higher-level brain functions. These include interpreting the signals sent from the sensory receptors in the body, reasoning, and memory. The outer surface of the cerebrum, called the cortex, is composed of gray matter that is deeply folded. The folds, called gyri (jy' ry), increase the surface area of the cortex. The grooves between the gyri are called sulci (sul' sigh). The general pattern of gyri and sulci are similar in all brains, although there are some minor variations from person to person. Indeed, there are even variations from one hemisphere to another in the same brain. The cortex is not very thick, but it contains 75% of our neuron cell bodies. Underneath the cortex lies white matter with interspersed clumps of gray matter called nuclei. The cerebrum is an important part of the brain that deserves more attention. We will therefore return to it in a later section.

The last major division of the brain is called the cerebellum (ser uh bel' uhm). Most of the functions controlled by the cerebellum are ones that occur without conscious thought. There is some new research that indicates moods and emotions may be at least partially controlled by the cerebellum. Based on our current understanding, however, the cerebellum is mostly considered the control center for subconscious motor functions. What do we mean by subconscious motor functions? These are the functions of voluntary (skeletal) muscles that we perform without really thinking about them. For example, consider muscle tone. As discussed in module 5, our skeletal muscles are usually at least partially recruited. That is, there is some degree of contraction in virtually every skeletal muscle in the body. That is muscle tone, and it is maintained in part by the cerebellum.

The cerebellum also controls equilibrium, or balance. Think about the physics behind standing up. Have you ever tried to get a pencil to balance on its eraser? It is not easy, is it? Why not? The pencil must be perfectly balanced. Even when you get it balanced, it might eventually tip over because air currents in the room might push it out of balance. Well, it turns out that it is at least as hard for us to stand up straight. You do not think it is hard, because you do not have to think about it. The cerebellum controls it without any thought on your part. Unconsciously, however, we are maintaining the proper amount of muscle contraction and adjusting the contraction to maintain our balance. The cerebellum assists with that.

The cerebellum also assists with the sequencing of muscle contractions. Let's just imagine what has to happen to grab a coin and put it in your pocket. First, your forearm has to extend. Then, your fingers must flex in just the right way so as to get the coin in your grasp. Then, your forearm has to flex to bring the coin back to your body. Then, your upper arm has to extend to get to your pocket. Then your forearm has to extend again to get into the pocket. Finally, your fingers must extend to release the coin. All of this has to happen with precise timing in the sequence, or you will not get the coin into your pocket. The cerebellum controls this precise sequencing. If a person's cerebellum is not working properly, he or she will lack coordination because the muscle-contraction sequencing is not working as it should.

The cerebellum is also involved in muscle preset. What do we mean by this? Well, suppose you open your refrigerator and see a paper carton of milk. We are not talking about a clear, plastic carton. We are talking about a carton that you cannot see through. You do not know how much milk is in there. You pick it up, and it almost flies up because, unconsciously, you thought it was full. However, the carton was nearly empty, so the force you used to pick it up was far too great. Or, have you ever stepped down a set of stairs in the dark, but you slammed your foot on the floor because you thought, unconsciously, that there was one more step? Why do things like that happen? When you are about to perform a task, you often unconsciously preset your muscles to a certain strength of contraction. You do this because in the past, you have learned about the amount of effort needed to complete the task. For example, in the situation we just discussed, you have learned how heavy a milk carton is when it is full, and you know the amount of strength necessary to lift the full carton. As a result, you preset your muscles for that strength. If the milk carton is not full, you get surprised because you exert way too much force in lifting the carton. That is muscle preset, a predetermined correct amount of contraction to perform a task. Your cerebellum is a major part of that process.

Dampening is another situation that the cerebellum takes care of implementing. When you walk quickly or run, your upper limbs could swing around wildly, since they are very similar to pendulums hanging down at your sides. That usually does not happen, however, because your cerebellum sends inhibitory signals to the motor neurons that control your arms. As a result, there is more or less an even swinging of the upper limbs back and forth. That inhibition is called dampening, and the cerebellum controls it.

The last structure we want to mention is the corpus (kor' pus) callosum (kuh loh' sum). The cerebrum consists of a right and a left half, as you will see in the next section. Those halves must communicate with one another. This communication is accomplished through several connections between the hemispheres. The corpus callosum is white matter, and it forms the largest of these connections.

That is the overall structure of the brain. In the next few sections, we will concentrate on the cerebrum, as it is the most complex part of the brain.

COLORING BOOK EXERCISE 8.1
Use pages 111-121 to review the structures of the brain that you have learned about so far. There is a lot of detail on some of the pages, and you need only color those structures discussed, although you may do more, if you choose.

ON YOUR OWN

8.2 Although the human brain is significantly more complex than the brains of other vertebrates, the basic layout is the same. However, one part of the brain is *significantly* larger in humans than in any other vertebrates. What part of the brain is that?

8.3 Amphibians typically move in a jerky, uncoordinated fashion compared with other vertebrates. What portion of their brain is not as well developed as it is in other vertebrates?

8.4 Based on what you have learned in this section, what portion of the brain do you think is affected by tranquilizers (medication used to calm individuals with certain mood disorders and to encourage sleep)?

THE CEREBRUM IN MORE DETAIL

Now that you have seen the major structures in the brain, we want to zero in on the cerebrum. Let's start with figure 8.3.

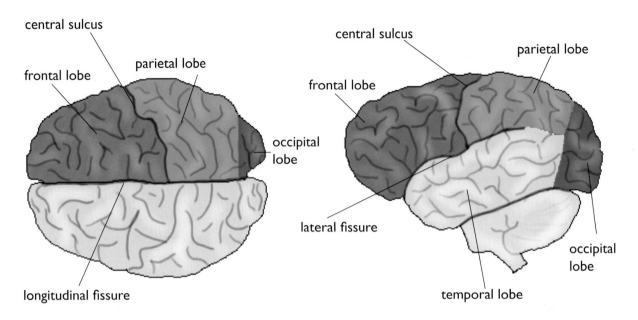

FIGURE 8.3
Superior and Lateral Views of the Cerebrum
Illus. by Megan Whitaker

The cerebrum is divided into two hemispheres by the longitudinal fissure. Each of these hemispheres can be divided into lobes, and those lobes are named for the skull bones that lie directly above them. The temporal lobe is the easiest one to spot, at least from the side. It is separated from the rest of the brain by a lateral fissure. This lobe is involved in the senses of hearing and smell, and it also plays a role in memory and abstract thought. The frontal lobe is also relatively easy to find. The central sulcus intersects with the lateral fissure, forming the boundary of the frontal lobe. This lobe is involved in motor function and smell. It is also involved in mood, emotions, foresight, and memory. The occipital lobe is not easy to detect, as it has no sulcus or fissure as a boundary. However, its function is very clear. It receives and integrates your visual sensory information. The parietal lobe is involved in receiving all of the sensory information we have not discussed so far. It handles all sensory information except that of smell, vision, and hearing. It receives information from receptors of touch from the entire surface of the body.

A wide range of research into the brain has allowed us to locate many specific functional areas in the cerebrum. These areas are illustrated in the cerebral cortex map of figure 8.4.

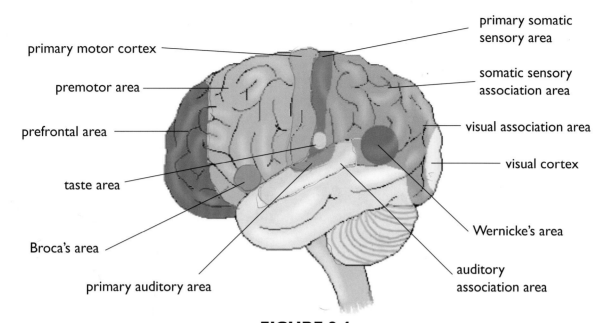

primary motor cortex

premotor area

prefrontal area

taste area

Broca's area

primary auditory area

primary somatic sensory area

somatic sensory association area

visual association area

visual cortex

Wernicke's area

auditory association area

FIGURE 8.4
Functional Areas of the Cerebrum
Illus. by Megan Whitaker

Let's start with the primary somatic sensory area, which is also called the primary somatic sensory cortex. When discussing the cerebral cortex, the words *area* and *cortex* are often used interchangeably. The term *somatic* refers to the body as a whole. So, this area of the cerebrum receives generalized sensory input from all over the body. Where is it located? Look at the figure. It is located mostly on a single gyrus. That gyrus is just posterior to the central sulcus, so it is called the postcentral gyrus. Notice that the primary somatic sensory area does not take up the entire gyrus. It does, however take up a good portion of it. Now please understand the difference. The postcentral gyrus is the *physical location* of this functional area on the brain. The functional area is the primary somatic sensory area. So, the functional area tells you what is *done* in that region of the brain. The physical location tells you where it is on the brain.

What does the primary somatic sensory area do with the sensory input it receives? Well, this area of the brain actually has little sections that correspond to every part of your body's surface. There is a section in the primary somatic sensory area that receives action potentials from the receptors in your elbow. There is another section in this area that receives signals from your tongue. This goes on and on. In other words, there is a little area on the primary somatic sensory area that corresponds to pretty much every part of your body's surface. So, when a signal comes in to the primary somatic sensory area, the brain knows *where* the signal came from. So, we say that this area *localizes* the sensations that come from the body.

Think about it. If a bee stings you, you do not have to look around to see where that bee is. You know where the bee is because, if it stings you on your elbow, the neurons in your elbow will send action potentials via a sensory neuron to CNS neurons, which are hardwired to the section of your primary somatic sensory area contolling the elbow. That way you immediately know *where* the pain is. If you jam your big toe, you will know that it is your big toe because the pain signals will be sent via afferent neurons to the big-toe section of the primary somatic sensory area. That is what we mean by localization.

Interestingly enough, neurologists actually have mapped the primary somatic sensory area to tell you exactly where the elbow section is and exactly where the toe section is. How did they get that map? The history is rather interesting. In the 1950's there were a lot of experiments conducted by surgeons who would open up a person's skull to expose the brain. Then, while the patient was *conscious*, they would lightly shock areas of the primary somatic sensory area to create action potentials. Then, they would ask the patient what he or she felt. If the patient felt a tingling in his or her elbow, then the surgeon would know that the elbow section of the primary somatic sensory area had been stimulated. If the patient felt a sensation in the big toe, then the surgeon would know that the big-toe section of the primary somatic sensory area had been stimulated.

Are you feeling sorry for the patient? You shouldn't. You see, the brain has no pain receptors. They are all located in the skull, brain coverings, and large blood vessels. These experiments were conducted on patients who were given local anesthetics that numbed the pain receptors on the skull. That way, they felt no pain from the skull being opened up and, since there are no pain receptors in the brain, they felt no pain from the shocks. Other than the sensations, then, the patients felt nothing.

When a patient has brain surgery for, say, a brain tumor, this technique is still used today. The brain is exposed using general anesthesia, and after that the patient is awakened and only a local anesthesia is used. Then, gentle shocks are given while the patient is awake. The patient may be asked to speak or to identify objects as this is done. That way, the surgeon can plan the best route to cut into the patient's brain to remove the tumor. As you can guess, the best route is the one that allows for removal of the tumor with the least possible damage to higher centers in the brain.

Next, we move to the somatic sensory association area. This area of the cerebrum determines the *meaning* of the sensation. For example, if a person pokes you with his or her finger, it is unpleasant. If the person touches you with his or her finger to get your attention, it is not as unpleasant as a poke. Your somatic sensory association area makes these distinctions for you, so that when you turn around, you know whether or not to be annoyed at the person who was touching you. Also, the somatic sensory association area has a sensory memory to which it refers. So, if you have experienced the sensation before, your somatic sensory association area will put it in the proper context. For example, even without looking, you can easily distinguish between the feel of an ordinary bath towel versus the feel of a paper towel. What you have learned from your sense of touch is stored in the somatic sensory association area.

In the occipital lobe, we find the visual cortex. This region receives the action potentials from the optic nerves that are attached to the eyes. In this region of the cerebrum, the action potentials are interpreted to give the basics of vision: shape, color, and size. Action potentials then pass from the visual cortex to the visual association area. Much like the somatic sensory association area discussed above, the visual association area compares this image with past experience in order to give you context. This is how we recognize a face. We get the basic size, color, and shape from the visual cortex, but then the information passes to the visual association area, where it is connected to our past experience. At that point, recognition occurs, and you identify the person at whome you are looking. As soon as we are born, we start filling that visual association area with recognition and meaning, so that even a young baby soon recognizes his mom's face, as well as objects of interest, such as food or toys.

The primary auditory area on the temporal lobe is responsible for the basics of sound: volume and pitch. Remember those experiments we discussed earlier? If you stimulate this area of the brain in such an experiment, the patient will hear various pitches or volumes but will not be able to relate them to anything. When you actually hear something, however, the signals also pass to the auditory association area which, you may guess, puts the signals into historical context for you. So, you can recognize the melody of a song or the fact that you hear the ringing of a doorbell.

As you might imagine, then, the auditory association area also enables us to make sense out of speech. However, there is more to it than that. Another area of the cortex plays a crucial role here: Wernicke's area. We want to try to describe for you how these three areas work together to help us hear and comprehend speech. As we have already said, auditory signals first hit the primary auditory area in order for us to hear volume and pitch. Then, the signals move to the auditory association area, which put those sounds into historical context. If the historical context indicates that the sounds are speech, they are sent to Wernicke's area, where the speech is then comprehended. These three areas must work together so that you can actually understand the words that reach your ears. Think about that if you are learning a foreign language as part of your high school education. Yes, you can hear those new sounds. But, at first, they have no meaning. As you learn the language, what had before been recognized only as sounds with particular pitches and volumes becomes organized in your brain so that you recognize new words and phrases with meanings that you can comprehend.

think about this

Stop for one moment and try to comprehend just how magnificently you were created. You do not merely see or hear, but rather you see, hear, and understand. Your Creator loved you so much as to give you the gifts of comprehension, not just instinct; communication, not just sound; and recognition, not just sight!

The taste area interprets taste. Not surprisingly, the olfactory area interprets the signals from the nose, in order to give us our sense of smell. This area is not shown in figure 8.4 because it is on the inferior surface of the frontal lobe, within the lateral fissure.

That covers the major sensory input to the cerebrum, but we also need to see how the cerebrum controls *motor* neurons. We begin with the primary motor area, which can also be called the primary motor cortex. Where is it? Like the primary somatic sensory area, it is localized mostly to one gyrus on each side. This gyrus is anterior to the central sulcus, so we call it the precentral gyrus. Just like the primary somatic sensory area, this area has been tested in experiments, and we know that it has regions that correspond to motor neurons that control specific areas of muscles. There is a "leg" area, a "thigh" area, a "tongue" area, and so forth. What happens in this area of the cerebrum? It controls our basic skeletal movements. The actions of making a fist, extending the forearm, or flexing the head are the result of signals sent from here.

Although the signals that cause our basic skeletal muscle movements come from the primary motor area, they do not necessarily *originate* from there. When we need to make skilled muscle movements for actions like typing, handwriting, jumping rope, and so forth, the sequence of action potentials needed for this fine motor movement is actually worked out ahead of time by the premotor area. As its name implies, this area of the brain does all of the preparatory work, deciding what action potentials must be sent, how quickly, and in what order. Impulses are then generated in this area and sent to the primary motor area. The primary motor area then "follows the instructions" and causes those movements to take place.

Broca's area, also called the motor speech area, is a subsection of the premotor area. Broca's area works out the detailed sequencing that needs to take place to carry out the finest of muscle movements--those related to speech. Remember Wernicke's area? It comes into play here. When you want to say something, Wernicke's area determines what words will convey the meaning that you wish to impart. This generates action potentials that are then sent to Broca's area. Broca's area then works out the precise sequence of muscle movements needed to produce the words that Wernicke's area has decided to use. Then, Broca's area sends action potentials to the primary motor area, which initiates the muscle movements worked out by Broca's area. The result: intelligible speech!

The prefrontal area is a large part of the cerebrum. It is dedicated to our ability to reason, to think things through, and our ability to foresee what is going to happen. It is also dedicated to our motivation. It helps us to inhibit out impulses. We might say that the many aspects of our personality are controlled in the prefrontal area. Have you ever heard of prefrontal lobotomy? Before the advent of medications that could modify behavior, prefrontal lobotomy was a surgical procedure used to control violent or disturbed people by just removing that part of the brain. Did it work? Well, have you read the book *The Fitzgeralds and the Kennedys* by Doris Kearns Goodwin? It includes information about the late President John F. Kennedy's sister Rosemary, who was mentally disabled. She had a prefrontal lobotomy as a young woman. The procedure damaged her personality enough that, sadly, she ended up in an institution for the rest of her life. Prefrontal lobotomy is not done anymore. Fortunately, there are effective drugs these days for treating disturbances in behavior.

Now remember, the brain is split into two hemispheres. As we mentioned before, the *left* side of the brain receives sensory information and controls the motor functions of the *right* side of the body. That is because of decussation, which occurs in the medulla oblongata and certain other parts of the brain, or even in the spinal cord. The two hemispheres share much of this information, however. They do this through structures called commissures.

Commissures—Connections of neuron axons that allow the two hemispheres of the brain to communicate with one another

The largest of the commissures is the corpus callosum, which was discussed in the previous section.

Although the two hemispheres of the brain are very similar, there are differences between them. Although most of the functional areas of the cerebrum are in both hemispheres of the brain, that is not always the case. Broca's area, for example, is almost always on the left hemisphere and not on the right hemisphere. As a result, the left hemisphere of the brain is more involved in speech than is the right hemisphere. In addition, the left hemisphere seems to be more active in mathematical reasoning. The right hemisphere, on the other hand, tends to dominate in determining spatial relationships, music, and face recognition.

Because the hemispheres are not quite equal, humans tend to have a dominant side. For example, if you are right-handed, then the left side of your brain is dominant when it comes to manipulating objects with your hand. The majority of people are not only right-handed, but they are right-eyed, right-legged, and right-eared. In each case, the right side of the body (and, therefore, the left side of the brain) is dominant over the other. Interestingly enough, this fact is unique in Creation. All vertebrates have two hemispheres in their brains. However, humans are the only vertebrates through-out the entire population that tend to have one side (most often the left hemisphere) dominant over the other. An individual rat, for example, might be right-eyed, but there are roughly as many right-eyed rats as left-eyed ones. The overall rat population has no dominant side. Human beings, however, are mostly right-side (and thus left-brain) dominant. Quite frankly, we have no solid explanation as to why this is the case. In fact, we really have no idea why individuals have a dominant side at all, much less why most people tend to be right side dominant.

ON YOUR OWN

8.5 Suppose someone hits his or her head and has a concussion. If that person has a difficult time speaking but has no problem thinking of the words he or she wants to say, what area of the brain was, most likely, damaged?

8.6 Blindness can occur in certain brain injuries, even though both eyes are uninjured. Which two areas of the brain are involved with vision? Which physical part of the brain was damaged?

OTHER IMPORTANT STRUCTURES IN THE BRAIN

In the previous section, we dealt with the cerebral cortex. Remember, however, that the cortex is just the *surface* of the cerebrum, which is composed of gray matter. Below the surface of the cerebrum, we find white matter. Some of that white matter is made up of the commissures, which allow the two hemispheres to communicate with one another. In addition to the white matter, however, there are lumps of gray matter, which we call basal nuclei. These areas can be seen in figure 8.5.

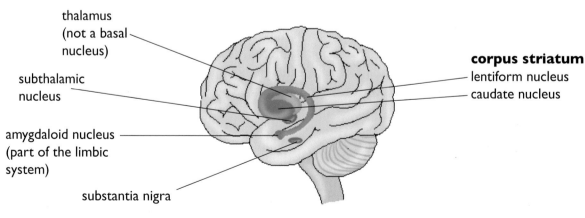

thalamus (not a basal nucleus)

subthalamic nucleus

amygdaloid nucleus (part of the limbic system)

substantia nigra

corpus striatum
lentiform nucleus
caudate nucleus

FIGURE 8.5
The Basal Nuclei
Illus. by Megan Whitaker

The two basal nuclei in the cerebrum, the lentiform (len' tih form) nucleus and the caudate (kaw' dayt) nucleus are called the corpus striatum. They are the largest of the basal nuclei. The other two nuclei are not technically in the cerebrum. The subthalamic (sub thal' uh mik) nucleus is in the diencephalon, and the substantia (sub stan' she uh) nigra (ny' gruh) is in the midbrain.

What do the basal nuclei do? They are involved in the planning, initiation, maintenance, and termination of motor activity. They also maintain muscle tone and are involved in the adjustments necessary to maintain posture. When everything works well, we are unaware of our basal ganglia. When there is damage there, there may be muscle tremors (involuntary shaking) or other dysfunctions of muscle coordination.

Notice that there are two structures labeled in figure 8.5 that are not a part of the basal nuclei. First, notice the thalamus. We have discussed the thalamus already, but this gives you a side view so that you can see its size better than you could in the midsagittal section shown in figure 8.2. The other structure in the figure is the amygdaloid (uh mig' duh loyd) nucleus. This nucleus is a part of the limbic system.

The limbic system is a series of nuclei and commissures that run through the cerebrum and the diencephalon. The limbic system influences mood, emotion, fear, and the senses of pain and pleasure. The limbic system also seems to play a vital role in survival instincts. The desire for food, water, and reproduction seem to be centered in the limbic system.

Interestingly enough, the amygdaloid nucleus is also involved in memory. There is a structure in the temporal lobe called the hippocampus (hip oh kam' pus). This structure is shaped like a sea horse (that is where it gets its name), and it takes care of a significant part of your memory. For example, the memory of a person's name is stored in the hippocampus. The amygdaloid nucleus, however, is involved in remembering the emotions that you relate to that person. When you see a person and think of his or her name, then, the name comes from the hippocampus, while the emotions that you attach to that person (friendship, love, anger, etc.) come from the amygdaloid nucleus.

This interaction between the limbic system, which is heavily involved in mood and emotion, and the hippocampus, which is heavily involved in memory, has led some to think that your emotions and your mood serve as gates in the brain. These gates determine what you remember on a long-term basis.

One other very important set of structures in the brain is the cavities, which are referred to as ventricles (figure 8.6). When the CNS develops in a fetus, it begins as a hollow tube. That hollow tube grows with the fetus, changing shape. The top of the tube develops lobes that eventually form cavities in each of the hemispheres of the brain. The bottom of the tube expands and forms cavities in the diencephalon as well as in the midbrain. We call these the ventricles of the brain.

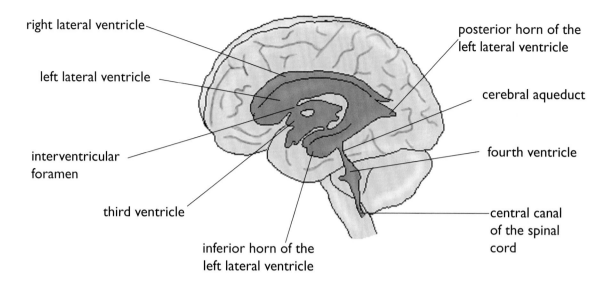

right lateral ventricle

left lateral ventricle

interventricular foramen

third ventricle

inferior horn of the left lateral ventricle

posterior horn of the left lateral ventricle

cerebral aqueduct

fourth ventricle

central canal of the spinal cord

FIGURE 8.6
The Ventricles of the Brain
Illus. by Megan Whitaker

What is the function of these ventricles? They are hollow spaces filled with cerebrospinal (ser ee' bro spy' nuhl) fluid (CSF), a clear fluid that cushions and protects the brain. The ventricles are lined with ependymal (ep en' duh muhl) cells, neuroglia cells that you learned about in the previous module. The ependymal cells produce and secrete the cerebrospinal fluid into the ventricles. Of course, since the ependymal cells are alive, they need an ample supply of nutrients and oxygen. So, there are blood vessels that supply them. In addition, in some locations with the ventricles, there are other specialized cells that support the ependymal cells in their function. The ependymal cells, their support cells, and the blood vessels that supply them with oxygen and nutrients together form the choroid (koh' roid) plexuses. The term *choroid* means "lacey," because the tissue has a lacey look to it. The choroid plexuses produce CSF.

Notice in the figure that the largest ventricles are the lateral ventricles. There is one in each hemisphere of the brain, so they are called the left lateral ventricle and the right lateral ventricle. About 80% of the CSF is produced in these two ventricles. The remainder is produced in the other two ventricles, which are called the third ventricle and the fourth ventricle. The third ventricle is a narrow space within the diencephalon, while the fourth ventricle is a widened cavity in the midbrain. Notice that below the fourth ventricle, the cavity continues and becomes the central canal of the spinal cord.

Now, it is important to understand that these cavities are all connected to one another. The two lateral ventricles are connected to the third ventricle by two foramina called the interventricular foramina. The third ventricle is connected to the fourth ventricle by a thin tube called the cerebral aqueduct. These connections allow CSF to flow freely from the lateral ventricles all of the way down to the fourth ventricle and then onto the surface of the brain or around the spinal cord. We will discuss the details of this process in the next section.

COLORING BOOK EXERCISE 8.3

To review the ventricles of the brain, follow the instructions on page 127 of the coloring book.

ON YOUR OWN

8.7 Sometimes people develop a disorder in which their hands shake uncontrollably, even when they are sitting still doing nothing. Which part of the brain might be the source of this type of tremor?

8.8 Some fear reactions seem to be a natural part of the brain that requires no learning. For example, an infant rodent will be afraid of a cat, even though it has never seen a cat before. Where, most likely, is this information stored?

PROTECTION OF THE BRAIN

The brain, of course, is the most complex and sensitive organ in the body. Its neurons do not undergo mitosis after babyhood. They are dependent on an uninterrupted supply of glucose and oxygen from the blood. The brain is a delicate organ that must be protected. It is not surprising, then, that the Designer of the body went to great lengths to ensure that the brain is well protected. The many layers of protection are shown in figure 8.7.

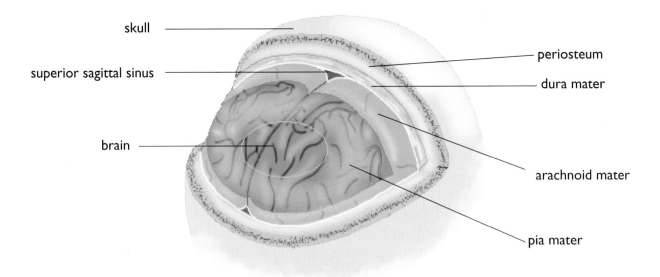

FIGURE 8.7
The Meninges of the Brain
Illus. by Megan Whitaker

The protection of the brain begins with the skull. Below the skull, however, three specific layers of tissue, collectively called the meninges (muh nin' jeez), surround and protect the brain, as well. The meninx (singular of meninges) right beneath the skull is called the dura mater (may' ter). It is firmly attached to the periosteum (discussed in module 3) of the skull so that they form one layer. The dura mater extends down into the major fissures of the brain. Where the dura mater extends into the longitudinal fissure, a tube-like opening occurs. This is called the superior sagittal sinus, and it is actually a vein that collects the blood that returns from the brain, as well as CSF, as discussed in detail below. This and other blood sinuses empty into large veins that leave the skull.

Below the dura mater we find the next meninx of the brain, the arachnoid (uh rack' noid) mater. The arachnoid mater gets its name from class Arachnida, which contains the spiders. It is given this name because the tissue resembles thick webbing like old dusty cobwebs that are found in barns. You will see this more clearly in figure 8.8. The space between the dura mater and the arachnoid mater is called the subdural space. It is filled with a small amount of fluid that moistens the tissue.

Below the arachnoid mater, we find the third meninx, the pia (pea-uh) mater. The word pia means "affectionate." The pia mater is so named because it binds tightly (affectionately) to the brain itself. The pia mater cannot be separated from the brain because of this connection. The space in between the arachnoid layer and the pia mater is the subarachnoid space, which contains web like strands of arachnoid mater and is filled with CSF. The CSF in the subarachnoid space cushions and protects the brain.

The term meninges might seem familiar to you because you have probably heard the term meningitis (men in jye' tis). This is a potentially life-threatening infection that can be caused by viruses or bacteria. Meningitis is an inflammation of the meninges. Since the meninges are so important in the protection of the brain (and spinal cord as you will see in the next section), an inflammation of these tissues can be quite dangerous. Pus formed as a result of the inflammation can accumulate in the subarachnoid space, blocking the flow of CSF. This can lead to pressure on the brain's neurons, in turn leading to paralysis, coma, and even death.

Let's look at all of this in a slightly different way, so that we can analyze where all of the meningeal layers are and how the CSF fits into the picture. Figure 8.8 is a schematic diagram that illustrates the flow of CSF in the brain. It also gives you a different view of the meninges in the brain. Note that in the figure, the white arrows denote the flow of CSF, while the black arrows denote the flow of blood as it leaves the brain and heads back to the heart.

The choroid plexus of each ventricle produces CSF. Remember, however, that the lateral ventricles produce the majority of the CSF. The choroid plexus is made up of tiny "fingers" of tissue called villi. These villi are composed of ciliated and non-ciliated ependymal cells. The ciliated cells move the CSF so that the flow pattern pictured below can be maintained. It is the pressure of production that maintains the flow.

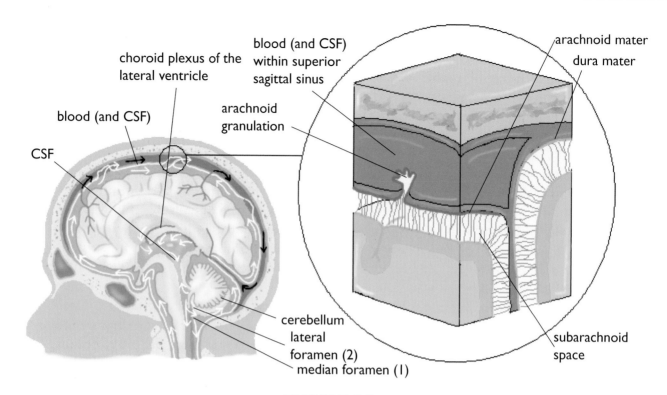

FIGURE 8.8
The Flow of Cerebrospinal Fluid
Illus. by Megan Whitaker

When the ependymal cells of the choroid plexus make the CSF, it enters the ventricle. If the CSF is made in the lateral ventricles, it flows under the pressure of its own production through the interventricular foramina into the third ventricle, and then down through the cerebral aqueduct into the fourth ventricle. There are three foramina in the fourth ventricle (the single median foramen and two lateral foramina are shown in the figure), which then allow the CSF to leave the ventricles and enter the subarachnoid space. The CSF then flows up and around the brain or down around the spinal cord, as shown by the white arrows.

Now you might wonder what causes the pressure that pushes the CSF out of the ventricles and into the subarachnoid space. The major cause of this pressure is simply the fact that more CSF is being made by the choroid plexus. So, the CSF that has already been made has to leave the ventricles in order to make room for the new CSF that is being made. The ciliated ependymal cells help facilitate the flow, but the impetus for the flow comes from the pressure of new CSF being made. This is why a blockage of CSF flow can be deadly. Since new CSF gets made constantly, the pressure would just build and build until the pressure on the brain destroyed neurons.

Why does new CSF have to be made? Well, the CSF that is flowing through the subarachnoid space over the surface of the brain and spinal cord eventually flows toward the top of the head, where it reaches arachnoid granulations. These are like tiny "sewers" that dump the CSF into the superior sagittal sinus. The arachnoid granulations are not microscopic; instead, they look like small cauliflower-shaped warts on the arachnoid mater near the superior sagittal sinus. The CSF mixes with used blood that has already supplied the brain tissue with nutrients and oxygen. The blood and the CSF that is mixed in with it are carried by veins back to the heart. CSF, which is a derivative of the blood, then, is eventually returned to the blood.

Notice what is happening, then. The CSF flows through the subarachnoid space and eventually gets recycled back into the bloodstream. This, of course, requires the production of more CSF in order to keep the subarachnoid space filled. What happens if the subarachnoid space is not filled with CSF? Consider this story from a student.

A student went to the doctor with symptoms of a stiff neck, headache, and a fever. The doctor was concerned that the student might have meningitis, so the doctor did a spinal tap, which allowed the doctor to take a sample of CSF from around the spinal cord in order to determine whether or not there was an infection in the meninges. So, the doctor took the CSF from the student, and the student was told to stay flat on his back in the hospital bed for the next 24 hours. He said that he did not feel very bad, and, as he lay there, his bladder filled up. Eventually, he decided that he would just get up and go to the restroom. When he got up, he said he was hit with a "thunderbolt" of a headache and just fell down on the floor in pain. This student, however, did *not* have meningitis!

What happened to the student? His *brain moved*! When the doctor removed the CSF, there was less fluid than what is necessary to fill the subarachnoid space. The student was supposed to lie flat for 24 hours in order to allow his body to replace all of that missing CSF. When he got up, before that time was over, his brain was not held in place by the cushion of CSF, and that actually allowed enough shifting to pull on the dura mater and shift the blood vessels, which is *very* painful. A normal level of CSF prevents that from happening. *The function of CSF is to cushion and protect the brain!*

THE SPINAL CORD

We have spent a lot of time on the brain because it is such a complex organ. Remember, however, that the spinal cord is an integral part of the CNS as well. It is the communications link between the PNS and the brain. Without it, the brain would not receive much of the sensory information from the body and it could not control much of the body. The spinal cord is, in fact, continuous with the brain, and you can think of it as the brain's "ponytail."

COLORING BOOK EXERCISE 8.4
To review the meninges and the flow of CSF, follow the instructions on page 129 of the coloring book.

ON YOUR OWN

8.9 Besides the large superior sagittal sinuses, there are smaller dural sinuses. Damage to any of them can cause bleeding into the subdural space. This is called a subdural hematoma. What effect would this condition have on the brain?

8.10 When someone fractures a skull, the meninges can be torn. This can cause CSF to leak out of the nose or the ear. This situation is dangerous not only because it indicates severe damage to the head, but also because it increases the risk of meningitis. Why would leakage of CSF out of the body increase the risk of meningitis?

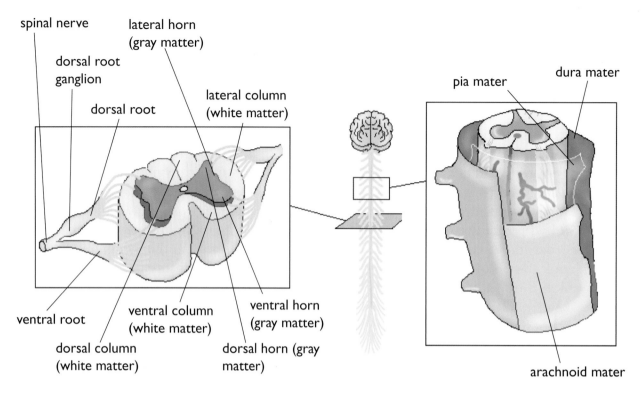

spinal nerve

lateral horn
(gray matter)

dorsal root
ganglion

dorsal root

lateral column
(white matter)

pia mater

dura mater

ventral root

ventral column
(white matter)

ventral horn
(gray matter)

dorsal column
(white matter)

dorsal horn (gray
matter)

arachnoid mater

FIGURE 8.9
The Spinal Cord
Illus. by Megan Whitaker

The spinal cord, as you will recall, is encased in the vertebral column. However, it is not quite as long as the entire vertebral column; it reaches only to the second lumbar vertebra. There are 31 pairs of spinal nerves that exit the spinal cord and travel out of the vertebral column through the intervertebral foramina.

In general, the spinal cord gets slightly smaller in diameter as it goes from the brain to the lower back. However, there are two areas of exception. The cervical enlargement is an area where the spinal cord's diameter increases so that the nerves of the upper limbs can enter and exit the cord. In the same way, the lumbar enlargement is a region of increased diameter where the nerves of the lower limbs enter and exit the spinal cord. Just below the lumbar enlargement, the spinal cord tapers to a cone-like structure called the conus medullaris. This structure and the many strands of axons that attach to it are often called the cauda equina because, together, they look like a horse's tail. Cauda equina means "horse's tail."

On the left side of the figure, we show a drawing of a cross section of the spinal cord. The gray portion in the center is gray matter, while the lighter portion is composed of white matter. This white matter is organized into three basic columns: the dorsal (posterior) column, the lateral columns, and the ventral (anterior) column. Since the term dorsal means "back" and ventral means "belly," the dorsal column is the column on the backside of the spinal cord, while the ventral column is on the belly side of the spinal cord. Posterior and anterior are synonyms for dorsal and ventral in the human. The term lateral refers to the side, so the lateral columns are on the side of the spinal cord. These columns are further divided into fasciculi (fuh sik' you lie), which are also called nerve tracts. Axons that carry action potentials to or from the brain are grouped together so that axons that carry the same type of information are found in the same fasiculus (singular). The term column is used because the axons are oriented vertically in anatomical position.

The central gray matter in the spinal cord is organized into horns. Axons from the *sensory* neurons synapse with association neurons in the dorsal (posterior) horn. The cell bodies of the *motor* neurons are found in the ventral (anterior) horn, while the cell bodies of the *autonomic* neurons are found in the lateral horns. As this shows, the nervous system is hardwired in a highly organized way!

On each side of the spinal cord, we find dorsal (posterior) roots and ventral (anterior) roots. The dorsal root enters the spinal cord at the dorsal horn, and it carries *afferent* signals from the sensory receptors to the spinal cord. Each dorsal root also contains a ganglion, which is made up of the cell bodies of afferent neurons. Remember, afferent neurons are unipolar. Their axons travel all the way from the receptors to the spinal cord, and the cell body hangs off the axon. The dorsal (posterior) root ganglion is where these sensory cell bodies are housed. The ventral root leaves the spinal cord at the anterior horn, and it carries *efferent* action potentials from the spinal cord to the effectors. The ventral roots have no ganglia because the motor neuron cell bodies are located within the gray matter of the spinal cord. The dorsal and ventral roots come together to form a spinal nerve. Can you see why the spinal nerves are all mixed nerves? Are you amazed at the precise anatomical arrangement of the nervous system?

On the right side of the illustration, we show a drawing that highlights the meninges of the spinal cord. Remember, the spinal cord, as part of the CNS, is continuous with the brain and needs to be protected, just like the brain. It has three meningeal layers continuous with the brain's layers. The spinal cord is covered with pia mater. The space between the pia mater and the arachnoid mater (the subarachnoid space) is filled with CSF, just as it is in the brain. There is also a subdural space between the arachnoid mater and the dura mater.

At this point, however, we reach a difference between the meninges in the spinal cord and the meninges of the brain. In the brain, the dura mater is attached to the periosteum of the skull. However, in the spinal cord, the dura mater is not connected to the bone of the vertebral column. There is a space, the epidural space, between the vertebral column and the dura mater. This space contains spinal nerves, blood vessels, connective tissue, and fat. In epidural anesthesia to relieve pain, the anesthetic is injected into this space, and it prevents the spinal nerves from sending pain signals to the brain. It is frequently used in childbirth.

think about this

Organization within the human body is truly astonishing. One of this textbook's authors has this life story to share with you:

"Years ago, when I was a young instructor, I dissected a cadaver for the first time. I did so along with an older professor who had taught human anatomy and physiology for a long time. One time as we were dissecting, I commented, 'What amazes me is that we look at the dissection manual, find out where to cut, and when we make the cut, there is what we're looking for, right where the manual says it is.' The old professor replied thoughtfully, almost reverently: 'Generation after generation…'

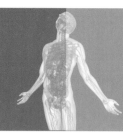

COLORING BOOK EXERCISE 8.5
To review the structure of the spinal cord, follow the instructions on page 131 of the coloring book.

ON YOUR OWN

8.11 Where are the cell bodies of the neurons that make up the ventral root?

THE REFLEX ARC

When you think about what controls your muscles, the brain immediately comes to mind. However, it is important to realize that the brain is not always involved in the control of your muscles. Often, your spinal cord is! Think about the situation in which you touch a hot stove and automatically pull your hand away from it. The speed at which you do this is surprising. In fact, it is not uncommon for someone to react by saying, "Wow, I pulled my hand away before I even knew what I was doing!" In fact, that is exactly right. In a situation like this, your hand responds *before* your brain knows what happened. How is that possible? It is possible because the nervous system has been elegantly designed with a system we call the reflex arc. The reflex arc, in fact, is the basic functional unit of the nervous system.

When you touch something hot, the pain receptors (part of the PNS) in your skin are stimulated. As a result, they send an afferent message to the spinal cord (part of the CNS). The spinal cord integrates that information using the interneurons within the gray matter and makes a "judgment" as to what to do. It sends an outgoing message to a flexor muscle in your arm, telling it to contract. This results in your hand pulling away from the stove. Realize that this happens *without the brain needing to be involved*.

The reason for such an ingenious design is obvious. Your hand needs to pull away from the heat *quickly*. Otherwise, your skin would be burned beyond repair. If your nervous system had to send a message from your hand to your brain, and then if your brain had to make a decision and send a message to the flexor muscle in your arm, it would take a longer time. The reflex arc allows you to react quickly to the pain, saving your skin from being burned to the point that it cannot be repaired.

Suppose you really wanted to see what would happen if you held your hand on a hot stove for a long time. In an effort to determine this, you put your hand on the stove, concentrating on trying to keep it there for a long time. Would you be able to do that? Not really. Why not? *Reflexes are preprogrammed*. They happen automatically. Since the reflex bypasses the brain, it is very hard for the brain to counteract the reflex. Of course, it also would not be a very smart thing to try to do.

We want to make sure that you really appreciate the ingenuity of the reflex arc, so we will discuss it in some detail. Figure 8.10 gives a schematic representation of the reflex arc. Now remember, this involves the spinal cord, not the brain. The left side of the figure, then, is a cross section of the spinal cord, like the one shown in figure 8.9. First, notice the afferent nerve. Where is its cell body? It is in the dorsal root ganglion. It synapses with an association neuron in the dorsal horn, as discussed above. Finally, notice the motor nerve. Its cell body is in the ventral horn, as discussed previously.

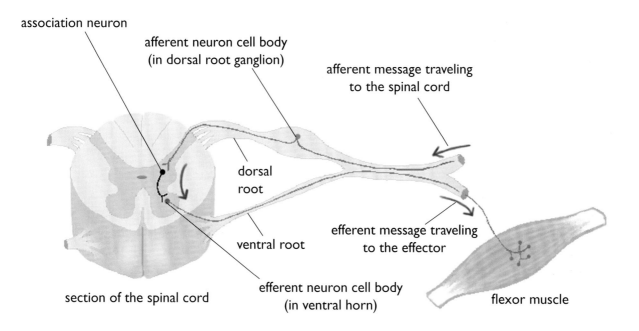

association neuron

afferent neuron cell body
(in dorsal root ganglion)

afferent message traveling
to the spinal cord

dorsal
root

ventral root

efferent message traveling
to the effector

efferent neuron cell body
(in ventral horn)

section of the spinal cord

flexor muscle

FIGURE 8.10
A Reflex Arc
Illus. by Megan Whitaker

MOD 8

The reflex arc begins with sensory information. The sensory information from the afferent PNS nerve is sent into the spinal cord. In the figure, the afferent nerve involved in the reflex arc is a pain receptor in the skin.

The afferent message reaches the spinal cord and is sent to an association neuron that directs the message to an efferent neuron. The efferent neuron then sends the message to an effector in order to generate a response. In this case, the effector is a flexor muscle, which causes your forearm to flex.

This is a pretty amazing design, isn't it? However, it's not the end of the story. Think about it. In figure 8.10, the afferent nerve sends a signal to the spinal cord, and then an association neuron in the spinal cord sends a signal to the correct effector muscle. This allows us to respond to stimuli quickly. However, if that were the end of the story, we would never *learn* from the experience. Once again, think about the situation in which your hand touches a hot stove. The reflex arc allows you to pull your hand away quickly. However, if your brain never learns about this experience, you would not know to *avoid doing it in the future*. In order to keep you from doing the same thing again, your brain has to be informed about the experience.

There is still something else to consider as well! Although it is wonderful that our effectors can be controlled by reflex arcs, that cannot be all there is. After all, we not only need to move our limbs by reflex, but we must also be able to move them as a result of conscious thought. Our brains must be able to send signals to the effectors too. So, in addition to the reflex arc, we need to have signals sent from the afferent nerves to the brain. In addition, the brain must be able to send signals down the efferent nerves to control effectors like muscles and glands.

How does all of this happen? Well, think about what you learned at the end of the previous module. Neurons are arranged in circuits. These circuits are crucial to the design of the nervous system. The way these circuits are used is shown in figure 8.11.

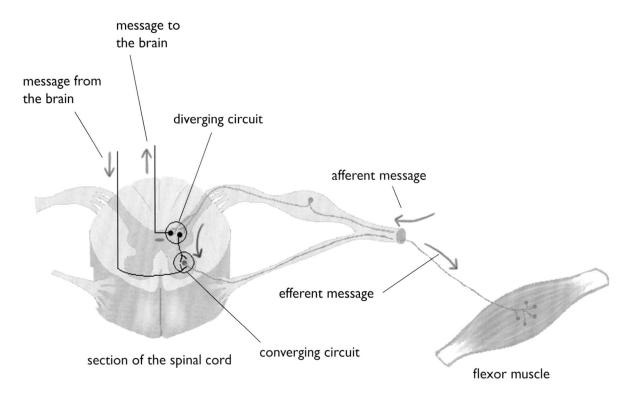

FIGURE 8.11
Circuits in the Spinal Cord
Illus. by Megan Whitaker

In this figure, concentrate on the circle labeled diverging circuit. What does this circuit accomplish? Well, as the afferent message travels into the spinal cord, the axon divides and synapses with many different neurons, two of which we will consider.
One neuron is the association neuron that stimulates the reflex. The other neuron is one that sends a message to the brain. What does this circuit do? It allows the afferent signal not only to initiate the reflex, but also to go to the brain. That way, the reflex allows you to react quickly, but the message to the brain helps you learn from the experience.

Now look at the circle labeled converging circuit. In this circuit, two neurons both synapse with the same effector neuron. The first neuron is the association neuron in the reflex arc. The other is a neuron coming from the brain. What does this accomplish? It allows the effector (in this case, a flexor muscle) to be controlled by *both* the reflex arc and the brain. Your forearm will flex quickly in reaction to pain, but it can also flex in reaction to a conscious thought, as it normally does.

Now think about this design for a moment. It is truly remarkable. If we were designing such as system, it would not be nearly as elegant. For example, our first thought would be to send one set of nerves from the brain to the effectors in order for the effectors to be controlled consciously. In addition, we would have another set of nerves going from the spinal cord to the effectors so that they could be controlled by reflex. Then, of course, there would also have to be two sets of afferent nerves. One set of nerves would go from the receptors to the spinal cord in order to stimulate the reflexes, and the other set of nerves would go from the receptors to the brain so that the brain could learn from experiences. The Designer of the body, however, is *much* more intelligent than we are! He has used diverging and converging circuits in the nervous system so that all of these tasks can be done with a minimum of neurons! Please keep in mind that this example is simplified, but the reality is based on this.

ASCENDING AND DESCENDING PATHWAYS IN THE SPINAL CORD

Obviously, reflex arcs are a very important function of the spinal cord. However, let's not forget its other main function. The spinal cord serves as a conduit for messages from the brain to the PNS and from the PNS back to the brain. So that you get a better understanding of how this information travels in the spinal cord and brain, we want to go through two specific pathways, a motor pathway and a sensory pathway.

Motor pathways are called *descending pathways*. Why? Think about it. The motor neurons carry signals from the CNS to the muscles. The conscious decision to move a muscle starts in the brain and action potentials travel *down* the spinal cord and then to the muscle. This information descends from the brain to the muscles. On the other hand, sensory pathways are called *ascending pathways*, because the action potentials begin at the receptors of the PNS and then travel *up* the spinal cord to the brain.

Let's start this discussion with an example of a motor pathway. Suppose you decide to perform a simple movement, such as clenching your fist. What happens in order for you to do this? The answer to this question is illustrated in figure 8.12.

ON YOUR OWN

8.12 When you touch a hot stove, your hand pulls back quickly as a result of the reflex arc. However, when you touch warm water, you do not pull your hand back quickly. Apparently, the reflex arc has a decision-making mechanism that interprets the afferent signals and determines whether or not the reflex should be activated. Which neuron in the reflex arc is responsible for this?

PLEASE NOTE:
In this figure, the brain and spinal cord are not drawn to scale.

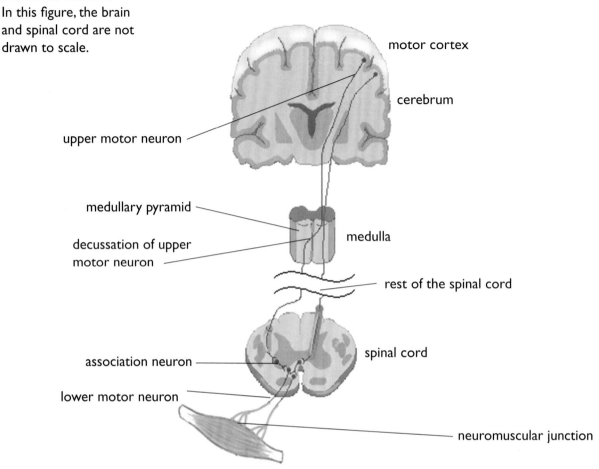

motor cortex

cerebrum

upper motor neuron

medullary pyramid

decussation of upper motor neuron

medulla

rest of the spinal cord

association neuron

spinal cord

lower motor neuron

neuromuscular junction

FIGURE 8.12
A Motor Pathway
Illus. by Megan Whitaker

When we initiate a movement, such as clenching a fist, the action potentials must originate in the primary motor cortex, which is on the precentral gyrus. Because the left side of the brain controls the right side of the body, a decision to clench your right fist will start in the primary motor cortex on the left side of the brain. The goal, of course, is to get that signal down to the muscles that will actually flex the fingers. How does that happen? This kind of motion is a conscious muscle movement, so it will take a direct pathway from the brain to the muscles. It only takes *two motor neurons and an association neuron* to do this job! What is the significance of that? There is a very close connection between what we voluntarily choose to initiate in the brain and how it is conducted to the skeletal muscle.

The neuron in the motor cortex, called the upper motor neuron, sends action potentials down through the midbrain, through the pons, and to the medulla. At the medulla, the axons travel through a structure called the medullary pyramid. In the pyramid, approximately 80% of the axons cross over. Remember, this is called decussation. To represent this, the axon in the figure crosses from the left to the right. The other 20% of the axons in other motor pathways cross over in the spinal cord.

Once past the medulla, the axon travels to the portion of the spinal cord that contains the spinal nerves, which in turn will contain the efferent neurons that go to the flexor muscles that flex the fingers. When the axon reaches the spinal cord, it synapses with an association neuron. The association neuron then synapses with a lower motor neuron, which will carry the action potentials to the neuromuscular junction of the muscle. The lower motor neuron is the same neuron we originally learned about when we first studied skeletal muscle in module 5.

Look at what we have in this example of a motor pathway. Upper motor neurons, which originate in the motor cortex, send their axons all of the way down the spinal cord without a synapse. These axons cross over to the other side of the body at the medulla oblongata. They then synapse with association neurons, which in turn, synapse with lower motor neurons, which send the action potentials to the muscles of interest.

If you think about it, this represents a very direct route from the motor cortex to the muscle. There are only two synapses involved. First, there is a synapse with an association neuron, and, second, that association neuron synapses with a lower motor neuron. The particular pathway in this example is called the *lateral corticospinal tract*. The word lateral refers to the fact that it travels down the side of the spinal cord. The word corticospinal refers to the fact that the route is direct from the cerebral cortex, down the spinal cord, and to the muscle.

Your entire body is innervated in a similar manner, so that you can choose to flex your toes, or bend your knee, or whatever. Yet that same lower motor neuron may receive 500 or more synapses from other neurons, so that it is responding to signals about muscle tone, posture, adjustments to other movements, its part in learned sequences, and so forth.

Let's switch gears now and look at a sensory pathway (figure 8.13). As we mentioned before, sensory pathways are called ascending pathways, because they send signals from the receptors to the brain. Like motor pathways, there are several different sensory pathways. The particular pathway we want to use as an example is called the anterior spinothalamic tract. The word anterior means that this bundle of neurons is located in the anterior (ventral) part of the spinal cord. The word spinothalamic refers to the fact that the signals travel from the spinal cord to the thalamus. This tract carries the signals that come from light touch, tickle, and itch receptors.

PLEASE NOTE:
In this figure, the brain and spinal cord are not drawn to scale.

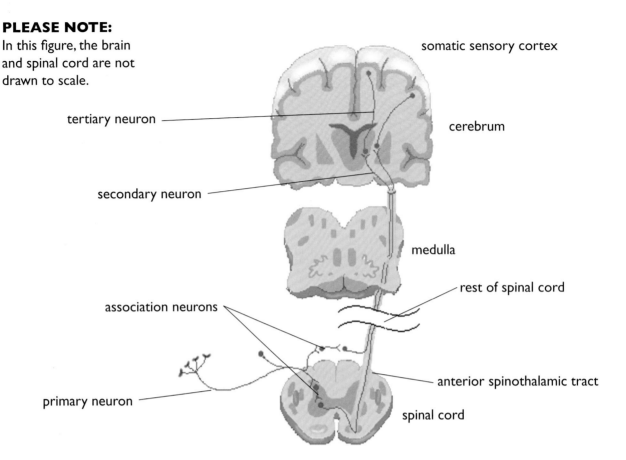

somatic sensory cortex

tertiary neuron

cerebrum

secondary neuron

medulla

rest of spinal cord

association neurons

anterior spinothalamic tract

primary neuron

spinal cord

FIGURE 8.13
A Sensory Pathway
Illus. by Megan Whitaker

Since this is an ascending pathway, it begins at the bottom of the figure and works its way up to the somatic sensory cortex. The pathway begins with receptors, which are very superficial in the skin. A very light touch will activate them, and action potentials will be produced in the primary neuron. In this illustration, the axon diverges, and each end synapses with an association neuron. Each association neuron then synapses with a secondary neuron. The axons cross over at the spinal cord and travel up the anterior spinothalamic tract.

The secondary neurons travel up to the thalamus and synapse with tertiary neurons. This is why we say that the thalamus is a relay station for sensory information, and why there may be crude interpretation of sensory information in the thalamus. The thalamus gives us some awareness of touch because of the synapses there. To really interpret the signals, however, they must be sent on to the somatic sensory area, which is where the tertiary neurons carry the signals.

Notice that there are three synapses in this pathway, compared to only two in the descending motor pathway. This should make sense. After all, sensory information must be regulated and perhaps inhibited. If we were to receive all of the sensory information gathered by our sensory receptors, we could not handle it! All this incoming information must be limited. There are more synapses in the sensory pathway to do just that. How so? Axons faithfully carry all the information they receive, because they conduct action potentials from one end to the other without any decrease in the strength or number of action potentials. The synapses, oppositely, can inhibit the formation of action potentials on the next neuron, or they can otherwise prevent irrelevant information from going through. Still, the conscious center of your brain, in this example the somatic sensory cortex, is literally closely "in touch" with information provided to it by the touch receptors. Only three major sensory neurons complete the link from receptor to conscious center.

Before you begin studying your notes on this module in preparation for the test, sit back and think about what you have learned. The CNS is an incredibly complex system. The brain itself is more complex than the most sophisticated computer network ever created by human science. It sends signals out via the spinal cord to hundreds of thousands of different effectors while, at the same time, receiving and processing millions and millions of signals from the sensory receptors all over the body. This whole system is packed securely in many layers of protection. The CNS is probably the pinnacle of complexity in design, and it cries out in testimony for its Designer!

ANSWERS TO THE "ON YOUR OWN" QUESTIONS

8.1 They can use other sources of nutrition so as to save the glucose for your neurons. This really does happen. As your blood glucose level drops, some other cells, such as skeletal muscle cells, catabolize glycogen, fats, and amino acids in order to allow the neurons to get the glucose that is left.

8.2 The cerebrum is much larger in humans as compared with other vertebrates. Remember, the cerebrum deals with higher-level functions.

8.3 The cerebellum deals with fine muscle movements. Amphibian cerebellums are much smaller and less developed than those of other vertebrates.

8.4 Since the reticular activation system deals with the sleep-wake cycle, tranquilizers must affect that part of the brain.

8.5 Most likely, Broca's area has been affected. Wernicke's area is what we use to *determine* what to say. Broca's area then stimulates the muscle movements needed to make the appropriate words. If the person knows what he or she wants to say, Wernicke's area is working fine. If he or she just cannot say it, that means that Broca's area is damaged.

8.6 The visual cortex and visual association areas are damaged. The visual cortex receives basic information about size, shape, and color. The visual association area interprets the meaning of the size, shape, and color. An injury to the back of the head, where the occipital lobe of the brain is found, can cause blindness even with two healthy eyes. That is because the visual cortex and visual association areas are located there.

8.7 This is a problem with the basal nuclei, which maintain muscle tone and posture. Tremors are a sign that there is something wrong with the basal nuclei.

8.8 This information is stored in the limbic system.

8.9 This would lead to pressure on the brain. If the dural sinuses fill up, the pressure will push on the brain, which can lead to unconsciousness since neurons are very sensitive to pressure, which among other things decreases their blood supply.

8.10 If CSF is getting out, that means bacteria and other pathogens can get in. Since bacteria and viruses cause meningitis, this increases the risk of meningitis.

8.11 The ventral root carries efferent information to the effectors, and the signal originates in the spinal cord. This means that the cell bodies are in the ventral horn of the spinal cord.

8.12 Sensory (afferent) neurons must be responsible for this. Afferent neurons from pain receptors synapse with association neurons that in turn synapse with the appropriate efferent neurons to the flexor muscle, as in the illustration. Afferent neurons from other receptors, such as for light touch or warm temperature, are not part of this particular reflex. The reflex has no decision-making function outside of its own hardwiring.

STUDY GUIDE FOR MODULE 8

1. Define the following:
   a. Gray matter
   b. White matter
   c. Decussation
   d. Vital functions
   e. Commissures

2. What is hypoxia? Why is it dangerous to the nervous system?

3. What is hypoglycemia? What can that do to the brain?

Choose your answers to questions 4-12 from the following:
midbrain, hypothalamus, pons, medulla oblongata, thalamus

4. Arrange the structures listed above from inferior to superior.

5. Which of the structures is a part of the brainstem?

6. Which of the structures is a part of the diencephalon?

7. In which of the structures does most of the decussation of neurons take place?

8. Which of the structures has nuclei that control many of the body's vital functions?

9. Which of the structures have nuclei specifically dedicated to reflexes involving the senses of hearing and sight?

10. Which of the structures relays messages from the cerebrum to the cerebellum?

11. Which of the structures controls the pituitary gland?

12. Which of the structures performs a crude interpretation of sensory information and then relays that information to the cerebrum?

13. If you were to think of the cerebrum as a series of hills and valleys, would the gyri be the hills or the valleys? What about the sulci?

14. Which major structure in the brain deals with the motor functions that we perform without consciously thinking of them?

15. What is the purpose of the corpus callosum? There are other structures in the brain and spinal cord that perform the same task. What is the general term that describes all of these structures?

16. Identify the following structures:

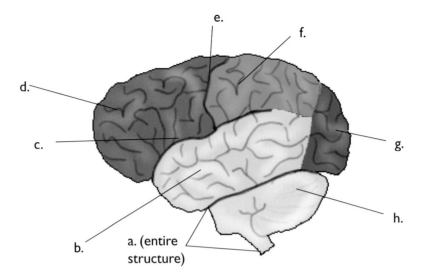

17. Identify the functional areas below, and indicate what functions they perform.

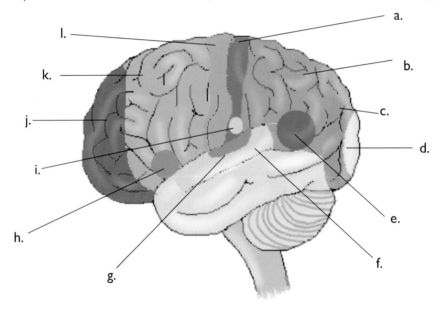

18. Where is the majority of the cerebrospinal fluid produced?

19. Where is the rest of the cerebrospinal fluid produced?

20. What is the purpose of cerebrospinal fluid?

21. What three structures covering the skull protect the brain? What are they called collectively? Name them from outermost to innermost.

22. What are arachnoid granulations, and what do they do?

23.   Identify the structures in the figure below:

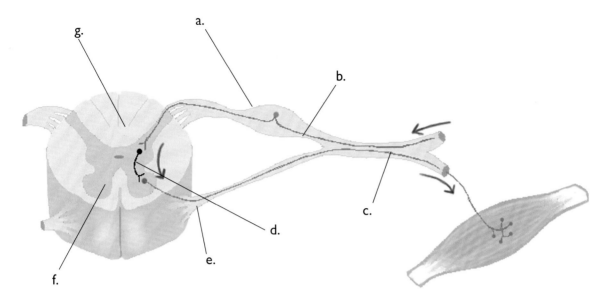

24.   What are the three neurons in a reflex arc, and in what order are they activated?

25.   Where can you find the association neuron in the reflex arc?

26.   Of the three neuron circuits we discussed in the previous module, which type of circuit is formed by the afferent neuron in the reflex arc?

27.   In the reflex arc, of which kind of circuit is the efferent neuron a part?

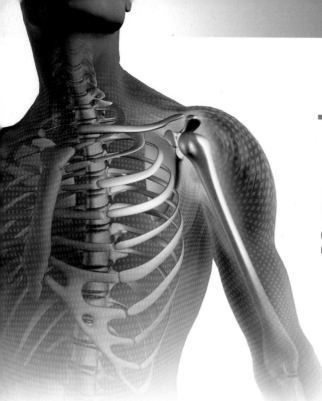

THE PERIPHERAL NERVOUS SYSTEM

In the previous module, we discussed the central nervous system (CNS). In this module we will explore the peripheral nervous system (PNS). As we investigate this extraordinarily designed system, we will also discuss the senses.

As you already learned in module 7, the PNS can be split into two divisions, both anatomically and functionally. These are the efferent and the afferent divisions. Efferent motor neurons send signals from the CNS to the effectors, while the afferent sensory neurons send signals from receptors back to the CNS. We will discuss both divisions in this module, starting with the efferent division. Remember that the efferent division of the PNS can be further subdivided into two systems: the somatic motor nervous system (SMNS) and the autonomic nervous system (ANS). We will concentrate on the autonomic nervous system, but before we do that, we want to note the differences between the SMNS and the ANS.

The most obvious difference between these two systems is the effectors they control. While the SMNS controls skeletal muscle, the ANS controls smooth muscle, cardiac muscle, and glands. This leads us to the next difference. Skeletal muscles are *voluntary* muscles. The SMNS can be *voluntarily* controlled, as for example, when you choose to bend your knees or clap your hands. Even though this is obvious, many activities of the skeletal muscles are controlled automatically—for example, muscle tone. Yet, you can easily decide to move your muscles.

heart of the matter

Blaise Pascal wrote, "All bodies, the firmament, the stars, the earth and its kingdoms, are not equal to the lowest mind; for mind knows all these and itself; and these bodies nothing." Your interpretation of and interaction with your world is generated by your nervous system. Your entire understanding of your world is formed by how your central and peripheral nervous systems interact as they interpret your senses. The wonder of what you see, hear, feel, taste, and smell is the creation of a loving God who wants you to interact and know your surroundings.

On the other hand, the ANS is *involuntary*. Although it can be affected by conscious thought, it cannot be directly controlled by conscious thought. Significant anatomical differences between the SMNS and the ANS are shown in figure 9.1.

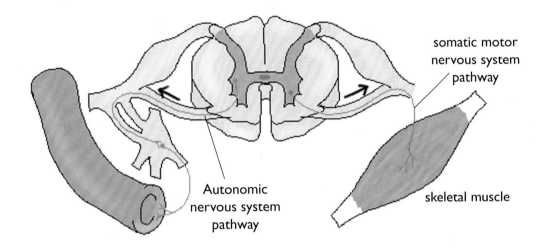

somatic motor
nervous system
pathway

skeletal muscle

Autonomic
nervous system
pathway

FIGURE 9.1
Neuron Arrangements in the SMNS and the ANS
Illustration by Megan Whitaker

In the SMNS, *a single* neuron whose cell body is located in the CNS extends from the CNS to the effector. In the ANS, there are *two* neurons extending from the CNS to the effector: the preganglionic neuron and the postganglionic neuron. The cell body of the preganglionic neuron is located in either the spinal cord or the brain stem. (In the illustration, we use the spinal cord.) The axon then travels out into the body, synapsing with the postganglionic neuron at an autonomic ganglion. The cell body of the postganglionic neuron is found in the autonomic ganglion, and its axon extends to the effector that it controls. Remember that a ganglion is neuron cell bodies outside the CNS.

Even the structure of the neurons themselves allows us to distinguish between the SMNS and the ANS. In the SMNS, the neuron axons are myelinated. In the ANS, the preganglionic neuron's axon is myelinated, but the postganglionic neuron's axon is not. Another difference between these two systems lies in the neurotransmitter used. The SMNS uses only acetylcholine (ACh) at the neuromuscular junction. The preganglionic neurons of the ANS use ACh. Some postganglionic neurons use another neurotransmitter known as norepinephrine (nor' ep uh neh' frin) to control their effector organs. Other postganglionic neurons use ACh to control their effector organs. As a reminder, the effector organs for the ANS are smooth muscle, cardiac muscle, and glands.

Finally, the response from the effectors is a bit different, as well. The SMNS is an excitatory system; it can only excite its effectors. In other words, when it releases its neurotransmitter ACh in response to action potentials, the ACh signals skeletal muscle to contract. The ANS, however, is both excitatory and inhibitory. For example, some ANS neurons can excite the smooth muscles of the stomach during periods of digestion, but other ANS neurons can inhibit those muscles during periods of exercise.

ON YOUR OWN

9.1 Another difference between the SMNS and the ANS is the number of synapses in a given nerve pathway between the CNS and the effector. How many synapses are in an SMNS pathway between those two points? How many synapses are in an ANS pathway between those points?

DIVISIONS OF THE AUTONOMIC NERVOUS SYSTEM

In module 7, you learned that the ANS is divided into the sympathetic division and the parasympathetic division. The function of the sympathetic division is to rouse your body for physical activity. The sympathetic division increases the rate and strength of your heartbeat and raises your blood pressure. It stimulates your liver to release glucose in the blood, providing a source of quick energy. The parasympathetic system, on the other hand, slows your heart rate and, therefore, lowers your blood pressure. In addition, it takes care of "housekeeping" activities such as causing the smooth muscles in your stomach to churn while you are digesting a meal.

Just as there are anatomical differences between the two motor divisions of the PNS (the SMNS and the ANS), there are also anatomical differences between the two divisions of the ANS, the sympathetic and parasympathetic divisions. The first one we will discuss is shown in figure 9.2.

This figure is a little complicated, so let's make sure you understand what it is showing you. First, both the sympathetic and parasympathetic nerves exit both sides of the CNS, of course. For convenience, though, we are showing the sympathetic division only on the left, and the parasympathetic division only on the right. Second, notice that some nerves from the parasympathetic division exit from the brain, while others exit from the lower (sacral) region of the spinal cord. Third, note that all sympathetic nerves exit from the thoracic and lumbar regions of the spinal cord. Finally, notice the (+) and (-) signs. These represent the kind of activity produced by the neurons shown. Neurons labeled with (+) signs *increase* the activity of the organs they innervate, while neurons with (-) signs *decrease* the activity of the organs they innervate.

Now, notice that in the sympathetic division (left-hand side of the figure), there is a chain of ganglia near the spinal cord, and there are three ganglia just a bit farther away. Those are the autonomic ganglia of the sympathetic division. These are actually *two* sympathetic chains of ganglia, a right and a left, though only one is shown. Notice, then, that the preganglionic neuron is *short*, because it gets to the autonomic ganglion soon after it leaves the spinal cord. On the other hand, the postganglionic neuron is *long* because it must reach from the ganglion to the effector organ.

Compare that with the neurons of the parasympathetic division (right-hand side of the figure). In this division, the preganglionic neuron stretches far from the brain or spinal cord and synapses with the postganglionic neuron near to the organ. Thus, in the parasympathetic division, the preganglionic neuron is *long*, while the postganglionic neuron is *short*.

This turns out to be a general rule and therefore is a means of distinguishing between the neurons of the two divisions. In the sympathetic division, the preganglionic neurons are short and the postganglionic neurons are long. In the parasympathetic division, on the other hand, the preganglionic neurons are long and the postganglionic neurons are short. In addition, the preganglionic neurons of the sympathetic division diverge quite a bit and thus synapse with many postganglionic neurons. This enables the sympathetic division to innervate a range of effectors at the same time. Those of the parasympathetic system do not diverge much.

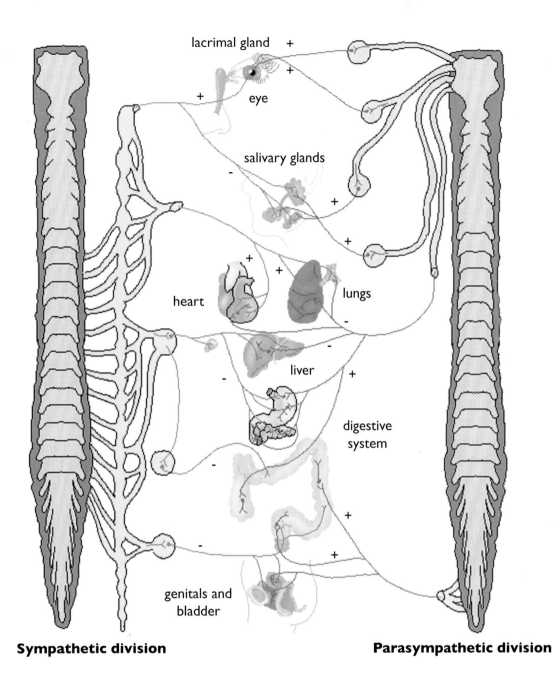

lacrimal gland   +
+
eye
+
salivary glands
-
+
+
+
heart   +
lungs
-
-
liver   +
digestive
system
+
+
genitals and
bladder

Sympathetic division   **Parasympathetic division**

MOD 9

FIGURE 9.2
The Sympathetic and Parasympathetic Divisions of the ANS
Illustration by Megan Whitaker

Another easy way to distinguish between the divisions is to notice where the preganglionic neuron cell bodies are housed. All of the preganglionic neurons originate in the CNS; however, the nerves of the sympathetic division come from the thoracic and lumbar regions of the spinal cord, while those of the parasympathetic division are found in the brain stem and the sacral regions of the spinal cord. Since the neurons originate in different parts of the body, it is not surprising that they are found in different parts of the body, as well. Sympathetic nerves can be found all over the body, while parasympathetic nerves are located in your head and trunk only.

Now that you know the anatomical differences between the sympathetic and parasympathetic divisions of the ANS, it is time to discuss the functions of these two systems. Remember, these systems function without conscious thought. They unconsciously regulate and control many processes that occur in the body. The sympathetic system controls certain body functions that the parasympathetic system does not control at all. There are many bodily functions that both divisions control. In those instances, the two divisions usually produce opposite effects.

Consider, for example, control of the heart. The neurons of the sympathetic division send action potentials, which increase the rate and force at which the cardiac muscle contracts. This, of course, increases heart rate and the strength of the heart's contraction. On the other hand, the nerves of the parasympathetic division send action potentials that slow the rate at which the cardiac muscle contracts. This may seem confusing, so let's restate it. *More* action potentials running along parasympathetic nerves to the heart *inhibit* the rate at which the heart beats. This, of course, slows the heart rate. In the heart, then, we see the two divisions of the ANS working opposite of one another. When you need increased blood flow in order to supply your body with a lot of energy, the sympathetic division kicks in, increasing the heart rate. When that increased blood flow is no longer needed, the parasympathetic division sends action potentials to decrease the heart rate. Right now, assuming you are sitting and reading, you have high parasympathetic activity (meaning many action potentials) to your heart. That's why it is beating at a slow rate.

Another example of the balancing relationship between the two divisions of the ANS can be found in the lungs. The lungs are filled with tubes called bronchial (bron kee' uhl) tubes. The sympathetic division of the ANS sends action potentials that cause these tubes to dilate. This means that they widen in diameter. What will that do? It will let more air flow into the lungs. If your body needs to take in more air in order to supply tissues with more oxygen, the sympathetic division of the ANS takes over, dilating the bronchial tubes in your lungs. However, if you do not need to take in as much air, the parasympathetic division sends action potentials to the lungs that cause the bronchial tubes to constrict. This decreases the amount of air intake.

In these two cases, the sympathetic division tends to excite the system it innervates, while the parasympathetic system tends to relax the system it innervates. After all, the sympathetic division increases heart rate and airflow while the parasympathetic division decreases heart rate and airflow. In the digestive system, we see exactly the opposite trend. The sympathetic system slows the activity in the digestive system. When it is active, digestive juices are not secreted, the digestive organs do not push digesting food along, and the blood flow to the digestive organs decreases. The parasympathetic division, on the other hand, increases secretion and movements of the digestive system. For example, the salivary glands are stimulated by the parasympathetic division to secrete more saliva, while the sympathetic division inhibits the secretion of saliva. Can you see why people talk about having a dry mouth when they get nervous? Which division predominates when you are really nervous?

Two more important functions in which the sympathetic and parasympathetic divisions work oppositely are vision and urination. The sympathetic division stimulates dilation of the pupil of the eye in order to let more light in, while the parasympathetic division stimulates contraction of the pupil to reduce the amount of light that enters the eye. The sympathetic division also relaxes the muscle that controls the eye's lens, allowing you to see things that are far away. The parasympathetic division, however, contracts that muscle so that the lens becomes more round and allows you to see things up close. Finally, the parasympathetic division contracts the bladder in urination, while the sympathetic division relaxes the bladder. The parasympathetic and sympathetic divisions also play a role in the control of the genitals for reproduction. We will discuss that in a later module.

Those are the major functions in which the sympathetic and parasympathetic divisions oppose each other. The organs and muscles that control these functions, then, must be innervated with neurons from each division. So, the eye contains both parasympathetic nerves and sympathetic nerves, as do the heart, the bladder, the lungs, and many parts of the digestive system. Note that all of these are either in the head or trunk. That is because parasympathetic nerves can only be found in the head and trunk.

As we mentioned previously, however, there are many functions that are regulated by only one of the two ANS divisions. The structures that control these functions, then, are innervated by only one division or the other. The lacrimal glands in the eyes, for example, are controlled only by the parasympathetic division. These glands produce tears. Now please realize that your lacrimal glands are always producing some tears. They bathe the eye to keep it moist and disinfected. These tears are normally drained away through a canal near the eye so that you never notice them. When you cry, your lacrimal glands are just producing more tears than can be drained away, so the tears run out of the eyes and onto the skin.

The sympathetic division of the ANS controls many functions not controlled by the parasympathetic division. The sympathetic division, for example, innervates blood vessels all over the body. It constricts the blood vessels in the abdominal organs, allowing the blood to flow more freely to the tissues that need extra nutrients and oxygen. As we mentioned previously, it also stimulates the liver to increase the amount of glucose released into the blood. This provides the body with quick energy. It also constricts blood vessels in the skin and contracts the arrector pili muscles. As discussed in module 3, this causes the hair on your skin to stand up, making goose bumps.

The sympathetic division of the nervous system also gives us a glimpse into one of the few positive-feedback systems in the body. Remember from module 1 that your body is controlled mainly by negative-feedback systems, which regulate homeostasis. If a body variable gets too high, the negative-feedback system will stimulate functions that lower the value of the variable. In the same way, if the body variable gets too low, the negative-feedback system will stimulate functions that will increase the value of the variable. This is the normal type of feedback that controls the body.

The sympathetic division, however, operates one of the body's positive feedback systems. It can stimulate the adrenal glands, which are located atop each kidney, to produce and secrete epinephrine and norepinephrine, which are hormones. Epinephrine in the blood causes the liver to release more glucose into the bloodstream and constricts the blood vessels in the abdominal organs. Epinephrine and norepinephrine in the blood cause the heart rate to increase. Now, notice that these are all effects that the sympathetic division *directly creates,* as well. As we already mentioned, the sympathetic division innervates the liver so it can control the release of glucose into the blood. It also innervates the blood vessels in the abdominal organs to make them constrict, and it innervates the cardiac muscle to increase the heart rate. Why, then, does it cause the adrenal medulla to release hormones that cause the same effect?

This is another example of the incredible design that you see again and again in the body. The sympathetic division can cause these changes quickly by directly activating nerves, which arouse the body for sudden activity. However, it can also *prolong* the effect by releasing sympathetic hormones into the bloodstream. This is a slightly longer-term control, however, because it takes time for the hormones to get into the bloodstream and then be transported to the organs that they affect.

Take, for example, the heart rate. If the body needs to increase the heart rate, the sympathetic division of the ANS directly controls the cardiac muscle so that it happens quickly. To prolong the effect, however, it also stimulates the adrenal medulla to release the two hormones mentioned above. This causes the heart rate to increase *even more*. In other words, it is a positive feedback. A body variable (the heart rate) is increased, and then, because of the same system creating that increase, it is increased again.

As mentioned in module 1, however, positive-feedback systems cannot go on forever. After all, if the heart rate just keeps increasing, the heart will simply not be able to function at some point. So, this positive-feedback system must turn off. It turns off when the sympathetic division of the ANS stops stimulating the heart and adrenal medulla. However, because the two adrenal hormones (epinephrine and norepinephrine) are still in the bloodstream when the sympathetic system turns off, the heart rate is still increased for a while. The heart rate eventually goes back to normal, however, because the hormones are quickly taken up by body tissues and either metabolized or excreted. Of course, the term quickly needs to be defined. In general, the lifetime of these two hormones in the blood stream is on the order of a few minutes. So, the release of these two hormones causes a short-lived, positive-feedback mechanism.

Now, if you think about all of the functions that are controlled by this system, you will see that, in general, the sympathetic division is associated with those functions that are related to increased overall activity in the body. After all, increased heart rate, increased levels of glucose in the blood, and dilated bronchial tubes in the lungs are all associated with activity. In addition, the sympathetic division tends to "turn down" those functions of the body not associated with activity, such as digestion. This allows the body to use its resources for physical activity. On the other hand, the parasympathetic division is generally associated with those functions that are related to body rest. At rest, for example, your heart rate is low, the level of glucose in the blood is not as high as it is when you are active, and you tend to devote your efforts to "housekeeping" activities such as digestion and urination. In addition, some responses of the reproductive systems are regulated by the parasympathetic division of the ANS.

COLORING BOOK EXERCISE 9.1

To review the structures controlled by the two divisions of the ANS, follow the instructions on pages 149-151 of the coloring book.

ON YOUR OWN

9.2 One other way to distinguish between the parasympathetic and sympathetic division is by the location of the autonomic ganglia. In one division, the autonomic ganglia are close to the spinal cord, while in the other they are close to the effector. In which division are the autonomic ganglia close to the spinal cord?

9.3 A neuroscientist is studying an autonomic nervous system pathway that extends from the spinal cord to the little finger. Is the ganglion of this pathway nearer to the finger or the spinal cord?

CONTROL OF THE AUTONOMIC NERVOUS SYSTEM

Now that you know the major structures controlled by the ANS, you might wonder about what actually controls the ANS itself. The sympathetic division, for example, can increase the heart rate, and the parasympathetic division can decrease the heart rate. But what controls whether the parasympathetic division or sympathetic division is in control of the heart? The answer to that question begins with a discussion of the autonomic reflexes.

You have already learned about reflex arcs. They control reflexes in the skeletal muscles, for example. How do they work? An afferent neuron sends sensory information to an association neuron. If need be, the association neuron sends a signal to an efferent neuron, which causes a skeletal muscle to contract. Autonomic reflexes work in much the same way. A sensory neuron sends information to an association neuron. The association neuron then interprets the information. If something needs to be done, the association neuron then initiates a signal in either the sympathetic or parasympathetic division, depending on what exactly needs to happen. Figure 9.3 gives you a specific example of how this works. Do keep in mind that the sensory neuron and the association neurons are not part of the ANS. Only the efferent neurons, sympathetic or parasympathetic, are part of the ANS.

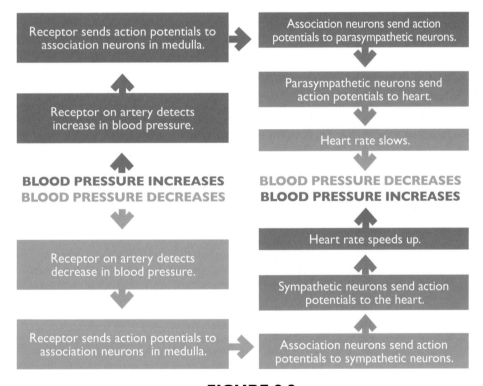

FIGURE 9.3
Autonomic Reflex

Consider blood pressure. If the blood pressure gets too high, it must be lowered. On the other hand, if it gets too low, it must be raised. In the body, there are receptors in the large arteries near the heart. These receptors detect changes in the blood pressure and send that information to the medulla oblongata of the brain. If the information indicates that the blood pressure has increased, association neurons in the medulla activate para-sympathetic neurons. Those neurons then send action potentials to the heart, slowing the heart rate. The result is that the blood pressure decreases. If, on the other hand, the receptors detect a decrease in the blood pressure, the association neurons in the medulla activate other association neurons, which in turn activate the sympathetic division nerves (which originate in the spinal cord), and the heart rate goes up, increasing blood pressure. That is an autonomic reflex.

Of course, there is actually more to it than that. Remember, the human body is an elegantly designed organic machine. You would expect any system in that machine to be backed up by other systems that not only operate as a fail-safe mechanism, but also aid in the efficiency of the overall process. That is certainly the case in terms of blood pressure. In addition to the negative-feedback system discussed above, there are also sympathetic nerves that innervate blood vessels throughout the body. They send a steady stream of action potentials to these blood vessels, keeping them partially constricted. This increases blood pressure. If the body needs to decrease the blood pressure, the sympathetic nerves reduce the frequency of the action potentials, and the blood vessels dilate. If the body needs to raise blood pressure, the frequency of action potentials is increased, and the blood vessels constrict.

The control centers for the autonomic reflexes are concentrated in several regions of the CNS, including the medulla oblongata, the spinal cord, and the hypothalamus. These reflexes are influenced not only by the sensory neurons that bring information to the association neurons in the reflex, but also by other parts of the CNS. Consider, for example, the limbic system in the brain. Remember, the limbic system contains information regarding emotions, such as fear. If you see something that your limbic system associates with fear, it will stimulate the sympathetic division of the ANS to increase your heart rate, release glucose into the bloodstream, and activate the adrenal glands. This makes your body instantly ready for action so that you can either confront the source of the fear or run. This is the fight-or-flight response.

ON YOUR OWN

9.4 Sensory receptors in your eye detect a foreign object that is irritating the eye. An autonomic reflex is initiated that produces tears which wash the object out of the eye. Does this reflex activate sympathetic division nerves or parasympathetic division nerves?

THE AFFERENT DIVISION OF THE PERIPHERAL NERVOUS SYSTEM

Up to this point you have learned about each major division of the nervous system except for the afferent division. In module 8, you learned about the CNS. In module 5, you learned about the somatic motor nervous system, which is the branch of the PNS efferent division that innervates skeletal muscle. Finally, in this module, you learned about the autonomic nervous system, which is the other branch of the PNS efferent division. The only division left to learn about, then, is the afferent division of the PNS. The afferent division of the PNS, as you learned in module 7, sends action potentials from the sensory receptors of the body to the PNS. It can also be called the sensory division of the PNS.

In studying the afferent division of the PNS, then, it's good to start with the definition of a sensory receptor.

Sensory receptor—An organ that responds to a specific type of stimulus by triggering an action potential on a sensory neuron

The cochlea of the ear, for example, is a sensory receptor. It responds to vibrations (sound) by triggering action potentials on a cranial nerve. As you might imagine, there are an enormous number of sensory receptors throughout the body, so we need to classify them in some way in order to make some sense out of them.

The first classification system is based on location. There are three ways we can classify receptors based on location.

Somatic receptors—Sensory receptors in the skin, muscle, and tendons

Visceral receptors—Sensory receptors in the internal organs

Special receptors—Sensory receptors in specific locations

The term somatic refers to the body. The somatic receptors are on or near the surface of the body, in the skin, muscles, and tendons. Visceral (vis' uh ruhl) receptors are located in viscera, which is a Latin term meaning "internal organs." You don't think of having sensory receptors on your organs, but they are there. Although you don't normally feel anything from your kidneys, if you are unfortunate enough to have a kidney stone, you *will* realize that the kidneys have pain receptors! Many of our internal organs, if not most, are endowed *only* with pain receptors. Some also have pressure receptors. For example, our sense of blood pressure comes from such receptors. We don't feel this sense consciously, but nevertheless, it is there. The sense of a full bladder is a pressure sensation, and (fortunately) it is conscious. Special receptors have specific locations. Of the five senses you learned about when you were in grade school (touch, taste, smell, hearing, vision), all but touch are mediated by special sensory receptors. The sense of touch is mediated not by special receptors, but rather by the somatic receptors.

Location is not the only means by which we can classify receptors. We can also classify the sensory receptors by their type: what they respond to. After all, in order to trigger an action potential, a sensory receptor must respond to some energy source.

Mechanoreceptors—Sensory receptors that respond to movement, whether it is light touch, vibration, or pressure

Thermoreceptors—Sensory receptors that respond to heat or cold

Photoreceptors—Sensory receptors that respond to light

Chemoreceptors—Sensory receptors that respond to chemicals

Nociceptors—Sensory receptors that respond to several types of excess stimulation, which is termed pain

Mechanoreceptors respond to movement. How do you know when a mosquito lands on your skin? Because when it lands, it causes movement of very delicate superficial touch receptors. The sense of hearing is also governed by mechanoreceptors, because sound is caused by vibrations (movement) in the air. This ultimately causes vibration of hair cells, which are located in the fluid-filled cochlea of the inner ear.

Thermoreceptors respond to heat or cold. Heat receptors increase the frequency of action potentials as they get warmer. Cold receptors, on the other hand, increase the rate of action potentials as they get colder. These receptors are generally located on the surface of the body, and there are many more cold receptors than heat receptors.

Photoreceptors, of course, respond to light. There is only one place you find these receptors—in the retina of the eye.

Chemoreceptors respond to chemicals. Frogs have chemoreceptors over most of the undersurface of their body so they can "taste" the water they are in. You do not taste with your skin. However, you do have chemoreceptors in several parts of your body. The sense of taste, for example, is provided by chemoreceptors. So is the sense of smell. There are also internal chemoreceptors of which you are not consciously aware, such as those that monitor pH and the level of oxygen in the blood.

Nociceptors (noh' see sep' ters) are pain receptors. Instead of responding to light, chemicals, heat, or movement, they respond to many intense types of stimuli. So, whether we get a chemical burn (too much of a chemical) or a pinch (too much movement) or a regular burn (too much heat), the nociceptors will respond. As you might expect, these receptors have a high threshold, meaning they are stimulated only by an intense stimulus.

There is one final way to classify receptors. We can classify them as simple or complex. This classification is a bit deceptive because even the simplest receptor is amazingly complex. However, some receptors are more complex than others, so we could also say that we can classify receptors as complex or very complex. However, the standard terminology is simple or complex, so we will go with that. Simple receptors are relatively small. As such, they can be distributed more widely over the body. The complex receptors are those that provide the five special senses. The five special senses are a bit different than those you probably learned when you were in grade school, because touch is not a special sense. It is distributed widely throughout the body. The five special senses, all of which are classified as complex, are taste, smell, hearing, balance, and vision.

So, that is how we classify receptors. Receptors, of course, are an important part of our senses, but they are not the only part. For example, let's imagine an individual who has severed their spinal cord at the level of the waist. Remember, those CNS neurons in the spinal cord cannot regenerate their axons. So, the spinal cord will not transmit signals from below the waist to the brain. Nevertheless, after a certain amount of healing goes on, it is possible that when you pinch that person's toe, he or she will pull the toe away from your fingers.

How can that happen? The reflex arc! Remember, in order to generate a reflex, the signal does not need to get to the brain. It simply needs to get to the spinal cord. So, as long as the spinal cord below the point at which it is severed is undamaged, the reflex arcs will still work. However, think about this: When you pinch that person's toe and get that withdrawal reflex, is he or she going to feel it? Is it going to hurt? The answer is *no*. If the signal cannot get to the brain, it will not be interpreted as pain. Nevertheless, as long as it can get to the spinal cord, it will generate a reflex.

If we are to be *aware* of a stimulus, then, there are certain requirements that must be met. To start with, we have to detect the stimulus from the environment. That takes a receptor that can respond to the stimulus. If you work in an environment where there may be radiation, you have to wear a badge that monitors that radiation so that you are not exposed to too much of it. Why? Because you do not have sensory receptors that respond to radiation. So, you are unaware of it. In other words, we do not have sensory receptors for everything. If we do not have a receptor that responds to a particular stimulus, then, we cannot be aware of it.

Not only must we have a receptor to respond to a stimulus, that stimulus must be equal to or greater than the receptor's threshold. For example, think about mosquitoes. You can feel some mosquitoes when they land on you. Those usually don't last very long because you slap them before they bite you. However, have you ever gotten an itchy lump from a mosquito bite and wondered when you got it? You never felt a mosquito, but nevertheless, one obviously bit you. Why? It was a sneak attack mosquito that did not trigger your receptors. The touch stimulus of the mosquito was *subthreshold*!

To be aware of a stimulus, then, we must first have a receptor that is stimulated at or above its threshold. The receptor will then cause action potentials to be generated in the afferent neuron in the PNS that is associated with the receptor. The action potentials will be conducted without decrease to the synapse within the CNS, which will trigger action potentials on an association neuron. That neuron synapses with an association neuron that will then send the action potentials on to several other neurons. Action potentials will be sent to the brain via afferent association neurons. The action potentials will then be interpreted in the brain, and at that point, we become aware of the stimulus. One of the points of interpretation, of course, is the strength of the stimulus. Remember from module 7 that action potentials are all-or-nothing. So, the nature of a single action potential is independent of the strength of the stimulus. Instead, a strong stimulus will cause a high rate of action potentials on the sensory neurons, while a weak stimulus will cause a low rate of action potentials.

Have you ever heard ringing in your ears when there is no sound? You probably get that when a stimulus *other than vibration* triggers the receptors in your ear. Perhaps you have an infection in your ear that is causing pressure. The pressure might cause your receptors to generate action potentials. However, sound is the **appropriate stimulus** for the receptors of hearing. Even though a large amount of pressure can generate action potentials in

think about this

Take a moment to receive all of the sensory input you can in about 30 seconds. Were there any sounds in the background of which you were not aware until you focused? Did you notice something that you had not seen earlier? Your sensory responses change to suit your environment. When you are quietly studying, you are mostly aware of your textbook. If you were sitting near a lake and contemplating nature, you would be more aware of the surrounding noises and objects. Your body was designed to adapt to its surroundings. There are times when concentration is essential, just as there are times when it is critical to be aware of your total surroundings and the dangers that may be present.

those receptors, that stimulus is inappropriate. Those actions potentials will go to the brain, but the brain will not interpret them as pressure, since nerves from the ear send action potentials to the auditory cortex. Instead, the brain will interpret them as sound, such as ringing or clanging. The same thing can happen to other receptors as well. If you hit your head hard enough to see stars, the intense motion triggered action potentials on your nerves for vision. However, since movement is not the appropriate stimulus for the neurons associated with vision, your brain does not interpret the signals as motion. Instead, it interprets them as light, and you see little points of light that are not really there.

Normally, the cerebral cortex accurately interprets the signals from our receptors. If the stimulus of the receptors is appropriate, the brain interprets the signals as something reasonable. However, if the stimulus is not appropriate, the brain still interprets the signal, and the result is not reasonable (a ringing in the ears when there is really no sound, for example). It turns out that the cerebral cortex also has other roles to play in interpreting those signals. For example, the cerebral cortex can tell us *where* a stimulus occurs. This is called projection. When a bee stings you, you know exactly where the sting occurred because of projection.

The cerebral cortex also determines the modality of the stimulus. What does that mean? Remember when we were classifying receptors according to their type? There were mechanoreceptors, thermoreceptors, and so forth. Each of those kinds of receptors responds to a different kind of stimulus. Your brain determines which kind of receptor is sending signals so it can determine what kind of stimulus caused the action potentials. That is called modality. How is that accomplished in the cerebral cortex? Well, there are thin layers in the cerebral cortex, and each layer is stimulated by a different kind of receptor. The mechanoreceptors stimulate one layer of neurons; the thermoreceptors stimulate another layer, and so forth. So, the brain interprets the modality of the signal by the layer of the cortex that is stimulated.

Before we move on to a discussion of the senses, there is one more thing that you need to know about receptors. Receptors can adapt. That is good because if receptors did not adapt, we would be overloaded with information. Adaptation means that the receptor physically stops responding or slows its response, even if the stimulus remains constant. There are many examples of this. For example, are you wearing a wristwatch right now? To answer that question, you might have to look and see. Sometimes you might try to look at your watch, not realizing that you forgot to put it on. Why? The pressure of that band or the touch of that band is there all day long. However, the mechanoreceptors in your skin do not respond now the same way that they did the first time you put it on in the morning. They decrease their response to the constant stimulus. As a little time goes on, you no longer feel your watch.

Here is another example. Imagine jumping into a swimming pool on a hot summer day. At first, the water feels cold and uncomfortable. In a few moments, however, you get used to it, and the water is actually very pleasant. That is adaptation. The water temperature did not change. Instead, thermoreceptors for cold stopped responding or slowed their response to the temperature of the water. Adaptation of the sense of smell can be almost complete. Have you ever walked into a room with an odd smell, but in a few moments, you no longer noticed the smell? It is not that you forgot about the funny smell, and it is not that the smell went away. Instead, the chemoreceptors in your nose stopped responding to the smell, and as a result, you no longer smell it.

The amount of adaptation in a receptor and the speed at which it occurs vary depending on the kind of receptor. For example, pain receptors adapt very slowly. Pain is a message that protects us. The pain receptors were designed to make you aware of pain for a long, long time. After all, if you could leave your hand on a hot stove and allow the pain receptors to adapt, you would soon have no skin on your hand! In order to protect us, the pain receptors are slow at adapting.

THE GENERAL SENSES

We have been talking about the senses in general, but now we want to talk about the general senses. That's is a strange statement, isn't it? Well, to a person who knows the nervous system, it makes perfect sense. When we say the general senses, we mean something very specific. We are referring to the senses that are located in the skin, skeletal muscles, and tendons. In other words, we are talking about the somatic senses.

There are two types of somatic receptors: cutaneous (kyou tay' nee ous) receptors and proprioceptors (proh' pree oh sep' ters).

Cutaneous receptors—
Receptors in the skin

Proprioceptors—Receptors in the skeletal muscles and tendons

ON YOUR OWN

9.5 A sensory receptor on a blood vessel within the kidney is stimulated when the blood vessel stretches. Is this a somatic, visceral, or special receptor? Is it a mechanoreceptor, thermoreceptor, photoreceptor, chemoreceptor, or nociceptor?
9.6 A doctor is trying to determine whether or not a patient's lower spinal cord has been severed. The doctor pokes the patient's foot with a pin, and the patient jerks his foot away. What question should the doctor ask to see whether or not the spinal cord has been severed?
9.7 You feel a sharp pain from stepping on a tack. What type of receptor was stimulated? What did the cerebral cortex's projection tell you about the stimulus? What did the cerebral cortex's determination of modality tell you about the stimulus?

Let's start our discussion with the cutaneous receptors. Figure 9.4 is an illustration of the skin and the many types of receptors that we can find therein.

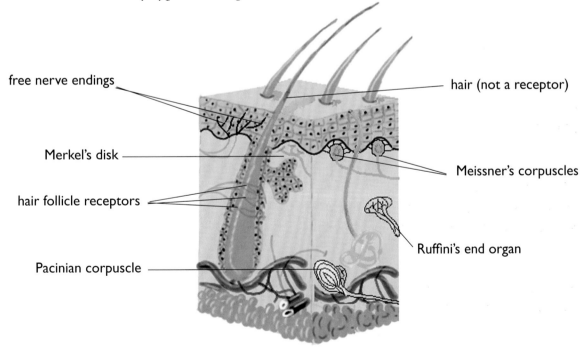

FIGURE 9.4
Cutaneous Receptors
Illustration by Megan Whitaker

The simplest and most common receptors are free nerve endings. In these receptors, neurons simply extend into the epidermis and branch out until they end. Free nerve endings are the type of receptors we have for heat, cold, itch, and pain. They can be either superficial or deep in the skin. There are different free nerve endings for each modality.

There are also hair follicle receptors in the skin. Remember from module 3 that the hair follicle is epidermal tissue that goes deep into the dermis. The hair growing out of the follicle is wrapped in a receptor, which is similar to a coiled free nerve ending. As a result, when you wiggle the hair, it moves the hair follicle receptor, which triggers an action potential on its associated neuron. Have you ever wondered why you don't feel anything when you cut your hair, but you can feel something when the wind blows through your hair? That is why. The hair has no receptors, but the follicles do.

Deep in the dermis, we find Pacinian corpuscles. These receptors look like tiny onions innervated by a sensory neuron. Pushing on these receptors generates an action potential in the neuron, so these are pressure receptors. They react to pressure and vibration deep within the dermis. Ruffini's end organs are also found in the deeper part of the dermis. They respond to both pressure on the skin and stretching of the skin. These are typically the receptors involved in responding to continuous touch or pressure.

In the most superficial layers of the skin are Merkel's disks. These are light touch receptors. They look like tiny disks, and many of them are associated with the same sensory neuron. They are so sensitive that they can respond to skin that moves as little as 1/25,000th of an inch! Now, that is a really light touch!

Meissner's corpuscles are found throughout the dermal papillae (the bumps on the dermis). These receptors are involved in two-point discrimination. What do we mean by that? Perform the following experiment to find out.

Experiment 9.1
Two-Point Discrimination

Supplies:

- Two toothpicks, each pointed at least on one end
- A metric ruler
- A person, called your subject, to help you. He or she should wear shorts and a short-sleeved shirt.

Purpose: The density of receptors including Meissner's corpuscles helps determine how sensitive skin is to distinguishing two touches that are close to one another.

Procedure:

1. Hold the two toothpicks between your thumb and forefinger so that their tips are 0.5 cm apart.

2. Tell your subject that you are going to randomly poke him or her with either one toothpick or two. Assure your subject that you will not poke hard enough to cause pain (and don't!). Your subject should then tell you whether it feels like one poke or two distinct pokes.

3. Tell your subject to close his or her eyes.

4. Now you need to poke your subject in various places: the tips of the fingers, the palms, the backs of the hands, various parts of the arms, various parts of the legs, and the lower back (lift up the back of the shirt to do this). You should only poke bare skin, but be gentle. You want to create a touch sensation, not a pain sensation!

5. Poke some spots with one toothpick and some with two so that your subject does not catch on to what you are trying to find out. You can poke with one toothpick by just tilting your hand so that only one toothpick touches the skin. Vary the order in which you do it so that your subject will not recognize any pattern.

6. Ignore what your subject says when you poke with one toothpick, but pay attention when he or she says you are poking with two toothpicks. Record the parts of the body for which your subject correctly identified two pokes. In a separate section, record the body parts where you poked with two points, but the subject reported feeling only one.

7. Repeat the experiment, this time with the toothpicks 1.5 cm apart.

In the experiment, you should have found that on certain parts of the body, such as the fingers, your subject was able to distinguish between the two toothpicks, even when they were only 0.5 cm apart. In other parts of the body, like the legs, he or she was not able to distinguish. When you increased the distance, the number of places in which your helper could distinguish between the two toothpicks increased. Why? There are many more receptors in places like the fingers than in places like the legs. The ability to distinguish between touches that are close together (two-point discrimination) is therefore easier in the fingers than in the legs. The tongue has one of the highest concentrations of these receptors. It is very good at two-point discrimination. This is why even the tiniest irregularity in your teeth can be very annoying to your tongue!

Let's leave the cutaneous receptors, and consider the other type of somatic receptors, the proprioceptors. There are two basic types of proprioceptors, and both are shown in figure 9.5.

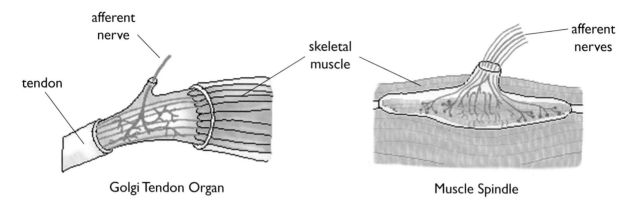

afferent nerve

skeletal muscle

afferent nerves

tendon

Golgi Tendon Organ

Muscle Spindle

FIGURE 9.5
Proprioceptors
Illustration by Megan Whitaker

A muscle spindle is a mechanoreceptor located within the skeletal muscle. This receptor responds to stretch. When we stretch the muscle, we stimulate the spindle. When is a muscle stretched? When it is relaxed and passively stretched out by gravity or by another muscle. So, this receptor lets us know when the muscle is relaxed. The Golgi tendon organ is found (you guessed it) in the tendon. This receptor responds to tension. When we pull or tighten up the tendon like pulling a rope tight, this receptor generates action potentials in its associated neuron. When do you tighten a tendon? When the muscle contracts. Golgi tendon organs tell you that a muscle is contracted. The action potentials from proprioceptors, then, send messages to our brain telling it how much a skeletal muscle is contracted or how much it is relaxed. That lets the brain know the status of a muscle at all times. Additionally, it provides us with the sense of body position. For example, without looking, can you sense whether your toes are flexed or extended right now? Of course you can! You may have considered that part of your cutaneous sense, but it is not; it is part of the sense of body position, also called proprioception.

ON YOUR OWN

9.8 Of the cutaneous receptors we discussed, which type are thermoreceptors? Which type are mechanoreceptors? Which type are nociceptors?

THE SENSE OF SMELL
Now that we have discussed the general senses, let's spend some time on the special senses. We will start with the sense of smell, which is called olfaction (ole fak' shun). Figure 9.6 is an illustration of the anatomy involved in olfaction.

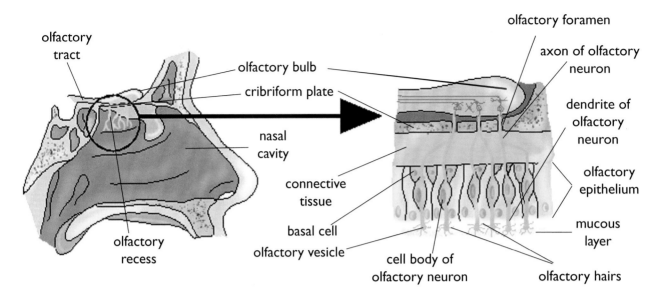

FIGURE 9.6
The Olfactory Recess and Epithelium
Illustration by Megan Whitaker

What we have here is a midsagittal view of the nasal cavity. Notice the position of the olfactory epithelium, where the receptors for the sense of smell reside. It is in the superior part of the nasal cavity. You do not have a sense of smell over your entire nose, then. It is only in the upper part of the nasal cavity, at the olfactory epithelium.

Now, what we really want to concentrate on is the magnified drawing on the right side of the figure. Both olfactory bulbs are directly superior to the cribriform plates, which are bones that protect the olfactory bulbs. Tiny holes in the cribriform plates, called olfactory foramina, allow the axons of the olfactory neurons to reach the olfactory bulb and synapse with association neurons there. At the other end of the olfactory neurons (the end that is exposed to the air in the nasal cavity), we have olfactory vesicles that end in olfactory hairs. If you look at the shape of the olfactory neurons, you will see that they are *bipolar*. There is one dendrite, and there is one axon. Notice also that the olfactory hairs are encased in a mucous layer. That becomes important in a moment.

Interestingly, the entire olfactory epithelium and all of the neurons are lost about every two months. This doesn't happen all at once, of course! You lose it a little bit at a time. The lost cells are replaced by the basal cells, which can even replace the olfactory neurons. This is a unique situation among neurons. You have learned that neurons are permanent cells that cannot be replaced. Olfactory neurons are the only exception to that rule!

Now that you know the anatomy, we can discuss the process of olfaction. Think about a rock. Does it have a smell? Probably not. However, if you paint the rock, then it might have a smell. The reason for this is simple: For a chemical to be smelled, it has to be airborne. If the rock does not deliver molecules that are airborne, we are not going to be able to smell it. A substance that can evaporate into a vapor so that it becomes airborne is called a volatile substance. So, we can only smell volatile substances.

Even though we can only smell volatile substances, there are some volatile substances we cannot smell. Why? Well, first, in order for us to smell a substance, the airborne molecules must reach the olfactory hairs. That cannot happen unless it can get through the mucous layer, which is watery. So, the substance must be somewhat water-soluble. In addition, the substance must also be somewhat lipid-soluble so that it can get through the plasma membrane.

Once the airborne substance reaches the olfactory hairs, there are receptor molecules in these hairs that will bind to the molecule. When that binding happens, a chemical reaction occurs, and, if enough of the reaction occurs, an action potential can be generated. Interestingly, this process is probably one of the least understood processes in human physiology. Once the action potential has been generated, it travels along the axon to the olfactory bulb. The axon synapses with specialized association neurons that can modify the information and send it on to the brain.

As we just mentioned, the whole process of how an airborne molecule binds to a receptor molecule on an olfactory hair and generates an action potential is still poorly understood. In the past, scientists thought that there were seven different primary sensations. That is, we thought there were perhaps seven different basic receptor molecules that would bind to the airborne molecules. Those seven receptors would each initiate some level of response, and all of the various smells that we can smell are just a combination of the intensity of those seven basic responses.

This thought is being replaced with new information that indicates that there may be as many as fifty primary sensations and, therefore, fifty different receptors, which bind to various airborne molecules. The smell, then, is the result of combining as many as fifty primary sensations rather than just seven. That is not an established fact yet, but new research is pointing in that direction.

think about this

If your sense of smell is so sensitive, why does it seem so poor compared to that of many mammals, especially dogs? The acute sense of smell of dogs has more to do with their slower adaptation of the olfactory sense compared with ours. We humans just might be able to recognize the smell of the clothing that is used to get a bloodhound to search for a particular person, but our awareness of that smell would soon adapt out. In addition, we humans prefer our sense of vision and hearing and touch for detailed recognition of the world around us, whereas for many breeds of dog, odor is a primary means of recognizing what is important to them. Our brains process olfactory information differently than do the brains of dogs.

We do know that the threshold for smell is very low. Now, what does that mean? If the threshold of a sense is low, that means it doesn't take much stimulation to trigger an action potential. So, that means we can smell things even when they are at a very, very low concentration in the air. Of course, as we recently mentioned, our olfactory receptors adapt rather quickly. So, after the olfactory hairs have been stimulated constantly for a short period of time, the action potentials are not sent anymore.

One of the best ways to illustrate how our sense of smell works is to discuss methane, which is the natural gas we burn in gas stoves, gas water heaters, and gas furnaces. Methane is odorless, which just means that it does not bind to our olfactory hairs to create an action potential. So, we cannot smell it because our olfactory system is not designed to detect it. However, since methane is explosive under the right conditions, it would be dangerous to use the gas if there were no way to detect leaks in natural gas appliances.

Gas companies deliberately add methyl mercaptan to natural gas. It is a chemical to which our olfactory hairs *do* bind. The smell is very distinctive, so it is easy to recognize.

Our sense of smell is so sensitive to this chemical, in fact, that we can detect the odor of about 4×10^{-11} grams of the chemical! Our sense of smell is *very* sensitive to the substances with which our olfactory hairs can bind. However, it is completely insensitive to many substances to which our olfactory hairs do not bind.

ON YOUR OWN

9.9 We often smell things without even trying. However, sometimes we have sniff to smell something. (Sniffing refers to shallow, rapid inhalation through the nose.) Why does sniffing help us smell things that we otherwise would not smell?

THE SENSE OF TASTE

Moving on to the sense of taste (called the gustatory sense), we want to start with the anatomy of the "taste organ," which is, of course, the tongue.

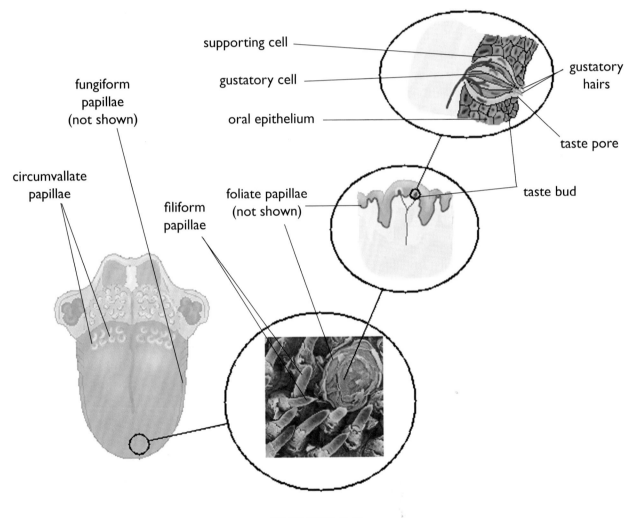

FIGURE 9.7

The Tongue

Illustration by Megan Whitaker | Photo © Phototake/Dennis Kunkel

The surface of the tongue is full of tiny bumps called papillae. If a cat has ever licked you, you have felt the cat's rough tongue papillae. The papillae on a human tongue, of course, are not as pronounced. However, they definitely exist. As you are almost

MOD 9

certainly already aware, the human tongue is also full of taste buds. How many taste buds do we have? Probably about ten thousand. Most of these taste buds are associated with papillae. Although taste buds are concentrated on the tongue, they can be found elsewhere. Especially in children, there are a few taste buds on the palate, the lips, and even the pharynx (throat).

As you can see from figure 9.7, there are at least four distinct forms of papillae on the tongue, the most numerous of which are the filiform papillae. Interestingly, these papillae do not have taste buds. The other three, however, do. Circumvallate papillae are the largest but least numerous of all papillae on the tongue. They are concentrated near the back of the tongue, as shown in the figure. Fungiform papillae, on the other hand, are distributed irregularly over the entire upper surface of the tongue. Finally, the foliate papillae are located on the sides of the tongue. Of these three types of papillae that have taste buds associated with them, the foliate papillae contain the most sensitive of the taste buds.

Now look at the structure of a taste bud (lower right-hand portion of the figure). You can see by this drawing why we call it a taste bud. It really looks like a tiny bud of a flower. In the bud, there are two types of cells, the gustatory cells and the supporting cells. The supporting cells form the bud shape. Notice that the bud has an opening in it called a taste pore. Projecting out of that hole is the actual receptor portion, called gustatory hairs. Notice the nerve fibers of the afferent neurons. Unlike the olfactory receptors, the gustatory receptors do not directly generate action potentials. Instead, they release neurotransmitters when stimulated. Those neurotransmitters then generate action potentials on the afferent nerves shown in the figure. This is the most common kind of receptor. Most receptors do not generate action potentials on their own. Instead, they release a neurotransmitter, which stimulates an action potential on an associated afferent nerve.

Now that you know the basic anatomy of a taste bud, you need to know how it all works. In order for our taste buds to function, the food we are eating must first be dissolved in our saliva. The saliva then enters into the taste pore. Chemicals dissolved in the saliva then bind to chemical receptors in the gustatory hairs, and the gustatory cell releases a neurotransmitter, which stimulates an action potential on the afferent nerve.

You may have learned in the past that there are four sensations of taste. In fact, in the past few years a fifth sensation has been discovered. Our ability to discriminate different foods depends on the combination of these five sensations, as well as on our sense of smell. If we can't smell the food, we can't always identify it adequately or taste it as well as when we can smell it.

The five taste sensations are sweet, salty, sour, bitter, and umami, which is the Japanese word for "savory." While the first four are self-explanatory, umami refers to the taste of amino acids, and so can be thought of as the taste of meat. Any taste bud can (at least in theory) respond to all five of these tastes, but a given taste bud usually will respond to one better than the others. So, as a practical matter, we say that there are taste buds for sweet; taste buds for sour, which are stimulated by acid (H^+ ions); taste buds for bitter; taste buds for salt; and taste buds for umami.

Adaptation of the taste receptors is generally rather fast. So, the intensity of a taste will be reduced after the first few bites. Taste intensity is also affected by temperature. The warmer something is, the better you can taste it, as long as it is not so hot that the pain receptors take over! The colder a substance is, the slower the taste bud can generate action potentials on the associated neuron, so the less intense the taste. That's why ice cream cones can be disappointing.

THE SENSE OF BALANCE

Although we rarely think about it, our sense of balance is incredibly important. When we stand, bend over to pick up a book, or lean against the wall, our muscles must make very complex adjustments in order to keep us from falling over. Those adjustments are made based on our sense of balance, which is located in our inner ear.

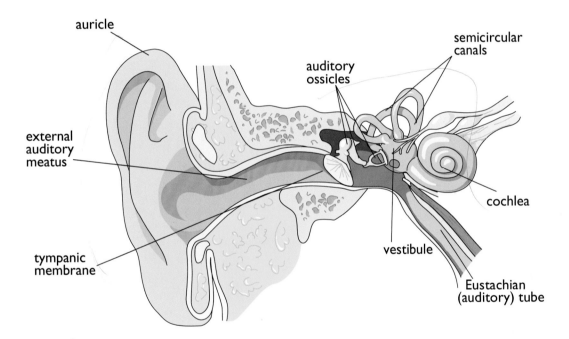

FIGURE 9.8
The Anatomy of the Ear
Illustration by LifeArt

The entire ear is composed of three components: the external ear, the middle ear, and the inner ear. The external ear extends from outside the body to the tympanic (tim pan' ik) membrane, which is also called the eardrum. The outer shape of the ear is formed by the auricle (aw' ri kuhl), and the external auditory meatus (mee aye' tus) is the canal that leads from the outside to the eardrum. The middle ear is a tiny, air-filled space right beyond the tympanic membrane. It contains the auditory ossicles, which you will learn about in the next section.

In this section, we will concentrate on the inner ear. The structure of the inner ear is carved out in minute and beautiful detail from the temporal bone, and it is all fluid filled.

The inner ear is divided into three regions: the vestibule (ves' tih buhl), the semicircular canals, and the cochlea (kok' lee uh). The cochlea is about the size of a sesame seed and consists of a set of narrow channels, or tubes, coiled in the shape of a spiral. Uncoiled, the entire structure would measure only about three centimeters long. Now remember, all of the inner ear is carved out of bone. When we talk about uncoiling the cochlea, we are really talking about unwinding the *epithelium* that lines the cochlea.

Now that you know the basic anatomy of the ear, we can discuss the sense of balance. Actually, the sense of balance is composed of two different senses: static equilibrium and dynamic equilibrium. These senses are related, but distinct anatomically and functionally.

Static equilibrium—determines the orientation of the head relative to the pull of gravity. In other words, it helps the body determine whether the head is being held up straight, bowed, leaned to one side, and so forth.

Dynamic equilibrium—helps determine the rotation and acceleration of the head. This allows us to maintain balance as we move.

Let's start with static equilibrium. The sense of static equilibrium takes place in the vestibule of the inner ear, as shown in figure 9.9.

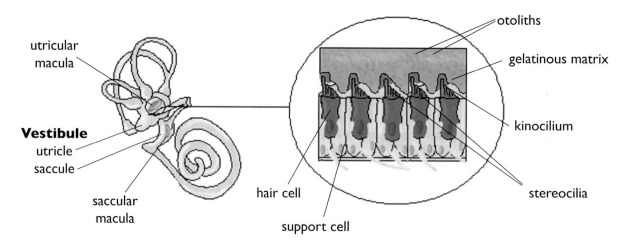

FIGURE 9.9
The Macula in the Vestibule of the Inner Ear
Illustration by Megan Whitaker

In the vestibule, we find the saccule (sak' youl), which means "little sac," and the utricle (you' trih kuhl), which means "little bag." Both the saccule and the utricle contain a patch known as the macula (mak' you luh), which in Latin means "spot." The macula in the utricle is oriented parallel to the base of the skull, while the macula in the saccule is oriented perpendicular to the base of the skull. The different orientations of the macula allow us to determine the position of our head relative to gravity. How? We're getting to that.

If we magnify the macula, we get what you see on the right-hand side of figure 9.9. The macula is made up of a gelatinous (juh lat' in us) matrix which has otoliths (oh' toh liths) suspended inside. What are otoliths? In Latin, the word otolith means "ear stone." Yes, we do, indeed, have rocks in our head! Those rocks are called otoliths, and they are suspended in the gel-like matrix of the macula. Buried within that gelatinous matrix, we also find hair cells that are supported by supporting cells. Attached to those hair cells are the associated sensory neurons. This whole complex (the support cells, the hair cells, the gelatin matrix, and the otoliths) is the macula. Now remember, macula means "spot." It is called a spot because it is small—on the order of just a couple of millimeters in diameter.

How does all of this give us our sense of static equilibrium? Look at the hair cells. Notice that there is one hair (cilium) that is longer than the others? That is called the kinocilium (kye noh sil' ee uhm). The other hairs (cilia) are called stereocilia. When the head moves, the heavy otoliths within the gelatinous matrix move, causing the stereocilia to move. If the stereocilia move toward the kinocilium, the hair cell causes an action potential to form on the sensory neuron. If the stereocilia move away from the kinocilium, the hair cell ceases to make action potentials on the sensory neuron.

Think about it, then. When the head is held still, there is a certain distribution of otoliths within the gelatinous matrix on the stereocilia. This produces a standing pattern of action potentials on the various neurons that make up the maculae (plural of macula) in both the saccule and the utricle. When the head moves, this causes the otoliths to shift, and a new pattern of action potentials is produced. Since one macula is oriented horizontal to the base of the skull and the other is oriented perpendicular to the base of the skull, and since all of this is happening in *both* inner ears, the movement of the otoliths and the corresponding change in the pattern of action potentials gives the brain the information it needs to determine the exact position of the head relative to gravity. That's our sense of static equilibrium.

Let's move onto the dynamic equilibrium. This sense is nearby, but it is not the same. You find your sense of dynamic equilibrium in the semicircular canals.

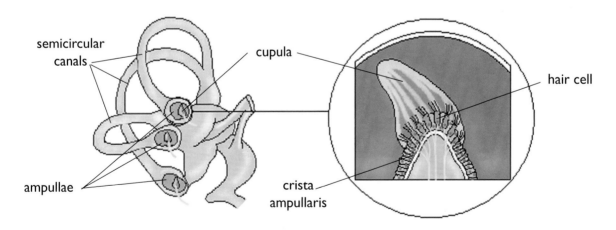

FIGURE 9.10
The Semicircular Canals and the Crista Ampullaris
Illustration by Megan Whitaker

The first thing to notice about figure 9.10 is the orientation of the semicircular canals. They are each laid out in a different plane, forming a three-dimensional X, Y, and Z grid, which you have probably studied in algebra. Now remember, the entire inner ear is filled with fluid. So, these canals are full of fluid as well. There are several bulges in the end of semicircular canals, which are called ampullae (amp' you lay), and they contain the receptors that gives us our sense of dynamic equilibrium.

This sense starts with a gelatinous cupula (coop' you luh) that acts like a float in the fluid of the inner ear. Although the cupula is gelatinous, it does not have otoliths in it. It bobs in the fluid, and when it is moved by the movement of the fluid, it will stimulate by its movement what we call the crista (kris' tuh) ampullaris (am pyou lar' us). In the crista ampullaris, we find hair cells that are embedded the cupula. Those hair cells respond to the motion of the cupula, creating action potentials on the associated sensory neurons.

This sense of dynamic equilibrium, then, does not tell you about the static position of the head. Instead, it responds to actual movements of the head. So, any movement that's big enough to get the fluid moving will trigger the hair cells in the crista ampullaris. As we turn our head, for example, the fluid in the inner ear moves, and that moves the cupula. This stimulates the hair cells, which will then stimulate action potentials in the sensory neurons. Those action potentials go to the balance center (the vestibular nucleus) in the medulla oblongata. From the medulla, information is sent to the cerebellum because, as you recall from the previous module, the cerebellum constantly adjusts our muscles so that we can keep our balance.

One of the best ways to understand how your sense of dynamic equilibrium works is to think about how you get dizzy. If you start to spin around and around, the fluid in the inner ear gets moving. When you stop, the fluid keeps flowing for a while because it has its own inertia. As it keeps flowing, it repeatedly moves the cupula, which stimulates the hair cells. Your dynamic sense of equilibrium tells your cerebellum that you are spinning. Meanwhile, the stimulation of the cupula and its hair cells initiates a reflex involving the eyes. This is how your eyes automatically "jump" ahead as you naturally turn so that you continue to see what's ahead of you. By over stimulating the hair cells within the semi-circular canals by spinning rapidly, you trigger that reflex. Even when you stop, the fluid flows, stimulating the feeling of movement. And as long as the fluid is moving rapidly, your eyes "jump ahead." That causes the room around you to seem to spin, both visually and through the sensation of movement. Little kids seem to enjoy this experience, and the little child's game of "Ring Around the Rosie" is based on it. "Ashes! Ashes! We all fall down" is a consequence of a rapid spin.

How did the dizziness result in the inability to walk? Well, the cerebellum wants to make adjustments for all of that spinning and visual input, but the cerebrum is telling the skeletal muscles to move forward. The result is summarized as "we all fall down."

This brings us to a final point about our wonderful sense of balance. To study it, we have separated it into its component parts, static and dynamic equilibrium. Yet the overall, integrated sense of balance depends also on our vision, our proprioceptors, and our cutaneous receptors. When a spinning dancer or ice skater spots, he or she focuses on a stationary object in the distance, turning his or her head at the last second and quickly refocusing on the object. The steady visual input helps prevent dizziness and loss of balance. Even under normal conditions, not spinning, your eyes orient you to your environment relative to gravity, greatly aiding your sense of balance. That's why the expression "Watch where you're going" is so common! Your proprioceptors additionally send the brain information about the contraction of your postural muscles. Try standing on one foot for a minute with your eyes closed, and you will feel the constant corrections that your muscles make to maintain your balance. The feel of the floor beneath your feet (cutaneous receptors) contributes information that the brain uses for balance. Another example of cutaneous receptors used to maintain balance is the use of a handrail while on a set of stairs. The handrail really isn't supporting you as your hand glides over it. Instead, the information from your cutaneous receptors in your palm and fingers provides extremely valuable information to your brain as to your vertical posture, helping you to maintain your balance. We've also heard, "Hold onto the railing" many times!

ON YOUR OWN

9.11 Space sickness is a disorder in the sense of balance experienced by astronauts who spend time in zero gravity. The disorder is the result of the brain not receiving the expected amount of sensory information from the inner ear. Would the disorder be the result of too much sensory information or too little sensory information getting to the brain?

THE SENSE OF HEARING

Although the inner ear is where we find the receptors for the sense of balance, the ear is best known for providing us with the sense of hearing, called the auditory sense. How does it work? Before we can answer that question, you need to know a bit about the physics of sound. Sound is really just a series of waves within a medium. The medium can be a solid, liquid, or gas, such as air. Sound waves travel through a medium by vibrating the material. Unlike light waves, which travel through a vacuum, sound cannot travel through a vacuum. They need to have some medium in which to vibrate.

Like any wave, sound waves have two fundamental qualities: amplitude and frequency. In sound waves, the amplitude determines the loudness of the sound. The bigger the waves, the louder the sound. The frequency of the sound waves determines the pitch. The higher the frequency, the higher the pitch. Although not a fundamental quality of sound waves, timbre (tam' ber) is nevertheless an important characteristic of a sound. We distinguish one person's voice from another person's voice based on timbre. You can tell the difference between the same melody played on a piano, guitar, or a French horn based on timbre. What is timbre? It's actually a very complex subject, but in brief, when we produce a sound, we do not just produce one frequency. For a given pitch, there is a fundamental frequency that determines the pitch, but there are other frequencies produced as well. The types of frequencies produced, along with the fundamental frequency and their relative loudness, combine together to form the timbre of a sound.

That's a brief description of sound. Now, how do we hear it? Sound waves, remember, are vibrations in the air. Those vibrations are collected in the auricle, the outer ear (see figure 9.8), and travel down the external auditory meatus to the tympanic membrane. The tympanic membrane then vibrates in response to the sound waves hitting it. So, the tympanic membrane converts the vibrations in the air to vibrations of itself.

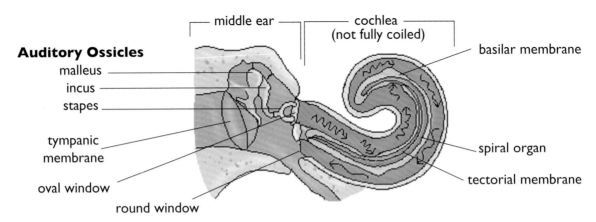

FIGURE 9.11
The Structures Related to Hearing
Illustration by Megan Whitaker

As is illustrated in figure 9.11, the malleus (mal' ee us) is attached to the tympanic membrane. When the tympanic membrane vibrates, the malleus vibrates as well. The malleus is connected to the incus (ing' kus), which is connected to the stapes (stay' peez). When the malleus vibrates, the incus and the stapes vibrate. The malleus, incus, and stapes collectively form the auditory ossicles, or ear bones. These three tiny bones concentrate sound energy from the tympanic membrane onto the flexible oval window. Why? It takes more force to vibrate an object in fluid than to vibrate it in air, right? The oval window is closed, and it has *air* on one side (the middle ear is filled with air) and *fluid* on the other side (the inner ear is filled with fluid).

The oval window leads to the cochlea. The organ of hearing, called the spiral organ (or organ of Corti), is coiled up, two and one-half turns within the cochlea. It is composed of sensory receptors for sound called hair cells and sits on the basilar membrane. The cochlea is filled with fluid. The gel-like tectorial (tek tor' ee uhl) membrane sits atop the spiral organ and touches hair cells of the spiral organ.

What happens to the vibration? Once the oval window vibrates, those vibrations cause the fluid in the cochlea to vibrate. So far, vibrations in the air were converted into vibrations of the tympanic membrane. Those vibrations were then converted into vibrations of the ear ossicles, which then were converted into vibrations of the fluid in the inner ear.

If the vibrations in the fluid within the cochlea are of high frequency and so are coming from a high-pitched sound, they cause a vibration in the basilar membrane at its base. In other words, the high-frequency vibrations disturb the basilar membrane near the oval window. This causes vibrations in the tectorial membrane. As the tectorial membrane vibrates, it brushes against the hair cells of the spiral organ. The movement of these hair cells at the base of the spiral organ then triggers action potentials in their associated sensory neurons.

think about this

Take a final look at figure 9.11. We have not mentioned the **round window,** but it has an essential role in the auditory sense. Fluid is incompressible, so when the oval window vibrates, in turn vibrating the fluid within the cochlea, something has to give. The round window, tiny but flexible, allows for that *give*. Our Creator pays attention to the smallest details!

If, on the other hand, the vibrations are of low frequency, they cause vibrations in the basilar membrane at the apex, or far end of the spiral organ. Once again, this triggers vibrations in the tectorial membrane, which touches the hair cells at the apex of the spiral organ. The movement of these hair cells triggers action potentials on their sensory neurons.

Do you see the beauty of this system? One of the two fundamental qualities of sound is frequency. The ear distinguishes frequency based on *where* the vibrations occur on the spiral organ. The higher the pitch of the sound (and so the higher the frequency of the sound waves), the closer to the oval window the basilar membrane will vibrate. The lower the pitch of the sound (and so the lower the frequency of the sound waves), the closer to the apex the basilar membrane will vibrate. Associated sensory neurons from near the oval window send action potentials that the auditory cortex of the brain interprets as high-pitched sound. Associated sensory neurons from hair cells at the apex (far end) of the spiral organ indicate low-pitched sounds when the auditory cortex receives them.

Of course, not only does the ear have to determine frequency, it must also determine volume. That's fairly easy. Remember, loudness is determined by the *amplitude* of the sound waves. Well, the bigger the amplitude of the sound wave, the bigger the amplitude of the vibrations in the tympanic membrane, the bigger the amplitude of the vibrations in the ossicles, the bigger the vibrations in the fluid of the cochlea. In the end, then, the location of the vibrations in the spiral organ determines the pitch, while the amplitude of the vibrations in the spiral organ determines the loudness of the sound. How? A big amplitude of vibrations triggers a high rate of action potential. The auditory cortex interprets the high rate of *action potentials* (not vibrations) as a loud sound.

THE SENSE OF VISION: EYE ANATOMY

We want to end this module with the sense of vision, and perhaps this wonder is best captured with a quote from Leonardo da Vinci:

"Who would believe that so small a space could contain the image of all the universe?"

COLORING BOOK EXERCISE 9.3

To review the senses of hearing and balance, follow the instructions on pages 167-173 of the coloring book.

ON YOUR OWN

9.12 The major structures involved in hearing are listed below. Order them in terms of when they vibrate. Start with the structures that vibrate first and end with those that vibrate last.

incus, oval window, tympanic membrane, spiral organ, fluid of cochlea, malleus, stapes

Think of some of the most breathtaking images you have ever seen. Your eyes impress upon your mind the miracles that surround you! They witness important events and deliver those events to your brain, where they will be cataloged and stored until your memory retrieves them. Your eyes are truly your windows to the world. Of all your senses, this is probably the most complex and most interesting.

Let's start with the anatomy of the eye. Before we talk about the eye itself, however, we should mention two structures that are designed to protect the eye. Since the eye is so complex and delicate, it needs special protection. The first layer of protection comes from the palpebrae (pal pee' bree), which are commonly known as the eyelids. The eyelids and their lashes protect the eye from foreign particles. They also aid in spreading tears, which is the second layer of protection we want to mention. The lacrimal (lak' rih muhl) glands produce tears, which moisten the eye and wash away foreign objects that make it past the eyelids and lashes. Tears also contain antibodies and an enzyme called lysozyme, which is antibacterial. Because of these two powerful disinfectants, the eye rarely gets infected. The lacrimal glands produce, on average, about one milliliter of tears each day. Under normal conditions, the tears are drained away into the nasal cavity via four ducts, one on each palpebra, called lacrimal canaliculi. You can see the openings called puncta by gently pulling your lower eyelid and looking medially for a dark "dot." There is another one on the upper eyelid. However, if you produce too many tears, they cannot be drained away quickly enough, and they spill out onto the skin. That, of course, is what we call crying.

There are two conditions under which we cry. If we have a foreign substance in our eyes, our eyes become irritated. In response, the lacrimal glands produce a large volume of tears, trying to wash the foreign substance out. So, when you slice onions or get a piece of dirt in your eye, you cry. However, we can also cry as a result of emotion. Amazingly enough, the tears that we cry when our eyes are irritated are chemically quite different from the tears we cry as a result of emotion!

Figure 9.12 illustrates a lateral view of the eye, so that you can see most of the important features.

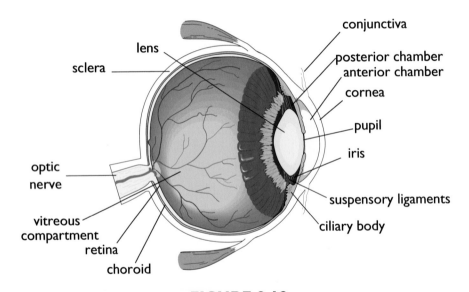

FIGURE 9.12
The Anatomy of the Eye
Illustration by LifeArt | Inset illustration by Megan Whitaker

The eye is composed of three coverings, or tunics of tissue. The outermost tunic is called the fibrous tunic, and it is composed of the sclera (skleher' uh) and the cornea. The sclera is the firm white outer layer of connective tissue, which covers the entire eye except for the cornea. Its job is mostly to maintain the shape of the eye, protect the inner components of the eye, and provide a point of attachment for the muscles that move the eye. The cornea covers the part of the eye that the sclera does not. This is the clear "window" of the eye through which light enters. Obviously, then, the cornea is transparent.

Even though the cornea is transparent, it is also made of connective tissue, like the sclera. The difference is that the collagen fibers in the cornea are thinner than those in the sclera, and there is much less water in the tissue of the cornea than in the tissue of the sclera. These two factors cause the cornea to be transparent, while the sclera is white. Although it is common to think of the cornea as just a "covering" for the window of the eye, the cornea is actually a part of the focusing system of the eye. It does not move, but it automatically refracts light that enters into the eye, bending it before it reaches the lens. We will discuss this more in a moment.

Even though the cornea and the sclera are considered the outer covering of the eye, there is an outer membrane called the conjunctiva (kon junk tie' vuh). This is an additional thin, transparent epithelial membrane that actually covers the inner surface of the eyelids and the anterior portion of the sclera. This slick membrane helps to protect and lubricate the eye. The whites of the eyes around each iris are shiny white because of the smooth, transparent conjunctiva overlying the white collagen of the sclera. The disease known as pinkeye is the result of an inflammation of this membrane that is caused by a bacterial or viral infection. However, the smoothness of the conjunctiva normally prevents infection, as bacteria cannot easily cling to such a surface. When we consider that the conjunctiva is bathed with tears, it's no wonder we seldom get an eye infection!

The next layer of the eye is the vascular tunic. It is called the vascular tunic because it contains most of the blood vessels in the eye, which supply the eye tissues with oxygen and nutrients. The choroid (kor' oyd) is the layer of vascular tissue that is just beneath the sclera. It is about 0.1-0.2 mm thick, and it appears black in color because it contains many cells that produce the dark brown pigment known as melanin (see module 3). The choroid does not extend to the area of the eye near the cornea. In that portion of the eye, the vascular tunic is composed of the ring-shaped ciliary (sil' ee air ee) body. The ciliary body contains smooth muscles called ciliary muscles. Tiny projections of the ciliary body, called ciliary processes, surround the lens of the eye and are attached to the lens by ligaments called suspensory ligaments. As you will see in a moment, the ciliary muscles control the shape of the lens, which is another step in the process of the eye focusing the light that it receives.

The final section of the vascular tunic is the iris. This is the colored part of the eye, which varies in color—blue, green, gray, brown - from person to person. The iris is made of smooth muscle that surrounds the opening in the eye, called the pupil. The iris regulates how much light gets into the eye by varying the size of the pupil. The larger the pupil, the more light gets into the eye. As you learned earlier in this module, the sympathetic division of the ANS is responsible for increasing the size of the pupil, a process called dilation. The parasympathetic division of the ANS controls decreasing the size of the pupil, which is called constriction.

The final tunic is called the nervous tunic, and it is composed of the retina. It's about the size and thickness of a postage stamp, and it is full of blood vessels. In fact, that's the reason you get a red-eye effect when you take someone's picture with a flash bulb. The light reflects off of the vessels of the blood in the retina, giving a vivid, red spot on the eye. The retina houses the photoreceptor cells called rods and cones. There are about 120 million rods and 7 million cones in the retina of each eye. There is one spot on the retina, the optic disk, that contains no photoreceptors. This is the point at which the blood vessels enter the eye. It is also the point at which the axons of the neurons in the retina exit the eye and join the optic nerve, which goes to the brain. Since there are no photoreceptors in the optic disk, we cannot see any light that is focused there. As a result, it is called the blind spot of the eye.

Near the center of the retina, on the posterior side of the eye, there is a small (about 4 mm in diameter), yellow spot called the macula lutea (mak' you la loo' tee uh). In the center of the macula lutea is a small pit called the fovea (foh' vee uh) centralis, which is normally the spot on which light is focused. This area (not shown in figure 9.12) gives us the sharpest image, because the photoreceptor cells for detailed, colored vision are packed very tightly in this region.

Since the retina is the tissue that contains the photoreceptors, let's spend some time on its histology. Figure 9.13 shows the major cells in the retina.

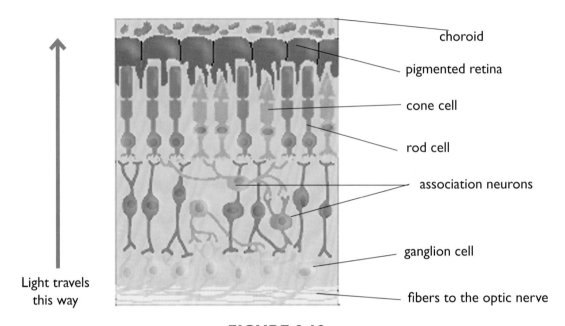

FIGURE 9.13
The Histology of the Retina
Illustration by Megan Whitaker

Starting at the deepest part (the last layer that light hits, top of figure 9.13), we find the pigmented retina. This component of the retina consists of one layer of epithelial cells, which are full of melanin. As a result, the layer is black. When light hits it, the light is absorbed. This increases the sharpness of the image we see, because light is not reflected back into the photoreceptors. If that were to happen, it would cause the photoreceptors to create extra action potentials, which would cause "noise" in the signal, reducing the quality of the image. Although the black pigment layer increases the sharpness of the image, it is not essential for sight. People with albinism experience visual problems caused by the bounce back of light, since they lack melanin all over the body, including the deepest layers of the retina. Their vision is compromised additionally by a reflex stimulated by the bounce back of light. This reflex causes *nystagmus*, or the constant involuntary shifting of the eyes by the skeletal muscle usually used to turn the eyes on an object of interest.

Mammals whose eyes glow in the dark do not have a black choroid to absorb light and therefore increase acuity, or sharpness, of the image. Instead they have a shiny, or iridescent, coloring on the choroid. This reflects the light back by design. Why? When light is bounced back, yes, distortion of the image occurs, but the retina gets stimulated twice, once as the light enters, and once as it bounces back. Such animals may not have good perception of detail, but they see better than humans in the dark. Cows, sheep, goats, deer, and other such prey animals can detect movement, even at night. Predator animals, such as cats, can do so, also.

Right before striking the pigmented retina, light hits the photoreceptor cells, which are called rods and cones. Although they both respond to light, their jobs are quite different. In effect, they give us two systems for vision—a daytime, bright-light system, and a night-time, dim-light system. Let's look at rods and the dim-light system first.

Rods are extremely sensitive to even small amounts of light. These are the cells that do most of the work when you are seeing under dim-light conditions. However, these cells cannot distinguish the color of the light that hits them. Consequently, no color information is sent to the brain by the rod cells. All of the information sent to the brain by the rod cells is interpreted as varying shades of gray. Have you ever noticed that, as the light levels in a room decrease, the colors of the objects in the room become less vivid? That's because as the rod cells take over, you lose color information.

Cones, on the other hand, require much more light than rods. They are active only when there is enough light available. They enhance the sharpness of the image, and they can distinguish the wavelengths of the light that hits the retina. Since the color of light is determined by its wavelength, this allows the brain to interpret the signals sent by the cones in order to produce a color image. How is this done? We will go over that in the next section.

The rods and cones synapse with bipolar neurons, which in turn synapse with ganglion cells. Surprisingly, the axons from those ganglion cells then pass over the *surface* of the retina and converge on the optic disk (see figure 9.12), so that they can become a part of the optic nerve, sending the information from the rods and cones to the brain. There are also some association neurons in the retina, which serve to regulate some of the signals before they hit the brain. So, the retina itself does some pre-processing of the signal before it gets to the brain. Interestingly enough, the axons of the ganglion cells *do not* pass over the retina at the fovea centralis, where light is primarily focused. This causes the fovea centralis to be a bit thinner than the rest of the retina, so it looks like a tiny pit in the retina. That is, in fact, how it gets its name, since fovea means "pit." Now remember, light has to pass through those axons in order to reach the retina. This does not happen in the fovea centralis, however, since the axons are not present there. That, in combination with the high density of cones, makes the fovea centralis the source of best vision on the retina. That's why the eye focuses light on that point of the retina.

In addition to the tunics we have described above, there are two other major components of the eye. The vitreous humor is found in the large *vitreous compartment* in the posterior part of the eye. The vitreous humor is composed of a transparent, gel-like protein that is holding water. The protein attracts water to form a gel, and the result is probably the most inert and the oldest substance in the body. It is so inert that we probably have the same vitreous humor now as we did when we were in the womb. What does it do? It maintains the general shape of the eyeball by acting as a filler. *Vitreous* means "glass-like" and, of course, it's crystal clear, unless you have a floater in your eye. Floaters" are usually strings of protein in the vitreous humor that have come out of solution. They can be seen as out-of-focus strands in the visual field.

Aqueous humor is similar to cerebrospinal fluid in its composition. Aqueous humor is found in both the anterior chamber and the posterior chamber of the eye (see figure 9.12). It is produced by the ciliary processes, flows through the two chambers, and ultimately drains

COLORING BOOK EXERCISE 9.4

To review eye anatomy and retina histology, follow the instructions on pages 159-165 of the coloring book.

ON YOUR OWN

9.13 As light hits the eye and ends up on the retina, it passes through many (but not all) of the parts of the eye. Using the parts labeled in figures 9.12 and 9.14, list the parts of the eye in the order in which light hits them. Then, in a separate list, point out those parts of the eye that are never hit by the light that enters the eye.

back into the blood via a circular vein near the edge of the iris. The aqueous humor is responsible for some of the automatic refraction that helps the eye focus light. It helps maintain the exact pressure within the eye, gently pushing the cornea so that it bulges outward. Its ability to maintain proper pressure in the eyeball is critical to our vision. If pressure would drop too low, the retina would detach from the choroid. If the pressure is too high, it gradually kills the neurons within the eye, causing progressive loss of vision called *glaucoma*. If you have had an eye exam in which the optometrist directed a tiny blast of air at your cornea, that was a test for the pressure within your eyeball. The bounce of your cornea in response to the air is being tested, so that glaucoma, which is treatable, can be detected early. Finally, the aqueous humor provides nutrition to certain tissues. The cornea, for example, has no blood vessels, so the aqueous humor provides the nutrition that the tissue of the cornea needs.

Experiment 9.2
Cow's Eye Dissection

Supplies:

- Cow's eye
- Dissection kit
- Paper towels

Purpose: The cow's eye is a reasonably good model of the human eye, so dissecting it is a good review of eye anatomy.

Procedure:

1. If necessary remove any attached palpebra (eyelids) with scissors, so that you have only the eyeball. Notice that the eye is somewhat collapsed since the natural fluids have been removed and preservatives injected.

2. The sclera is the tough outer layer of the eye. Posteriorly, it is grayish and rough (it is made of dense irregular connective tissue). Some of it may be covered with fat. Remnants of the extrinsic eye muscles may be seen attached to it. Find the optic nerve. It will look like a round, flat, whitish disk, since it will be cut close.

3. Anteriorly, the cornea, which is perfectly clear in life, is blue-gray due to the preservative. Beginning at the edge of the cornea and smooth covering the anterior part of the sclera is the conjunctiva. It may be clear, giving the anterior sclera the shiny, white appearance of the human eye. More likely it is pigmented black, but it will still be smooth. It adheres to the sclera about as tightly as an adhesive bandage adheres to the skin. Use the forceps to pull up one edge of it.

Dissecting the eye

4. Turn the eyeball so that the cornea is upward. Using scissors cut the eye in a circle, about 1.5 cm from the edge of the cornea. Don't cut any deeper than is necessary.

5. Gently separate the two parts. If the dissection is done correctly, you will have a "cup" and a "saucer." The smaller part ("saucer") should be the anterior part of the eye. Carefully dump the lens and preservative fluid from the eye onto the dissecting pan.

The anterior eye from within: pupil, iris, and ciliary body.

6. Turn the anterior eye over with forceps so that the inside is up. The pupil is the hole that can enlarge or contract to regulate light entry. In these animals it is oblong, improving the animal's lateral vision, a useful trait for prey animals that must look out for attacks from behind.

7. The iris is the thin black tissue surrounding the pupil. Around the iris, the radial fibers of the ciliary body are evident. (The ciliary body attaches to the lens via suspensory ligaments. It has intrinsic muscles that can change the shape of the lens.)

The posterior eye from within: retina, choroid (with tapetum lucidum), and sclera.

8. The retina would be a thin, delicate, tan layer, much like a wet tissue, smoothly spread out against the entire back of the eyeball, and held in place by the pressure within the eye. Instead, because pressure dropped when you opened the eyeball, it probably looks like a wet, tan, crumpled piece of tissue in the back of the eye. Probe it with a blunt probe. Can you see its attachment at the optic disk, where the optic nerve exits?

9. The stiffer, thin, middle layer, the choroid, can be gently probed away from the sclera at the edge of the dissection. In sheep and cattle, the choroid is colored with the iridescent tapetum lucidum. This reflects light back over the retina, improving vision in dim light. It causes the animal's eyes to glow in the dark. The human choroid is all black.

10. Pull away a bit more of the choroid to see the sclera again from the inside. Its name means "hard" or "tough."

The lens and lens capsule, suspensory ligaments, and vitreous humor

11. In life the lens is soft and perfectly clear. The preservative has hardened the lens and clouded it like a bad cataract. It will look like a yellowish marble inside a small clear "sack," the lens capsule. The black pigment adhering to the edges of the capsule shows where the suspensory ligaments attached the lens to the ciliary body. Gently pick up the lens in the capsule by using the sharp probe to pierce and pick up the capsule along the black edge.

12. A small amount of vitreous humor may be attached to the lens capsule. It will look like a thick, clear gel. Once you have carefully observed the above, remove the lens from the capsule.

13. With your scalpel, cut the lens in two. It is made of concentric layers of epithelial cells, arranged like the layers of an onion. It is avascular.

14. Spend some time reviewing the anatomy.

15. Put everything away.

THE SENSE OF VISION: PHYSIOLOGY OF THE EYE

How does the eye actually work? There are three main steps to the physiology of vision. First, the light must be focused onto the retina where the photoreceptors can be stimulated by it. Second, the photoreceptors react to the stimulus. Third, the action potentials produced as a result of the stimulus are sent to the visual cortex where they are interpreted.

Let's start with the first step: focusing the light onto the retina. Remember, that's where the photoreceptors are. If the light can't get to the retina, then it will not be detected. How does this happen? Let's start with figure 9.14.

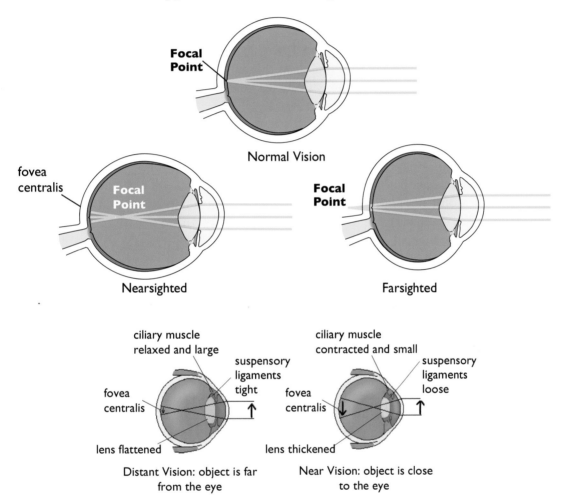

FIGURE 9.14
The Optics of Vision
Illustration by LifeArt

In order for us to see something, light must bounce off it and into our eyes. The lines represent rays of light. In order for us to see the entire image, then, the rays must be focused onto the retina.

When the light rays enter the eye, they are bent so that they end up on the fovea centralis, where the cones are most concentrated. Notice that in the figure, those light rays are first bent by the cornea. The cornea is a very important part of the focusing process. It can automatically do as much as 80% of the light bending that is necessary to get the image to the fovea. Next, the light hits the aqueous humor, which also bends the light. Then, the light hits the lens.

The lens is attached to the ciliary muscle by the suspensory ligaments on the ciliary processes. It is crystal clear and elastic, so it tends to round up like a ball if not pulled into another shape. Because it is elastic, the ciliary muscle can change the shape of the lens. That changes the fundamental property of the lens called the focal point. Every lens has a focal point, and lenses shaped like the eye's lens (called converging lenses) bend horizontal light rays so that they all converge on the focal point. As you can see in the drawings, the light rays converge at the focal point. It is important to understand that the retina is *not* at the focal point. The focal point must be anterior to the retina, or the image will not focus on the retina.

Now, notice the differences between the drawings in the figure. One illustration represents a situation in which the object being viewed is far from the eye. In this situation, the ciliary muscle is completely relaxed. This pulls on the lens making it flat. Remember, a relaxed muscle is *longer* than a contracted one. In a circular muscle, like the ciliary muscle, this makes a *wider* ring, which pulls on the lens. We are accustomed to a contracted muscle doing the pulling, but in this situation, the circular ciliary muscle pulls when it is relaxed. The light then passes through the flattened lens with little bending. The closest point at which this can happen is called the far point of vision (about 20 feet from the eye). If an object is at the far point of vision or beyond, the ciliary muscle is completely relaxed, and light naturally bends so that the image is focused upside down on the fovea. This assumes, of course, that you have good vision and do not need glasses. If the object moves closer than the far point of vision, three reflexes must occur to bring the image to proper focus on the retina: *accommodation of the lens, constriction of the pupil, and convergence of the eyes.*

Accommodation of the lens is accomplished with the contraction of the ciliary muscle. When the ciliary muscle contracts, the ciliary body moves closer to the eye because the ring of muscle gets smaller. This reduces the tension on the suspensory ligaments. As the tension is released, the elastic lens naturally rounds up, becoming more like a ball. Because it is now curved, not flat, it increases the amount that the light rays bend. In other words, the focal length of the lens decreases. This moves the focal point farther from the retina, making a larger upside-down image, as shown.

Accommodation is an amazing process and really needs to be emphasized. Have you ever watched a photographer operate a camera with a manual focus? If you have, then you have seen the photographer twisting the lens of the camera back and forth. Why does he do that? Well, to get a good picture, the image that he is trying to photograph must be focused precisely onto the film in the camera. When the photographer twists the lens, he is not actually twisting it. Instead, he is *moving* it back and forth. In a camera, the photographer changes the focus by moving the lens.

That works quite well for a camera, but it would be an inefficient design for a person! Why? Well, a person needs to change the focus of his or her eyes quickly. It takes time to move a lens back and forth. Also, if the lens moves, there must be room for it to move. In cameras, the lens moves back and forth within a tube that is on the front of the camera. The larger the range of focus you want, the larger the tube has to be. To give us the range that we need for focusing by that method, human eyes would have to have their lenses mounted on long tubes that would stick far out of the eye.

The eye needs to focus the light from the object onto the retina, but doing so by moving the lens is simply too inefficient. Thus, the eye *changes the shape of the lens* instead. This accomplishes the same task as taking a lens of fixed shape and moving it back and forth. However, this process is more efficient and takes no extra room. Isn't that marvelous?

You can now understand now why spending a lot of time looking at something up close causes eyestrain. While looking at something up close, your ciliary muscle must stay contracted to keep the lens rounded. That takes energy, and after a while, the muscle can get tired. That's eyestrain. Also, you can now understand why looking off in the distance (especially at a beautiful scene) can be so relaxing. To see things far off, the ciliary muscle is completely relaxed. If the far-off scene you are seeing is pleasant, that makes it even better!

Accommodation does has its limits. At some point, the lens just can't get any rounder. That limits how close an object can be to the eye if you want to view it clearly. If you move an object too close to your eye, it becomes blurry. The point at which the blurring starts is called the near point of vision, and that point changes as you grow older. In children, the near point of vision is about 2 to 3 inches. It grows to 4 to 6 inches in a young adult, and it reaches up to 60 inches when a person is in his or her 80s! The accommodation of the lens changes as a result of age because, as we get older, our lenses become less flexible and they remain flat. When the accommodation ability of the lens degenerates to the extent that the near point of vision is greater than 9 inches, we say that the eye has presbyopia (prez bee oh' pee uh), which is Latin for "elder vision."

It is important to note that, although accommodation is an incredibly well-designed process, it can have defects. If a person has myopia (nearsightedness), the combination of the lens and cornea bends light too strongly, or the eyeball is too long, and the image is formed too far in front of the retina. A nearsighted person naturally moves the object closer. This moves the tiny upside-down image backward, where it lands on the fovea. Myopia can be corrected with a lens that bends light away from the center of the eye. This is called a diverging lens, and it corrects myopia by bending the light rays the opposite way that the eye does, in order to make up for the fact that the eye bends the light too strongly or is too long. A person can also have hyperopia (farsightedness). This condition arises when the cornea and lens cannot bend light strongly enough or the eyeball is too short. As a result, the image is formed behind the retina. This can be corrected with a lens that bends light toward the center of the eye. This lens, called a converging lens, simply helps the lens and cornea by bending the light in the direction it needs to bend before it hits the eye.

After accommodation, the second reflex in trying to see something up close is pupil constriction. Remember, the pupil is the opening that allows light into the eye. The more dilated the pupil is, the more light gets in. As the pupil constricts, less light gets in. So, as you are trying to look at something up close, your pupil automatically constricts to let less light in. How does that help? Well, by constricting the pupil, you are reducing the number of light rays that come into the eye. As your pupil constricts, it starts blocking out rays that are not coming straight in from the object to the eye. Constricting the pupil ensures that the light rays coming from the object are traveling very straight. This increases your depth of focus, which is the range of distances over which you stay focused. To understand depth of focus consider that reading in bright light is less tiring than reading in inadequate lighting. Why? Bright light automatically causes pupil constriction, which improves depth of focus. That means that whether the book is 12, 16, or 20 inches from your eyes, no additional work by the ciliary body is necessary for the book's print to stay in focus. If the pupil is dilated too much, you would only be focused, say, at 16 inches, and any movement of the book forward or backward forces your ciliary body to adjust the lens, increasing eyestrain.

The last reflex for near vision is convergence. This has to do with the fact that you have two eyes. When you are looking at a distant object, the light rays hitting your eyes are nearly parallel to one another. As a result, you can look more or less straight ahead with each eye. As the object moves closer, however, the eyes must be rotated to make up for the fact that the light rays are not parallel anymore. This is called convergence, and the skeletal muscles outside the eyeball do it. Convergence, which allows both eyes to see the same object, improves depth perception. Depth perception is the ability to judge distance, especially of close objects. If you want to see how important convergence and depth perception are, try threading a needle with one eye closed!

As we mentioned before, the object is actually focused upside down on the retina. However, we do not see things upside down, do we? Why not? The answer is actually simple: we get used to it! While we are infants, we learn to link the image we see on the retina to the object in the outside world. Since we spend time as infants touching everything, we learn the correct orientation of everything, so our visual cortex becomes accustomed to flipping the image, so that we see right side up. The actual images on our retina, however, are upside down.

Now that the light is focused on the retina, what happens? Well, if you recall figure 9.13, the light must travel through the axons of the ganglionic cells, through the bipolar cells, through the association neurons, and to the rods and cones. Those are the photo-receptors. Now remember, rods are for dim, black and white vision. They are located toward the periphery, that is, the edges of the retina. So, there are very few on the fovea. This leads to an interesting effect. If you want to see a really dim light, you should *not* look directly at it. If you look directly at it, your eye will focus it on the fovea. However, if it is dim, you want what little light there is to hit your sensitive rods. There are not many rods in the fovea. Astronomers, for example, learn that when they want to look at a dim star, they look away from it, and view it peripherally, out of the corner of their eye. That's where they'll see it because the light will focus onto rods. Conversely, have you ever stared at a dim star on a dark night until it disappears? If not, try it! You had been seeing it out of the corner of your eye, but when you focused it onto your fovea, there were not enough rods there to send a neural message.

Cones are the photoreceptors for detailed color vision. They are concentrated in the fovea and require considerably more light than the rods. There are three types of cones, each having a different protein complex that is sensitive to a different set of light wave-lengths. Since the wavelength of light determines its color, you could also say that the cones are sensitive to different *colors* of light. There are cones sensitive to red light, cones sensitive to blue light, and cones sensitive to green light.

That's the way our eyes detect color. Now wait a minute. We see *many* more colors than red, green, and blue. If our cones are sensitive only to those colors, how can we see so many different colors? Well, red, green, and blue are the additive primary colors. Any other color can be made by simply adding different amounts of red, green, and blue. When a certain color of light hits our cones, the red-sensitive cones stimulate action potentials in proportion to how much red is in the color; the green-sensitive cones stimulate action potentials in proportion to how much green is in the color; and the blue-sensitive cones stimulate action potentials in proportion to how much blue is in the color. The brain adds those colors together in those proportions, producing the image of color that originally hit the cones.

Neither rods nor cones produce action potentials; instead, when enough light hits them, they release neurotransmitter, which ultimately controls the rate of action potentials on the bipolar neurons. The action potentials then travel down the ganglion cell axons and into the optic nerve. Most of those neurons go to the thalamus, where they synapse with other neurons that take action potentials to the visual cortex. Those that do not synapse in the thalamus go directly to the midbrain, where they form part of the visual reflex system that allows us to react reflexively to visual threats. For example, if you turn your head and see a rock heading toward you, you duck without thinking. That is a visual reflex controlled in the midbrain.

It is time to move on to other organ systems in the human body. Before we leave this fascinating topic on the nervous system, however, we want you to sit back and think about what you have learned. The design of the CNS is amazing, but the CNS would not be very useful without the PNS. The PNS is a well-engineered system of detection and response. Reflex arcs and autonomic reflexes make your body respond quickly to stimuli. Your body is full of amazingly complicated receptors to provide your CNS with all of the information it needs, and the special senses are truly incredible.

Your senses are responsible for forming your view of your world. They detect the vibrations of sound and allow you to hear and identify everything from a loud blender to your favorite melody. You're capable of discriminating odors, which can be pleasing or serve as a warning that something is wrong. Taste gives you the opportunity to crave chocolate or your favorite food. The miracle of sight gives shape to your world, and touch makes it all tangible. Your nervous system takes it all in, translates it, makes sense out of it, and presents to you the mystery and wisdom of your world.

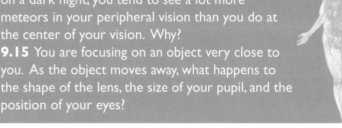

ON YOUR OWN

9.14 If you have ever watched a meteor shower on a dark night, you tend to see a lot more meteors in your peripheral vision than you do at the center of your vision. Why?

9.15 You are focusing on an object very close to you. As the object moves away, what happens to the shape of the lens, the size of your pupil, and the position of your eyes?

ANSWERS TO THE "ON YOUR OWN" QUESTIONS

9.1   In the SMNS, the neuron cell body is in the CNS, and the axon goes straight to the effector (the skeletal muscle). So, there is only one synapse between the CNS and the effector in the SMNS. In the ANS, there is a ganglion between the CNS and the effector. At the ganglion, the presynaptic neuron from the CNS synapses with the postsynaptic neuron, which then carries the signal to the effector. So, there are two synapses between the CNS and the effector in the ANS.

9.2   In the sympathetic division, the preganglionic neuron is usually short, while the postganglionic neuron is long. Therefore, in the sympathetic division, the autonomic ganglia are close to the spinal cord. After all, if the neuron going from the spinal cord to the ganglion is short, the ganglion must be close to the spinal cord. In the parasympathetic division, the preganglionic neuron is long, and the postganglionic neuron is short. Oppositely, in the parasympathetic division, the autonomic ganglia are far from the spinal cord.

9.3   This question requires you to remember that only the sympathetic division of the ANS extends beyond the head and the trunk of the body. Since it goes all of the way to the little finger, it must be a *sympathetic* nerve, which means the ganglion is close to the spinal cord.

9.4   The parasympathetic division nerves are involved here. Remember, the parasympathetic division controls the lacrimal glands. So, if tears are produced, it must be the result of parasympathetic control.

9.5   This is a visceral receptor, since it is in the internal organs. It is also a mechanoreceptor, since it responds to the motion of stretching.

9.6   The doctor should ask the patient whether or not he feels the pin prick. The reflex arc will cause the foot to jerk away. However, the patient will not feel a prick unless the pain signal gets to the brain.

9.7   Pain receptors are nociceptors. The cerebral cortex's projection tells you where the pain is. In this case, then, projection told you the pain is in the foot. The modality tells you what *kind* of receptor was stimulated. So, the modality is pain.

9.8   Thermoreceptors sense heat or cold. They are free nerve endings. Hair follicle receptors, Pacinian corpuscles, Ruffini's organs, Merkel's disks, and Meissner's corpuscles are mechanoreceptors, since they respond to motion of the skin or hair. Pain receptors are free nerve endings (but not the same ones as for heat or cold).

9.9   Sniffing brings the air up to the superior part of the nasal cavity where the receptors are. If we are trying to smell something, we must make sure that the molecules reach the top of the nasal cavity.

9.10 As mentioned in the text, the sense of smell works together with the taste buds to provide a sense of taste. In a head cold, the nose is often stopped up, making it difficult to smell. Since smell works together with taste buds to produce taste, without a good sense of smell, the sense of taste is not at its peak.

9.11 The disorder is the result of too little information getting to the brain. Remember, in the sense of static equilibrium, the otoliths in the gelatinous matrix push down on the hair cells, sending a constant signal to the brain. With no gravity, they would not push down on the hair cells, and the brain would not get the information it is expecting.

9.12 The sound starts at the auricle and heads to the tympanic membrane. That vibrates the ossicles, and they vibrate the oval window, which vibrates the fluid of the cochlea, which vibrates the spiral organ. The order, then, is:
tympanic membrane, malleus, incus, stapes, oval window, fluid of cochlea, spiral organ

9.13 The light passes through the layers in front of the pupil, through the pupil, and to the retina. Thus, the order is:
cornea, anterior chamber, pupil, posterior chamber (aqueous humor), lens, vitreous humor, retina

The structures in the figure that light doesn't pass through are the conjunctiva, ciliary body, the suspensory ligaments, the choroid, the sclera, and the optic nerve.

9.14 When watching a meteor shower, you are looking for dim lights against the sky. Therefore, you are using your rods as light receptors. Rods are concentrated away from the fovea centralis, so you see the meteors better when the light hits away from that region of the retina. This occurs in your peripheral vision.

9.15 When you are looking at something up close, the lenses have rounded up, your eyes are rotated so that they both are turned toward the object, and your pupils are constricted to give you good depth of focus. As the object moves away, the lenses flatten out, the eyes rotate away from each other to a position looking straight ahead, and the pupils dilate slightly.

STUDY GUIDE FOR MODULE 9

1. Define the following terms:
   a. Sensory receptor
   b. Somatic receptors
   c. Visceral receptors
   d. Special receptors
   e. Mechanoreceptors
   f. Thermoreceptors
   g. Photoreceptors
   h. Chemoreceptors
   i. Nociceptors
   j. Cutaneous receptors
   k. Proprioceptors

2. The cell body of a neuron is housed in the spinal cord, and its axon travels all the way to the effector it controls. Is this an autonomic neuron or a somatic motor neuron? What is the effector?

3. Compare the sympathetic and parasympathetic divisions of the ANS according to:
   a. Length of the neurons
   b. Where in the body the neurons can be found
   c. Position of the autonomic ganglia

4. Given the following receptors, classify them first as either somatic, visceral, or special. Then classify them again as either a mechanoreceptor, thermoreceptor, photoreceptor, chemoreceptor, or nociceptor.
   a. Hair follicle receptors
   b. Olfactory neurons
   c. Taste buds
   d. Pain receptors in the kidney
   e. Free nerve endings in the skin that detect cold temperatures
   f. Rods and cones
   g. Hair cells in the macula of the vestibule
   h. Golgi tendon organ

5. You feel someone poking you in the back of the head. It is painful. What does the cerebral cortex's interpretation of projection tell you about this touch? What does the cerebral cortex's interpretation of modality tell you?

6. Identify the cutaneous nerves pictured below, and list their major functions:

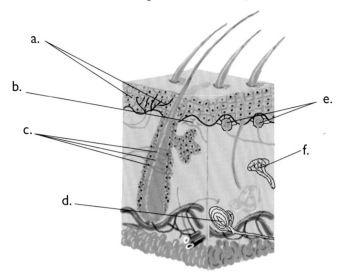

7. Which proprioceptors detect the extent to which a muscle is relaxed (extended)? Which detect the extent to which the muscle is contracted?

8. There are at least four conditions that must be met before we can smell a substance. What are they?

9. You walk into a house and smell a musty odor. The residents of the house do not smell it. Why not? Will you continue to smell the odor?

10. What types of papillae are found on the tongue? Which of these papillae have taste buds associated with them?

11. Name the five taste sensations. Which is the taste of amino acids?

12. Identify the structures in the following figure:

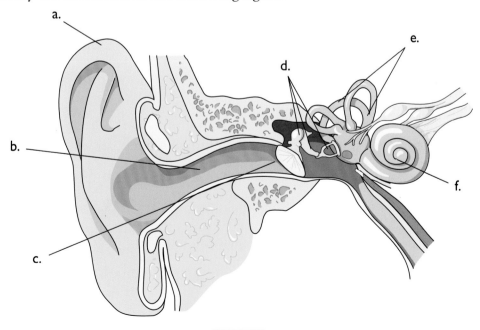

MOD 9

13.   Identify the structures in the following figure:

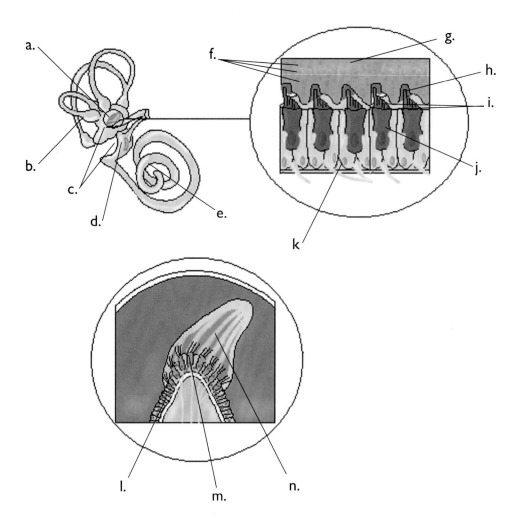

14.   Which of the structures above are involved in the sense of static equilibrium? Which are involved in the sense of dynamic equilibrium?

15.   The major structures involved in hearing are listed below. Order them in terms of when they vibrate. Start with the structures that vibrate first and end with those that vibrate last.

incus, tympanic membrane, tectorial membrane, malleus, basilar membrane, stapes

16. Identify the structures in the following figure, and list the function of each.

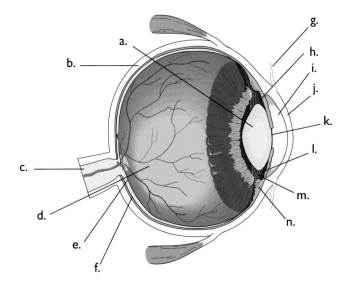

17. Which cells are responsible for the detection of color? Which are responsible for detecting low levels of light?

18. Where are the cones concentrated in the retina?

19. What is accommodation?

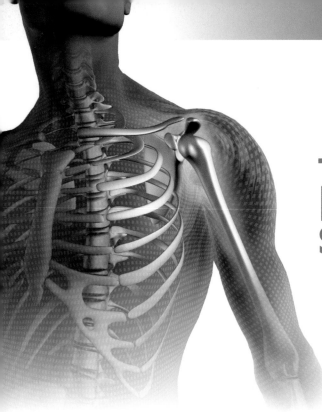

THE ENDOCRINE SYSTEM

In several previous modules, we mentioned the adrenal glands, the pituitary gland, and a few hormones. These are all a part of the endocrine (en' doh krin) system. That's what we will concentrate on in this module. Along with the nervous system, the endocrine system regulates the body in order to achieve homeostasis. The word endocrine comes from two Greek words: endo, which

heart of the matter

Communication has always had significant purpose throughout civilization. God has used prophets and angels to deliver important messages to His people. Inside your body, your Creator designed chemical messengers to transfer fundamental information and instructions. The ability of your endocrine system to communicate effectively with other body systems is necessary to carry out the vital functions of life.

means "within," and crino, which means "separate." So, the endocrine system is a control system that secretes chemicals within the body in order to control tissues that are far (separate) from the source of the secretion. Now remember, the goal of the endocrine system is to regulate the body. That is also the goal of the nervous system. So, these two systems work in tandem with one another. As a start, it's useful to contrast one with the other.

First, let's look at what they have in common. They are both *control centers for feedback systems*. In other words, when the body detects that a variable is getting either too high or too low, it will initiate a response to bring that variable back in order to maintain homeostasis. Sometimes, the nervous system controls the response. Sometimes, the endocrine system controls the response. Often, both systems play a part in the response.

Although these systems are both control centers for feedback in the body, they end up approaching this task in several different ways. Consider, for example, *the speed of response*. The nervous system is *fast*. We can measure its response time in milliseconds. The endocrine system, on the other hand, is slow compared with the nervous system. We would measure its response time in seconds, minutes, or even days.

Similarly, the duration of influence (the time that influence lasts after the control has been stopped) for each system is quite different. For example, if your nervous system suddenly stops functioning, how long could you stand? Not very long at all, because your skeletal muscles are stimulated by your nervous system. You might be able to stand for a tenth of a second or so, but no more. Thus, the duration of influence of the nervous system is brief. That's not the case for the endocrine system. For example, when a woman gives birth, after the child is born, the placenta is expelled. The placenta, the organ that regulates blood flow between mother and fetus, manufactures many hormones that are no longer produced once it is gone. Nevertheless, the influence of those hormones will last about three days. The duration of influence for the endocrine system is long.

Another difference between these two systems is the *effectors they control*. The nervous system controls only two types of effectors: muscles and glands. The endocrine system, on the other hand, can control practically all of the cells in the body!

Think also about the difference in the *strength of the signal* for the two systems. In the nervous system, the signal is the action potential. Its strength is fixed. The nervous system distinguishes between weak and intense stimuli not by the *size* of the action potentials, but by the *rate* of the action potentials. For the endocrine system, the *strength* of the signal varies, and the effectors respond in proportion to the strength. A small amount of hormone makes a small difference. A large amount makes a bigger difference.

Importantly, the endocrine system's signal strength can be varied in another way, as well. In order for a particular hormone to affect a cell, the cell must have receptors for that hormone. Cells with receptors to a particular hormone are called target cells for that hormone. **Receptors** are proteins made by the target cell that bind like a lock and key to a specific hormone, and, like a key turning a car's ignition, they cause profound changes in the target cell once a hormone binds to them.

If a cell has no receptors for a particular hormone, the hormone cannot affect it. So, the strength of the endocrine system's signal can also be controlled by increasing the ability of the target cell to respond. How can that be done? Well, if the cell makes more receptors, it will be able to respond to even a small amount of hormone. We will explore this topic a little later. A target cell with more receptors will respond better to the hormone.

The last thing to consider is *repair*. The endocrine system is composed of glands, which are epithelial tissue. Endocrine glands are made of *stable* cells; that is, if the endocrine glands are injured, they can be repaired. The nervous system, remember, is not like that at all. With the exception of olfactory neurons, neurons cannot be replaced. If they die, you lose them forever. Even the severed axon of a neuron can only be repaired if it is in the PNS and lined up close to the portion of the axon from which it was severed. Compared with the nervous system, the endocrine system is very good at repairing itself.

ON YOUR OWN

10.1 Two cells react differently to the same level of a particular hormone. The first cell does not seem to react to the presence of the hormone, whereas the second cell quickly begins manufacturing proteins in response to the hormone. What is the difference between the two cells?

THE ENDOCRINE SYSTEM AS A WHOLE

The endocrine system consists of hormone glands or hormonal cells that secrete hormones into the blood. The blood then serves as a transport medium that quickly takes the hormones to cells that can be quite distant from the cells that secreted them. For example, parathyroid hormone (PTH) affects osteoclasts, stimulating them to break down bone (figure 4.5). The osteocytes may be distant from the parathyroid glands, which secrete PTH, but the hormone is transported to the osteoclasts by the blood. As PTH travels through the blood, however, it is exposed to many cells. Why is it that osteoclasts respond to the hormone? They have the receptors for the hormone! The blood will transport the hormone to many cells, but if those cells do not have receptors for the hormone, it will not affect them.

To give you some idea of the overall scheme by which the endocrine system works, let's look at a figure 10.1.

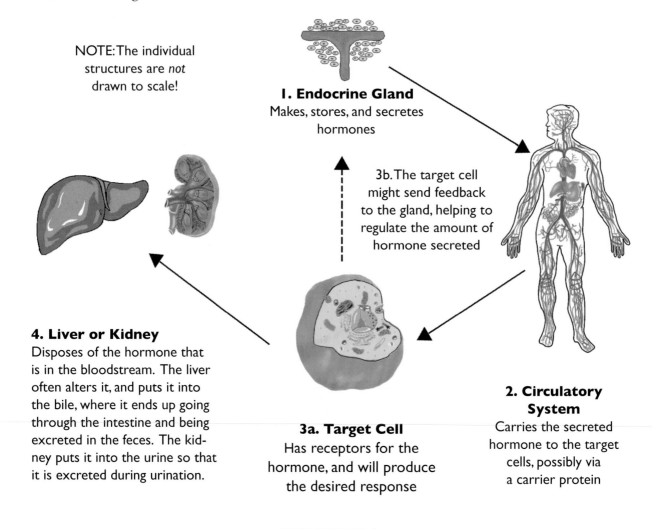

NOTE: The individual structures are *not* drawn to scale!

1. Endocrine Gland
Makes, stores, and secretes hormones

3b. The target cell might send feedback to the gland, helping to regulate the amount of hormone secreted

4. Liver or Kidney
Disposes of the hormone that is in the bloodstream. The liver often alters it, and puts it into the bile, where it ends up going through the intestine and being excreted in the feces. The kidney puts it into the urine so that it is excreted during urination.

3a. Target Cell
Has receptors for the hormone, and will produce the desired response

2. Circulatory System
Carries the secreted hormone to the target cells, possibly via a carrier protein

FIGURE 10.1
The Overall Scheme of the Endocrine System
Illustration by Megan Whitaker; liver from the Future Graph collection.

The endocrine system's functions begin with the endocrine gland. The gland will synthesize the hormone and may store it until it is needed. Over time, the gland will release the appropriate amount of the hormone into the blood. Once the hormone is in the blood, it might have to be bound to a carrier protein. Why? If the hormone is lipid-soluble, it's going to need a protein to bind it because blood is a watery fluid, and a lipid-soluble chemical is poorly soluble in water. To become a part of the blood, it will have to bind to a special protein that is found in the blood. In essence, then, the hormone will "hitch a ride" on the carrier protein since it cannot mix into the blood directly.

Eventually, the hormone will be released near the target cells with receptors for the hormone. The target cells will then produce the response that the hormone signals. The hormone may also provide a feedback signal. That is, its presence in the blood may "tell" the original gland that the job is done and that there does not need to be any more hormone secreted, or it may also "tell" the gland that more hormone needs to be secreted. The hormone will eventually be disposed of by the liver or the kidney. The kidney will put it into the urine, and the liver will usually put it into the bile. Bile is secreted into the small intestine, and the hormones in the bile end up in the feces.

Now, if you think about it, urine tests can tell us a great deal about what's going on in the endocrine system. After all, if the hormone is disposed of in the urine, by testing the urine, you can test what hormones the body is producing. For example, there are many home pregnancy-testing kits that involve testing a sample of a woman's urine. The tests work because they detect a particular hormone that's produced only if a woman is pregnant. Since the hormone is disposed of in the urine, it is easy to test for it there.

The fact that hormones are often excreted in the urine can be handy for something else, as well. Women produce estrogen, which is a sex hormone. As women age, estrogen eventually drops, and some women use estrogen as a medication. This is called estrogen replacement therapy. Well, one of the popular versions of this drug is named Premarin. This name stands for pregnant mare urine, because the estrogen is distilled from female horse urine during the time that the horse is pregnant. Pregnant horses produce a lot of estrogen, and once it is excreted in the urine, it can be purified and used as estrogen replacement therapy! If this offends your sensibilities, just be glad they're not getting it from where the liver would dispose of it!

MOD 10

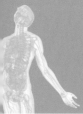

ON YOUR OWN

10.2 Home pregnancy tests are rarely wrong when they indicate that a woman is pregnant. That is, they have few false-positive readings. However, home pregnancy tests are sometimes wrong when they indicate that the woman is not pregnant. In other words, they do give false-negative readings. Why are false-negatives more likely than false positives?

ENDOCRINE GLANDS AND HORMONES

Now that you have seen the big picture on how the endocrine system works, we want to spend some time on the major glands and hormones that make up this system.

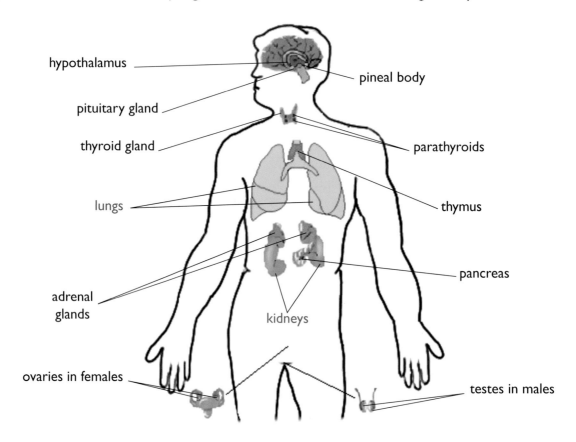

FIGURE 10.2
The Major Endocrine Glands
Illustration by Megan Whitaker

Let's go through this figure, discussing each of the glands that are pointed out (organs labeled in blue are reference points). Let's start with the hypothalamus, situated on the underside of the brain. You studied the hypothalamus when you studied the central nervous system (CNS). Although the hypothalamus is a part of the CNS, it is also an endocrine gland. In fact, the nervous system and the endocrine system converge here. The hypothalamus responds to a variety of stimuli, and in response, it can secrete hormones that regulate the pituitary gland, which is located just under it.

Since the hypothalamus produces hormones that control the pituitary gland, we consider them special hormones. Basically, the hypothalamus secretes two types of hormones: releasing hormones (which cause the pituitary gland to secrete more hormones) and inhibiting hormones (which cause the pituitary gland to secrete fewer hormones). What are these hormones? To understand that, you need to learn a little bit about the pituitary gland.

Although it is small, the pituitary gland is actually two different endocrine glands: the anterior pituitary gland and the posterior pituitary gland (see figures 10.3 and 10.4). They differ both structurally and functionally. Since they are attached to one another, we lump them into one gland, the pituitary gland.

The anterior pituitary produces several major hormones: growth hormone (GH), thyroid stimulating hormone (TSH), adrenocorticotropic (uh dree' no kor' tih koh troh' pik) hormone (ACTH), luteinizing (loo' tin eye zing) hormone (LH), follicle stimulating hormone (FSH), prolactin (pro lak' tin) (PRL), and melanocyte stimulating hormone (MSH). Now that's a long list of hormones, so let's go through them one by one.

Growth hormone stimulates growth in most tissues. One of the most important tissues that GH affects is bone. GH stimulates bone growth, as you learned in module 4. Because growth is more important during youth, GH levels are usually higher in young people than in adults. Although GH is mostly thought of as a hormone that stimulates growth, it does perform other functions. It is one of the major regulators of metabolism. For example, GH levels rise during exercise, and prevent the body from breaking down body proteins at that time.

Thyroid stimulating hormone increases the secretion of thyroxine (thigh rok' sin) from the thyroid. Adrenocorticotropic hormone increases during times of emotional or physical stress, which in turn increases the stress hormone cortisol, which is secreted from the adrenal glands. Luteinizing hormone and follicle stimulating hormone stimulate the ovaries or testes, which are part of the reproductive system. Prolactin stimulates milk production in the breasts and is also present in males, where it plays several minor roles. Finally, melanocyte stimulating hormome increases the synthesis of melanin by the melanocytes.

Notice that most of the hormones secreted by the anterior pituitary glands actually stimulate other endocrine glands. TSH, for example, stimulates the thyroid gland, and ACTH stimulates the adrenal glands.

Because the pituitary actually controls some other endocrine glands, it is often called the master endocrine gland. Hormones that stimulate other hormones to secrete are called tropic hormones. This master endocrine gland, however, has its own master. As mentioned before, the hypothalamus regulates the pituitary gland. For example, it releases the growth hormone releasing hormone (GHRH). As its name implies, this hormone stimulates the anterior pituitary gland to secrete growth hormone. Another hormone secreted by the hypothalamus, corticotropin (kor' tih koh troh' pin) releasing hormone (CRH), stimulates the anterior pituitary gland to secrete ACTH. Gonadotropin (goh' nad oh troh' pin) releasing hormone (GnRH) increases the anterior pituitary gland's secretion of both FSH and LH. FSH and LH stimulate the ovaries and testes, which are called the gonads. Another releasing hormone, thyrotropin releasing

MOD 10

hormone (TRH) stimulates the anterior pituitary gland to release TSH. Finally, the hypothalamus also produces an inhibiting hormone called prolactin inhibiting hormone (PIH), which reduces the amount of PRL that is secreted by the anterior pituitary gland. As you can see, then, the hypothalamus is actually the master of the master endocrine gland.

The posterior pituitary produces two major hormones. Antidiuretic (an' tie die you ret' ik) hormone (ADH) also called vasopressin, increases the amount of water retained by the kidneys. As a result, urine production decreases. Oxytocin (OT) increases the contractions of the uterus during birth and promotes the release of breast milk when a baby nurses. The hypothalamus is truly the master of the posterior pituitary, also, because neurons within the hypothalamus synthesize ADH and OT; these hormones are transported down the axons of the neurons, which end in the posterior pituitary. Can you see why ADH and OT can be called neurohormones?

The thyroid gland sits at the base of the neck, just like a little bow tie in size, shape, and location. It secretes two major hormones: thyroxine (thigh rok' sin) (TH) and calcitonin (kal sih toh' nin). TH increases the metabolism rate of most cells in the body with wide-ranging effects throughout the body. It controls the oxygen usage of the cells. Excessive secretion of TH generally results in weight loss, anxiety, and an elevated metabolic rate. A significant lack of TH secretion can cause fatigue, weight gain, diminished mental activity and accumulation of mucus material in the skin, giving the person a "puffy" appearance. If a baby is born without enough TH, he or she will fail to grow well, and will develop a kind of mental retardation called cretinism. Fortunately, it is easy to test newborn babies for TH, and it is easy to replace TH if it is too low. In fact, most states require that newborn babies be routinely tested for TH soon after birth.

Calcitonin is a more limited hormone. It selectively targets osteoclasts, the cells that break down bone, inhibiting their activity so that calcium levels in the blood decrease. How? When less calcium-rich bone is broken down, less calcium is released into the blood. This effect helps to lower blood calcium levels, but it is not essential, since the kidneys can actually excrete excess blood calcium.

The four tiny parathyroid glands are embedded in the edges of the thyroid gland. Their job is to secrete parathyroid hormone (PTH). As you learned in module 4 (see figure 4.5), PTH produces the opposite effect of calcitonin. It stimulates osteoclast activity, raising the blood calcium levels. PTH also stimulates the intestines to absorb more calcium and the kidneys to retain calcium, which both raise the blood calcium level. PTH is essential for life. Without it, calcium levels would drop, and due to complex changes that follow, excess action potentials occur, which overstimulate skeletal muscle and cardiac muscle. Fortunately, PTH levels seldom drop that low, but if a surgeon must remove a patient's thyroid gland, care must be taken to leave at least one of the parathyroid glands in place.

The adrenal glands are actually two glands in one. They sit near the very top of each kidney. The inside of each gland is the adrenal medulla, and the outer layer of the gland is the adrenal cortex. The adrenal medulla produces epinephrine (E) and norepinephrine

(NE). As you learned in the previous module, these hormones increase the fight-or-flight response of the sympathetic division of the autonomic nervous system.

The adrenal cortex, on the other hand, produces about 50 hormones, including cortisol (kor' tih sol) and aldosterone (al dos' ter ohn). The amount of cortisol secreted from the adrenal cortex rises during times of stress. Cortisol does a number of things, but the main thing we want you to remember is that it increases the breakdown of protein and fat in many tissues. This is important because in times of stress, your brain needs a good supply of glucose. By stimulating the other tissues to break down fats and proteins, cortisol saves the glucose so that it can be used by the neurons in the brain. The other hormone, aldosterone, stimulates the kidneys to retain sodium, and therefore water, by the process of osmosis. In effect, when the body is low in salt, aldosterone levels rise to correct this imbalance. The pancreas is a part of both the digestive system and the endocrine system. Its job in the endocrine system is to produce insulin (in' suh lin) and glucagon (gloo' cuh gone). These hormones are produced in the pancreas by cells called pancreatic islets (also known as islets of Langerhans). Certain cells of the islets, called beta cells, secrete insulin. This hormone stimulates most cells of the body to take in glucose. The net effect of insulin, then, is to lower blood glucose levels. Other cells, called alpha cells, secrete glucagon, which has the opposite effect. It stimulates the liver to release glucose, which in turn increases the glucose level of the blood.

An interruption of the endocrine function of the pancreas leads to the condition known as diabetes mellitus (mel' ih tus). There are actually two types of diabetes mellitus. Type 1 diabetes mellitus, also called *insulin dependent diabetes mellitus*, occurs when the pancreas fails to produce insulin. As a consequence, cells do not readily take in glucose, and the blood glucose level stays high. Symptoms include eating and drinking in excessive amounts, as well as excessive urination. Typically, people with Type 1 diabetes mellitus are weak and lethargic, as their cells are forced to break down fats and proteins for energy rather than burning glucose. They tend to lose weight because of the breakdown of body fat. People with Type 1 diabetes mellitus can be treated with regular insulin injections or even implanted with insulin pumps so that the body gets the amount of insulin that it needs.

Type 2 diabetes mellitus, also called *non-insulin dependent diabetes mellitus*, illustrates the importance of receptors for hormones. It is caused by the body's cells being unable to respond to insulin efficiently due to few or no insulin receptors. Type 2 diabetes mellitus, which is more common but less severe than Type 1, is typically treated by controlling the diet, reducing excess body weight, and exercising. Medications are also used.

Many people familiar with diabetes mellitus simply call it diabetes. This is not really correct, however, since there is a completely different type of diabetes called diabetes insipidus. This diabetes is not related to the pancreas, however. It is the result of too little ADH, which, as you learned above, is secreted by the posterior pituitary gland. Compared with diabetes mellitus, however, this disease is quite rare. If untreated, people who have it urinate huge volumes of dilute urine daily, and must drink huge amounts of water to stay hydrated. As we mentioned before, ADH's job is to cause the kidneys to *retain* water.

MOD 10

The reproductive systems also have endocrine glands. In females, they are the ovaries, which produce estrogen and progesterone. In males, the reproductive endocrine glands are the testes, which produce testosterone. These sex hormones will be discussed in more detail when we discuss the reproductive system. For now, just realize that they promote the changes that occur at puberty and our reproductive capabilities.

The pineal (pine' ee uhl) body is a fascinating endocrine gland. As shown in figure 10.2, the pineal body is in the brain. It doesn't get light directly; however, nerve signals from the eyes profoundly affect the output of hormones from the pineal gland. When your eyes receive light, the pineal body produces serotonin (sayr uh toh' nin). When the eyes stop detecting light, it switches and starts producing its major hormone, melatonin (mel uh toh' nin). What does that do? It affects day-night cycles and reproductive readiness.

For example, the reproductive readiness of some animals is dependent on the relative length of night and day. When the days get shorter and the nights become longer, some animals become ready to reproduce. When this happens, we say that the female animals go into estrus (heat). Some animals like sheep, goats, and deer, go into estrus in the fall and winter because their pineal bodies react to shorter days and longer nights. Birds, on the other hand, react in the opposite way. Their pineal bodies stimulate reproductive readiness in the spring as the days become longer and the nights become shorter. Interestingly enough, in either case the young are born in the spring. This is because the time needed for pregnancy in the mammals mentioned above is longer than the time it takes for a bird's egg to hatch. For the young to be born in the spring, then, the mammals must be ready for reproduction sooner than the birds.

Well, that's how the pineal gland affects animals, but how does it affect humans? By releasing melatonin, it affects the release of GnRH by the hypothalamus. What does that do? The answer is that we don't really know. We do know certain things. We know that blind girls reach puberty sooner than sighted girls. We assume that this is related to the pineal body, as it receives light information from the eye. We do know that Inuits (Eskimos) in the Far North have a lower fertility rate compared with Eskimos

think about this

Expectations are usually established through the use of reliable patterns that predict what the outcome might be. Your life is filled with examples of things you take for granted. For example, the sun will set in the evening and rise in the morning. Changes in nature signal the passing seasons. Even though you may not be consciously aware of the changes, your body registers them and in some cases reacts to them!

who live farther south. As near as we can tell, it has to do with the unusual daylight cycle at the North Pole, which once again points to the pineal body. In addition, some researchers have noted that in cultures without electric lights, the female menstrual cycle (we will discuss that in more detail when we deal with reproduction) tends to be linked to the cycle of the moon. Once again, there is probably a light/pineal body connection. We also know that tumors that destroy the pineal body result in early sexual development, while tumors that result in too much secretion by the pineal body result in delayed sexual development. In the end, then, the pineal body affects human reproduction, at least to some degree.

There's also another completely different area of research involving the pineal gland, and that is how it affects sleep cycles. Remember, once the eyes stop detecting light, the pineal body begins producing melatonin. So, as soon as you turn out the lights, you start producing melatonin, which is a natural sleep aid. You can actually go out and buy a bottle of melatonin at a pharmacy, but don't waste your money. You can make your own; just turn out the lights! That is why we sleep better with the lights off; melatonin levels rise in the dark. In fact, a good tip for people with trouble sleeping is to sleep in an absolutely black room, because even small amounts of light go through the eyelids and affect the pineal body. Did you know that caffeine also reduces melatonin? Perhaps you're wondering how babies and little kids seem to sleep well even in bright light? Well, melatonin levels are high in youth and drop with age. That also helps to explain why older folks often complain of the inability to sleep well.

The last endocrine gland we want to discuss is the thymus (thigh' mus) gland. It secretes the hormone thymosin (thigh' moh sin), which is involved in the development of the immune system. We will be dealing with the immune system later, and we will discuss thymosin a bit more at that point.

Now it is important to note that the glands we have discussed in this section are considered the classic endocrine glands. However, there are other organs in the body that release important hormones. The heart, for example, produces a hormone called atrial natriuretic hormone, which causes the kidneys to excrete salt and water. The stomach and the small intestine produce hormones that control many aspects of digestion. The kidneys produce a hormone, erythropoietin, which stimulates red blood cell production in the bone marrow. Fatty tissue produces a hormone call leptin that signals the hypothalamus that you have had enough to eat. When a woman is pregnant, the placenta is also a major hormone gland. New hormones are being discovered all the time; that's why we want to emphasize that we are listing *major* hormones from major endocrine glands. There are many, many other hormones!

Endocrine Gland	Hormone Produced	Hormone Function
Hypothalamus	Growth hormone releasing hormone (GHRH)	Increases the release of GH from the anterior pituitary
	Corticotropin releasing hormone (CRH)	Increases the release of ACTH from the anterior pituitary
	Thyrotropin releasing hormone (TRH)	Increases the release of TSH from the anterior pituitary
	Prolactin inhibiting hormone (PIH)	Decreases the release of PRL from the anterior pituitary
	Gonadotropin releasing hormone (GnRH)	Increases the release of FSH and LH from the anterior pituitary
Anterior Pituitary	Growth hormone (GH)	Increases growth in most tissues
	Thyroid stimulating hormone (TSH)	Increases the release of thyroxine from the thyroid gland
	Adrenocorticotropic hormone (ACTH)	Increases the release of cortisol from the adrenal cortex
	Luteinizing hormone (LH)	Stimulates ovaries or testes
	Follicle stimulating hormone (FSH)	Stimulates ovaries or testes
	Prolactin (PRL)	Stimulates milk production in the breasts
	Melanocyte stimulating hormone (MSH)	Increases the synthesis of melanin in melanocytes
Posterior Pituitary	Antidiuretic hormone (ADH)	Increases the retention of water by the kidneys
	Oxytocin (OT)	Increases the contractions of the uterus during birth and promotes the release of breast milk

TABLE 10.1
A Review of the Major Endocrine Glands,
the Hormones Produced, and the Hormone Function

Endocrine Gland	Hormone Produced	Hormone Function
Thyroid	Thyroxine (TH)	Increases the metabolic rate of most cells
	Calcitonin	Lowers blood calcium levels
Parathyroid glands	Parathyroid hormone (PTH)	Increases blood calcium levels
Adrenal medulla	Epinephrine (E)	Increases sympathetic response
	Norepinephrine (NE)	Increases sympathetic response
Adrenal cortex	Cortisol	Increases protein and fat breakdown in most tissues
	Aldosterone	Increases the retention of sodium and water by the kidneys
Pancreas	Insulin	Lowers blood glucose by stimulating cells to take in glucose
	Glucagon	Raises blood glucose by causing liver to release glucose
Ovaries	Estrogen	Reproductive hormone in females
	Progesterone	Reproductive hormone in females
Testes	Testosterone	Reproductive hormone in males
Pineal body	Melatonin	Affects release of GnRH by hypothalamus; affects day/night sleep cycles
Thymus	Thymosin	Develops immune functions

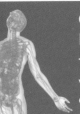

COLORING BOOK
EXERCISE 10.1

To review the endocrine system as a whole, as well as the individual glands, follow the instructions on pages 175-189 of the coloring book.

HORMONE CHEMISTRY

Hormones are chemicals that are designed to produce a response in a target cell. So, it is important to know a bit about the chemistry of hormones. We can classify hormones into three different groups: amine (uh meen'), steroid, or protein/peptide. Amines are hormones that have been derived from an amino acid. Steroid hormones are made from cholesterol. The majority of hormones are neither amines nor steroids; they are proteins or peptides. Now remember, a protein is a long chain of amino acids. A peptide is just a short chain of amino acids. You can therefore think of a peptide as a "mini-protein."

Epinephrine, norepinephrine and thyroxine are all amine hormones; that is, they are derived from amino acids. Now, here's an interesting principle. If hormones have similar chemical characteristics, they will tend to be able to fit into each other's receptors. As a result, they will overlap in their functions. Well, it turns out that these three hormones—E, NE, and TH—are all derivatives of the same amino acid, called tyrosine. As a result, they have similar characteristics, and, therefore, overlapping activities. As you already know, E and NE are very similar in their activity. After all, they elevate heart rate, elevate blood pressure, and increase blood glucose levels. Well, even TH can do this. If a person's thyroid gland secretes too much TH, a condition called hyperthyroidism, the symptoms are elevated heart rate, elevated blood pressure, and a high metabolism. The person will even feel anxious. Melatonin is also an amino acid derivative. It's from a completely different amino acid, called tryptophan, so it does not produce overlapping effects with the first three we just mentioned.

Estrogen and progesterone are steroids, as they are derived from cholesterol. They are also chemically similar, so their functions overlap to some extent. The male sex hormone, testosterone, is also a steroid. (The sterone in progesterone and testosterone indicates that they are derivatives of cholesterol.) In addition, the hormones of the adrenal cortex, cortisol and aldosterone, are steroids. If a hormone is from the ovary, the testes, or the adrenal cortex, then, it is a steroid hormone.

If a hormone is neither an amine nor a steroid, it's a peptide or protein. So, all of the other hormones mentioned in the previous section (parathyroid hormone, insulin, oxytocin, etc.) are either peptides or proteins. In this course, we will not distinguish between peptide hormones and protein hormones, but they can be distinguished. This, of course, is based on size. Proteins are huge molecules, while peptides are much smaller. Protein hormones may contain 50 to several hundred amino acids, whereas peptides may contain only about ten amino acids. Protein/peptide hormones can be quite different from one another, or rather similar. Like amines and steroids, if they are chemically similar, they may be able to bind to the same receptors and cause similar responses in the target cell.

HORMONE SECRETION CONTROL

Remember from figure 10.1 that the control scheme of the endocrine system starts with the endocrine glands. Hormones are synthesized, stored, and secreted by these glands. The target cells cannot respond to the hormone until it is secreted into the bloodstream, so it is

interesting to study how the gland "knows" when to secrete a hormone and when to stop secreting it. This is, of course, an important process, since the endocrine system must not secrete hormones at random times! After all, the adrenal medulla secretes the hormones epinephrine and norepinephrine, which speed up the heart rate, raise the blood pressure, and cause the body to prepare for fight-or-flight. You certainly don't want that to happen while you are trying to sleep! What, then, controls the release of hormones?

There are three major ways that hormone release is controlled in the body. The first is called nonhormonal regulation. In this process, a chemical *other than a hormone* is involved in regulating the release of a hormone. An example of this can be found in the pancreas. The release of insulin is mainly controlled by the level of glucose in the blood. When blood enters the pancreas, the blood glucose level directly affects the islets, which form the endocrine portion of the pancreas. If blood glucose levels are high, the islets secrete more insulin. This causes most of the cells of the body to take in glucose, therefore lowering blood glucose levels. When the blood glucose levels are low, the pancreas secretes less insulin, reducing the amount of glucose taken in by the cells of the body. This, in turn, helps to maintain blood glucose levels. This negative-feedback system is controlled directly by the level of glucose in the blood. That's nonhormonal regulation. For another example of nonhormonal regulation, see figure 4.6, which shows that blood calcium, a nonhormonal substance, controls the secretion of PTH.

The second mode of regulation is the direct neural control of the hormone gland by the nervous system. The field of physiology called neuroendocrinology focuses on how the nervous system exerts control over the endocrine glands. In direct neural control, this field of study has shown that the nervous system can control the endocrine system via *neurotransmitters* or *neurohormones*.

A good example of direct neural control by neurotransmitter comes from the adrenal medulla. Stimuli such as stress or exercise activate the sympathetic division of the ANS. Sympathetic neurons synapse directly with the cells of the adrenal medulla. When action potentials travel along these neurons, they release neurotransmitter at the synapse. In response, the cells of the adrenal medulla release epinephrine and nor-epinephrine as hormones into the blood. Once the stress disappears, the sympathetic division stops sending action potentials down the neurons, and the secretion of the neurotransmitter stops. In the absence of the neurotransmitter, the cells of the adrenal medulla reduce their secretion of E and NE.

Not only does the nervous system control certain endocrine glands via the release of neurotransmitter, it also controls other endocrine glands via the release of neurohormones. How does that work? Well, consider figure 10.3.

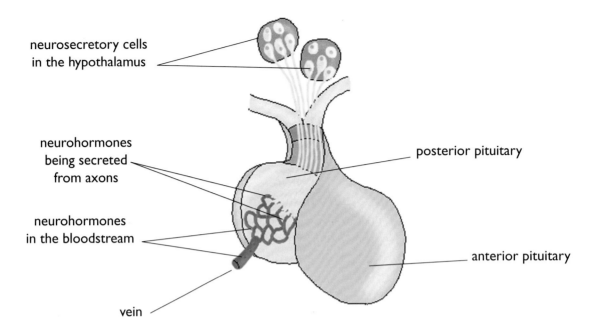

neurosecretory cells
in the hypothalamus

neurohormones
being secreted
from axons

neurohormones
in the bloodstream

posterior pituitary

anterior pituitary

vein

FIGURE 10.3
Hypothalamus Control of the Posterior Pituitary Gland
Illustration by Megan Whitaker

Now remember, the pituitary gland is made up of two separate glands: the posterior pituitary gland and the anterior pituitary gland. In this figure, we are concentrating on the means by which the hypothalamus controls the posterior pituitary gland. In the hypothalamus are neurons whose axons travel down the infundibulum (in fun dib' you lum), which is the connection between the hypothalamus and the pituitary gland. These axons travel all the way to the posterior pituitary where they secrete chemicals. These chemicals, however, are not neurotransmitters. They are *neurohormones*.

What are these neurohormones? They are products of neurons, but they are secreted into the blood. There are two major neurohormones in the posterior pituitary, oxytocin (OT) and ADH. Now, wait a minute. Didn't we say earlier that OT and ADH are hormones released by the posterior pituitary gland? Yes, we did. Look at the figure. Although the neurons originate in the hypothalamus, they store the hormones in the posterior pituitary gland. As you can see in the figure, the hormone is released by the neurons into the veins that run through the posterior pituitary gland. Since these neurons are specialized, in that they secrete neurohormones into the blood rather than neurotransmitters, we call them neurosecretory cells.

Neurosecretory cells—Neurons of the hypothalamus that secrete neurohormones rather than neurotransmitters

You can think of the posterior pituitary gland as an extension of the hypothalamus. It is the neurons whose cell bodies are in the hypothalamus that actually synthesize the hormones of the posterior pituitary gland. It is action potentials on the axons of these neurons that stimulate the release of the neurohormones.

What causes the hypothalamus to signal the release of these two hormones by action potentials on the axons? In the case of OT, neural signals from the uterus during labor, or neural signals from the breast as a baby nurses, are sent to the hypothalamus. In response, the neurosecretory cells that produce oxytocin undergo action potentials, and oxytocin is released into the blood.

In the case of ADH, which causes the kidneys to retain water, other neurosecretory cells are involved. We need to retain water when fluid is in short supply in our body. As our body loses water, all cells begin to shrink a bit. That tiny shrinkage of the hypothalamic neurosecretory cells for ADH is the actual signal for these cells to produce ADH! This is an amazing example of negative feedback, as the ADH signals the kidneys not to produce much urine. ADH also stimulates thirst.

Both oxytocin and ADH are peptide hormones, and they are somewhat similar to one another chemically. They have slightly overlapping functions. For example, when a woman nurses a baby, the OT causes milk letdown, so that the milk moves forward in the milk ducts of the breast. At the same time, she often suddenly feels thirsty!

The third way that hormone release is controlled is called hormonal control. A good way to illustrate this is to show how the hypothalamus controls the *anterior* pituitary gland, as shown in figure 10.4.

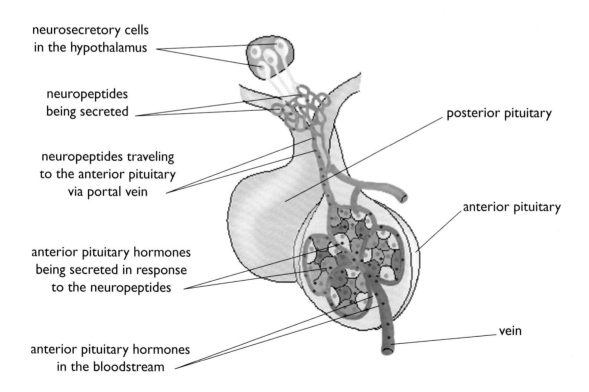

neurosecretory cells
in the hypothalamus

neuropeptides
being secreted

posterior pituitary

neuropeptides traveling
to the anterior pituitary
via portal vein

anterior pituitary

anterior pituitary hormones
being secreted in response
to the neuropeptides

vein

anterior pituitary hormones
in the bloodstream

FIGURE 10.4
Hypothalamic Control of the Anterior Pituitary Gland
Illustration by Megan Whitaker

In figure 10.4, you see the pituitary gland again, but this time, the figure concentrates on the anterior pituitary gland. Notice how this figure differs from the previous one. In the posterior pituitary gland, the neurosecretory cells extend from the hypothalamus into the gland and release the neurohormones into the bloodstream. In figure 10.4, however, the neurons do not extend into the gland. Instead, they release their hormones, called neuropeptides, into the blood, and the blood carries the hormones directly to the anterior pituitary gland via a special vein called the portal vein. Most of these neuropeptides then stimulate the anterior pituitary gland to release its own hormones. In some cases, the hypothalamus secretes hormones that *inhibit* specific anterior pituitary hormones.

Do you now see why we say that the anterior and posterior pituitary glands are completely different glands? The hormones of the posterior pituitary gland are secreted into the bloodstream directly by the neurosecretory cells of the hypothalamus. The hormones of the posterior pituitary gland are, in reality, produced by cells of the hypothalamus. That is not the case in the anterior pituitary gland. In this gland, the hormones are secreted by the cells of the gland itself. Anterior pituitary cells are *controlled* by hormones released by the neurosecretory cells of the hypothalamus.

In order to make this a little clearer, we want to give you a concrete example. Let's consider the thyroid hormone, thyroxine. The release of this hormone is ultimately controlled via hormones from the hypothalamus. How? First, the hypothalamus is stimulated. For example, the hypothalamus has a control center for temperature. Long-term, cold temperatures resulting in low body temperature stimulate the hypothalamus to produce thyroid stimulating hormone releasing hormone (TSH-RH), most often called thyrotropin releasing hormone (TRH). This "releasing hormone" goes into the portal vein on a direct concentrated route to the anterior pituitary gland. Once cells of the anterior pituitary gland with receptors to TRH bind to this hormone, it stimulates them to release their own hormone, thyroid stimulating hormone (TSH). The TSH then enters the bloodstream.

Once in the bloodstream, TSH travels all over the body. However, it only affects one part of the body: the thyroid gland. Why? The thyroid gland is the only part of the body whose cells have *receptors* for TSH. So, the TSH travels all around the body, but it only stimulates cells in the thyroid gland. What does it cause them to do? It causes thyroid cells to release thyroxine into the bloodstream. Now, unlike TSH, thyroxine affects most body cells, causing them to increase their oxygen usage by burning more cellular fuel. This produces heat, which warms the body. Thyroxine affects the hypothalamus in a particular way. When the hypothalamus detects a certain level of thyroxine in the blood, it "knows" that it has succeeded in stimulating the thyroid, and so it decreases its production of TRH.

We really want to make sure you understand this, so let's summarize it with figure 10.5.

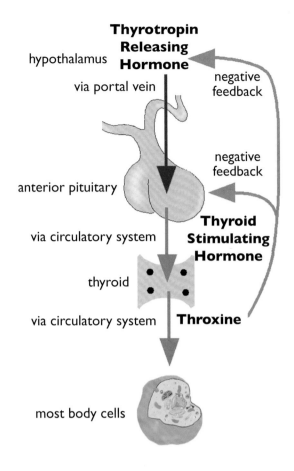

FIGURE 10.5
Control of Thyroxine Secretion by the Hypothalamus
Illustration by Megan Whitaker

A disease called Graves' disease occurs when antibodies abnormally block the hypo-thalamus from sensing thyroxine. In effect, then, the hypothalamus doesn't sense the thyroxine. What do you think it will do? It will continue to release TRH. This, of course, will increase the release of TSH from the anterior pituitary gland, which will in turn increase the release of thyroxine from the thyroid. The result is hyperthyroidism. If left untreated, the thyroid will grow big, and the metabolism rate will get too high. The enlarged thyroid is called as hyperthyroid goiter. Because of the overlapping function of chemically similar hormones, this results in fight-or-flight effects similar to what happens when epinephrine and norepinephrine are released. As we already men-tioned, the three hormones are chemically related.

Of course, other problems affect this system. For example, your thyroid gland needs iodine to make thyroxine. There are parts of the world where it's difficult to get iodine. It used to be true in parts of the United States, but we iodize salt so that everyone can easily get iodine.

MOD 10

What happens if you can't get iodine? Without iodine, your thyroid gland simply cannot make thyroxine. As a result, the hypothalamus does not detect thyroxine in the blood, so it continues to release TRH. The anterior pituitary gland, in turn, continues to release TSH. However, since the thyroid cannot make thyroxine, this does not lead to an increase in thyroxine levels. Without thyroxine, the body's cells cannot be stimulated to increase their metabolic rate. Nevertheless, the hypothalamus is still releasing TRH, and the anterior pituitary is still releasing TSH. What happens, then? The TSH promotes growth of the thyroid gland, but no thyroxine is released. This leads to hypothyroidism, in which the low metabolism causes weight gain, a sense of being too cold, and many other problems. In this condition, the enlarged thyroid is called a hypothyroid goiter.

ON YOUR OWN

10.4 Although we separated out the three means by which hormone secretion is controlled, a given hormone might be controlled by two or more of these mechanisms. For example, the release of insulin from the pancreas can be stimulated in any of the following ways:

    a. Increased blood glucose levels are the major stimulus for the pancreas to release insulin.

    b. Both divisions of the ANS innervate the pancreas. Action potentials in the parasympathetic division cause an increase in the release of insulin, while action potentials in the sympathetic division decrease the release of insulin.

    c. Hormones released by the stomach and small intestine increase the release of insulin by the pancreas.

For each situation (a, b, and c), indicate which mode of control (nonhormonal, direct neural, or hormonal) is being used.

10.5 The hypothalamus is releasing an inhibiting hormone. Is it affecting the posterior pituitary gland or the anterior pituitary gland?

PATTERNS OF HORMONE SECRETION

Now that you have learned how hormone secretion is *controlled*, it is important to realize that this control is designed to cause a given *pattern* of hormone secretion. For example, we spent a lot of time in the previous section discussing how the release of thyroxine is increased or decreased by hypothalamic control. However, what is the normal mode of thyroxine secretion? In other words, is thyroxine *only* secreted when the hypothalamus is stimulated, or is there some standard level of thyroxine secretion that is simply modified by the hypothalamus? Well, in the human body, the control mechanisms result in three distinct patterns of hormonal secretion control.

The first pattern of secretion is constant secretion. Hormones that conform to this pattern are produced by the body in a more or less even amount. The control mechanisms that act on these hormones maintain this constant level of secretion. Thyroxine is an excellent example of such a hormone secretion

pattern. If you live mostly indoors, thyroxine levels are fairly stable. However, the hypothalamus *can* either raise or lower this constant level through changes in TRH, in order to adjust to stresses such as a change in climate.

The second pattern is called acute response. In this pattern of hormone secretion, the hormone is at low levels in the body until a particular stimulus occurs. Then, the production of hormone increases quickly in response to the stimulus. Once the stimulus goes away, the production drops off quickly. Epinephrine and norepinephrine are excellent examples of acute response hormones. They are produced in response to emotional or physical stress. A stressful stimulus will cause them to be secreted, and, the larger the stress, the larger the amount of epinephrine and norepinephrine.

The third pattern of secretion is cyclic secretion. Hormones that follow this pattern are secreted on a regular, predictable cycle. For example, estrogen and progesterone in women are secreted on a monthly cycle, which is called the menstrual cycle. The male hormone, testosterone, is secreted on a daily cycle. The level of testosterone in a male is higher in the morning and lower by evening.

HORMONE RECEPTORS IN THE BODY

If you want to call or text a friend, you need a phone, of course. If your friend is to receive your message, he or she must also have a phone. In the same way, hormone glands and hormones cannot do their work unless the target cells can *receive* the message. Hormone receptors are proteins on or within target cells that complete the link. They are essential to the work of the endocrine system. For example, Type 2 diabetes mellitus is a disease caused by a lack of receptors for insulin. We must have both hormones *and* receptors in order to achieve endocrine control of the body.

There are two types of hormone receptors: membrane-bound receptors and nuclear receptors. As the name implies, membrane-bound receptors are located on the plasma membrane of the target cell. The hormone binds to the receptor like a key fits into a lock. Unless a chemical has a very similar shape to a given hormone, then, it will not affect that hormone's receptor, because it cannot fit into the "lock."

It's easy to remember what kinds of hormones stimulate membrane-bound receptors: protein and peptide hormones, and amine hormones except thyroxine. Why? Proteins and peptides are very large, water-soluble (polar) molecules. They're too big to enter the cell, so they can only affect the cell from the outside. So, the receptor for the hormone must reside on the cell membrane. Most amine hormones are also slightly too big and too polar to enter cells, so they also require membrane-bound receptors. Thyroxine is an exception; it can enter its target cells.

ON YOUR OWN

10.6 he graphs below illustrate the level of hormones in the body at a given time. Indicate which of the three secretion patterns they represent.

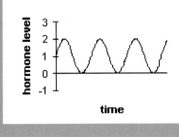

a.

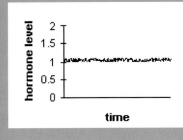

b.

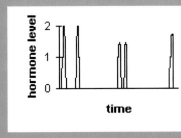

c.

think about this

The membrane-bound receptor/hormone reaction actually fits the lock and key analogy very well. Consider what happens when you put a key in the ignition of a car and turn it. The car starts, right? The car has everything it needs to start (engine, gasoline, etc.) before you turn the key. When you turn the key in the ignition, that gives the car a signal to initiate a sequence of events that ends with the car starting.

When a hormone interacts with a membrane-bound receptor, something similar happens. The cell already has the complex cellular machinery needed to produce the response. The hormone/receptor interaction is just the signal telling the cell to get it all going. So, this interaction activates enzymes or other molecules that are already inside the cell. Because of this, the membrane-bound receptor/hormone interaction produces a relatively fast response, perhaps a few seconds to a few minutes.

Compare this to what happens when hormones interact with nuclear receptors. In this process, the hormone actually diffuses into the cell, travels through the cytoplasm and into the nucleus. There, the hormone binds to a receptor protein in the nucleus, and that receptor/protein complex activates a specific gene in the DNA. What is the result? The activated gene is transcribed to make mRNA, which in turn contains the information to make a protein or enzyme, according to the protein synthesis mechanisms you learned about previously. That new protein or enzyme is what produces the response of the target cell.

ON YOUR OWN

10.7 What kind of receptor is used to respond to the sex hormones (estrogen, progesterone, and testosterone)?

10.8 Epinephrine increases certain smooth muscle contractions by stimulating the release of calcium ions which were already inside smooth muscle cells. Is the receptor nuclear or membrane-bound?

This kind of interaction, then, helps the cell produce something that was not in the cell before. Unlike the membrane-bound receptor/hormone interaction, this interaction is relatively slow; the cell must synthesize the proteins that are needed. Steroid hormones stimulate cells via nuclear receptors because they are lipid-soluble. Remember from module 1 that lipid-soluble molecules can diffuse right through the plasma membrane, so steroids have ready access to the inside of the cell, even the nucleus. Although thyroxine is an amine hormone, it also has nuclear receptors.

As we've said, receptors are equally as important to endocrine function as the hormone itself. Hormones are carried all over the body, but only cells with receptors (target cells) respond to particular hormones. But, there is yet another way that receptors contribute to endocrine control. They can increase or decrease!

Up-regulation occurs when target cells make more of a receptor. Can you see that that will make the target cell more sensitive to the hormone? Sometimes one hormone influences a target cell to make more receptors to another hormone, so that the cell becomes more responsive to the second hormone. At puberty, up-regulation explains many of the changes that occur within cells.

Two drugs used in childbirth provide a good example of up-regulation. Pitocin is a drug that strengthens contractions of the uterus in order to speed up labor. How does it work? It is an artificial version of oxytocin (ox' ih toh sin), the hormone that causes the uterus to contract. The increased hormone gives increased response. Another drug, called Cytotec, also speeds up labor, but it does so by stimulating uterine cells to increase the number of receptors for oxytocin. Do you see the difference there? The first drug increases the concentration of the hormone to increase the response; the second drug increases the number of receptors in order to increase response.

Down-regulation of receptors occurs when a target cell loses receptors to a particular hormone, making the target cell less sensitive to that hormone. Since receptors are proteins, they naturally break down over time. If a target cell does not make as many receptors as it had been making, down-regulation occurs.

PROSTAGLANDINS

Prostaglandins (pros stuh glan' dinz) are not hormones, but they are an important example of chemicals that are secreted into the interstitial fluid around the cells that secrete them. Prostaglandins do not travel far from the cells that secrete them, but they are powerful signal molecules even in tiny amounts.

> **Prostaglandins**—Biologically active lipids that produce many effects in the body, including smooth muscle contraction, inflammation, and blood clotting

There are three major classes of prostaglandins, Pg 1, Pg 2, and Pg 3. All are derivatives of fatty acids, but they often have opposite effects on various body tissues. For example, some prostaglandins increase smooth muscle contraction, blood clotting, and inflammation. People refer to these prostaglandins as bad ones, though of course our body needs the right amount of smooth muscle contraction, blood clotting, and inflammation. (Inflammation may be unpleasant and cause pain, but it enables the body to fight infection.) They are called bad only because they are often too plentiful in the body, producing too much of these responses.

Other prostaglandins do exactly the opposite, relaxing smooth muscle, decreasing blood clotting, and decreasing inflammation. They are sometimes referred to as good prostaglandins, because they may be in short supply in the body, and we generally need more of them.

Since prostaglandins are derivatives of fatty acids, and since fatty acids are obtained from the diet, new research shows how the quality of the diet affects the production of bad versus good prostaglandins. Healthy oils such as fish oil contain the precursor molecules for the good prostaglandins. If you have heard the expression "heart-healthy fish oil," it refers to the fact that the good prostaglandins prevent excess blood clotting that can block heart vessels. They also relax the smooth muscle that lines the arteries. That helps lower blood pressure. Inflammation in blood vessels is also reduced by the good prostaglandins. That's healthy, because inflammation is related to the hardening of the arteries that raises blood pressure and clogs the arteries that supply the heart.

Maybe you have heard of adults who take a low dose of aspirin daily for heart health. For many years aspirin was known to be an anti-inflammatory agent, but no one knew how it worked. Now we know that aspirin works by reducing the formation of prostaglandins, especially the bad ones, which tend to be more plentiful (probably because of our modern diet). The low-dose aspirin helps prevent excess blood clotting and inflammation, both of which are damaging to the circulatory system.

By understanding prostaglandins, we can understand how aspirin can do so many different things. How can it relieve a headache, a backache, or a sore thumb that you slammed in a door? Now you know: It decreases prostaglandins that cause inflammation!

As promised, this module was a little shorter than the previous one so as to even out the difficulty somewhat. Do not be fooled by the size of the module, however. Just as the size of a book in the Bible is not indicative of that book's importance, the size of this module does not imply that the endocrine system is less important than other systems in the body! Learning about your body's communication systems and chemical messengers is important to your study of physiology.

ANSWERS TO THE "ON YOUR OWN" QUESTIONS

10.1 The first cell has no receptors for the hormone. The second cell has receptors for the hormone. Remember, for a hormone to affect a cell, the target cell must have receptors.

10.2 The home pregnancy tests are trying to detect a particular hormone in the urine. If the hormone is detected, about the only explanation is that the woman is pregnant. However, there are many explanations for *not detecting* the hormone. For example, the woman may not be far enough along in the pregnancy to produce a lot of hormone. So, the hormone levels might be below the testing threshold. Also, the testing materials might be out-of-date or the urine might have been tested too long after it had been collected.

10.3 a. Epinephrine, norepinephrine, thyroxine, and melatonin are all amines.
 b. The sex hormones and the hormones of the adrenal cortex are steroids. The rest are proteins or peptides.

10.4 a. This is nonhormonal control, as the glucose causing the insulin to be secreted is not a hormone.
 b. This is direct neural control, as the nerves are controlling the glands.
 c. This is hormonal control, as hormones are causing the endocrine response.

10.5 The hypothalamus controls the posterior pituitary because its neurons reach down into the posterior pituitary and directly release the hormones. Therefore, it must be controlling the anterior pituitary in this case, because only the anterior pituitary secretes releasing or inhibiting hormones, which then cause the desired pituitary response.

10.6 The graph in (a) represents the cyclic secretion, since the hormone appears in a repeated cycle. The graph in (b) is constant secretion, since the level is reasonably constant. The wiggles just show the minor variations needed to preserve homeostasis. The graph in (c) represents acute response, since the hormone appears and disappears quickly in no repeating pattern. There must have been a stimulus for each peak even though they are not shown.

10.7 Sex hormones are steroids, so they must reach nuclear receptors.

10.8 The cell is not making something new. So, this is a membrane-bound receptor.

STUDY GUIDE FOR MODULE 10

1. Define the following:
   a. Neurosecretory cells
   b. Prostaglandins

2. Compare the nervous and endocrine systems in terms of:
   a. speed of response
   b. duration of influence
   c. effectors controlled
   d. strength of the signal
   e. ability to be repaired

3. Under what conditions would a hormone need a carrier protein?

4. What two ways are hormones eliminated from the body?

5. Identify the glands in the following figure:

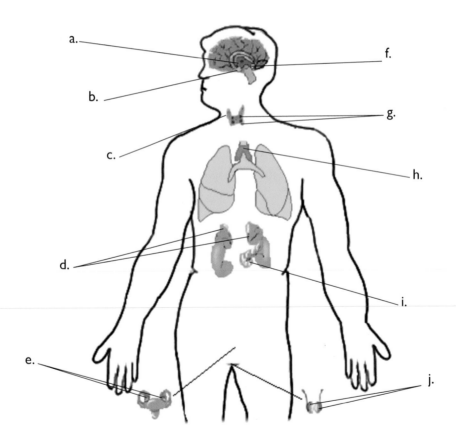

6. For each of the glands shown above, list the hormones produced and the effects of those hormones. For the pituitary and adrenal glands, split them into their two parts (i.e., anterior pituitary and posterior pituitary) when you make the list.

7. What are the three basic types of hormones? Which stimulate membrane-bound receptors only? Which stimulate nuclear receptors only?

8. List the three ways that secretion of hormones is controlled. Briefly describe each one.

9. The level of a particular hormone in the body varies widely. Although it varies, the level can be predicted based on the time of day that it is measured. Which pattern of secretion is this?

10. A hormone interacts with a receptor, stimulating the cell to synthesize and secrete a new protein. Is the receptor a nuclear receptor or membrane-bound?

11. A target cell for a particular hormone seems to respond more strongly than it did in the past. List two ways that this could occur.

12. If a person has a painful, bleeding injury to the nose, should aspirin be given to help? Why or why not?

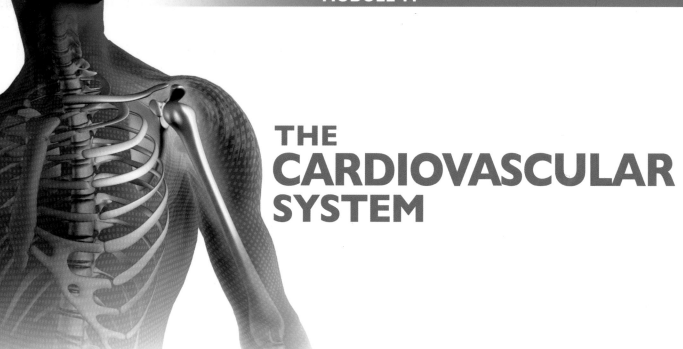

THE CARDIOVASCULAR SYSTEM

Think for a moment about these two words: *heart* and *blood*. Are there any words for bodily parts that have deeper meaning in our everyday speech? "Blood is thicker than water," we say (meaning we need to put up with our relatives because they are related to us). We worry about "bad blood" between former friends. In the news we hear about the possibility of "bloodshed" between warring nations. We talk about people's passions, their motivating force, as their very "lifeblood." When it comes to our Lord Jesus Christ, we claim His blood as the price of our salvation.

heart of the matter

There is great emotion tied up in the anatomical word *heart*. We give our heart, share our heart, and pour out our heart. We win our lover's heart. We can be bighearted, but truly great people are greathearted. We can be tenderhearted and softhearted—but hopefully not hard-hearted! A heart can be broken; a heart can ache. We might be fainthearted, though we try to be stouthearted. Yes, heart is a hearty word, filled with layers of meanings that we hold in our heart of hearts. Check out the concordance of your Bible for some of the most beautiful uses of the word heart in the English language.

He is so rich in kindness and grace that he purchased our freedom
with the blood of his Son and forgave our sins.
—Ephesians 1:7, NLT

Why should these words have such intense meaning? As we will see, "lifeblood" comes close to answering that question. Blood means life. Loss of enough blood means death. The way that the heart responds to emotions by speeding up and pounding has given us those rich words that mean love, courage, loyalty, generosity, or deep sincerity—heart!

340

The cardiovascular system, the topic of this module, puts the blood together with the heart, which pumps the blood through the blood vessels. As you will soon appreciate, it is not just the blood, but the *flow of blood*, that is essential for life. Blood is a transport medium first, but it must have a power source to move it, and it must have vessels through which to flow. If we compare the blood to an electric commuter train, then the heart is the power source that moves the train, and the blood vessels are the rails that carry the train.

Like the commuter train that picks up and drops off people and goods all day long as it goes round and round the tracks, blood is a transport medium. It picks up oxygen (O_2) from the lungs and drops it off in the tissues. At the same time it picks up carbon dioxide (CO_2) from the tissues and drops it off in the lungs. Meanwhile, it is transporting nutrients from the small intestine to the liver first, and then to all body cells. Simultaneously, it transports wastes from the tissues to the kidneys, and hormones from the endocrine glands to the cells throughout the body. Talk about multitasking!

How fast does your blood circulate over its "rails"—the blood vessels? Every minute all of your body's blood goes through your heart, even when you are at rest. So, blood travels at a quick pace. If you are doing vigorous exercise, your blood travels so quickly that all your blood travels through your heart three or four times as fast—every 15 to 20 seconds. If you are a trained athlete, your blood may be able to travel five or six times as fast as it does at rest. It is the heart, of course, that produces that amazing power.

Blood is a transport medium, but it is also a regulatory tissue. It regulates fluid volume. Blood picks up fluid from the intestines and quickly moves it around the body, so that all tissues receive the fluids they require. In addition, it equalizes temperature differences between warm and cold parts of the body. If you are outside in cold weather, your skin gets cold. Why? To help regulate the body's temperature, the blood vessels of the skin constrict, squeezing the blood away from the surface to the deeper, warmer parts of the body. Yet, if the skin gets too cold, those same vessels open up, allowing the blood to return to the surface to warm up the skin again. The blood regulates the pH of the tissues as well. The blood and tissues are highly sensitive to pH, but the blood keeps a tight control over acid-base changes through chemicals called buffers.

Blood is a protective tissue. It's protective against fluid loss. When you get a cut and start bleeding, there are mechanisms right within the blood to stop the bleeding. That process is called hemostasis, and we will soon discuss it. Blood is also protective against infection because of the function of the white blood cells. These cells, like a defensive army, circulate around the body, detecting foreign invaders and calling in reinforcements—other white blood cells—to fight infections, which foreign invaders such as bacteria and viruses cause.

THE COMPOSITION OF BLOOD

Now that you know the functions of this vital connective tissue, it's time to learn more details about the makeup of blood. As you know, blood is a liquid. One of the most descriptive aspects of a liquid is its viscosity.

Viscosity—The resistance to flow and alteration of shape due to cohesion

That's a mouthful, isn't it? The layman's term for viscosity is thickness. Consider honey and water. If you tip a glass of water, the water flows out of the glass freely. Honey, on the other hand, does not flow easily. It you tip a jar of honey over, it slowly oozes out of the jar. Also, a balloon full of honey would be much harder to squeeze into various shapes than a balloon full of water. Honey is more viscous than water. In the same way, blood is about three times more viscous than water. The old saying, then, is true. Blood *is* thicker than water! It is actually the red blood cells (RBCs) that give the blood this property. These cells have a slight cohesion (stickiness) that causes them to resist flowing to a small extent.

Another important description of any type of matter is its density. Blood has a plenty of water in it, but it is still slightly denser than water. That's because RBCs contain iron, which is very dense compared to water. If you donate blood, the person preparing you for your donation may check you for iron-deficiency anemia by taking a drop of your blood and dropping it into a solution. They will time how quickly it drops to the bottom of the tube. Denser blood drops faster, indirectly indicating its iron content.

The pH of blood must be tightly controlled because many of the chemical reactions of the body work properly only within a narrow range of pH. The pH of blood ranges from 7.35 to 7.45. You should be very impressed with how tiny this range is! After all, you put acids and bases into your body all the time. Many fruits and fruit juices are acidic. Orange juice has a pH between 4 and 5, for example. Nevertheless, your blood's pH does not fall lower than 7.35 under normal conditions. That's because it is designed with an elegant buffering system.

Blood volume is also a physical property to consider. A typical adult has about 5 to 6 liters of blood in his or her body. That's about 8% of an adult's body weight. If you think about it, that's not really a lot! Nevertheless, it can transport all of the raw materials that cells need, and it can carry all of the waste products away from them.

What is blood actually made of? Blood can be separated into two basic parts: plasma and formed elements. This can be seen in figure 11.1.

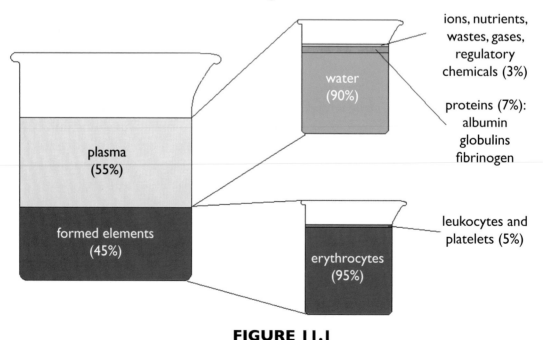

FIGURE 11.1
The Composition of Blood
Illustration by Megan Whitaker

Plasma—The fluid portion of the blood, which is mostly water, about 55% by volume

Formed elements of blood—The red blood cells, white blood cells, and cell fragments called platelets, about 45% by volume

Blood plasma is a pale, yellow liquid that is about 90% water. The other 10% consists mainly of proteins, and also gases, nutrients, ions, and waste products. There are three basic types of proteins in plasma: albumin (al byou' min), globulins (glob' you linz), and fibrinogen (fye brin' oh jen). Albumin is a small protein, synthesized by the liver, that regulates the movement of water between tissues and the blood by the process of osmosis. It makes up more than half the proteins in the plasma. The globulins constitute just over one-third of the proteins in the plasma. Some globulins act as carrier proteins, while others, called gamma globulins, are antibodies responsible for fighting off infections. Fibrinogen is an inactive protein, but it plays a critical role when injury occurs. It can be activated to form a blood clot if bleeding occurs.

We lose water constantly from the kidneys as urine, from the lungs as water vapor, and from the skin as perspiration. We gain water from the intake of fluids and foods. Despite variations in all of these, the amount of plasma in the blood stays fairly constant.

What about the formed elements of blood? Figure 11.2 is a wonderful electron photomicrograph image of blood, showing you some of the formed elements. To get this image, blood is smeared out, and then a scanning electron microscope goes over and over the smear. The results of these scans are fed into a computer, and the computer then generates the image you see. The colors are added later because electron microscopes do not detect color as they use electron beams, not light, to view the sample.

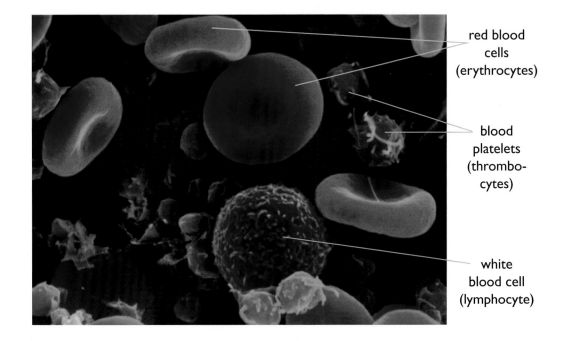

red blood cells (erythrocytes)

blood platelets (thrombo-cytes)

white blood cell (lymphocyte)

FIGURE 11.2
Electron Micrograph of Blood
Photo © Phototake/Dennis Kunkel

The first things you probably noticed in the image were the red blood cells (RBCs), which make up about 95% of the formed elements of blood. Red blood cells are disk-shaped, but the disk is flattened, like thumbprint cookies. Technically, they are called erythrocytes (uh rith' roh sights). These cells carry the O_2 between the lungs and the cells.

Erythrocytes—Red blood cells that carry the O_2 in blood

Now, why do we need a carrier for O_2? Oxygen is nonpolar. So, it does not mix well with the water in the blood. Less than 2% of the O_2 that your body needs can dissolve in the watery plasma. As a result, O_2 must have a carrier in order to be able to travel in blood. The RBCs contain that carrier, the iron-containing protein complex called hemoglobin.

The remaining 5% of the formed elements in blood are leukocytes (loo' koh sights), which are commonly known as white blood cells, and thrombocytes, which are also called platelets.

Leukocytes—White blood cells that perform defensive functions in blood

White blood cells perform various functions related to protecting the body in times of infection or inflammation. There are five types of leukocytes, and we will discuss them all in the next section of this module.

Thrombocytes, on the other hand, are not cells. That is why they look so small compared to RBCs in the electron micrograph of figure 11.2. Thrombocytes are actually fragments of white blood cells called megakaryocytes, which are found in the bone marrow. If activated, thrombocytes function in preventing blood loss after an injury to a blood vessel.

Thrombocytes—Cell fragments in blood that help prevent blood loss

ON YOUR OWN

11.1 Why must blood flow?

11.2 What are the basic functions of blood?

11.3 What percentage of blood is composed of water?

11.4 If the percentage of RBCs in the blood goes up above the normal 45%, what happens to the viscosity of the blood? Why?

11.5 If the percentage of RBCs in the blood goes down to 33% (which is sufficient to sustain life), would it be harder or easier for the heart to pump blood? Why?

11.6 One type of blood test is a white blood cell count, in which the number of white blood cells in your blood are counted. If your white blood cell count is high, what might that mean?

THE FORMED ELEMENTS IN BLOOD

Now that you know the basic makeup of blood, we want to spend some time discussing blood cells. Let's start with the erythrocytes, which make up approximately 95% of the formed elements in blood. As shown in figure 11.2, these cells are biconcave disks, with the edge of the cell thicker than the center. The diameter of the average erythrocyte is about 7.5 micrometers, making them rather small cells. This shape is the perfect design for transport of O_2 through the blood vessels. Why? Well, try taking a small amount of kids' play dough and rolling it into a ball. Then flatten it. When does that play dough have more surface area exposed? When it is flattened, right? In the same way, the shape of a red blood cell gives it more surface for the same volume than if it were a sphere. Since gases move through the surface, this allows the diffusion of O_2 and CO_2 to occur rapidly. In addition, the cell can bend and deform around the thin center, making it easier to get through the twists and turns of the tiniest blood vessels.

How do RBCs carry O_2? They do so with an iron-protein complex called hemoglobin (hee' moh gloh' bin). Hemoglobin is responsible for the red color of blood. It is one of the most amazing chemicals in your body, designed so that it can respond exactly to the needs of the cells to drop off the O_2 they need and to pick up their CO_2.

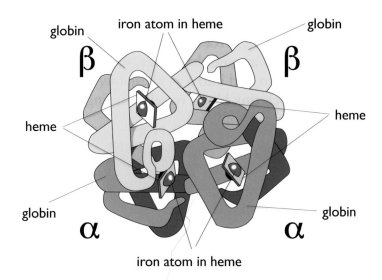

FIGURE 11.3
Hemoglobin
Illustration: LifeArt

Hemoglobin is composed of four protein chains (called globins), each of which is neatly folded into a particular shape. The middle of each globin holds a flat molecule called heme. An iron atom (Fe) is bound in the middle of each heme. The iron atoms in the hemes can each bind to one O_2 molecule. Therefore, four O_2 molecules can bind to the iron in the hemoglobin, and when all four hemes are loaded with O_2, the hemoglobin turns bright red. When the hemoglobin drops off the O_2 its color darkens. There is so much hemoglobin in each red blood cell that we can think of them as tiny bags, about one third full of wonderful hemoglobin.

There are several differences between erythrocytes and other cells. Erythrocytes contain hemoglobin; other cells do not. Mature erythrocytes, the ones in the blood, do not have a nucleus. As a result, we say that RBCs are anucleate (ay new' clee ate). Since RBCs have no nucleus, they have only a limited metabolism. Without DNA, they don't have much cellular machinery. They carry O_2 but they do not use O_2 for their own purposes. Why not? With their limited cellular machinery, they are able to generate a small amount of ATP through glycolysis, which does not require O_2. Think about your Creator's wisdom—what would it be like if the very cells that are designed to pick up and drop off O_2 were using it up along the way? Could your other cells survive? Without a nucleus, RBCs cannot repair themselves, and so they live only four months. Because RBCs die off rather quickly, you make them at a very fast pace in your red bone marrow—about two million per second! Of course, if you make about two million every second, that means about two million die off every second, as well.

Diapedesis—Passage of white blood cells through pores
in blood vessel to get into the tissue spaces

Why would they do this? Well, white blood cells in the blood vessles are actually traveling. They do their work in the tissue spaces. They are attracted to dead cells or foreign materials by chemotaxis (keem oh tak' sis).

Chemotaxis—Attraction of cells to chemical stimuli

For example, when a bacterium or virus gets into tissue, white blood cells are attracted by chemotaxis to the point of infection, and move out of the bloodstream by diapedesis. That way, the white blood cells, like protective soldiers, can get right to the attack.

Figure 11.5 illustrates the five basic types of white blood cells. Now, please realize that white blood cells are transparent. So, they look like this only when you stain them for observation under a microscope.

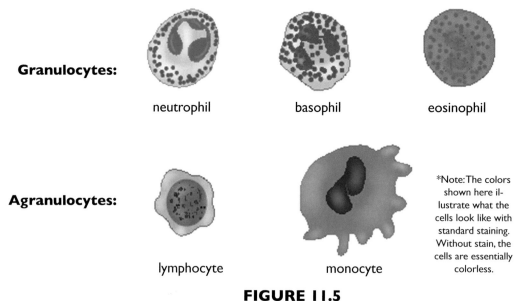

Granulocytes:

neutrophil   basophil   eosinophil

Agranulocytes:

lymphocyte   monocyte

*Note: The colors shown here illustrate what the cells look like with standard staining. Without stain, the cells are essentially colorless.

FIGURE 11.5
The Five Types of Leukocytes
Illustration by Megan Whitaker

When classifying leukocytes, we first split them into two classes: granulocytes (gran' you loh sights) and agranulocytes (aye' gran you loh sights). Granulocytes have vesicles that are filled with a substance that stains easily. This makes the vesicles visible in a microscope and gives the cell a grainy, or granular, look. Agranulocytes also have vesicles, but they are small and not easily stained. They cannot be seen with a microscope, and as a result, the cell appears to be smooth.

The first granulocyte shown in figure 11.5 is a neutrophil (new' troh fil). These are the most common of the white blood cells. They're distinguished by a nucleus with several lobes in it. In addition to their multilobed nucleus, the granules in a neutrophil are rather small and not very dense. You can hardly see the granules under a microscope. These cells are the first responders when an infection occurs. They are attracted to foreign invaders by chemotaxis and they are capable of phagocytosis. In other words, they eat (engulf) the rapidly. In addition, the cell can bend and deform around the thin center, making it easier to get through the twists and turns of the tiniest blood vessels.

How do RBCs carry O_2? They do so with an iron-protein complex called hemoglobin (hee' moh gloh' bin). Hemoglobin is responsible for the red color of blood. It is one of the most amazing chemicals in your body, designed so that it can respond exactly to the needs of the cells to drop off the O_2 they need and to pick up their CO_2.

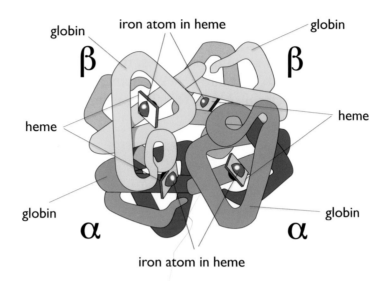

FIGURE 11.3
Hemoglobin
Illustration: LifeArt

Hemoglobin is composed of four protein chains (called globins), each of which is neatly folded into a particular shape. The middle of each globin holds a flat molecule called heme. An iron atom (Fe) is bound in the middle of each heme. The iron atoms in the hemes can each bind to one O_2 molecule. Therefore, four O_2 molecules can bind to the iron in the hemoglobin, and when all four hemes are loaded with O_2, the hemoglobin turns bright red. When the hemoglobin drops off the O_2 its color darkens. There is so much hemoglobin in each red blood cell that we can think of them as tiny bags, about one third full of wonderful hemoglobin.

There are several differences between erythrocytes and other cells. Erythrocytes contain hemoglobin; other cells do not. Mature erythrocytes, the ones in the blood, do not have a nucleus. As a result, we say that RBCs are anucleate (ay new' clee ate). Since RBCs have no nucleus, they have only a limited metabolism. Without DNA, they don't have much cellular machinery. They carry O_2 but they do not use O_2 for their own purposes. Why not? With their limited cellular machinery, they are able to generate a small amount of ATP through glycolysis, which does not require O_2. Think about your Creator's wisdom—what would it be like if the very cells that are designed to pick up and drop off O_2 were using it up along the way? Could your other cells survive? Without a nucleus, RBCs cannot repair themselves, and so they live only four months. Because RBCs die off rather quickly, you make them at a very fast pace in your red bone marrow—about two million per second! Of course, if you make about two million every second, that means about two million die off every second, as well.

One common problem associated with erythrocytes is anemia (uh nee' me uh). Many people define anemia as iron-poor blood. However, that's not a proper definition. Anemia is really a lack of sufficient O_2 carrying capacity by the blood. This is caused by either a lack of normal RBCs or a lack of hemoglobin (often due to nutritional deficiencies, which could include a lack of iron). In the first type, anemia can be the result of a person not producing enough erythrocytes, or loss of the ones that are already produced, as in hemorrhage (excessive blood loss) or parasitic infection.

There's also the possibility that the hemoglobin doesn't work properly. In sickle cell disease, for example, due to a genetic error hemoglobin is not properly shaped. When O_2 levels are low, which is normal around the tissues, the hemoglobin clumps together, causing the entire red blood cell to fold into a sickle shape, as seen in figure 11.4. In turn, the abnormally shaped cells block tiny blood vessels, causing pain and more serious consequences, as the tissues are deprived of O_2.

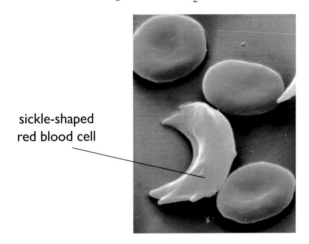

sickle-shaped
red blood cell

Figure 11.4
Sickle Cell Disease
Photo © 2008 University of Michigan

The symptoms of anemia aren't usually definitive. Because anemia results in less O_2 getting to the tissues, probably the most obvious symptom is fatigue. You can be fatigued for many reasons, however, so fatigue does not necessarily mean that you have anemia. Pallor (looking pale) is another symptom. Of course, people can look pale for many reasons, including the fact that they might just have very light skin. Once again, then, pallor is not a definitive symptom. Another common symptom is breathlessness on exertion. However, breathlessness as a result of exertion may just mean that you're out of shape. The best way to determine if someone is anemic is to test his or her blood. A hematocrit blood test, for example, tests the percentage of RBCs in the blood. The RBCs in adult males make up about 44%-48% of the blood. In adult females, they make up about 38%-45% of the blood. If the hematocrit test comes out much lower, it indicates anemia. In addition, a hemoglobin test can determine how much hemoglobin is in those RBCs. A healthy adult has 12-16 grams of hemoglobin per 100 mL (1 deciliter) of blood. Once again, if the hemoglobin test is much lower than that, the test shows anemia.

Iron is needed to prevent or overcome anemia, but many other vitamins and minerals are also involved in making erythrocytes: the B vitamins, including vitamin B_{12}

and folic acid; vitamin C, which helps the intestines to absorb iron; vitamin E, which prevents overly rapid breakdown of the RBCs; and other minerals, including copper, cobalt, manganese, and zinc.

When a person is anemic, we worry about his or her ability to get enough O_2. Yet no one seems too concerned about the ability of the body to get rid of CO_2 during anemia. Here's why: Even though cells produce an average of one CO_2 molecule for each O_2 molecule that they use, only about one-fourth of the CO_2 is carried by hemoglobin, and it is not carried bound to the iron, but rather to the globin. Most of the CO_2 is actually carried in the plasma. That's because CO_2 is much more soluble in plasma compared to O_2. In addition, your amazing RBCs contain an enzyme, called carbonic anhydrase, which quickly catalyzes the following reaction:

$$CO_2 + H_2O \longleftrightarrow \underset{\text{carbonic acid}}{H_2CO_3} \longleftrightarrow \underset{\text{bicarbonate + hydrogen ion}}{HCO_3^- + H^+}$$

This formula shows that CO_2 plus water, catalyzed by carbonic anhydrase, reversibly forms carbonic acid, which reversibly dissociates (comes apart) to form bicarbonate and hydrogen ion.

Most of the CO_2 is carried in the blood in the form of the bicarbonate as shown above. Near the tissues, where CO_2 is produced, the chemical reaction shown above favors the left-to-right direction, forming more bicarbonate. Near the lungs, where CO_2 leaves the body, the chemical reaction favors the right-to-left direction, reforming and releasing the CO_2.

Although erythrocytes obviously have an essential job to do in the blood, so do the leukocytes. As we mentioned in the previous section, leukocytes are commonly called white blood cells. You probably already know that white blood cells help fight off infection. However, you probably didn't know that there are actually five different kinds of white blood cells in the blood, and they all have specific tasks in the body.

White blood cells are not nearly as common as RBCs. In healthy adults, the ratio of RBCs to white blood cells is 700:1, but they are larger, nucleated cells that have many interesting abilities. RBCs cannot move on their own; they are simply carried along by the flow of blood. Most white blood cells, however, can move on their own by a process known as amoeboid movement. This means they can push out an extension of themselves (a pseudopod) and then flow into it. This allows them to squeeze through pores in the microscopic blood vessels and move into the tissues, a process called diapedesis (dye' uh puh dee' sis).

think about this

Hemoglobin is sensitive to the environment around it. When O_2 levels are high, as is the case near the lungs, hemoglobin is affected in such a way that it chemically attracts just about as much O_2 as it can carry, which is four O_2. Near the cells of the tissues, which are constantly using O_2, the lower level of O_2 causes an opposite change in hemoglobin, and it automatically drops off about one-fourth of its O_2 – just what the cells need. When hemoglobin passes by cells that are especially active, such as exercising muscles cells, the very low O_2 levels and the high acid environment that these cells produce causes hemoglobin to drop off about three-fourths of its O_2—just where it is vitally needed! Hemoglobin is an incredibly designed molecule.

Diapedesis—Passage of white blood cells through pores
in blood vessel to get into the tissue spaces

Why would they do this? Well, white blood cells in the blood vessels are actually traveling. They do their work in the tissue spaces. They are attracted to dead cells or foreign materials by chemotaxis (keem oh tak' sis).

Chemotaxis—Attraction of cells to chemical stimuli

For example, when a bacterium or virus gets into tissue, white blood cells are attracted by chemotaxis to the point of infection, and move out of the bloodstream by diapedesis. That way, the white blood cells, like protective soldiers, can get right to the attack.

Figure 11.5 illustrates the five basic types of white blood cells. Now, please realize that white blood cells are transparent. So, they look like this only when you stain them for observation under a microscope.

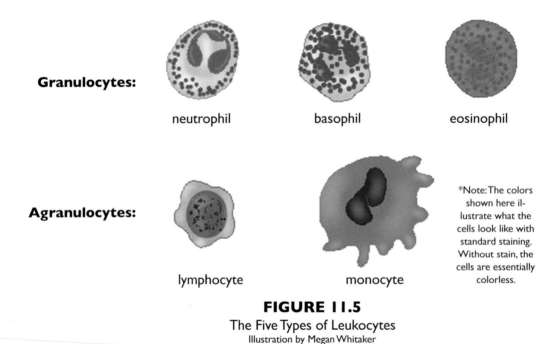

Granulocytes:

neutrophil   basophil   eosinophil

Agranulocytes:

lymphocyte   monocyte

*Note: The colors shown here illustrate what the cells look like with standard staining. Without stain, the cells are essentially colorless.

FIGURE 11.5
The Five Types of Leukocytes
Illustration by Megan Whitaker

When classifying leukocytes, we first split them into two classes: granulocytes (gran' you loh sights) and agranulocytes (aye' gran you loh sights). Granulocytes have vesicles that are filled with a substance that stains easily. This makes the vesicles visible in a microscope and gives the cell a grainy, or granular, look. Agranulocytes also have vesicles, but they are small and not easily stained. They cannot be seen with a microscope, and as a result, the cell appears to be smooth.

The first granulocyte shown in figure 11.5 is a neutrophil (new' troh fil). These are the most common of the white blood cells. They're distinguished by a nucleus with several lobes in it. In addition to their multilobed nucleus, the granules in a neutrophil are rather small and not very dense. You can hardly see the granules under a microscope. These cells are the first responders when an infection occurs. They are attracted to foreign invaders by chemotaxis and they are capable of phagocytosis. In other words, they eat (engulf) the bacteria or other foreign matter that is infecting tissue. It has been estimated that a neutrophil can devour about ten bacteria before dying. The white pus that you see, for example, around an infected site caused by a splinter in your skin, contains dead neutrophils.

Phagocytosis—Literally, cell-eating. The process by which a cell engulfs and ingests a foreign or dead cell or cell part

Pus—A mixture of dead or dying white blood cells, foreign cells such as bacteria, and fluid

The basophils (bay' soh filz) are the rarest of the granulocytes. They get their names because they are attracted to a basic blue dye. A basophil has a two-lobed nucleus, but the granules in the cell are so big that they tend to obscure it. So, the nucleus is a bit difficult to see under a microscope. These leukocytes increase in numbers during allergic reactions. They release histamine (hist' uh mean) and heparin (hep' uh rin). Histamine promotes inflammation. As mentioned in the previous module, inflammation stimulates the immune system. Heparin prevents the blood from clotting locally. That's actually a good thing. After all, if the blood clots at the area of the infection, the white blood cells, antibodies, and other immune factors can't get through. After a while, the heparin will be deactivated in order to allow the blood to clot.

Eosinophils (ee oh sin' oh filz) are uncommon, but are more plentiful than basophils. They have two-lobed nuclei, and their granules stain red. That's where they get their name, since eosin means "red." These leukocytes also increase in number during allergic reactions. They tend to balance out the basophils because they decrease inflammation. They also increase in number during parasitic infections. In the U.S., however, such infections are fairly rare in humans.

Now let's move on to the agranulocytes. There are two types of agranulocytes: lymphocytes and monocytes. Figure 11.2 shows an electron microscope image of a lymphocyte. Lymphocytes are only a little larger than erythrocytes, and they are the smallest white blood cell. After neutrophils, they are the second most common type of white blood cell. They have a dark-staining nucleus with just a little rim of cytoplasm. We will discuss them in more detail in the next module, when we study the lymphatic (or immune) system. Why? These cells produce antibodies, which are proteins that specifically protect against foreign invaders. They provide other immune protection for us, as well.

Monocytes are the biggest white blood cells, but they are uncommon in terms of numbers. They have a kidney-bean-shaped nucleus and more cytoplasm than the lymphocytes. These cells destroy invading organisms and foreign material by phagocytosis. Compared to neutrophils, however, these cells are much more phagocytic. It's estimated that they can engulf

COLORING BOOK EXERCISE 11.1

To review the makeup of blood, follow the instructions on page 195 of the coloring book.

ON YOUR OWN

11.7 What is the maximum number of O_2 molecules that can be carried by one hemoglobin molecule?

11.8 A blood cell is seen moving on its own. Is it an erythrocyte or a leukocyte?

11.9 Common over-the-counter medicines you buy often contain antihistamine. Based on what you have learned in this section, what type of white blood cell does this medicine affect?

100 bacteria before they die. Monocytes leave the bloodstream by diapedesis and take up residence in the tissues. When they are in the tissues, they're called macrophages (mac' roh faj ez), which means big eaters. For example, in your lungs, deep down where the simple squamous epithelium is very delicate, you have what are called dust cells. They're actually just macrophages that live in the tissue, swallowing up any tiny particles that get into your lungs. Macrophages are also found in your lymphatic tissue, where they assist the lymphocytes in recognizing foreign invaders. Have you heard of mononucleosis? It's a chronic viral disease characterized by fever, fatigue, sore throat, and a loss of appetite. The disease gets its name because it stimulates the body to produce an enormous number of monocytes.

Now that you have seen all of the formed elements of blood, you might be wondering where they are made in the body. Well, the process of blood cell formation is called hemopoiesis (he' moh poy ee' sis).

Hemopoiesis—The process by which the formed elements of blood are made in the body

Hemopoiesis occurs in the red bone marrow, though early in development lymphocytes move out to lymphatic tissue and are made there (lymph nodes, spleen, and other tissues). All blood cells, including the white blood cells that form platelets, come from just one type of cell, hemocytoblasts, also called stem cells. Red bone marrow is full of stem cells, which are undifferentiated cells that are capable of dividing to produce daughter cells that can form any of the blood cells that we mentioned! Which kind of blood cell is formed is a carefully controlled process that ensures you have as much of each type of blood cell as you need.

EXPERIMENT 11.1
Examining a Blood Smear

Supplies:

- Microscope
- Prepared slide: normal human blood smear

Purpose: In this section, we discussed the types of blood cells and their appearance when stained and observed under a microscope. You will now examine a blood smear and try to identify the cells.

Procedure:

1. Place the slide under the microscope at 40x magnification. Find some red tissue and focus.

2. Change the magnification to 100x and focus again. You should see little red dots. Most of those dots are erythrocytes.

3. Change the magnification to 400x and focus again. Now the cells should be much clearer. The vast majority of cells that you see will be circles of red. Those are erythrocytes. Remember, erythrocytes have no nucleus. Draw an erythrocyte.

4. Scan the slide, and you will see cells that look NOTHING like the erythrocytes. Those are the leukocytes. Using figure 11.5 as a guide, try to identify one of each. You might have a hard time finding basophils, eosinophils, and monocytes, but spend some time looking. When you find each type of leukocyte, draw an example. Remember, the monocytes will be the biggest cells. Lymphocytes will look like they are mostly, if not all, nucleus. The neutrophils, which are most common, will have many lobes in the nucleus the basophils will be very granular with a hard-to-see nucleus and the eosinophils, which are rare, will have bright red granules.

5. If you see clumps or cells that are significantly smaller than the erythrocytes, those are blood platelets. They stain purple and are sometimes clumped together.

6. OPTIONAL: You might want to prick yourself with a sterile needle and look at a drop of your own blood under the microscope. Smear the drop on the slide with the edge of a second slide. Let it dry, and then scan near the thin part at the edge of the smear. Note how different blood looks without the benefit of a stain.

7. Put everything away.

BLOOD AS A CONNECTIVE TISSUE

You probably don't think about blood as a connective tissue, but it does fit the definition. Connective tissue has cells. Blood has cells. Connective tissue has an extracellular matrix. Blood has an extracellular matrix, which is the liquid plasma. Connective tissue has protein fibers. Blood has protein fibers. Wait a minute. Blood has fibers? Where are they? They are only activated during blood coagulation. Nevertheless, the fibers have the potential to form. So, blood is a connective tissue. The best way to understand how blood acts as a connective tissue is to study hemostasis (he' moh stay' sis).

Hemostasis—The process by which the body stops blood loss

Have you ever heard of a hemostat? A hemostat looks like a pair of medium-sized scissors. Instead of having blades that cut, however, a hemostat has blades that pinch together. A hemostat is used during surgery to stop bleeding. That might help you remember the definition of hemostasis.

There are three stages of hemostasis, and after an injury that breaks blood vessels, they occur in a particular order: First, the vasoconstriction stage; second, the platelet plug stage; and third, the coagulation (koh ag you lay' shun) stage. Why three stages? The purpose of hemostasis is to stop the bleeding so that a wound can mend. Let's compare it for a minute to sewing. Perhaps you or your mother sews, and if so, you are aware that before your mom sews a seam on the sewing machine, she first pins the pieces together. She may then take a needle and quickly take big stitches to hold the pieces a little better. Then she'll remove the pins. Now, with the cloth temporarily held together, she'll use the sewing machine to actually do the final job of holding the two pieces together. Hemostasis is like that. The first two stages are quick fixes that limit the bleeding so that the slower, final stage, which does the job the best, has time to occur without too much blood loss.

Let's think about the word *vasoconstriction*. Blood vessels are made of vascular tissue. Vaso refers to blood vessels. Vasoconstriction, then, refers to a blood vessel constricting. When a blood vessel ruptures, a reflex contraction of the broken ends of the smooth muscle that surround the vessel occurs. This contraction of the smooth muscle helps close down the tear in the blood vessel. That's what happens in the vasoconstriction stage. This is a local reflex, and interestingly enough, the more damage that occurs, the more the reflex is stimulated. You can see this by comparing how much a sharp, clean cut bleeds compared with a jagged, rough cut. A paper cut, for example, bleeds quite a bit. Why? Clean cuts do not promote vasoconstriction reflex as well as jagged, rough cuts do. More damage promotes more vasoconstriction.

The second stage of hemostasis is the platelet plug stage. When a blood vessel is damaged, the damage causes a positive-feedback mechanism by which blood platelets swell, get sticky, and stick to both the blood vessel and to each other. This, of course, causes the platelets to "pile up" at the point of damage, plugging the tear. That's why it's called the platelet plug stage, because the platelets form a plug to stop blood from leaking out of the tear.

How does platelet plug formation happen? Well, when a blood vessel is damaged, the damage exposes collagen fibers that are in the outer layers of the blood vessel. Only when a blood vessel is damaged will the blood be exposed to collagen. Platelets bind to the collagen. So, the blood platelets bind to the blood vessel at the point of damage because that's the only place that will have collagen exposed to the blood! When the platelets bind to collagen, they are stimulated to release several chemicals. The one we want you to remember is thromboxane (throm bok' zayn). This chemical is derived from a prostaglandin, which you read about in the previous module. The release of this chemical stimulates several chemical processes that cause other platelets to stick.

The trigger for platelet plug formation, then, is exposure of collagen to the blood. The collagen causes the platelets to bind to the blood vessels, and that stimulates the process by which platelets secrete chemicals that cause other platelets to stick together, forming the plug. That plug is called a thrombus. Overall, a thrombus is a good thing, because it prevents blood loss. However, there are situations in which a thrombus can be a bad thing. If a person has hardening of the arteries, the lining of the blood vessels can be very rough. This damaged lining might trigger the formation of a platelet plug, even though there is no actual tear in the blood vessel. As a result, a plug could form, blocking the blood vessel. This could decrease the flow of blood to an organ, causing a major problem.

A coronary thrombosis is commonly called a heart attack, and it is caused when one of the major arteries that supply the heart muscle itself with blood gets plugged up by a thrombus that should not be there. This is why people at risk for a heart attack are often encouraged to take a small dose of aspirin daily. Since thromboxane is derived from prostaglandins, taking aspirin reduces the release of thromboxane, reducing the chance of forming a thrombus when a blood vessel is not torn.

Another type of clot is an embolus. This happens when a clot forms, usually in a vein of the legs, and then breaks loose and travels through the veins toward the heart. This is particularly bad, because an embolus can end up in the lungs and can be deadly. People who travel long distances on airplanes are often encouraged to get up and walk around every couple of hours. This helps maintain good circulation in the legs. When blood flows well, the chance of a thrombus forming abnormally is reduced, and so the chance of an embolus occurring is decreased also.

Now that we've covered vasoconstriction and platelet plug formation, it is time to move on to the most complex stage of hemostasis: coagulation. Before we go into detail on the coagulation process, we want to give you a simple overview with figure 11.6.

FIGURE 11.6
The Three Steps of the Coagulation Process

When a blood vessel and surrounding tissue are damaged, certain factors in the blood react. The damage sets off an incredible cascade of chemical reactions that, in the end, produce a substance called prothrombinase (pro throm' bin aze). Prothrombinase is an enzyme. Like most enzymes, it has a descriptive name. The suffix ase means "enzyme." The first part of an enzyme's name is the chemical on which the enzyme works. Prothrombinase works on prothrombin.

How does prothrombinase work on prothrombin? The liver produces prothrombin, an inactive protein, and sends it into the bloodstream. So, prothrombin is always in the blood, as long as the person is healthy. The enzyme prothrombinase converts prothrombin into its active form, thrombin. Thrombin is an enzyme also, though its name does not end in –ase. That's the second stage of blood coagulation.

The third stage occurs when thrombin activates fibrinogen (fi brin' uh jen). Fibrinogen is made by the liver, and is the inactive, water-soluble protein in the plasma that has the potential to become a fiber. When thrombin activates fibrinogen, it is converted into fibrin, which is no longer soluble in water. Instead, it forms long fibers, which form a blood clot. Yes, blood really is a connective tissue!

That's the basic scheme of blood coagulation. Tissue damage causes prothrombinase to form. Prothrombinase activates `prothrombin that is already in the blood to make thrombin. Thrombin then activates fibrinogen, which is also already in the blood, to form fibrin. How does this clot the blood? Look at the electron microscope image in figure 11.7.

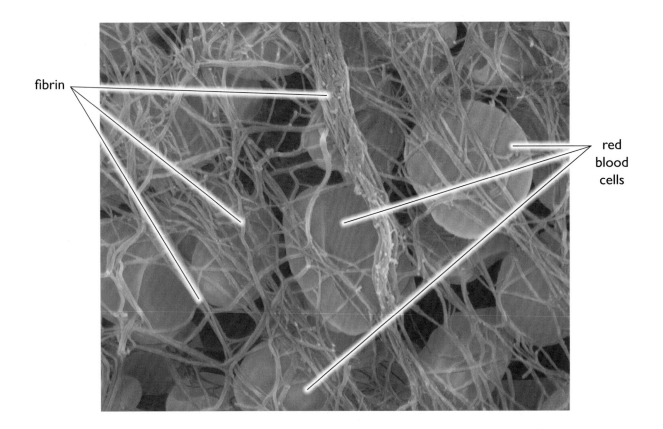

FIGURE 11.7
Fibrin Forming a Blood Clot
Photo © Phototake/Dennis Kunkel

Essentially, fibrin forms a net, trapping the blood cells, platelets, and plasma inside the blood vessel. If you think that's amazing, you haven't seen anything yet! Those are the three basic steps that lead to blood coagulation, but how do they happen? Where, for example, does the prothrombinase actually come from? The answer to that question begins with a discussion of coagulation factors.

Coagulation factors—Proteins in blood plasma that help initiate the blood coagulation process

Your liver forms most coagulation factors. The production of these proteins is complex, and for many the liver requires vitamin K to get the job done. You get vitamin K from your diet as well as from bacteria that live in your intestines. Without the proper level of vitamin K in your body, the liver cannot make adequate blood coagulation factors, and your blood cannot coagulate properly.

Blood coagulation factors used to have names such as *Christmas factor*. Some also were named to honor certain scientists. That has all changed, and they are now referred to by Roman numerals. They now have names such as factor VII and factor IX. Unfortunately, they do not become activated in numerical order! What do these factors do? Let's start with figure 11.8.

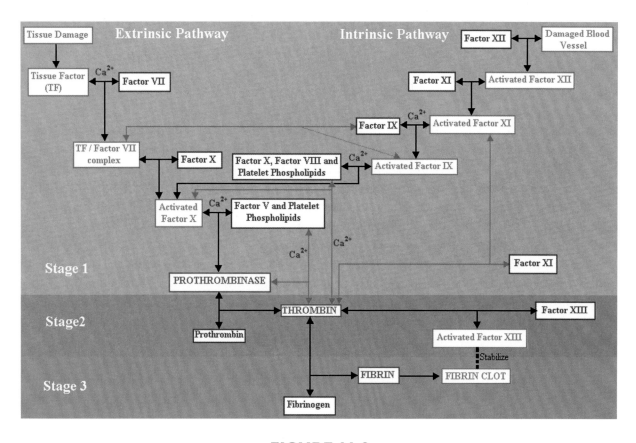

FIGURE 11.8
The Entire Blood Clotting Process
Illustration by Megan Whitaker

Now, this figure can seem very daunting, but take it one step at a time. First, notice that it is divided into three sections: stage 1, stage 2, and stage 3. Those are the stages about which you have already learned. Next, look at the three green boxes with green words. Those three boxes represent the final products of each stage. Prothrombinase is the product of stage 1, thrombin is the product of stage 2, and fibrin is the product of stage 3. All of the other information in the figure just tells you how each of these products is actually made. Notice also that there are red boxes and blue boxes. The red boxes represent substances that are made as a result of the blood coagulation process. The blue boxes represent substances already in the blood before the blood coagulation process. For right now, ignore the pink lines and arrows. We will come back to them later.

What does all of this mean? Well, start at the top of the figure. Notice that there are two branches leading down the figure. Those two branches represent the two pathways that can initiate blood coagulation. The extrinsic pathway begins when damage brings substances from outside the blood into the blood. That should make sense. The term extrinsic means "outside of." The intrinsic pathway initiates blood coagulation without contact from substances outside the blood. This should also make sense. The term intrinsic means "inside of." So, the intrinsic pathway begins with chemicals that are already in the blood. As you can see in the illustration, the extrinsic and intrinsic pathways join to become the common pathway. Common means "combined."

Let's start with the extrinsic pathway. When tissues are damaged, they release lipoproteins and phospholipids into the blood. The mixture of these chemicals is called tissue factor. When tissue factor interacts with Ca^{2+} ions and a protein already in the blood, factor VII, the result is a larger molecule called the tissue factor/ factor VII complex. This complex, in turn, reacts with another protein that is already in the blood, factor X. This interaction activates factor X. What does activates mean? Well, without the tissue factor/ factor VII complex, factor X is inactive. However, after reacting with the tissue factor/ factor VII complex, it readily participates in the chemistry of the blood coagulation process. That's what we mean by activated.

Once activated, factor X then reacts with factor V, phospholipids on the blood platelet membrane, and calcium ions. That reaction produces prothrombinase, the ultimate goal of stage one. The activation of factor X is particularly significant because it is the beginning of the common pathway.

Let's summarize what happens in this pathway so far. A series of reactions takes place, each of which has a unique trigger. Tissue factor triggers the reaction that makes the tissue factor/factor VII complex. That complex then triggers the reaction that makes activated factor X and begins the common pathway. In the common pathway, activated factor X then triggers the reaction that produces prothrombinase. This is called a reaction cascade because several chemical reactions happen in sequence once the first trigger occurs.

The extrinsic pathway is one of two ways that the blood coagulation process can begin. The other way is through the intrinsic pathway. Collagen from damaged blood vessel walls comes into contact with factor XII, a protein that is already in the blood. This interaction activates factor XII, and it then reacts with factor XI, which is also in the blood. This interaction activates factor XI. In the presence of Ca^{2+}, the activated factor XI reacts with factor IX to make activated factor IX. Finally, activated factor IX reacts with factor X to make activated factor X, and the common pathway continues. In the common pathway activated factor X reacts with factor V, phospholipids on the blood platelet membrane, and calcium ions to make prothrombinase.

In the end, then, both extrinsic and intrinsic pathways lead to the same result. They both lead to activated factor X, which then reacts via the common pathway to form prothrombinase. Remember those pink lines we told you to ignore earlier? Notice the pink line that connects the tissue factor/factor VII complex with factor IX. This is where the two pathways can interact. If the extrinsic pathway reaches the point where it can make the tissue factor/factor VII complex, that complex will not only react with factor X, it will also activate factor IX. So, once the extrinsic pathway reaches that point, it not only continues, but it also starts the intrinsic pathway midstream.

That's stage 1, and it is definitely the hardest! Once prothrombinase is made, it activates prothrombin, which is already in the blood. This produces the enzyme thrombin, the ultimate goal of stage 2. Thrombin, then, makes the blood clot. It does this by activating fibrinogen (already in the blood) to make fibrin threads, which ultimately form the blood clot. If thrombin does not do that effectively, it can also react with factor XIII to make activated factor XIII. This substance aids the blood clot by stabilizing it. Both of these jobs, then, directly affect the blood clot, and they are both done by thrombin.

There is one more thing that thrombin can do. Look now at the rest of the pink lines. These lines represent how thrombin can participate in a *positive-feedback system*. If thrombin encounters factor V, platelet phospholipids, and Ca^{2+}, it can actually produce prothrombinase, which will ultimately produce more thrombin. This, then, is one of the few examples of positive feedback in the body. If you make thrombin, that thrombin will cause you to make more thrombin.

Thrombin can participate in positive-feedback in at least two other ways as well. First, it can react with factor VIII, platelet phospholipids, and Ca^{2+} to make activated factor X, which can then make prothrombinase. Also, it can react with factor XI to make activated factor XI, which will continue down the rest of the intrinsic pathway until once again, prothrombinase is made.

That's the blood coagulation process, then. It involves two interacting cascades (intrinsic and extrinsic) of reactions that produce prothrombinase, then thrombin, and then fibrin. It's pretty complex, isn't it? Why? Why should the process be this complex? Why can't tissue factors directly produce fibrin? Why can't damaged blood vessels just react with fibrinogen to make fibrin? Why go through these long, complicated pathways?

To answer this question, we want to make an analogy. When you studied the nervous system, we told you that each time an axon synapsed with a neuron, the synapse provided the ability to regulate the signal. So, nerve information that needed to be regulated went to the brain via one or more synapses. If the nerve information did not need to be regulated much, it could go straight to the brain without any synapses.

You can think about the blood coagulation process in the same way. It involves several points at which one substance is made and then must react with another substance to continue the process. Each of those points represents a point of regulation. The complex nature of the blood coagulation process, then, is simply a reflection of the fact that it must be *regulated* carefully. ✗

Why must it be regulated so carefully? Think about it. You can't have clots appearing randomly in the blood. That would be devastating! Instead, clots can only appear when there is damage. But, not *all* damage should lead to blood clots. After all, some damage can be fixed with vascular constriction and platelet plug formation. And sometimes roughness in a blood vessel may activate some thrombins via collagen exposure. Why risk coagulating the blood unless it is really necessary? Yet, oppositely, the blood coagulation process must occur quickly if needed, in order to reduce blood loss. At the same time, however, it also needs to turn off quickly, or all of the blood would solidify!

ON YOUR OWN

11.10 Suppose you could watch the hemostasis process as it happened. You see a tear in a blood vessel; you see the blood vessel constrict, and then you see a platelet plug form. Assuming that you could immediately test the blood surrounding the plug for any chemical, what would be the first sign as to whether or not the blood was going to coagulate?

11.11 For the following list of chemicals, indicate whether or not the chemical is normally in blood or something that is produced in the blood coagulation process:
factor IX, prothrombinase, thrombin, prothrombin, tissue factor, factor VII, fibrin, fibrinogen

11.12 A person's blood seems to have enough of all the blood clotting factors, enough prothrombin, and enough fibrinogen. Nevertheless, the person's blood does not clot well. What might be the cause of the problem?

How does the blood coagulation process stop? In brief, the body produces anticoagulants (an' tye koh ag' you luntz), which prevent certain blood factors from being activated. So, the anticoagulants stop the coagulation pathways by stopping certain steps within the pathways.

BLOOD TYPES

There are four types of blood that humans have: A, B, AB, and O. What is the difference between these blood types? It is based on certain molecules located on the *surface* of the RBCs (the erythrocytes). These molecules are called antigens (an' tih jenz).

> **Antigen**—A protein or other molecule that, when introduced into the body, triggers the production of an antibody

Remember, your body produces antibodies as a way of fighting off invaders. Antigens trigger an immune response from the body. Type A blood, then, is blood whose erythrocytes have A antigens on their surfaces. If the erythrocytes have B antigens, the blood type is B. Blood whose erythrocytes have *both* A and B antigens is type AB blood. Finally, if the erythrocytes have neither A nor B antigens, the blood is type O.

That's the difference in the blood types of the ABO blood group. Why, does it matter? Well, your blood produces antibodies to fight infection. If you have type A blood, your body does not produce antibodies against A antigens. However, it *does* produce antibodies against B antigens. If you have type A blood and would be unfortunate enough to get type B blood transfused into you, the antibodies you have against the B antigens will begin attacking those type B erythrocytes. They attack those blood cells by binding to the antigens and building "bridges" from one erythrocyte to another. As a result, the B erythrocytes start clumping together, and that's bad. Such a clump can block blood vessels, cutting off blood flow to organs and tissues. You cannot receive blood that is incompatible with the antibodies that are already in your blood.

Now, let's think about this for a moment. A person with type A blood produces antibodies against the B antigen. You don't produce antibodies against your own blood. If you have type A blood, you will not produce antibodies against the type A antigen. You will, however, produce antibodies against the B antigen. Similarly, then, a person with type B blood will produce only the antibodies against the A antigen. What about type AB blood? What kind of antibodies will be in that blood? The answer is *neither!* After all, if the blood has both antigens, the body cannot produce either of the antibodies that attack them. Finally, type O blood will produce *both* antibodies, because the erythrocytes have *neither* antigen. This is illustrated in figure 11.9.

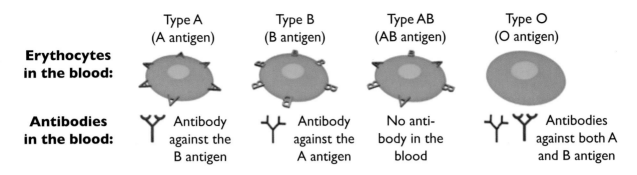

Figure 11.9
Blood Types and Blood Antibodies
Illustration by Striar Yunis

Interestingly enough, we are not exactly sure *how* the antibodies against the A and B antigen develop. You see, your body does not produce antibodies until it *needs* them. So, we would expect a person's blood not to contain antibodies against an antigen unless the blood is exposed to that antigen. However, from the time a baby is about two months old, if his or her blood type allows for the production of one or two of these antibodies, they will appear in the body. The best explanation for this is that food or other organisms such as bacteria carry the A and B antigen and, since everyone's blood is exposed to food and microorganisms, it is just a matter of a short time before everyone is exposed to both the A and B antigen in the intestine. As long as the blood type allows for the production of the antibodies, then, they will be made.

Type O blood is called the universal donor type. Why? Well, think about it. If the recipient has type O blood, everything is fine because the blood types are the same. If the recipient has type A blood, he or she will have antibodies against the B antigen. However, there are no B antigens on the O blood erythrocytes! The antibodies will have nothing to attack. In the same way, a recipient with type B blood will have antibodies against the A antigen. However, type O blood has no A antigens. There is once again nothing for the recipient's antibodies to attack. Finally, since AB blood has neither antibody in it, there will be nothing wrong with a recipient with AB blood receiving type O blood. That's why people with type O blood are considered universal donors.

Of course, the term universal donor needs to be used rather carefully. Even though the antibodies of the *recipient* will not attack the erythrocytes of the *donor*, the opposite situation can happen. Remember, people with type O blood produce both antibodies. So, when you put type O blood into a person, some of those antibodies will come with it. Those antibodies will attack type A, type B, and type AB erythrocytes. The antibodies of the *donor* will attack the RBCs of the *recipient*. This is a problem, but it is not a huge problem. Since the donor donates only a fraction of the total blood in the recipient's body, the donor's antibodies are dilute compared with the antibodies of the recipient. Also, the recipient will not make any more of those antibodies, because they belong to the donor and the donated antibodies will break down over time. Thus, the antibodies of the donor cannot cause nearly the problem that the antibodies of the recipient can cause. Please realize, however, that the problem is still there. It is best, therefore, for people to receive whole blood of exactly the same type as their own. However, type O blood can be used in an emergency.

What determines your blood type? Genetics do, of course. The allele for type O blood is recessive. The alleles for A and B are both dominant over O. However, they are not dominant over each other. If you get the A allele from one parent and O allele from the other, you will have type A blood. However, if you get the A allele from one parent and the B allele from your other parent, your blood type will be AB, because neither allele dominates in that situation. Figure 11.10 demonstrates the genetics of blood type.

A father with a blood genotype of AO and a mother whose blood genotype is BO have a baby. What are the blood types of the mother and father? What possibilities exist for the blood type of the baby, and what percentage chance exists for each type?

A and B are both dominant over O. So, the father is type A, and the mother is type B. To determine the possibilities for the baby, we must construct a Punnett square.

	A	O
B	AB	BO
O	AO	OO

The letters inside the boxes represent the possible genotypes for the baby. If the baby has AB, the blood type will be AB. If the baby has the BO genotype, he or she will have type B blood. The AO genotype will lead to type A blood, and the OO genotype will make O blood. Thus, there is a 25% chance of AB blood, a 25% chance of type B blood, a 25% chance of type A blood, and a 25% chance of O blood.

Figure 11.10
The Genetics of Blood Type

Although the A and B antigens on the RBCs are important, there is one other important blood antigen to consider: the Rh antigen. The *Rh* stands for "Rhesus monkey" because that's where the antigen was first identified. If the Rh antigen exists on the surface of the erythrocytes in blood, the blood is called Rh-positive (Rh^+). If there is no Rh antigen on the erythrocytes, the blood is Rh-negative (Rh^-). About 85% of people are Rh^+. Since the Rh antigen is an important part of the blood, whether or not a person is Rh^+ is usually listed with the blood ABO type. So, type O positive (O^+) blood is type O blood in which the erythrocytes do have the Rh antigen. O negative blood (O^-), obviously, is type O blood in which the erythrocytes have no Rh antigen.

How is this inherited? It is inherited independently of your ABO type, that is, there is a separate gene that determines whether or not your erythrocytes have the Rh antigen. Rh^+ is dominant and Rh^- is recessive. So, to be Rh^-, you must have an Rh^- allele from each parent. If you have just one allele for Rh^+, you will be Rh^+.

Since Rh is an antigen, antibodies can be produced against it. People who are Rh^+, of course, will not produce the antibody that fights the Rh antigen, because a body will not produce an antibody that attacks its own blood. However, people who are Rh^- can produce the antibody against the Rh antigen.

The antibody against the Rh antigen does not automatically appear in the blood as do the antibodies against the A or B antigen. Instead, a person who is Rh$^-$ must be exposed to Rh$^+$ blood to produce the antibody. How can that happen? Well, one way is through a mismatched blood transfusion. If an Rh$^-$ person receives Rh$^+$ blood, he or she will begin to produce antibodies against the Rh antigen. Interestingly, however, that particular blood transfusion will not result in really serious problems, because the production of antibodies is relatively slow, and the erythrocytes don't live very long to begin with, as you learned in the previous section. However, if the Rh$^-$ person is unlucky enough to get a second Rh$^+$ blood transfusion, then the antibodies against the Rh antigen will already be there, and a transfusion reaction will occur. Of course, this is only a concern for an Rh$^-$ person, because Rh$^+$ blood cannot produce the antibody against the Rh antigen.

However, there is an Rh problem that can occur naturally. If a mother is Rh$^-$, a potential problem may occur if children born to her are Rh$^+$. At the birth (not pregnancy) of an Rh$^+$ baby, it is possible that some of the baby's blood may mix with her blood.

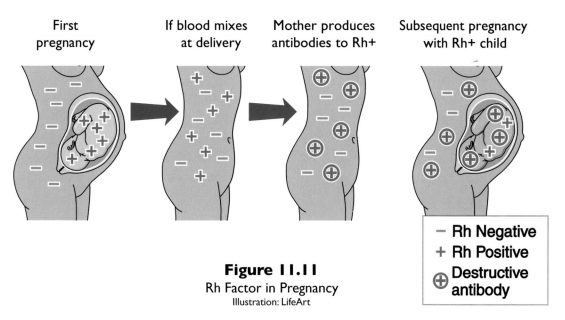

| First pregnancy | If blood mixes at delivery | Mother produces antibodies to Rh+ | Subsequent pregnancy with Rh+ child |

Figure 11.11
Rh Factor in Pregnancy
Illustration: LifeArt

- Rh Negative
+ Rh Positive
⊕ Destructive antibody

Since Rh factor is foreign to her body, she will make anti-Rh antibodies. Now this is harmless to the Rh$^+$ baby, who has already been born, and the anti-Rh antibodies in the mother's blood are harmless to her. However, if she has a second Rh$^+$ child, that child is at risk for hemolytic disease of the newborn. During the pregnancy, the anti-Rh antibodies of the mother cross the placenta (the organ of exchange between mother and fetus). The fetus is the child in the womb, and these antibodies attack the unborn baby's Rh$^+$ erythrocytes. This effect may be very small, or it can be serious, depending on how many antibodies the mother produces. With each Rh$^+$ child that she has, if mixing of blood occurs during childbirth, she will be exposed again to the Rh antigen and will make more anti-Rh antibody. So, the more Rh$^+$ children she has, the higher the risk to the developing Rh$^+$ fetus, whose erythrocytes are attacked. But, let's give a little perspective. First, most women (about 85%) are Rh$^+$ and cannot make anti-Rh, since Rh antigen is natural to them. Some of the children of Rh$^-$ women may be Rh$^-$, and so even if she has made anti-Rh from previous childbirth of Rh$^+$ children, the anti-Rh has nothing to attack on Rh$^-$ erythrocytes.

If hemolytic disease of the newborn occurs, it can be treated. The Rh^+ newborn is given a transfusion of its ABO type, except the donated blood is Rh^-. For example, if the baby is A^+, it is given A^- blood. Why? The A^- cells replace the A^+ cells attacked by anti-Rh antibodies in the womb, and since there are no anti-Rh antigens on the donated A^- blood, the anti-Rh antibodies that the newborn acquired from his or her mother cannot attack the donated A^- cells. The baby gets the O_2 carrying RBCs that he or she needs. The anti-Rh from the mother will breakdown gradually, and the baby will not make more, because he or she is Rh^+.

More commonly, the disease is prevented. How? As soon as a baby is born to an Rh^- mother, the baby's umbilical cord blood is typed. If it is Rh^-, there is no need for treatment. If the baby is Rh^+, the mother is injected with anti-Rh antibodies. Surprised? Aren't we trying to avoid having anti-Rh antibodies made by the Rh^- mother? Yes, but the injected anti-Rh will quickly attack Rh^+ cells that may have gotten into the mother's blood from the newborn during childbirth. That way, the mother's immune system will not be stimulated to make her own long lasting production of anti-Rh. The injected anti-Rh will break down within a few weeks. We say this prevents her from being sensitized to the Rh antigen.

A final question that you may have: Why doesn't this problem affect, say, a fetus with B blood, in the womb of a mother with A blood? As you have just learned, any adult with A blood has anti-B antibodies in the plasma. As it turns out, anti-B (and anti-A) antibodies are several times larger than anti-Rh, so they are too big to cross the placenta, and the fetus does not get exposed to these large antibodies.

ON YOUR OWN

11.13 A person with O⁻ blood donates blood. What blood types have no risk associated with receiving this type of blood? What blood types have a low risk?

11.14 In addition to a universal donor type, there is also a universal recipient type. People with this type of blood can receive transfusions with low risk of any blood type. What is the universal recipient type? To be a true universal recipient, should this type be Rh-positive or Rh-negative?

11.15 A person's blood type is A+. What possible genotypes could the person have for the blood type? What possible genotypes could the person have for the Rh antigen?

AN OVERVIEW OF BLOOD CIRCULATION

As you already know, the heart pumps blood throughout the body. In the human body, the blood travels in tubes called blood vessels. This is called a closed circulatory system since the blood is enclosed in blood vessels. This is not the only kind of circulatory system, however. Many creatures (like the arthropods) have an open circulatory system. In this type of system, the blood travels away from the heart in blood vessels, but the blood is then dumped directly onto the tissues. It is then collected and forced back into other blood vessels so that it can travel back to the heart. Although open circulatory systems are quite interesting, we will of course focus on the human circulatory system, which encloses the blood in blood vessels. There are three different types of blood vessels: arteries, capillaries, and veins.

Arteries—Blood vessels that carry blood away from the heart

Capillaries—Microscopic, thin-walled blood vessels that allow the exchange of gases and nutrients between the blood and body cells

Veins—Blood vessels that carry blood back to the heart

Away = Artery
Veins = to the heart

Starting from the heart, then, the blood flows away from the heart through the arteries. As the blood travels, the arteries branch so that there are more and more of them, but they get smaller and smaller. Eventually, the blood reaches the capillaries. These blood vessels are so thin that the erythrocytes must "squeeze" through them in a single file! Because they have thin walls, they allow for the exchange of gases (O_2 and CO_2) between the blood and the tissues. After passing through the capillaries, the blood returns to the heart by traveling through veins. Veins, which are small and numerous near the capillaries, form larger and larger vessels. At the same time, there are fewer and fewer of these larger vessels, so only a few large veins return blood directly to the heart.

Now, notice in the figure that there are really two divisions to this circulation: the pulmonary (pul' muh nair ee) circulation and the systemic circulation.

Pulmonary circulation—Circulation of the blood around the alveoli (air sacs) of the lungs

Systemic circulation—Circulation of the blood through the other tissues of the body

The pulmonary circulation sends blood from the right heart to the lungs and back to the left heart. The purpose of this circulation, of course, is to allow the blood to exchange gases with the tissues of the lungs. This allows the blood to pick up O_2 and release CO_2. Systemic circulation sends the blood from the left heart to the tissues, where the blood can deliver O_2 and pick up the CO_2 waste.

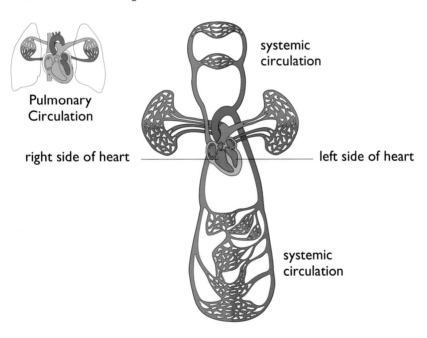

systemic circulation

Pulmonary Circulation

right side of heart — left side of heart

systemic circulation

FIGURE 11.12
The Basic Layout of Blood Circulation
Illustration: LifeArt

Notice the two colors that you see in figure 11.12. In some parts of the figure, the blood vessels are colored blue. In other parts, the blood vessels are colored red. In most human anatomy figures, blue is used to represent blood that has little O_2 in it. We call this deoxygenated blood. The color red, on the other hand, is used to denote blood that has plenty of O_2

MOD 11

in it. We call this oxygenated blood. Blood is never really blue in the body. Deoxygenated blood is dark red while oxygenated blood is bright red. Your blood vessels may appear to be blue when you look at them through the skin, if your skin is light-colored, because the skin does not transmit light very well. As a result, the color is distorted. The difference between dark red and bright red would be hard to see in a figure, however, so the usual convention is to use the colors red and blue to denote oxygenated blood and deoxygenated blood, respectively. It is common to use the terms red and blue as a shortcut instead of saying oxygenated and deoxygenated.

COLORING BOOK EXERCISE 11.2

To review the basic layout of blood circulation, follow the instructions on page 193 of the coloring book.

As a point of orientation, the sides of the heart are determined from the perspective of the person who owns the heart. In figure 11.12, the right side of the heart is on your left, because we are looking at the heart from the anterior (chest) side of the body. Notice that in the right side of the heart, the blood is deoxygenated. That's because the right side of the heart receives the blood that comes back from the body tissues, except for the lungs, and then pumps it to the lungs. Since the blood gives up O_2 to the tissues, it comes back to the right side of the heart lacking O_2. However, once the blood is pumped to the lungs by the right side of the heart, it picks up O_2. Then, the left side of the heart receives red, oxygenated blood from the lungs and pumps it out to the tissues of the body. In summary, the right side of the heart handles deoxygenated blood, while the left side of the heart pumps oxygenated blood.

HEART ANATOMY

The purpose of the heart is to pump blood through the circulatory system. Let's study this amazing organ in some detail, starting with its anatomy.

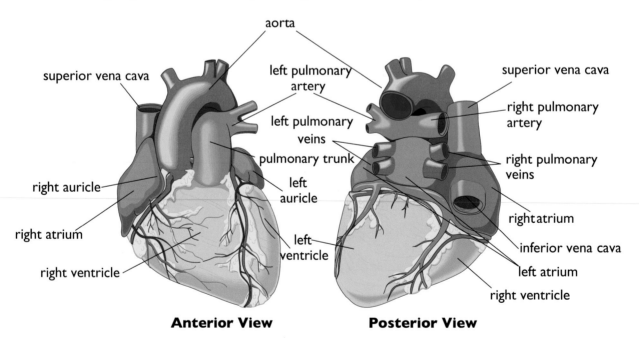

Anterior View   **Posterior View**

FIGURE 11.13
External Heart Anatomy
Illustration by LifeArt

The heart consists of four chambers: two atria (aye' tree uh) and two ventricles (ven' trih kulz). The term *atrium* (singular of atria) means "entrance," and the term *ventricle* means "belly." The atria, then, are the entrances"to the heart, and the ventricles are the bellies of the heart. The atria have thin walls, while the ventricles have thick walls. Both the right and the left atria have flap-like extensions, called auricles, that can be seen on the anterior side of the heart. At one time, the word auricle actually referred to the entire atrium, but that is old terminology that is not used today. The auricles slightly increase the capacity of each atrium.

Several large veins bring blood into the heart. The superior vena (vee' nuh) cava (kay' vuh) brings "blue" blood from the upper body tissues to the right atrium, while the inferior vena cava brings "blue" blood from the lower body tissues to the right atrium. In addition, the four pulmonary veins (two left pulmonary veins and two right pulmonary veins) bring red blood from the lungs to the left atrium. Two large arteries carry blood away from the heart. The pulmonary trunk carries "blue" blood out of the right ventricle toward the lungs. This artery quickly divides into the right and left pulmonary arteries, which carry the deoxygenated blood to the right and left lungs, respectively. The aorta is the large artery that exits the left ventricle, carrying red blood to the body tissues.

Notice in figure 11.13 the veins and arteries that run across the surface of the heart. Remember, the heart is made of living tissue, mostly cardiac muscle cells. These cells need a steady supply of O_2 and nutrients. They need to be supplied with blood, as well. That's the purpose of these arteries and veins, which together form the coronary circulation. When people talk about heart health, the ability of the coronary arteries to deliver blood to the heart muscle is a major concern.

Although the external anatomy of the heart is important to learn, a look at the internal anatomy of the heart is necessary in order to understand how blood flows in the body. This view can be seen in figure 11.14.

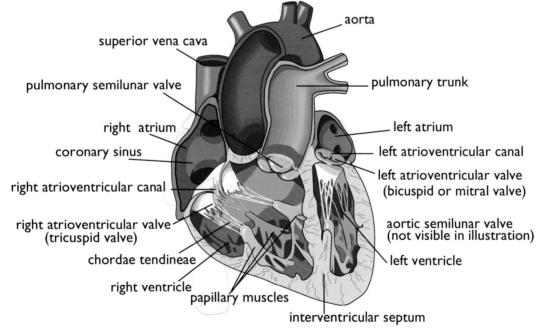

FIGURE 11.14
Internal Anatomy of the Heart (Anterior View)
Illustration: LifeArt

Notice that we have labeled the aorta, superior vena cava, and the pulmonary trunk. This allows you to get your bearings in the figure. Let's start our discussion of figure 11.14 with the right atrium. The right atrium receives "blue" blood from the superior vena cava, the inferior vena cava, and the coronary sinus (the major vein returning "blue" blood from the heart muscle itself).

The right atrium opens to the right ventricle through the right atrioventricular canal. The right atrioventricular valve, which is also called the tricuspid (try kus' pid) valve, ensures one-way blood flow through the canal. The valve is called tricuspid because it is made of three sheets of thin connective tissue, covered with smooth, slick epithelial tissue, each of which is called a cusp. This valve passively opens and closes based on the pressure differences that arise when the right ventricle contracts and relaxes.

The papillary muscles connect to the valve via strong, thin, connective tissue "threads" called chordae (kor' dee) tendineae (ten' dih nee ee), which are nicknamed "heart strings." The papillary muscles contract when the ventricles contract. This keeps the valve from opening into the atrium. That way, when the right ventricle contracts, the blood goes out the pulmonary trunk, and none of it can flow backwards into the right atrium.

The left atrium receives red blood from the four pulmonary veins. It is separated from the left ventricle by the left atrioventricular valve, which is also called the bicuspid valve or the mitral (mih' truhl) valve. This valve is made of two sheets of connective tissue instead of three. When this valve opens in response to pressure changes, blood flows from the left atrium, down the left atrioventricular canal, and into the left ventricle. The left ventricle empties into the large aorta. Like the right atrioventricular valve, the left atrioventricular valve closes off the left atrium when the ventricle contracts. This ensures that none of the blood in the left ventricle flows back into the left atrium. The left and right ventricles are completely separated by the thick interventricular septum, and the left and right atria (plural) are completely separated by the thinner interatrial septum.

The aorta and pulmonary trunk are separated from their ventricles by semilunar valves. The valves get their names because they are composed of three cusps of tissue that are each shaped like a half-moon. These three pocket-like cusps meet in the center of the vessel to block blood flow. Blood flowing out of the ventricles pushes against the valve, causing it to open. However, these valves ensure one-way flow. If blood flows backwards from the vessels and tries to enter the ventricle, the valves snap shut. So, these one-way valves ensure that blood does not flow back into the heart once it has been pushed out.

EXPERIMENT 11.2
Cow's Heart Dissection

Supplies:
- Cow's heart
- Dissection kit
- Paper towels

Purpose: The cow's heart is a reasonably good model of the human heart, so dissecting it is a good review of heart anatomy.

Procedure:
1. Take the cow's heart and examine the external anatomy. The best place to start is to determine left from right. This can actually be a little tricky. First, hold the heart with both hands so that the point (the apex) is pointing down. Use your thumbs to push against the heart. You should notice that one side yields to the push easier than the other. If you don't notice a difference, rotate the heart and try again.

2. The side that yields more easily to the push is the wall of the right ventricle. The muscle of the right ventricle is not as strong as the muscle of the left ventricle, because the right ventricle pushes blood to the lungs. The left ventricle pushes blood to all other parts of the body. The left ventricle exerts more force and therefore grows thicker and stronger.

3. Next, we will find the auricles. Rotate the heart so that the right ventricle is on your right side. If you did this correctly, you should be looking at the posterior side of the heart. Now examine the top of the heart. You should find two lobes of tissue that are darker than the fat surrounding the heart. We are not talking about the blood vessels. These lobes of tissue will have no openings in them. Instead, they lie flat against the heart. However, if you put your fingers under the end of each lobe that is farthest from you, you should be able to lift part of the lobe off of the heart. These are the auricles. The name means "ears." Can you see why?

4. One auricle should be on the right side of the heart (the auricle of the right atrium), and the other auricle should be on the left side of the heart (the auricle of the left atrium). You can distinguish the right auricle from the left one because the wall of the heart below the right auricle should yield to a push more readily than the wall under the left auricle.

5. Follow the right auricle back to the blood vessel that sits directly posterior to it. This is the superior vena cava. Check that this is the superior vena cava by sticking the blunt end of a probe in, opening the vessel. Explore with the blunt end of the probe, and you should be able to tell that the blood vessel opens into the right atrium.

6. Follow the left auricle back to the blood vessels that sit posterior to it. Those are the pulmonary veins. Check by sticking the blunt end of the probe into the holes. You should be able to tell that these vessels open into the left atrium.

7. Directly anterior to the superior vena cava, you should find the aorta. Most likely, it has been cut so that you just see what appears to be a short, thick Y-shaped tube pointing upward. The aorta is easy to spot because it has the thickest wall of all the blood vessels. Why? The aorta carries the blood from the left heart to the tissues of the body. It is receiving blood being pumped by the left ventricle. Remember, the left ventricle is the stronger ventricle, so the aorta carries the blood that is being pumped with the greatest force. It must be the strongest blood vessel.

Anterior to the aorta, you will find the pulmonary trunk.

8. Before you cut into the heart, note all of the white tissue. This is fat. The fat around the heart cushions and insulates it.

9. Now it is time to cut into the heart. Rotate the heart slightly so that the superior vena cava is directly in front of you. You want to cut the heart into two halves. You are not going to cut the right side from the left side. Instead you are going to make a cut that splits open the ventricles.

10. Stick your scalpel into the superior vena cava and cut straight down the wall of the heart that is facing you. You want to cut so that the superior vena cava will be split down the center. You will have to cut through a lot of meat. Don't worry about it. Cut away!

11. Continue the cut up the other side of the heart. Just as you wanted the vena cava to be split down the center, you also want the aorta to be split down the center.

12. Pull the two halves apart. Put down the half that is in your left hand, and look at the interior of the side that is in your right hand.

You should see two chambers. One will be thick and the other thin. The thick chamber is half of the left ventricle and the thin chamber is half of the right ventricle. The meat in between those two chambers is the interventricular septum.

13. Pry open the thin chamber (the right ventricle). You should see three flaps of tissue. Two flaps will be on one side of the chamber, and the third will be on the other side. Those three flaps make up the tricuspid valve. Note the stringy chordae tendineae, which attach to the tissue.

14. While still prying open the right ventricle, stick the blunt side of your probe down the pulmonary trunk. You should see the end of the probe in the right ventricle, because the right ventricle pushes blood into the pulmonary trunk.

15. Rotate this half of the heart so that you are looking down the pulmonary trunk. Pull it wide open so that you can see down it. If you can't see down it very well, cut it so that you can pull it open wide. Notice the three flaps of tissue down inside. Those flaps make up the pulmonary semilunar valve.

Now look at the interior of this half of the heart again. Look at the wide chamber (the left ventricle). Note how it opens at the top of the heart to the aorta. Note the flaps of tissue between the aorta and the left ventricle. Those flaps make up the aortic semilunar valve.

16. Draw this part of the heart.

17. Now look at the interior of the other side of the heart. Once again, you should see a thin chamber and a wide chamber. These are, of course, the ventricles. If you made the cut correctly, this side should give you a good view of the left atrium and left ventricle.

18. Push the blunt end of the probe down a pulmonary vein. You should see it come down through two flaps of tissue and into the left ventricle (the wide chamber). Those two flaps of tissue make up the bicuspid valve of the left atrium. Once again, note the chordae tendineae that connect the tissue to the muscles.

You should also see the other half of the aorta and the other half of the aortic semilunar valve.

19. Draw this side of the heart.

20. Clean everything up.

The Flow of Blood Through the Heart

After the blood has delivered O_2 to the various tissues of the body (except the alveoli of the lungs) and is deoxygenated, it travels back to the heart in veins. It enters the right atrium via the superior vena cava, the inferior vena cava, or the coronary sinus and flows into the right ventricle. Once the atrium is full, it contracts. This causes extra blood to flow through the tricuspid valve and into the right ventricle. The right ventricle then contracts, forcing the blood into the pulmonary trunk. Backflow into the right atrium is prevented by the closing of the tricuspid valve. Once the right ventricle relaxes, backflow of blood from the pulmonary trunk is prevented by the closing of the pulmonary semilunar valve.

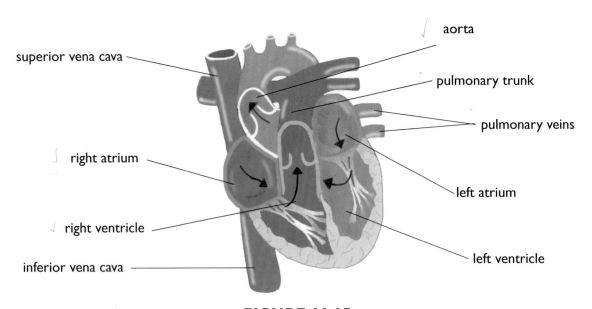

FIGURE 11.15
Blood Flow in the Heart
Illustration by Megan Whitaker

Now remember, this blood is deoxygenated because it transferred its O_2 to the body tissues. This blood needs to be oxygenated. The pulmonary trunk leads to one of two pulmonary arteries that take the blood to the right and left lungs. In the lungs, the blood gets oxygenated in the pulmonary capillaries (capillaries of the lungs) and turns red. Once oxygenated, the blood comes back via the four pulmonary veins. The red blood in the pulmonary veins enters the left atrium and flows into the left ventricle. The left atrium then contracts, forcing extra blood through the bicuspid valve. When the left ventricle contracts, blood flows up and out of the aorta through the aortic semilunar valve. The bicuspid valve closes, preventing backflow into the left atrium. When the left ventricle relaxes, the aortic semilunar valve closes, preventing backflow of blood into the left ventricle. You might be accustomed to thinking that veins carry deoxygenated blood and arteries carry oxygenated blood. That is true of *systemic* circulation, but in *pulmonary* circulation, it is just the opposite.

Although we talked about the right and left atria and ventricles contracting separately, they actually contract together in the body. That is, when the left atrium contracts, the right atrium also contracts exactly at the same time. A split second later, when the right ventricle contracts, the left one does also at the exact same time.

CARDIAC MUSCLE AND THE CARDIAC CYCLE

Cardiac muscle shares characteristics with both smooth muscle and skeletal muscle. It is striated, like skeletal muscle, but the striations are not as easily seen as those in skeletal muscle. Like smooth muscle, cardiac muscle is involuntary. Cardiac muscle tissue is made of elongated, branching cells which usually have a single nuclei. The cells are connected by intercalated (in ter' kuh lay ted) disks. These disks conduct action potentials from one cell to another.

Interestingly, the heart is self-stimulatory. This means it creates its own action potentials. Both smooth and skeletal muscle need action potentials produced by the nervous system. The action potentials of the heart, however, are self-generated. They can be influenced by the parasympathetic and sympathetic divisions of the ANS, but they are not generated by the ANS. Instead, they are generated by special bundles of cardiac muscle tissue known as nodes.

There are small nodes in the heart. The first is the sinoatrial (sigh' no aye' tree uhl) node (SA node), located in the

COLORING BOOK EXERCISE 11.3
To review the anatomy of the heart, follow the instructions on pages 197-201 of your coloring book.

ON YOUR OWN

11.16 If you could take blood from an atrium, how could you tell whether the blood came from the right or left atrium?

11.17 Deoxygenated blood is moving away from the heart. What ventricle was the blood just in? In what blood vessel did it leave the heart?

upper portion of the right atrium. The second is the atrioventricular node (AV node), located near the tricuspid valve in the right atrium. The sinoatrial node is often called the pacemaker, as it initiates the action potentials that cause the heart to beat.

Here's how it works. The SA node spontaneously generates action potentials that spread to both atria and signal them to contract. This causes the blood that is in the atria to be pushed into the ventricles, topping off the ventricles, which actually did most of their filling while both atria and both ventricles were at rest. The action potentials of the atrial cells stimulate an action potential in the AV node. After a split-second delay, the AV node sends action potentials into the atrioventricular bundles, which are special bundles of nodal tissue that travel through the interventricular septum and then branch and travel to each ventricle. These bundles further branch into fibers called Purkinje (per kin' jee) fibers, which send the action potential to the cells in the ventricles. This signals the ventricles to contract *after* the atria have contracted and topped off the ventricles.

When the ventricles contract, both atrioventricular valves close, and the blood is pushed out the aorta (from the left ventricle) and the pulmonary trunk (from the right ventricle). What causes the AV valves to close? Fluid, including blood, flows from high pressure to low. When the contraction of the ventricles raises the ventricular pressure, the blood begins to backflow, but it catches in the cusps of the AV valves, causing them to close! After contracting, the ventricles relax. At this point, the semilunar valves in the aorta and the pulmonary trunk close, preventing blood from rushing back into the ventricles. How does that happen? When the ventricles relax, their pressure suddenly drops. Blood that tries to flow from the now higher pressures in the pulmonary trunk and aorta catches in the cusps of the semilunar valves, snapping them shut and preventing backflow into the ventricles.

Once the pressure in the ventricles drops, the atrioventricular valves open because the pressure in the atria is now higher than in the ventricles, and blood in the atria begins flowing into the ventricles. This actually happens before the atria contract. This is called passive ventricular filling, and it is actually responsible for about 70% of the blood transfer from the atria into the ventricles. When the atria contract again, that just tops off the blood transfer, adding the other 30% to the ventricles.

MOD 11

The cycle we just described is called the cardiac cycle. It is split into two phases: systole (sis' toh lee), which means, "to contract," and diastole (dye as' toh lee), which means, "to relax." Not surprisingly, then, the systole phase is defined as the phase in which the *ventricles* contract, and the diastole is defined as the phase in which the *ventricles* relax.

> **Diastole phase**—The phase of the cardiac cycle in which the ventricles relax
>
> **Systole phase**—The phase of the cardiac cycle in which the ventricles contract
>
> **Cardiac cycle**—One complete round of diastole and systole

When you get your blood pressure measured, you are given one number over another number. The first number is the systolic pressure, and it reflects the pressure in the aorta when the left ventricle contracts (the systole phase). This is the maximum pressure that the aorta experiences. The second number is the diastolic pressure, and it reflects the minimum pressure in the aorta. This occurs right before ventricular contraction, during the diastole phase.

Have you ever listened to a heartbeat? A heartbeat contains two sounds, which are best described with the words lub-dupp. A series of heartbeats, then, sounds like:

lub-dupp, lub-dupp, lub-dupp, lub-dupp…

When you hear a heartbeat, what you are really hearing is the closing of the valves in the heart. When the ventricles contract, the atrioventricular valves close. That's the lub, pronounced "lube." It is a long, deep, booming sound reflecting the large size of the atrioventricular valves (which close at the same instant). The dupp is a short, snapping sound made by the two smaller semilunar valves when they close. The valves *open* silently.

COLORING BOOK EXERCISE 11.4

You can learn more about the cardiac cycle by following the instructions on page 203 of the coloring book.

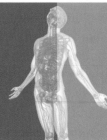

ON YOUR OWN

11.18 The terms atrial systole and atrial diastole are sometimes used in discussions pertaining to the heart. Based on what you have read, to what do these terms refer?

BLOOD VESSELS AND THE ENTIRE CIRCULATORY SYSTEM

So far, we have concentrated on blood and on the heart. However, we cannot end a discussion of the circulatory system without studying blood vessels and how they carry blood throughout the body.

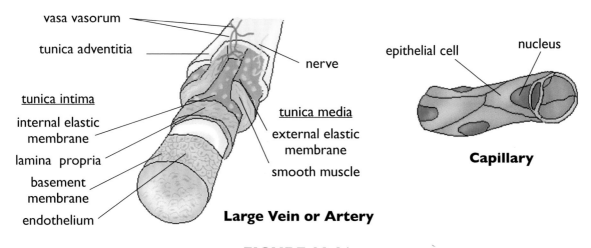

FIGURE 11.16
Blood Vessels
Illustration by Megan Whitaker

We've already talked about arteries, veins, and capillaries. It is now time to discuss their structure. Veins and arteries are composed of three tunics: the tunica intima (in' tih muh), the tunica media, and the tunica adventitia (ad ven tish' uh). The tunica intima is closest to the blood, and that's why it is referred to as intima, because it is "intimate" with the blood. It consists of a slick layer of simple squamous epithelial tissue, called the endothelium, resting on a basement membrane of connective tissue. The basement membrane is connected to a thicker layer of connective tissue called the lamina (lam' ih nuh) propria (proh' pree uh). Finally, this tunic is wrapped in a layer of elastic fibers called the internal elastic membrane.

The tunic in between the inner tunic (the tunica intima) and the outer tunic is appropriately called the tunica media. It contains the smooth muscle that wraps around the vessel and an outer covering of elastic fibers called the **external elastic membrane**. Finally, the outer tunic is a layer of connective tissue called the tunic adventitia. It blends into the surrounding tissue, holding the vessel in place. Notice also that there are nerves in the blood vessels. These nerves innervate the smooth muscle. Finally, you might not think about this, but large blood vessels themselves need blood vessels, since the vessel walls are composed of living tissue. So, the vasa (vas' uh) vasorum (vas or' uhm) is the set of blood vessels that supply the blood vessel walls with O$_2$ and nutrients.

Even though large arteries and veins have the same three layers, veins are much thinner walled than are arteries. From the outside, an artery and vein taking blood to and from a particular body organ look to be about the same diameter. But, the artery has a thick wall and less space for blood within it; the vein has a thin wall and more space for blood. In fact, about two-thirds of the body's blood is in the veins.

Compare the structure of veins and arteries with that of a capillary. Notice the capillary has no tunics. In fact, a capillary has only an endothelium and a basement membrane. Now remember the purpose of capillaries. They allow the exchange of gases and nutrients between the tissues and the blood. Obviously, then, capillaries must be thin. That's why they do not have tunics. We also know that capillaries are microscopically small. We told you at beginning of this module that capillaries are so small that erythrocytes must line up in single file as they pass through them.

There are also two more types of blood vessels: arterioles (ar tear' ee olz) and venules (ven' youlz).

Arterioles—The smallest arteries that still have three tunics

Venules—Small veins that do not have three tunics, but instead have only an endothelium, a basement membrane, and a few smooth muscle cells.

Obviously, then, arterioles are found between arteries and capillaries. Arteries get smaller and smaller as they get closer to the capillaries that they supply. The smallest artery that still has all three tunics is called an arteriole. Similarly, venules are found between the capillaries and the veins.

Now that you have all of the terminology related to blood vessels, you can learn a little more detail with regard to how blood travels throughout the body. First, let's take a look at some of the major veins and arteries in the body.

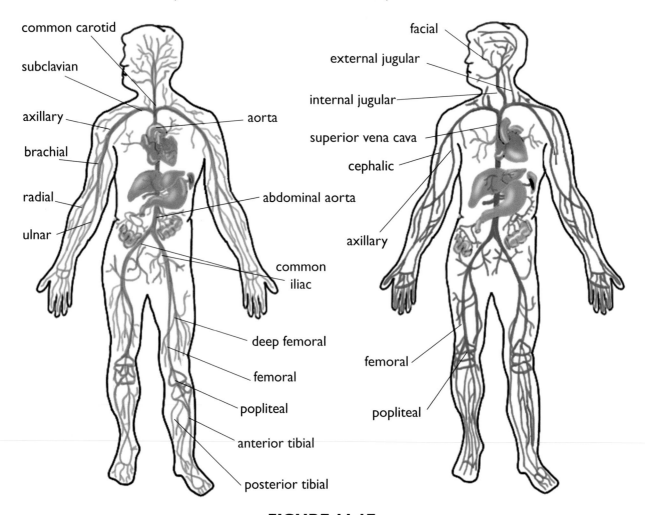

FIGURE 11.17
Some Major Arteries and Veins
Illustration by Megan Whitaker

Now, don't get caught up in memorizing the arteries and veins in figure 11.17. We will not require you to know them for the test. We are just showing them to you so that you get an idea of the system as a whole. Also, please realize that the veins and arteries shown here are just a few of the veins and arteries in the human body.

There are several things that you can observe from the illustration. First, arteries and veins tend to travel together in the body. However, there are more veins in the body than arteries. What you cannot see from the illustration is that all arteries are considered to be deep. Deep veins travel together alongside arteries, but there are also many superficial veins. You may be able to see some superficial veins as bluish vessels beneath your skin.

COLORING BOOK EXERCISE 11.5
An overview of blood vessels can be found on page 205 in your coloring book. Overviews for the arteries and veins can be found on pages 207 and 223.

ON YOUR OWN
11.19 Blood is traveling in the thigh down a large blood vessel towards the feet. Is it in a vein or an artery?

Now that you see the big picture, how does all of this work? Well, when the left ventricle of the heart contracts, blood is pushed through the arteries, creating pressure in the arteries. This pressure pushes blood away from the heart. As the blood travels, the arteries branch, getting smaller and smaller, eventually becoming arterioles. Finally, the blood reaches the capillaries, and it drops off the O_2 it is carrying in its hemoglobin to the tissues. At the same time, nutrients move from the blood to the tissues, and waste products are transferred to the blood from the tissues.

The deoxygenated blood then moves into the venules and into the veins. Please note that the action of the heart pumping *does not* pull blood back into the heart from the veins. Remember, *pressure* pushes the blood along. However, as the blood travels toward the capillaries, the pressure drops. By the time the blood gets through the capillaries and into the venules, the pressure is very low. So, the blood needs some help to get back to the heart. The help comes from movements of the nearby skeletal muscles, which squeeze the veins, helping to push the venous blood along. One-way valves in the veins of the limbs keep the blood from moving backwards, so when the skeletal muscles squeeze the veins, blood travels only toward the heart. Even breathing helps the blood return to the heart. As you inhale, "suction" is placed on the inferior vena cava. That pulls its walls outward, dropping its pressure so that blood flows into it.

Once the blood travels to the right heart, it must get rid of its CO_2 and pick up O_2. So, the right heart pumps the blood to the lungs. There, it drops off its CO_2 and picks up O_2. The blood then travels back to the left heart, ready to start the process all over again. At rest, all of the blood in your body, about 5 liters, completes this journey in one minute!

Every moment of every day, your cardiovascular system is at work. Tens of thousands of miles of blood vessels link every cell in your body to this lifeline. You can live a few days without water and weeks without food, but you can only live minutes without O_2. Blood is life-giving.

You've learned many important physiological details in this module. We hope that you have also managed to find time to contemplate the philosophical and spiritual wonders of your cardiovascular system.

ANSWERS TO THE "ON YOUR OWN" QUESTIONS

11.1 Blood must flow to take nutrients and O_2 to the cells, and to pick up CO_2 and wastes from the cells. It also picks up O_2 and drops off CO_2 as it flows through the lungs, and is purified as it flows through the kidneys.

11.2 Blood is a transport medium, a regulatory tissue, and a protective tissue.

11.3 On average, 55% of blood is plasma, and 90% of plasma is water. To get the percentage of water in all of blood, just take 55% times 90%, and you get about 50%. Indeed, half of blood is water.

11.4 The viscosity of the blood increases because the RBCs have a slight stickiness for each other. More RBCs means more stickiness, which means more resistance to flow, which means greater viscosity.

11.5 It would be easier for the heart to pump blood, because with fewer RBCs, the viscosity of the blood drops and it flows more easily.

11.6 Since white blood cells aid the body in times of infection or inflammation, then the body is either fighting an infection or is inflamed in some other way.

11.7 Hemoglobin has four hemes, each with an iron in the center. Each heme can carry an O_2 molecule, so a single hemoglobin molecule can carry up to four O_2 molecules.

11.8 Erythrocytes have no means of locomotion. They are simply carried along by the blood. So, it is a leukocyte, which can move on its own.

11.9 Antihistamines reduce production of histamine. They do this by reducing the activity of basophils, since basophils release histamine.

11.10 A blood vessel tear would start the intrinsic pathway of coagulation. If the vessel constriction and platelet plug formation were not enough, factor XII would be exposed to collagen, making activated factor XII. That would start the pathway. So, if activated factor XII is there, coagulation will begin.

11.11 This is important. Some things are made in the coagulation process; some are already in the bloodstream. Typically, factors exist in the blood, but activated factors are made. So, factor IX is already in the blood. Prothrombinase is produced at the end of stage 1. Thrombin is produced from prothrombinase and prothrombin. This means that prothrombin is already in the blood. Tissue factor is a result of tissue damage and is therefore produced. Like all factors, factor VII is already in the blood. Fibrin is produced when thrombin reacts with fibrinogen. So, fibrinogen is already in the blood.

11.12 There might be a problem with the calcium level in the blood. Many of the steps require Ca^{2+}. If they are not there, factors will not be activated.

11.13 Only O⁻ blood types have no risk. There is always the risk of the donor's antibodies in the recipient. However, all other blood types have low risk, because O is the universal blood type and the negative means there are no Rh antigens on the erythrocytes. Even if the person has antibodies against the Rh antigen, they will not affect the blood.

11.14 The universal recipient type is AB. After all, they produce neither the anti-A nor the anti-B antibody. Therefore, whether the erythrocytes being donated have A or B antigens or both doesn't matter because there are no antibodies to attack them. To be truly universal, however, it needs to be AB⁺. Remember, if you are Rh positive, you do not produce the anti-Rh antibodies. So, whether or not the donated blood is Rh positive will not matter.

11.15 A is dominant as long as there is no B, which is codominant. There cannot be a B allele in the genotype. That means the person could be AA or AO. For the Rh factor, positive is dominant. The person could have two alleles for positive (++) or one positive and one negative (+−).

11.16 Check to see if it is oxygenated. Blood in the right atrium comes from the body tissues and is deoxygenated. Blood in the left atrium comes from the lungs and is oxygenated. The oxygenated blood is bright red; deoxygenated blood is dark red.

11.17 If it is deoxygenated and moving away from the heart, it must be going to the lungs. It just came from the right ventricle. It left the heart through the pulmonary trunk.

11.18 The term systole refers to contraction. When nothing is put in front of it, we assume it means contraction of the ventricles. However, atrial systole means contraction of the atria. In the same way, atrial diastole means relaxation of the atria.

11.19 It is in an artery. If it is traveling down toward the feet, it is still traveling away from the heart. That makes the blood vessel an artery.

STUDY GUIDE FOR MODULE 11

1.   Define the following terms:
        a. Viscosity
        b. Plasma
        c. Formed elements of blood
      — d. Erythrocytes
      — e. Leukocytes
      — f. Platelets
        g. Diapedesis
        h. Chemotaxis
      — i. Hemopoiesis
        j. Hemostasis
        k. Coagulation factors
        l. Antigen
        m. Arteries
        n. Capillaries
        o. Veins
        p. Pulmonary circulation
        q. Systemic circulation
      — r. Systolic phase
      — s. Diastolic phase
        t. Cardiac cycle
      — u. Arterioles
      — v. Venules

2.   If you fill a balloon full of blood and throw it into the water, will the balloon sink
        or float?

3.   What is the pH range of blood? Why is it so critical?

4.   What are the two main components of blood? Roughly what percent of each is in
        blood?

5.   Blood is about 50% what?

6.   What makes up the majority of blood plasma? What other things are in
        blood plasma?

7.   What makes up the majority of the formed elements of blood? What other things are in the formed elements?

8.   What does hemoglobin do in the blood?

9.   What metal must be in hemoglobin in order for it to work properly?

10.   Why do RBCs have a short lifespan?

11.   What are the five types of leukocytes? Which are granulocytes? Which are agranulocytes?

12.   List the function of each leukocyte.

13.   Where are the formed elements in blood formed? From what type of cell are they formed?

14.   What are the three stages of hemostasis, in the order in which they happen?

15.   What is a thrombus?

16.   What is made in each of the three stages of blood coagulation?

17.   In which stage of blood coagulation do coagulation factors play a critical role?

18.   Do the presence of blood coagulation factors imply that blood coagulation is occur ring? What about the presence of activated blood coagulation factors?

19.   What is special about type O^- blood?

20.   What is special about type AB^+ blood?

21.   A father has type A blood and a mother has type B blood. What blood types are possible for these parents' children?

22.   A father and mother are both Rh positive. They have a child who is Rh negative. How is this possible?

23.   Explain the flow of blood. Start with blood going into the heart from the superior and inferior vena cava. Explain what parts of the heart it passes through, what kinds of blood vessels it passes through, and what happens to the oxygenation in the blood. In the description, name the major veins or arteries that feed directly into the heart or lead directly from the heart.

24.   A person's blood pressure is 120 over 80. Which is the systolic pressure and which is the diastolic pressure?

25.   What is the sinoatrial node? What is the atrioventricular node? Which is called the pacemaker?

26.   In which types of blood vessels is the blood pressure lowest?

27.   We often say that a lot of exercise in the morning "gets the blood pumping." For which kinds of blood vessels is this particularly true?

28.   Identify the structures in the following:

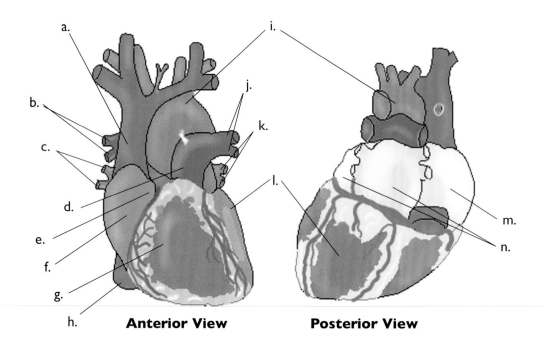

Anterior View   **Posterior View**

29. Identify the structures in the following anterior view of the inside of the heart.

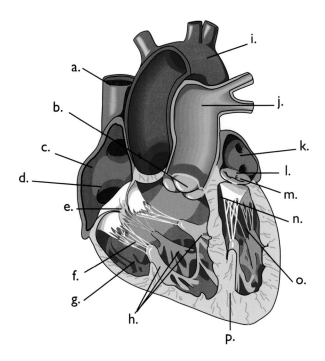

30. Suppose you could watch a drop of blood as it leaves the lungs and heads back to the heart. Take the structures in the figure above and list them in the order through which the drop would pass until it once again reaches the lungs. If the drop will not pass through the structure, just leave it out.

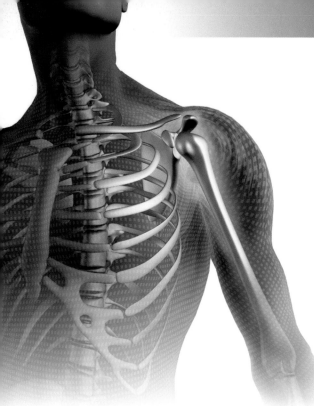

THE LYMPHATIC SYSTEM

Your lymphatic system labors in the shadows of the other well-known organ systems, but it is extremely important to your well-being. This system is crucial to your body's ability to stay healthy.

As you learned in the previous module, your circulatory system is composed of a vast network of blood vessels that cover your entire body. In addition, there is another vast network of vessels that run throughout your entire body. These vessels are called lymph vessels, and they form the infrastructure of the lymphatic system, which is illustrated in figure 12.1.

heart of the matter

Your lymphatic system is designed like a well-built fortress. Without it, invaders such as bacteria, viruses, and parasites would have free access to your body. Indeed, this world is a dangerous place in which to live, but your body's Designer has given you all that you need to stay well protected.

Notice that along the lymph vessels there are little bulges called lymph nodes. These lymph nodes are tiny organs containing lymphocytes, which as you recall from the previous module, are white blood cells that produce antibodies and otherwise protect you from foreign invaders. In addition, lymph nodes contain large numbers of another type of white blood cell called a macrophage. Macrophages are large white blood cells that are capable of phagocytosis of foreign invaders. In general, groups of lymphocytes and macrophages are referred to as lymphatic tissue.

The lymphatic system can be described as a system of lymph vessels and lymph tissue that serves three basic functions: fluid balance, fat absorption, and immunological (im' myou no loj' ih kuhl) defense. We will discuss each of these functions later on in this module.

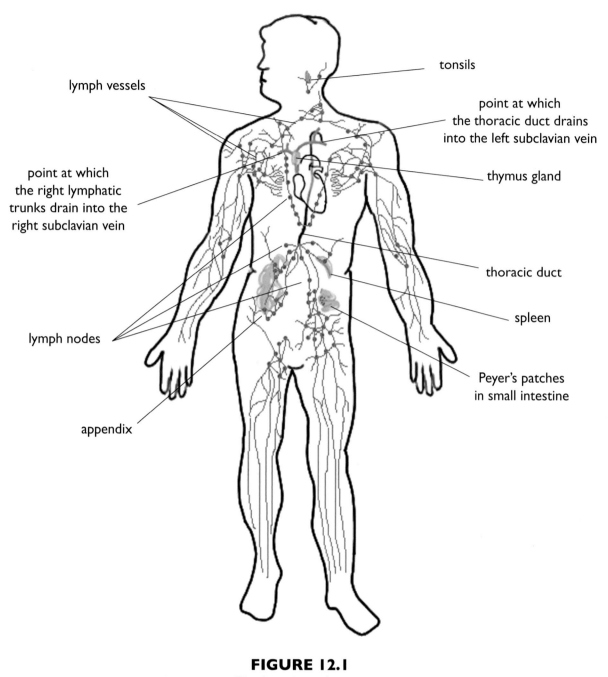

FIGURE 12.1
The Lymphatic System
Illustration by Megan Whitaker

Lymphatic tissue—Groups of lymphocytes and macrophages
that provide immune protection

Lymph nodes—Encapsulated masses of lymphatic tissue found along lymph vessels

LYMPH AND LYMPH VESSELS

Before we discuss how the lymphatic system performs its functions, we need to make sure that you understand the basics of lymph vessels and what they carry. Not surprisingly, lymph vessels carry a substance we call lymph, which means "clear."

Lymph—Watery liquid formed from interstitial fluid and found in lymph vessels

In module 10, we mentioned interstitial fluid, which is the fluid around and between cells. It is naturally produced by leakage of clear fluid out of the blood capillaries. About 90% of the interstitial fluid diffuses back into the capillaries and is carried away by the circulatory system. The blood capillaries do not pick up the remaining10% of the interstitial fluid. Instead, it is collected in the lymphatic vessels. When interstitial fluid enters a lymph vessel, it is renamed lymph. The lymph is eventually returned to the circulatory system by either the right lymphatic trunks or the thoracic duct, which dump the lymph into the subclavian veins as shown in figure 12.1.

Lymphatic vessels have porous, blind beginnings called lymph capillaries. In other words, they start out as dead-end capillaries, unlike blood capillaries, which are flow-through tubes and are part of the circulatory system.

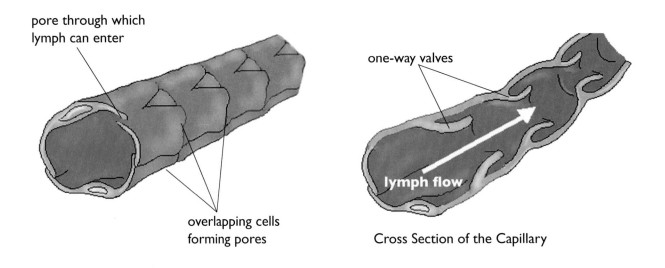

FIGURE 12.2
A Lymph Capillary
Illustration by Megan Whitaker

Epithelial cells, which overlap with one another, form these dead end capillaries. The overlap leaves spaces in between the cells, and interstitial fluid can easily flow into the vessel through these spaces. Now called lymph, the clear fluid travels through the vessel with the aid of three processes that we will discuss later. Notice the microscopic valves in the vessel, which are formed from the overlapping cells. These valves prevent the lymph from flowing backwards.

The lymph capillaries and vessels are found in all of the tissues in the body, except for the central nervous system, the bone marrow, and tissues without blood vessels, such as cartilage. The lymph capillaries flow into larger lymph vessels, which eventually flow through lymph nodes. You can think of lymph nodes as filtering stations, which clean the lymph of foreign organisms and dead cells. Eventually, lymph is returned to the circulatory system, where it again becomes part of the blood plasma.

You might be wondering how the lymph is able to flow through the lymphatic system. After all, the heart pumps blood through the arteries. Is there some organ that pumps lymph through the lymph vessels? No. Instead, lymph flows through the lymphatic system somewhat like blood travels through the veins. The contraction of skeletal muscles squeezes the nearby lymph vessels, "pumping" them. This pushes lymph through the vessels. One-way valves, similar to the semilunar valves of the heart, prevent the lymph from flowing backwards when the skeletal muscles relax. These delicate valves have only two small cusps (unlike the semilunar valves of the heart, which have three) and are found all along the larger lymphatic vessels.

In addition to the contraction of skeletal muscles, there are two other means by which lymph travels through the lymphatic system. There is smooth muscle in the larger lymph vessels. The contraction of this smooth muscle most likely adds to the force provided by the skeletal muscles. Also, when you breathe, pressure changes occur in the thoracic region. When the thoracic pressure drops, as you inhale, that tends to pull lymph into the thoracic duct and speed its return to the left subclavian vein (figure 12.1).

COLORING BOOK EXERCISE 12.1
An overview of the lymphatic system can be found on page 235 of your coloring book.

ON YOUR OWN

12.1 Imagine a person walking down the street to a bus stop. While walking to the bus stop, the person is referred to as a "pedestrian." When the person boards the bus, he or she is no longer considered a pedestrian but is now considered a "passenger." The person is exactly the same person, but as soon as he or she gets on the bus, the person is referred to in a completely different way. How is this similar to interstitial fluid and lymph?

FUNCTIONS OF THE LYMPHATIC SYSTEM

We now want to spend some time discussing how the lymphatic system accomplishes its three basic functions: fluid balance, fat absorption, and immunological defense. Let's start with fluid balance. Without the lymphatic system, your body would not be able to maintain fluid balance. The result would be a buildup of interstitial fluid, which would cause edema (uh dee' muh).

> **Edema**—a buildup of excess interstitial fluid in the tissues, which leads to swelling

How does this buildup occur? Think about your blood capillaries for a moment. They are thin-walled and porous, allowing for the exchange of gases, nutrients, and waste products with the cells. But how do they actually do their job? We will answer that question with figure 12.3.

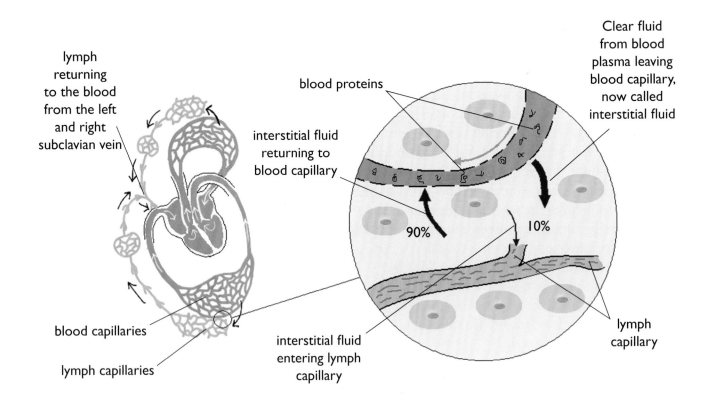

lymph
returning
to the blood
from the left
and right
subclavian vein

blood proteins

interstitial fluid
returning to
blood capillary

Clear fluid
from blood
plasma leaving
blood capillary,
now called
interstitial fluid

90%

10%

blood capillaries

lymph capillaries

interstitial fluid
entering lymph
capillary

lymph
capillary

FIGURE 12.3
Fluid Exchange between Capillaries, Tissues, and Lymph
Illustration by Megan Whitaker

As blood flows through a blood capillary, clear fluid is pushed out. This happens because the blood is flowing through the capillaries under pressure. The pressure pushes the fluid out of the pores in the capillaries. Blood cells and proteins, however, cannot get through the pores because they are too big. So, the fluid that leaks out of the capillaries is a clear derivative of the blood plasma, but it is not identical to blood plasma because it lacks proteins. It does have the oxygen and nutrients the cells need. Once it leaves the capillaries, it is called interstitial fluid. Interstitial fluid bathes the cells, giving them oxygen and nutrients and picking up carbon dioxide and other waste products. About 90% of this interstitial fluid is drawn back into the capillary after it has released its nutrients and picked up the cells' waste products. This happens mainly because of osmosis. The blood proteins cannot leave the capillary, but the clear fluid can. This increases the concentration of proteins still in the blood capillary, and this increased concentration of solutes pulls the interstitial fluid back into the capillaries at the far end via osmosis. About 10% of the interstitial fluid is not drawn back in to the capillaries, however. If that 10% were not drained out of the tissues in some way, the tissues would begin to swell with the excess fluid. Depending on the location and severity of the swelling, the results could be disastrous. Why? Too much interstitial fluid creates too wide a space between the cells and the all-important capillary blood supply, and diffusion of oxygen and nutrients to the cells is slowed. This can cause cells to die if the situation becomes severe enough.

Of course, the healthy human body is designed to prevent this. Instead, the lymph capillaries pick up the 10% remaining interstitial fluid. It is renamed lymph. The lymph capillaries send lymph into the larger lymphatic vessels, where it goes through one or more lymph nodes to be filtered. It then flows back into the blood. As figure 12.1 indicates, the lymphatic system deposits its lymph into one of the two subclavian veins in the shoulders. Lymph that ends up in the right lymphatic duct drains into the right subclavian vein, while lymph that ends up in the thoracic duct drains into the left subclavian vein.

The lymphatic system, then, helps maintain fluid balance by picking up the excess interstitial fluid in the tissues and returning it to the circulatory system. Have you ever heard of the disease elephantiasis? It's a tropical disease in which the legs swell and become huge, like those of an elephant, because of edema. That's because tropical parasites capable of getting into the lymph vessels block the flow of lymph. This causes a backup of lymph, and the interstitial fluid cannot drain into the lymph capillaries. So, the tissues swell with the excess fluid.

The second function of the lymphatic system is the absorption of fats from the digestive system. We'll discuss this in more detail in the next module, when we deal with digestion. However, we want to make you aware of the basics of this function right now. There are specialized lymph capillaries in the lining of the small intestine. These lymph capillaries, called lacteals (lak' tee uhlz), collect fats that are absorbed by the small intestine during the digestive process. Once these lymph capillaries absorb fat, the fluid inside takes on a milky-white color. At that point, the liquid is no longer called lymph, but instead is called chyle (kile). The chyle eventually is returned into the bloodstream at the left subclavian vein, along with lymph from other parts of the body. This is the means by which fats get into the circulatory system.

The final function of the lymphatic system is immunological defense. We will spend the majority of this module discussing this important function.

Immunological defense—The process by which the body protects itself from pathogenic invaders such as bacteria, fungi, parasites, and foreign substances

It's a tough world out there, but your body was created to withstand the challenges. You have a many-tiered defense system that protects your tissues in an amazingly efficient way. Lymph nodes filter foreign organisms and substances from the lymph. The spleen, as you will learn in a later section of this module, does the same kind of filtering of the blood. Also, white blood cells can travel to the tissues and destroy invaders right where they are doing their damage.

COLORING BOOK EXERCISE 12.2

Review of the material covered in this section can be found on pages 237 and 245 of your coloring book.

ON YOUR OWN

12.2 After a fatty meal, the blood looks like tomato soup—a rather cloudy red. After fasting, it is a clear cherry red. Why?

12.3 Which subclavian vein receives more lymph: the right subclavian vein or the left subclavian vein? (HINT: Look at figure 12.1.)

MOD 12

MUCOSA—ASSOCIATED LYMPHOID TISSUE (MALT)

As we mentioned previously, the main thing we want to concentrate on in this module is the immunological defense provided to the body by the lymphatic system. Such a discussion needs to start with mucosa-associated lymphoid tissue (MALT).

Mucosa-associated lymphoid tissue (MALT)—Concentrations of lymphatic tissue without a connective tissue capsule

MALT is located deep to the mucous membranes of the respiratory, digestive, urinary, and reproductive systems. This is by design of course, because these mucous membranes line passages that open to the outside of the body and are therefore prone to infection by foreign invaders. MALT is strategically located to intercept such invaders.

In its least-organized form, MALT is called diffuse lymphatic tissue.

Diffuse lymphatic tissue—scattered lymphocytes, macrophages, and other cells found deep to mucous membranes

Diffuse lymphatic tissue, because it has no boundaries, tends to blend with the surrounding tissue. Besides its location deep to mucous membranes, it is found around **lymph nodules** and in the spleen.

Lymph nodules—Lymphatic tissue arranged into compact, somewhat spherical structures, but without a capsule

When stained and put under a microscope, diffuse lymphatic tissue looks like a scattered grouping of purple dots. Lymph nodules, on the other hand, look like a lot of purple dots surrounded by a ring of even more dense purple dots. Perform the following experiment to see what we mean.

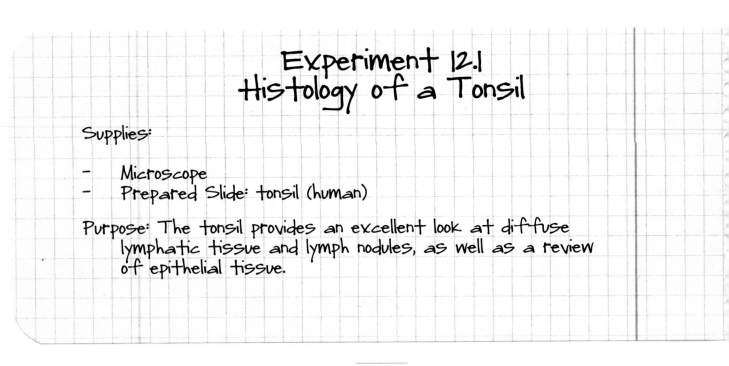

Experiment 12.1
Histology of a Tonsil

Supplies:

- Microscope
- Prepared Slide: tonsil (human)

Purpose: The tonsil provides an excellent look at diffuse lymphatic tissue and lymph nodules, as well as a review of epithelial tissue.

Procedure:

1. Mount the prepared slide on the microscope and focus in on some tissue at 40x magnification. Scan the slide to find the edges of the tissue.

2. You should be able to see that the edges of the tissue are surrounded by a thin band of cells that look different than the rest of the cells. This is the epithelial tissue of the tonsil.

3. In the tissue beneath the epithelial layer, you should see large ovals of purple dots inside unorganized masses of purple dots. These ovals can be hard to see, as they are not a lot different from the surrounding tissue. They have the same cells as the rest of the tissue below the epithelial layer, but the cells are just a bit more concentrated around the edges, forming an oval ring. Those are the lymph nodules.

4. Draw what you see, including the epithelial tissue. Label the lymph nodules.

5. Find a small lymph nodule and center it. You need a relatively small one, because the large ovals will not fit in the microscope field at 100x. Change to 100x and refocus.

6. You can now see the cells a little more clearly. Center the nodule. Notice that the cells inside the oval are really the same as the cells outside the oval, at least until you reach the epithelial layer. The tissue outside the oval (not including the epithelium) is the diffuse lymphatic tissue.

7. Draw what you see at this magnification, labeling the lymph nodule and the diffuse lymphatic tissue.

8. Without changing the position of the slide, increase to 400x and refocus. You are now looking at the tissue inside the lymph nodule. Draw what you see.

9. Go back to 100x magnification, refocus, and center on some cells outside the lymph nodule.

MOD 12

10. Change back to 400x and refocus. You are now looking at diffuse lymphatic tissue. Draw what you see. Notice that there is very little difference between the cells inside the nodule and outside of the nodule. That's because they are both really just lymphatic tissue. The tissue in the lymph nodules is just concentrated into an oval.

11. Go back to 40x and refocus. Find the thin band of cells, which is the epithelial layer. Center a portion of the band.

12. Change to 100x and refocus. If the epithelium is not centered, center it.

13. Increase to 400x and refocus. What kind of epithelial tissue is this? Look at module 2 if you can't remember the characteristics of the different types of epithelium.

14. Put everything away.

Lymph nodules can be found as single structures in the body, or they can be grouped together into larger clumps. That's what the tonsils (see figure 12.1) are. The palatine tonsils (most commonly referred to as "the tonsils") are an accumulation of lymphoid nodules located on each side of the throat. Also, there are lymphoid nodules located at the base of the tongue (lingual tonsils) and in the nasopharynx (adenoids). These lymph nodules form a protective ring around the throat, strategically located to protect the body from foreign invaders that may enter through the nose or mouth.

If the tonsils get infected, they can become inflamed and abnormally enlarged. This condition is called tonsillitis. If the condition is chronic, the tonsils can be removed in a tonsillectomy. Tonsils tend to get smaller as a person matures, and they can actually disappear altogether in an adult.

Peyer's (pie' yers) patches (see figure 12.1) are very similar to tonsils. They're groups of lymphocytes in lymph nodules that are in the last third of the small intestine and in the vermiform appendix. Once again, they're strategically located to deal with foreign invaders. They prevent the friendly bacteria that inhabit the large intestine from stirring up trouble in the small intestine.

LYMPH NODES

Scattered throughout the lymphatic system, we find encapsulated masses of lymphatic tissue called lymph nodes. As figure 12.4 shows, lymph nodes are far more organized than lymph nodules, and each may be considered a tiny organ.

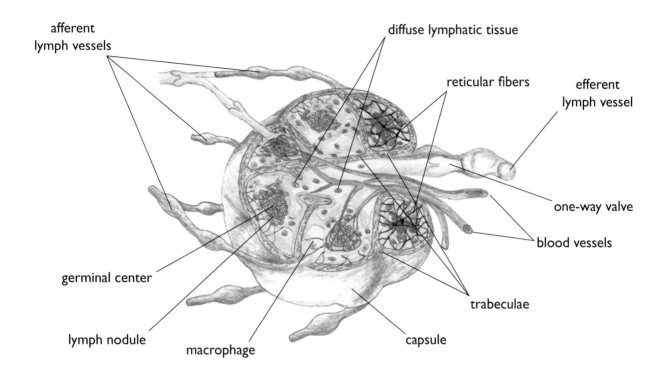

FIGURE 12.4
A Lymph Node
Illustration by Megan Whitaker

Unlike lymph nodules, lymph nodes are surrounded by a capsule of dense connective tissue. Extensions of this capsule, called trabeculae (truh bek' you lay), make up the "skeleton" of the node. Reticular fibers extend from the trabeculae, forming a net of connective tissue throughout the lymph node. A typical lymph node actually contains lymph nodules along its outer edge. These lymph nodules form germinal centers, where rapid mitosis of lymphocytes can take place in response to a foreign invader found in the lymph. Lymphocytes produced in the germinal centers are released into the lymph and eventually reach the blood, where they fight the foreign invaders. The lymph nodules within the lymph node are surrounded by diffuse lymphatic tissue.

Lymph nodes filter the lymph as it travels through the lymph vessels. They accomplish this task with macrophages, which are found along with lymphocytes in all lymphatic tissues. Several afferent lymph vessels feed the lymph nodes. However, lymph usually exits through just one efferent lymph vessel. A lymph node, then, not only filters the lymph, but it also acts as a transfer station, where many vessels combine their fluid into a larger vessel. It is likely that the efferent lymph vessel leading out of one lymph node will lead into another lymph node as an afferent vessel. This means that lymph usually travels

MOD 12

through more than one lymph node (and therefore gets cleaned more than once) before getting returned to the blood.

Think about how this works for a moment. Remember, only 10% of the fluid that leaked from the blood capillaries ends up becoming lymph. The rest returns to the blood due to physical forces, including blood pressure and osmosis. How important is this? Well, the blood needs fluid for the plasma. So, only a little bit of fluid can be lost when the capillaries exchange nutrients and wastes with the tissues. If the blood needs fluid, why should any of it be lost? Why didn't God just design the system so that all of the fluid in the plasma makes it back into the capillaries after it bathes the cells?

There must be some way to detect foreign invaders and deal with them. That's where the lymph vessels and lymph nodes come in. The lymph vessels collect a "sample" of the fluid from the blood. Then, they send that sample through the lymph nodes. There, the fluid is tested. If foreign invaders are detected, the lymph node can trap them. The presence of the foreign invaders stimulates the production of both macrophages and lymphocytes in the lymph nodes. Those lymphocytes then go to the source of the problem.

Lymph nodes, then, have three real functions. First, they are testing stations. They monitor the blood by receiving samples of the blood plasma. Second, if the sample is rife with foreign invaders, they activate macrophages and lymphocytes, which can destroy the invaders. In addition, the lymph nodes filter the lymph that they have, so that they return only cleaned fluid back to the blood. This is very similar to the way a city monitors its water supply. It would take too long and be too costly to test all of the water in a city's water supply. However, periodic samples of the water are taken and, if foreign material is detected, the water is treated to remove it. The lymphatic system does somewhat the same thing. Amazing, isn't it?

COLORING BOOK
EXERCISE 12.3

To review, follow the instructions on pages 239 and 243 of the coloring book.

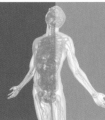

ON YOUR OWN

12.4 Which carries more lymph: an afferent lymph vessel or an efferent lymph vessel? Assume both vessels are connected to the same lymph node.

THE SPLEEN AND THE THYMUS GLAND

The spleen (see figure 12.1) is found in the upper left part of the abdomen and is roughly the size of a clenched fist. It is encased in a capsule and has a support network of trabeculae that extend into the spleen from the capsule. The capsule of the spleen contains smooth muscle tissue. Inside the spleen, there are two types of tissue: red pulp and white pulp. The white pulp is composed of diffuse lymphatic tissue and lymph nodules. This white pulp surrounds the arteries that enter the spleen. The red pulp is made up of specialized veins with reticular fibers. These veins receive blood that was in the capillaries of the spleen. About three-fourths of the spleen is red pulp.

Unlike lymph nodes, the spleen does not filter lymph. It is not a giant lymph node! It is a part of the lymphatic system because it filters the blood. As the blood passes through the white pulp of the spleen, foreign invaders stimulate a response from the diffuse lymphatic tissue or the lymph nodules. That's only the first of the spleen's three major functions, however. The red pulp of the spleen also works to clear the blood of worn-out erythrocytes. Remember, red blood cells have a short life span. As a result, roughly two million erythrocytes die every second! They must be removed from the blood, and that's another one of the spleen's functions. As the blood leaves the spleen through the veins, it passes through the red pulp. Old red blood cells are stiff, and their membranes break as they go through the reticular fibers of the red pulp. Macrophages in the red pulp engage in phagocytosis to remove the worn-out red blood cells.

The third function of the spleen is to act as a reservoir for oxygen-rich blood. The spleen actually holds more blood than it needs. This serves as a backup supply of blood in case of blood loss. If the body detects blood loss due to hemorrhage, the sympathetic division of the ANS stimulates the smooth muscle in the capsule of the spleen to contract. This pushes the backup supply of blood into the bloodstream, compensating, at least partially, for the blood loss.

Although the spleen is a part of the lymphatic system, you can live without it. If your spleen is ruptured due to injury, it can be removed in a splenectomy (splee nek' toh mee). This may be necessary in order to stop internal bleeding, because the spleen is very vascular. If the spleen is removed, the liver can take over the function of removing old red blood cells, and other lymphatic tissue in the body takes over the immunological defense function of the spleen. Of course, overall function is not quite as good as when the spleen is present in the body. As

COLORING BOOK EXERCISE 12.4

A review of the spleen can be found on page 241 of your coloring book.

a result, people who have had their spleens removed may be more susceptible to infection.

Just anterior to the heart and posterior to the upper sternum, is the thymus gland (see figure 12.1). We mentioned the thymus gland in module 10 as a part of the endocrine system; it produces the hormone thymosin. It is also a part of the lymphatic system. Like the tonsils, the thymus gland changes as a person matures. When a person is young, the thymus gland grows. During this stage of life, it is mostly lymphatic tissue. After puberty, it gradually decreases in size, becoming mostly fibrous and fatty tissue in old age.

What does the thymus gland do? Like many things in the human body, the scientific community has much to learn about the thymus gland. We know that especially during prenatal life and childhood, immature lymphocytes known as pre-T lymphocytes leave the red bone marrow (where they are made) and travel to the thymus. Through a remarkable maturation process sometimes referred to as *thymic education*, pre-T lymphocytes that are beneficial to the immune system become T lymphocytes (T stands for thymus), while pre-T lymphocytes that might evoke a detrimental immunological response are eliminated. For example, pre-T lymphocytes that might attack your own antigen are eleminated, but pre-T lymphocytes that could attack foreign cells are allowed to mature to T lymphocytes and enter the bloodstream, from which they take up residence in other lymphatic tissue. We will discuss the function of T lymphocytes shortly.

One function of the thymus gland, then, is to promote the maturation of T lymphocytes. However, we also know that the thymus is an endocrine gland. It produces hormones, principally the hormone thymosin. What does thymosin do in the body? It stimulates the maturation of T lymphocytes and undoubtedly has other functions that are not yet well understood.

IMMUNITY

Now that you know the basic structures of the lymphatic system, it is time to concentrate on immunity. To start the discussion, we want you to consider the words of Nobel Laureate Niels K. Jerne, Professor Emeritus of the Basel Institute for Immunology in Switzerland. In this quote, he compares the nervous system to the lymphatic system:

These two systems stand out among all other organs of our body by their ability to respond adequately to an enormous variety of signals. Both systems display dichotomies and dualisms. The cells of both systems can receive as well as transmit signals. In both systems the signals can be excitatory as well as inhibitory. The two systems penetrate most other tissues of our body...[and they both] learn from experience and build up a memory that is sustained by reinforcement.

In this statement, a great immunologist compares the lymphatic system to the nervous system! "These two systems stand out among all other organs of our body by their ability to respond adequately to an enormous variety of signals." The nervous system obviously does this, but so does the lymphatic system. "Both systems display dichotomies and dualisms." In other words, they display opposite functions and divisions of functions. "The cells of both systems can receive as well as transmit signals. In both systems, the signals can be excitatory as well as inhibitory. The two systems penetrate most other tissues of our body." They also learn from experience. Obviously, your brain learns from experience. Your lymphatic system does, too! That's why if you have had chicken pox, you most likely will not get it again. Even if you are exposed to the virus, your lymphatic system remembers it and knows how to destroy it. This memory is actually "sustained by reinforcement." What do we mean by that? Well, think about tetanus shots. You get a tetanus shot so that if you ever meet up with the tetanus toxin, it's not going to harm you. But, you have to get booster shots periodically. These booster shots stimulate the "memory" of your immune system so that if it ever meets the toxin, it will know what to do with it. Clearly, then, the immunological aspects of the lymphatic system are worth some investigation!

When we are talking specifically about immunity, we are actually talking about only one function of the lymphatic system: immunological defense. So, we often refer to the part of the lymphatic system that gives us immunity as the immune system. That's the focus of the rest of this module. Now remember, the systems of the body interact quite a bit. This is especially evident when discussing immunity. Many of the things that give us immunity are not a part of the lymphatic system. Instead, they are part of another system and simply aid the lymphatic system in its job. You will see what we mean in a moment. First, however, let's look at some disease-causing agents that might lay you low if it were not for your immune system.

First of all, there are pathogenic bacteria. There are harmless bacteria that do you no damage and can even benefit you, but pathogenic bacteria are the ones that give you sinus infections, infected cuts, and so forth. Second, there are pathogenic fungi. Most of the pathogenic fungi that your immune system must work against are the single-celled fungi which are commonly called yeast. Pathogenic yeast can cause athlete's foot or thrush on the tongue. There are parasites such as pinworms, roundworms, and tapeworms. There are also viruses, which are an information-containing unit of either DNA or RNA that is wrapped in its own protein coat. It has none of its own cellular machinery, so it invades a cell and hijacks that cell's machinery to reproduce itself. In the end, this ruptures the cell. Obviously, that's not good! In addition, we must deal with cancers, which are actually our own cells that have been genetically damaged and can no longer control their functions. Instead, they perform uncontrolled mitosis. This forms cancerous tumors. Finally, there are toxins, chemicals that are neither cells nor viruses, nor any of the things discussed above. They are just harmful chemicals that are foreign to the body. Botulism toxin, which is produced by anerobic bacteria in improperly canned foods, is an example.

There are two big divisions in the immune system: innate immunity and acquired immunity.

Innate immunity—An immune response that is the same regardless of the pathogen or toxin encountered

Acquired immunity (also called specific or adaptive immunity)—An immune response targeted at a specific pathogen or toxin after exposure

Innate immunity is the immunity that you have soon after you are born. Your body will respond the same way every time, no matter what. Acquired immunity is the immunity you get as a result of experiencing a pathogen or toxin. To understand the differences between these two divisions, consider distemper and chicken pox. Distemper is a disease that dogs get. If you've got a puppy with distemper, do you have to stay away from the puppy so that you don't get distemper? No. Why? Humans have innate immunity to the pathogen that causes distemper. We cannot catch the disease. On the other hand, consider the chicken pox virus. We have no innate immunity to it. When we are exposed to it, most of us get the disease. Once we get better, however, we usually do not get the disease again. Why? We get acquired immunity from our exposure the virus.

Innate immunity is called nonspecific immunity. That's because the innate immunity that you have does not seek out a particular pathogen or toxin. It simply protects you from many different disease-causing agents. Acquired immunity, however, is specific immunity. When you catch and then recover from a certain disease, you become immune to that specific disease. However, that immunity will not help you fight off another disease. For example, chicken pox immunity won't help you against measles virus. The immunity you acquire once you get chicken pox is specific only for the chicken pox virus.

THE FIRST LINE OF INNATE (NONSPECIFIC) IMMUNITY

As we mentioned in the previous section, many of the structures and processes that are a part of the immune system are not part of the lymphatic system. This is just another example of how the body's systems all interact. For example, consider skin. Skin is the major part of the integumentary system. As you learned in module 3, it has specific tasks that it performs. One of those tasks is to provide nonspecific immunity. The keratin in skin cells makes skin waterproof, and it allows the skin to act as a barrier, keeping foreign invaders out of the body. If something can't get into your body, it can't hurt you.

Not only does the skin act as a barrier, it also provides you with other types of non-specific defense. For example, skin has sweat glands (see module 3). Sweat washes the

MOD 12

surface of the skin. It also helps to lower the pH of the skin. Low pH environments inhibit the growth and activity of many pathogens. In addition to sweat glands, skin also has sebaceous glands (see module 3). The sebaceous glands secrete oil, which contains antibacterial substances.

In addition to sweat and oil, some epithelial tissues, such as those found in the sinuses and trachea, secrete mucus. This mucus traps and catches microorganisms so that they cannot go anywhere. In other words, mucus acts like flypaper, catching and holding pathogens. When you get a cold, for example, you must constantly blow your nose. Why? The epithelium in the sinuses is producing mucus to trap the cold viruses. Of course, once the pathogens are trapped in the mucus, the body needs to get rid of them. That is accomplished by cilia on certain cells that line the mucus-producing epithelium. These cells beat their cilia, moving mucus toward the mouth or nose. We can then blow our nose, cough, or swallow the mucus to get rid of it.

Wait a minute? We swallow our mucus? How does that help get rid of pathogens? After all, swallowing something sends it into the body, right? Yes, that's true, but when you swallow something, you are sending it to the stomach. The stomach contains gastric juice, which is very acidic (pH between 1 and 2). The acid in the gastric juice kills most pathogens. So, swallowing your own mucus helps you kill pathogens that are stuck in that mucus. In fact, the gastric juice of the stomach is considered another one of the first lines of nonspecific immunity. If you eat food that contains bacteria, and most food does, the gastric juice in your stomach kills those bacteria before they can do any damage.

Certain secretions give you chemical protection against organisms that would otherwise invade you. Consider, for example, tears. Tears contain an enzyme called lysozyme. This enzyme breaks down the cell walls of many bacteria. The term lyse actually means, "to break," so lysozyme is an enzyme that breaks cell walls. Lysozyme is the main reason that you rarely get eye infections. The tears bathe the eye in lysozyme, killing bacteria which try to infect it. However, sometimes even the lysozyme in tears is not enough to kill the bacteria invading the eye. When that happens, the eye does get infected. The most common bacterial infection of the eye is known as pinkeye, or conjunctivitis. Conjunctivitis can also be caused by a virus.

Although you might not think of it this way, urine is also a very important first line of nonspecific immunity. Why? It washes out the urinary tract. Remember, any opening to the outside is a potential place for infection. You must get rid of excess water and chemicals, so you need an opening to the outside for that purpose. However, that opening can become a pathway for pathogens. Urine washes out the tract that leads to the outside (the urethra). This helps fight off any organism attempting to enter the body that way. An interesting study on women indicated that women who have large bladders (and thus urinate less frequently) had a higher risk of urinary tract infections than women with small bladders (who urinate more frequently).

Now remember, every opening to the outside is a potential point of infection. In the female reproductive system, the vagina opens to the outside. So, the cervix, the opening between the vagina and the uterus, secretes cervical mucus. This cervical mucus is a nonspecific defense against infection. In addition, cervical mucus contains antibodies, which are a part of the acquired immune system. So, cervical mucus is a mixture of nonspecific and specific defense.

There is one more first line of innate immunity: symbiotic organisms. There are a host of symbiotic organisms that live throughout the body. Bacteria in your large intestine, for example, produce vitamin K and, in return, you provide food for them and a place for them to live. Those symbiotic bacteria flourish in your intestines, and their populations can actually crowd out populations of pathogenic bacteria that might get past the stomach. In addition, symbiotic bacteria and fungi that live on your skin and digest your sweat produce lactic acid, which inhibits pathogenic bacteria and fungi.

> **ON YOUR OWN**
> **12.5** You are given two vials of a salty liquid. One contains sweat and the other contains tears. What test could you perform to determine which was which?

The systems we discussed in this section act as the first line of defense. They either keep pathogens out (as is the case with the skin), or they trap or kill pathogens before they get very far in the body (as is the case with mucus and gastric juice). Much like the defenses of a well-designed fortress, however, the first line of defense is not the only defense available to the body. The vast majority of pathogens get stopped by the first line of defense. However, if they make it past that, there is a second line of nonspecific defense in the body. We will discuss that in the next section.

THE SECOND LINE OF INNATE DEFENSE

If a pathogen gets by the first line of innate defense, other defense mechanisms are activated to protect the body. These defenses are nonspecific, however, so they are still part of our innate immunity. The second line of defense begins with complement and interferon (in ter fear' on).

Complement—A series of about 30 plasma proteins activated by foreign cells or antibodies to those cells. They lyse bacteria, promote phagocytosis, and promote inflammation.

Interferon—Proteins secreted by cells infected with a virus. These proteins do not save the infected cell, but they stimulate nearby cells to strengthen themselves against a viral invasion.

Before you get wrapped up in the details of the definitions, notice two things. First, complement is antibacterial. It is involved in fighting foreign cells, which are generally bacteria. Second, interferon is antiviral. The interferon defense does nothing against living cells. It affects only viruses. These are two nonspecific defense mechanisms that work against different groups of invaders.

Now let's look at the details of the definitions. Complement is made up of about 30 plasma proteins. Where do they come from? The liver makes them and puts them into the blood. Like blood coagulation factors, these proteins stay inactive in the blood until something activates them. How do they become activated? Well, the foreign invader itself in some cases can activate the proteins, or the presence of antibodies bound to antigens can do the activation. Either way, this happens only when foreign cells are present.

What do these proteins do? First, they can lyse bacteria. Now remember, lyse means "to break." These proteins can actually break open bacteria! How do they do that? The complement proteins combine like pieces of a puzzle to form a "punch," which punches a hole in the plasma membrane of the foreign cells, particularly bacteria. This causes the bacteria's components to leak out, killing the bacteria. Not only does activated complement lyse bacteria, but it also attracts phagocytic cells. The phagocytic cells then destroy the bacteria by engulfing them. Finally, complement can help promote inflammation. You might think inflammation is bad, but it is necessary if a foreign invasion occurs. Inflammation occurs when there is a "war" going on between your body's defenses and an invader. Activated complement signals inflammatory agents to be activated. This signal "rallies the troops," bringing more disease-fighting mechanisms to bear.

Now let's move on to our innate viral defense. Interferon is a protein that is antiviral. Unlike the complement proteins, the liver does not produce it. Instead, it is produced by individual cells. If a virus infects a cell, that cell is going to be killed. There's really no hope for it once the virus enters. However, as the virus is attacking it, the cell produces interferon. The interferon won't save that cell, but it will affect neighboring cells and signal them to strengthen themselves against viral attacks. The neighboring cells respond by making their plasma membranes less permeable.

White blood cells make up another part of this second line of innate defenses. Any bacterium or any virus can potentially be attacked by white blood cells, so they are non-specific. Now remember, the neutrophils are phagocytes. That means they can engulf cells or cell parts. They are not very strong at doing this, but these are typically the first white blood cells to arrive at the scene of an infection. The second white blood cells to respond are the monocytes. These are the larger, highly phagocytic white blood cells. Once they enter the tissues, they are called macrophages, which means "big eaters." Basophils, as we've already discussed, promote inflammation by releasing inflammatory chemicals such as histamine, prostaglandins, and leukotrienes (loo koh try' eenz). We will discuss inflammation in more detail in a moment.

Natural killer cells are lymphocytes that attack tumor cells and virus-infected cells. There are a variety of lymphocytes in your body. Natural killer cells are just one type. This particular type of lymphocyte is nonspecific and, therefore, is a part of our innate immunity. Eosinophils are also a part of our innate immune response. Remember from the previous module that these cells reduce inflammation. Why would the body have one type of cell that promotes inflammation and another type that reduces it? Well, inflammation can be a good thing, but too much inflammation can damage healthy tissue. The inflammation must stay under control. Eosinophils contain enzymes that tend to break down inflammatory agents, keeping inflammation under control.

Let's look a little more closely at our second line of innate defense, inflammation. To understand inflammation, think about a bee sting. What happens when a bee stings you? Well, first of all, you feel pain. Then, the bee sting begins to swell, or puff up. That's typical of inflammation. The bee sting also turns red. Why does it do that? Inflammation results in an increased blood flow to the injury. That gives it a red color as well as swelling, and it also makes the area feel warm. The pain, the redness, the swelling, and the warmth are all a part of the inflammation.

What causes inflammation? Basophils and similar cells called mast cells, which are found deep to the skin, release histamines, prostaglandins, and leukotrienes. These chemicals stimulate vasodilation (vas' oh die lay' shun). Remember, vaso refers to the blood, and dilation means "to get larger." Vasodilation, then, means that the blood vessels get larger. This promotes the increase in blood flow mentioned above, causing the redness as well as the swelling. This brings in more complement to help fight the infection. It also makes the capillaries more porous, making it easier for phagocytic cells to leave the capillaries and enter the tissues that are infected. Now remember, complement not only kills invading cells, but it also attracts phagocytes into the tissues. The complement, therefore, is attracting phagocytes to the tissues, and the vasodilation makes it easier for the phagocytes to perform diapedesis (squeezing out of the blood vessels) in order to get there.

There are two types of inflammation. Local inflammation happens when infections are being fought in one area of the body. For example, the inflammation associated with an infection caused by a splinter in your skin is local inflammation. Systemic inflammation, however, occurs all over the body. That's what the term systemic means: "all over the body." When you have a bad case of the flu, you feel terrible all over. Everything hurts, your nose runs, and your stomach is upset. That's systemic inflammation. Chicken pox is another example of an infection that causes systemic inflammation.

When inflammation is systemic, you may find that you get a fever. What causes fever? In many cases, when you are sick, you have foreign invaders in your body. Sometimes those foreign invaders produce chemicals called pyrogens (pie' roh jenz), which are fever-causing agents.

Pyrogens—Chemicals that promote fever by acting on the hypothalamus

Sometimes, even your own white blood cells release pyrogens in order to cause a fever. These pyrogens travel through the body and affect the hypothalamus. Now remember from module 8 that the hypothalamus controls body temperature. Pyrogens affect the hypothalamus in such a way as to cause it to increase body temperature.

What good is an increased body temperature? Well, since chemical reaction rates increase with increasing temperature, a fever speeds up the immune response. The mitosis of the white blood cells goes faster, increasing the white blood cell population. Complement or interferon is made faster. Inflammatory chemicals are made faster. Also, a higher temperature is often inhibitory to the invading microorganism. Some bacteria like cooler temperatures. Increased body temperature itself, then, can actually fight infection.

ON YOUR OWN

12.6 One measure to prevent infection that was tested several years ago involved an interferon spray. Although the side effects are too serious to warrant its use, if a person sprays his or her nasal cavity with interferon, the person becomes more immune to certain infections. To what kind of infections would the person be more immune?

ACQUIRED IMMUNITY, PART I: HUMORAL IMMUNITY

Although we have already discussed a wide variety of mechanisms designed to defend the body from foreign invasion, we are not done. In fact, we have not even discussed the most interesting line of defense that our bodies have: acquired immunity (also called specific or adaptive immunity). Remember the quote from the immunologist, discussing the similarities between the nervous system and the immune system? He said that both systems have a memory. The memory of the immune system allows the body to remember how to defend itself against an infection. That way, if the infection occurs a second time, the body can defend itself more efficiently.

There are two types of acquired immunity: humoral immunity and cell-mediated immunity.

Humoral immunity—Acquired immunity provided by antibodies in the blood plasma

Cell-mediated immunity—Acquired immunity provided by T lymphocytes

The lymphatic system produces antibodies against specific antigens that can be found on the plasma membranes of cells. If a cell with that antigen is introduced into the body, the lymphatic system will fight that cell with antibodies specific to the antigen. In the case of blood types, if a person produces the antibody against the A antigen, then he or she cannot receive a transfusion of type A blood, because the person's antibodies will attack the donated erythrocytes that carry the A antigen. Antibodies are produced by lymphocytes that originally matured in the red bone marrow before traveling through the blood and taking up residence in the lymphatic tissues. These lymphocytes that produce antibodies are called B lymphocytes or B cells.

B lymphocytes, then, are responsible for humoral immunity. Since humoral immunity comes from the actions of antibodies, we should first concentrate on what antibodies are. First of all, antibodies are proteins. The basic layout of one of these proteins is given in figure 12.5.

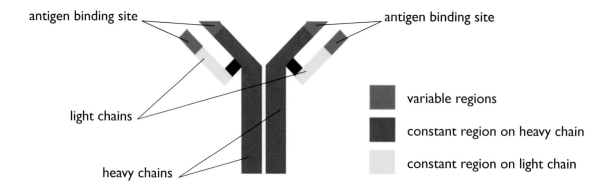

FIGURE 12.5
Schematic of an Antibody

Basically, antibodies are made of four polypeptide chains: two identical heavy chains and two identical light chains. These chains are arranged in a Y shape. The two tips of the Y vary from one antibody type to the next, and these tips allow the antibody to attack one kind of antigen specifically. These tips, called the variable regions of the antibody, are the point at which the antibody binds to the antigen. Because of this, they are also called the antigen binding sites. An antigen binding site binds to the antigen because the site fits the antigen like a key fits its lock.

The rest of each chain in the antibody is called the constant region. The characteristics of the constant region determine the class of antibody. There are five basic classes: IgG, IgM, IgA, IgE, and IgD. Each class of antibody fights antigens in a slightly different way. IgG antibodies, which are by far the most common type of antibody, help promote phagocytosis. They bind to the antigen with their variable regions, and then they bind to macrophages with their constant region. Macrophages then engulf the antigen. IgM antibodies are the largest antibodies; they are formed from five Y-shaped subunits. They bind antigens together with their variable regions, and then use their constant regions to activate complement proteins, which we discussed earlier. IgG antibodies can also fight antigens this way.

think about this

Because IgM molecules are so large, they cannot pass through the placenta from a mother's blood to her unborn child's blood. The plentiful IgG antibodies are small enough to do so. IgG antibodies provide the fetus with immunity before birth, and they even last for a few weeks after birth in the newborn baby's blood.

IgA antibodies are secreted antibodies. They look like two IgGs bonded together at the stems of the Y's. They are found in saliva, tears, and mucous membranes. They are also found in breast milk to provide immunity to an infant. IgE antibodies help initiate the inflammatory response. They do this by first attaching to an antigen with their variable region. Then they attach to a basophil with their constant region, stimulating the basophil to release inflammatory agents. IgD antibodies typically inactivate antigens by simply binding to them.

Antibodies, then, have several means by which they can fight antigens:

1. **Bind directly to the antigen**
2. **Bind the antigens together in groups**
3. **Activate complement**
4. **Stimulate phagocytosis**
5. **Stimulate inflammation**

Now remember, the variable region of an antibody determines the specific antigen that the antibody will fight. The constant region determines the method with which it will fight the antigen.

As we already mentioned, antibodies are produced by B lymphocytes (B cells), which are specialized lymphocytes. Like all blood cells, these lymphocytes are formed from stem cells in the red bone marrow, but they spread throughout the lymphatic tissues all over the body. They are formed with antigen binding sites on their plasma membranes. When exposed for the first time to the antigen for which they are specific, these sites bind to the antigen, and the B cells begin to undergo rapid mitosis. The mitosis produces two types of B cells: plasma B cells and memory B cells. The plasma cells release their antibodies into the plasma so that the antibodies can attack the antigens to which they can bind. The memory B cells are long-lived B cells that do not release their antibodies. Instead, they circulate in the body waiting for the next attack by the antigen. This allows the body to respond very quickly to any subsequent infection by the same antigen. These cells, then, give the immune system its memory.

Memory B cells are the means by which vaccinations provide immunity to certain pathogens. There are two basic types of vaccines. The first type contains a weakened form of the pathogen itself. In this kind of vaccine, the pathogen has been weakened or killed so that it cannot overtake your body's immune system. As a result, your lymphatic system recognizes it, makes the antibodies to destroy it, and then makes the memory B cells to "remember" the infective agent in case the organism attacks again. Since the pathogen is weakened (or dead), your body's immune system will destroy it before it can overtake your body. So, even though the vaccine may actually contain a disease-causing pathogen, the vaccine is safe because the pathogen is so weak that your immune system will destroy it.

The other type of vaccine contains a synthetic chemical that makes the body react the same as if a certain pathogen has entered the body. This type of vaccine, then, mimics a real pathogen, causing the immune system to react and produce antibodies as well as memory B cells. Regardless of the type of vaccine, the effect is the same. The vaccine causes your body to react as if it is being infected. It then forms B cells that produce plasma cells and memory B cells. The memory B cells remember the pathogen and provide a quick response to any future infections. Vaccines have virtually elimi-nated many of the childhood diseases that have claimed the lived of millions of children over the years. Because of the smallpox vaccine, for example, the smallpox virus exists only in laboratories. It has been wiped out because the vaccine stopped its ability to reproduce by infecting people. Many doctors in the United States have never even seen a real case of the measles because the measles vaccine has made that childhood disease a thing of the past.

Even though memory B cells are long-lived, they do not last forever. So, some vaccines require a booster to boost the memory of the infection. When the body is first exposed to a pathogen, the B cells will produce a primary response. This response, as stated above, fights the infection and produces memory B cells. The memory B cells will then produce a secondary response if the pathogen infects the body again.

We need to point out one more thing about the production of antibodies. Remember that a person normally cannot produce antibodies against antigens that he or she has in his or her own cells. For example, if you have Rh^- blood, you will not normally produce the antibody against the Rh antigen. However, if you are exposed to type Rh^+ blood, you will immediately start producing antibodies against the Rh antigen. Your lymphatic system "knows" your blood type and "knows" how to spot an erythro-cyte from another blood type. How does the lymphatic system "know" your blood cells from other blood cells?

There are about 20 specific glycoproteins (protein-carbohydrate complexes) that exist on the cell membrane of every cell in your body. This collection of proteins is called the major histocompatilibity complex (MHC). The structure of these proteins is determined by 20 genes in your DNA, each of which has more than 50 alleles. So, there are literally billions of combinations of these alleles, and each combination produces a unique MHC. As a result, it is virtually impossible for two people to have identical MHCs, unless they are identical twins. The MHC, then, is like a fingerprint for your cells. Any cell that has your MHC will not be attacked by your lymphatic system because the finger-print will be recognized.

ON YOUR OWN

12.7 A blood sample has plasma B cells in it. Must it also have memory B cells against the same antigen? Must a blood sample with memory B cells in it also contain plasma B cells against the same antigen?

ACQUIRED IMMUNITY, PART 2: CELL-MEDIATED IMMUNITY

The other kind of acquired immunity is cell-mediated immunity. This kind of immunity comes from the action of T lymphocytes, which are also called T cells. T cells originate in the red bone marrow, but they mature in the thymus gland, which gives them the name T. T cells, like B cells, have antigen receptors. However, these receptors are not associated with antibodies. Instead, they are attached directly to the surface of the T cell. They allow the T cell to recognize molecules that are on the plasma membranes of other cells. This helps the T cells distinguish between cells that belong in the body and cells that do not.

T cells are particularly useful against whole cells and intracellular agents. In other words, T cells tend to fight diseases that are caused by pathogens that invade cells, such as viruses and intracellular bacteria. They find cells that have these pathogens inside them and then react. How do the T cells know that there are pathogens inside another cell? Well, when a cell has been invaded, it often produces MHC proteins that are not a part of the fingerprint for the body's cells. This makes the cell look foreign to the T cells, and the T cells react. Even cancerous cells usually produce aberrant MHC proteins, which once again cause the T cells to respond.

When T cells respond to MHC proteins that are not a part of the body's fingerprint, they produce effector T cells and memory T cells. The effector T cells attach to the invading cell or infected cell. Memory T cells provide long-lasting immunity just like memory B cells do. There are two basic kinds of effector T cells: cytotoxic T cells and helper T cells. Cytotoxic T cells are the ones that recognize, bind to, and destroy foreign cells (or infected cells) by puncturing them, causing them to lyse. Helper T cells, on the other hand, stimulate the activities of both B cells and cytotoxic T cells.

Another type of effector T cell is the delayed hypersensitivity T cell. This kind of T cell responds to antigens by releasing chemicals that promote inflammation. They also promote phagocytosis by attracting macrophages through chemotaxis. These cells are particularly active in allergic reactions. For example, the burning and itching sensation caused by poison ivy is a delayed hypersensitive T-cell response to antigens produced by skin cells that interact with poison ivy.

TYPES OF ACQUIRED IMMUNITY AND AUTOIMMUNITY

There are four basic ways that acquired immunity can occur in the body. The first and most obvious is active natural immunity. This is the acquired immunity that comes from being exposed to a pathogen. For example, when you are first exposed to the chicken pox virus, you get sick. Your body must fight off the virus. However, after that, you don't get sick from the chicken pox virus again because your body has the memory B cells that will produce a quick and effective secondary response. Active natural immunity is long-lasting because the B cells continue to produce antibodies, and memory cells will be activiated if you are again exposed to the same pathogen.

You can also receive acquired immunity artificially, which is referred to as active arti-ficial immunity. This is the immunity you receive from a vaccine. The vaccine causes your immune system to react, forming memory B cells or T cells. This gives you acquired immunity to that disease, but the immunity is artificially induced. Like active natural immunity, it is long lasting.

Passive natural immunity occurs only between mother and baby. IgG antibodies, which include about 80% of all antibodies, can travel across the placenta during pregnancy, providing the unborn baby with the same immunity that the mother has. In addition, IgA antibodies are found in breast milk. So, through breast-feeding, the baby receives immunity from diseases to which the mother is immune.

The final means by which acquired immunity can occur is passive artificial immunity. In this situation, a different individual is exposed to a particular pathogen and thus creates antibodies. Those antibodies are then removed from the individual via blood donation and transferred to someone else. This provides immunity to the pathogen. Although this procedure is often done using another human, that is not always necessary. Sometimes, an animal such as a horse can be injected, and then the horse's antibodies can be transferred to the person who needs immunity. This is only a temporary fix, however, since the donated antibodies will break down and be removed from the person who received them within a relatively short period of time.

For example, most people in the U.S. are not immune to rabies. Even though rabies is a deadly disease caused by a virus, there is no need to immunize everyone because it is so rare and because of passive artificial immunity. On the other hand, veterinarians and some military personnel are immunized against rabies by being injected with the weakened rabies antigen. They make anti-rabies antibodies through active artificial immunity.

When such individuals donate blood, their anti-rabies antibodies can be separated from the whole blood. If a suspicious animal that cannot be caught and observed for signs of rabies bites someone, that person can be injected with the donated anti-rabies antibodies. That's passive artificial immunity. It gives rapid short-term protection, in this case, from rabies virus. Meanwhile, the individual who was bitten will begin active artificial immunity stimulation by being injected with weakened rabies antigen. See the difference?

One type of immunity that is not good is autoimmunity. In autoimmunity, the body cannot differentiate between the MHC of its own cells and that of others. It starts attacking its own cells. Multiple sclerosis, for example, is an autoimmune disease. The lymphatic system cannot distinguish between the neuroglia of the body and foreign neuroglia. As a result, the lymphatic system begins attacking the myelin sheaths of the nerves. This causes gradual loss of control of the skeletal muscles and

COLORING BOOK EXERCISE 12.5
The two types of immunity are reviewed in your coloring book on page 247.

a loss of sensation. There are a number of other diseases that are caused by autoimmune reactions: rheumatoid arthritis, myasthenia gravis, and lupus erythromatosis are examples.

As you journey through the human body and learn about its structures and functions, make sure you take a few moments to contemplate its complexity. Your body is wonderfully made and astonishingly resilient. At every moment it is being confronted by outside influences, and the adjustments that occur do so silently, so that your thoughts are not interrupted.

ANSWERS TO THE "ON YOUR OWN" QUESTIONS

12.1 When interstitial fluid enters lymph vessels, it is called lymph. It is the same fluid, but because it is now moving through the lymph vessels, it is called something different. This is just like a person who is a pedestrian while walking and a passenger when riding.

12.2 Remember, fat is brought into the blood via the lymphatic system. When it is in the lymphatic system, it looks milky-white. When it gets dumped into the blood, it gives the blood a cloudy appearance. So, the blood is cloudy because of fat that is being brought into the blood by the lymphatic system. When you are fasting, you are not taking in any food, including fat. So, there is no milky-white substance to cloud up the blood.

12.3 Notice that the thoracic duct empties into the left subclavian vein. The right lymphatic duct empties into the right subclavian vein. Since the thoracic duct is much larger than the right lymphatic duct, more lymph drains into the left subclavian vein. In fact, the thoracic duct drains lymph from the entire abdomen and lower body, as well as the right side of the upper body. The right lymphatic duct drains only the upper right part of the body.

12.4 There may be several afferent vessels coming into a lymph node, but there is usually only one going out. So, the efferent vessel carries more lymph.

12.5 Check for the presence of lysozyme. Lysozyme is in tears, giving tears antibacterial properties. Sweat has no such properties because it does not contain lysozyme.

12.6 Interferon is antiviral. So, **the person will be more resistant to viral infections**.

12.7 If the blood has plasma B cells, it must have memory B cells. These cells are made at the same time (when the B cells undergo mitosis). However, memory B cells are longer living. Thus, if the plasma B cells are there, memory B cells must be there as well. The plasma B cells will die long before the memory B cells, so blood that has memory B cells in it may not have plasma B cells in it.

STUDY GUIDE FOR MODULE 12

1. Define the following terms:
   a. Lymphatic tissue
   b. Lymph nodes
   c. Lymph
   d. Edema
   e. Immunological defense
   f. Mucosa-associated lymphoid tissue (MALT)
   g. Lymph nodules
   h. Innate immunity
   i. Acquired immunity
   j. Complement
   k. Interferon
   l. Pyrogens
   m. Humoral immunity
   n. Cell-mediated immunity

2. Interstitial fluid becomes lymph. What happened to the interstitial fluid to make it lymph?

3. How does interstitial fluid get into the lymph vessels? How does it get pumped through those vessels?

4. What are the three basic functions of the lymphatic system?

5. Is lymph the same throughout the lymphatic system? If not, what causes the difference?

6. What are tonsils? Where are they found in the body?

7. What are Peyer's patches? Where are they found in the body?

8. What is the difference between afferent lymph vessels and efferent lymph vessels? For a given lymph node, are there more afferent lymph vessels or more efferent lymph vessels?

9. What are the three basic functions of a lymph node?

10. What are the three functions of the spleen?

11. What are the two functions of the thymus gland?

12. Identify each of the following as a part of innate immunity or acquired immunity: skin, T cells, mucus, urine flow, B cells, stomach acid, antibodies, interferon, natural killer cells

13.   Identify the structures in the figure below:

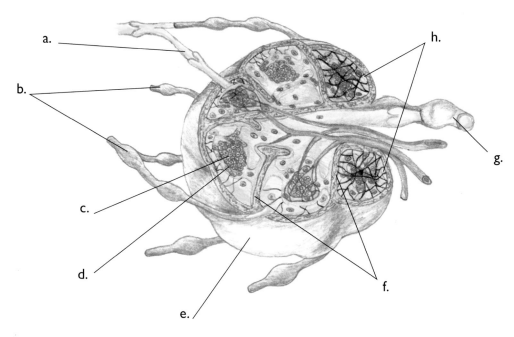

a.

b.

c.

d.

e.

f.

g.

h.

14.   For each of the things listed, describe its role in innate immunity:

a.   Skin
b.   Sweat glands
c.   Sebaceous glands
d.   Mucus
e.   Gastric juice
f.   Tears
g.   Urine
h.   Symbiotic organisms

i.   Complement
j.   Interferon
k.   Neutrophils and Mocrophages
l.   Basophils
m.   Eosinophils
n.   Vasodilation
o.   Pyrogens

15.   Which letter best represents the shape of an antibody?

16.   What part of an antibody determines whether it is an IgG, IgM, IgA, IgE, or IgD antibody?

17.   In what five ways do antibodies fight antigens?

18.   What is the function of a plasma B cell? What about a memory B cell? Which lives longer?

19.   How does the immune system recognize its own body's cells?

20.   What is the function of a cytotoxic T cell, the function of a memory T cell, and the function of a helper T cell?

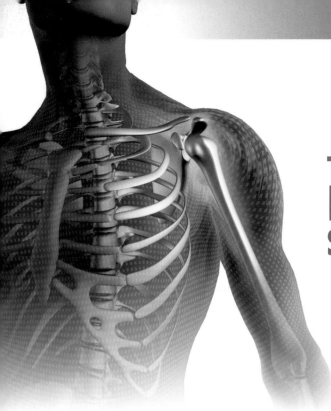

THE DIGESTIVE SYSTEM

You've probably heard the saying, "you are what you eat." Obviously, that's not a physical truth. Eating (ingestion) is only the first step in a long, complex process that allows you to absorb nutrients. The foods that you ingest are composed of large molecules that your body cannot absorb. In order to gain any benefit from the food, your body engages in a multistep process that includes physically breaking down the food that you eat, chemically breaking down the molecules in the food into smaller molecules, and absorbing those smaller molecules into your blood. Your blood then carries these nutrients to the body cells. In addition, anything that cannot be absorbed must be eliminated.

heart of the matter

It's easy to recall the warm feeling you get when you smell a favorite food cooking or the anticipation you feel waiting for it to arrive on the dinner table. Food is something we can all relate to because everyone has a favorite food. It's rare that you stop and look at the food you are eating as solely nourishment for your body. Additionally, there are many memories that become associated with meals and special foods eaten during important holidays. It's clear that food is significant in many ways that go beyond physical sustenance, but it is essential to remember that food is necessary to stay alive.

What do we mean when we say that the body must physically break down the food that we eat? When you eat a sandwich, you take a bite from it and then chew. This process is called mastication (mas tih kay' shun).

Mastication—The process of chewing

What does mastication do? It chops up the food into little bits. This is not a chemical change. It does not change the nature of the molecules in the food. It simply breaks down the food into smaller, more manageable chunks.

The digestive system physically breaks down food in other ways, as well. When your stomach churns, for example, it is breaking the food into even smaller bits. Also, food ultimately gets dissolved in the fluids of the digestive system. Remember, when a substance dissolves, it does not change the chemical nature of the substance. Instead, the molecules are just separated from one another by the dissolving fluid. So, this is a physical change as well.

Just breaking the food down into little bits is not quite enough, however. Once the digestive system breaks food down into its individual molecules, those molecules are usually still too large to be absorbed by the body's systems. So, the molecules must be chemically broken down into smaller molecules. That is the proper definition of digestion.

Digestion—The breakdown of food molecules into their individual components

When you eat proteins, for example, your body cannot absorb the proteins. Instead, they must first be broken down into their individual amino acids. Those amino acids can then be absorbed. In the same way, most of the carbohydrates that you eat are either disaccharides or polysaccharides. These must be chemically broken down into monosaccharides (simple sugars, such as glucose) in order to be absorbed. Finally, the fats that you ingest must be broken down chemically into their constituent fatty acid molecules.

Once the food has been physically and chemically broken down into small molecules, the digested products (the amino acids, monosaccharides, and fatty acids) can be absorbed into the blood. Some molecules, such as vitamins and minerals, are absorbed without being chemically changed. As you will soon see, this happens mostly in the small intestine. If a substance cannot be absorbed, it travels through the digestive system and is eliminated through the anus.

OVERVIEW OF THE DIGESTIVE SYSTEM

As you might imagine, the human digestive system is large and complex. It is illustrated in figure 13.1. The digestive system can be split into two parts: the alimentary canal (also called the alimentary tract, gastrointestinal tract, or GI tract) and the accessory organs. The alimentary canal is the canal through which food travels on its way from the mouth to the anus.

We will discuss many of the parts of the digestive system in greater detail later. For right now, however, we just want to give you a general overview. This figure points out the "major players" in the digestive system, so it is a good place to start. Note that the lungs, larynx (lare' inks), and trachea (tray' key uh) are in the figure for reference, but they are not a part of the digestive system.

MOD 13

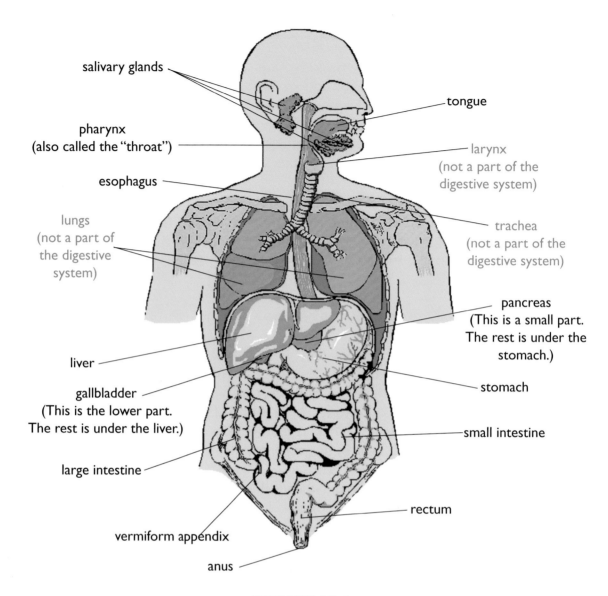

FIGURE 13.1
The Human Digestive System
Illustration from the Future Graph collection

Food enters your body through your mouth. It is cut, crushed, and ground into little pieces by your teeth. It is also moistened by saliva. Your tongue moves food around in your mouth. It also provides most of the taste sensation that you get when you eat. The food is then passed from the mouth to the pharynx (fare' inks), where it is then passed into the esophagus (ee sof' uh gus). Notice in the figure that the pharynx actually opens to the nose, the larynx, and the esophagus. When we talk about the mouth, pharynx, and esophagus individually, we will discuss the incredible process that occurs to make sure that food goes down into the esophagus rather than up into the nasal cavity or, worse, "down the wrong pipe" into the larynx.

Once in the esophagus, food is sent to the stomach. In the stomach, the food is churned and mixed with digestive fluids (juices) that the stomach secretes. Your stomach temporarily stores the food, but once it has been thoroughly mixed, it sends the mixture, which is now called chyme (kime), into the small intestine (in test' in). In the small intestine, the food molecules are digested, and most of the nutrients are absorbed into the bloodstream through the small intestine's lining.

The nutrient-filled blood then passes directly to the liver, which picks up and stores many of the absorbed nutrients. That's not the only thing the liver does, however. As the largest organ inside the body, it makes several proteins for the blood, such as fibrinogen and prothrombin (involved in blood clotting). In addition, it also cleanses the blood of toxins and wastes, and it produces a fluid called bile, which aids in the mechanical digestion of fats.

The bile from the liver is concentrated and stored in the gallbladder. The gallbladder then releases this concentrated bile into the small intestine, where it aids in the digestion of fats coming from the stomach. The pancreas (pan' kree us) produces its own digestive juice, which is also released into the small intestine to aid in the digestion of the food molecules. Remember that the pancreas also has endocrine functions, which are not directly related to digestion.

Once the chyme is completely digested and most of the nutrients have been removed, what has not been absorbed is sent to the large intestine. At this point, then, what remains must be eliminated from the body. Quite a bit of water is absorbed from the chyme entering the large intestine, and the remaining chyme becomes the feces (fee' sees), which are then sent to the rectum and expelled from the body through the anus.

That's the basic outline of what happens in your digestive system. How long does all of this take? It depends on the individual as well as on the kind and amount of food that is ingested. However, on average, it takes less than a minute for food to get chewed in the mouth and transferred to the esophagus. It is in the esophagus for only a couple of seconds, and ends up in the stomach. Typically, a meal remains in the stomach for two to four hours before being sent to the small intestine. However, carbohydrates (particularly the simple carbohydrates such as sugary junk food) leave the stomach rapidly and are quickly absorbed by the small intestine. Fatty foods and protein-rich foods significantly slow the emptying of the stomach. This explains why nutritionists recommend eating meals that contain carbohydrates, proteins, and fats. The proteins and fats slow the release of nutrients so that the meal can maintain blood glucose levels over the longest possible time.

The small intestine usually takes one to four hours to digest and absorb the food, depending on the type and amount of food. The food then gets passed to the large intestine. The amount of time the waste products stay in the large intestine varies *greatly* depending on the person involved and the food that was eaten. The shortest time the waste products from food normally spend in the large intestine is about six hours, but a refined meal low in fresh fruits, vegetables, and whole grains may take *several days* to make it through the large intestine. The food that you eat can spend as little as nine hours in your body or as long as a day or two. Remember, however, that most of the nutrients have been absorbed by the time the food leaves the small intestine. So, your body gets most of the nutrients from the food you eat within one to eight hours.

Notice that within this entire discussion, we have not mentioned the vermiform appendix. This little worm-shaped (vermiform means "worm-shaped") tube branches off the beginning of the large intestine. Scientists are not certain what the exact purpose of the appendix is, but recent studies have provided some information. Different bacteria populate your intestine and help your digestive system break down the foods that you eat. They also help your body fight off harmful bacteria that cause disease. In return for their service, your digestive system provides nutrition and safety to these beneficial microbes. A delicate layer of beneficial microbes, mucus, and immune system molecules exist on what are known as biofilms. These biofilms are found in your intestines and inside your appendix.

Because of the precise location and position of the appendix—just below the one-way flow of chyme into the large intestine—it is hard for anything to enter it as your intestines are emptied. If you experience a severe bout of diarrhea, you could shed the valuable biofilms in your intestines. Afterwards, good bacteria could safely emerge from your appendix and repopulate the lining of your intestine before more harmful bacteria could take hold.

Further research has shown that another function of the appendix appears to be to expose your immune system to the wide variety of foreign substances present in your digestive system. The appendix contains much lymphatic tissue, so there are some biologists who think that the appendix is an infection-fighting organ that specifically fights off infections of the large or small intestine. It helps your body distinguish between good and bad microorganisms. Your immune system maintains a balance between providing a safe environment for this vital community of beneficial biofilms while still protecting you against invasion from a pathogenic species.

For reasons not fully understood, the appendix can become infected, resulting in appendicitis. This results in pain and cramps near the right hipbone, usually accompanied by fever, nausea, and vomiting. If the appendix is not removed at this point through a surgical procedure called an appendectomy, it may burst, and the infection can spread throughout the abdominal area. If left untreated, it can lead to death.

COLORING BOOK EXERCISE 13.1

To review the digestive system, follow the instructions on page 267 of the coloring book.

ON YOUR OWN

13.1 List the structures in figure 13.1 that are a part of the alimentary canal. List the accessory organs. Do not list the organs labeled in blue, as they are not a part of the digestive system.

THE MOUTH, PHARYNX, AND ESOPHAGUS

Now that you have seen the digestive system as a whole, we want to break it down into its parts so that you can learn more of the details of how it works. We'll start, therefore, with a more detailed view of the mouth, pharynx, and esophagus.

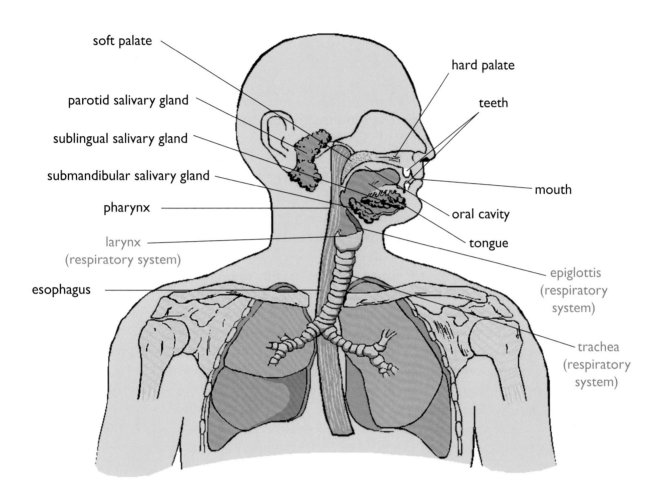

FIGURE 13.2
The Mouth, Pharynx, and Esophagus
Illustration from the Future Graph collection

The digestive system starts at the mouth. The teeth masticate the food, cutting, grinding, and crushing it into small bits. The teeth are made of hard, bone-like material and are surrounded by soft, shock-absorbent gums. It is important to realize that your mouth has specific kinds of teeth, each designed for a different purpose. These can be seen in figure 13.3. The incisor (in size' or) teeth are sharp and are used to cut food. The canine (kay' nine) teeth are used to tear food, while the premolars and molars are used to crush and grind food.

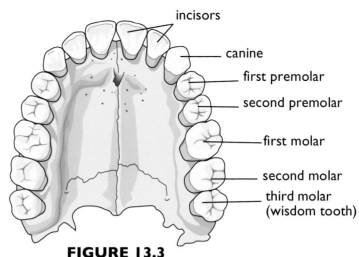

The teeth on this side of the mouth (and in the lower jaw as well) are arranged in the same way as pointed out on the other side of the figure.

incisors
canine
first premolar
second premolar
first molar
second molar
third molar (wisdom tooth)

FIGURE 13.3
Teeth in the Adult Human Mouth
(This is a drawing of the upper jaw.)
Illustration: LifeArt

Once the food is cut, torn, and ground into small bits, those bits are mixed with saliva that comes from the salivary glands. Saliva is a mixture of about 99% water and several different chemicals, each with a specific purpose. It is used to dissolve food, and it is essential for your sense of taste. In order for your taste buds to function, the food you are eating must first be dissolved in your saliva. This mixture can then enter the taste pore of the taste bud.

The other components of saliva are mucus, amylase (am' uh layz), lysozyme, and antibodies. The mucus provides for lubrication so that the food can travel more easily down the alimentary canal. Amylase is a digestive enzyme that helps to break down starch into maltose, which is a disaccharide (double sugar; maltose is two glucose molecules linked together). Have you ever noticed that crackers melt in your mouth even when you do not chew them? That's because crackers are starchy. Your saliva can help break them apart by breaking down the starch into maltose. By contrast, celery will not melt in your mouth, because it does not contain much starch. The lysozyme in saliva kills bacteria, and the antibodies, which are the secreted type (IgA), provide immune defense against potential invaders.

There are three major pairs of salivary glands, with three glands on each side of the mouth. The largest of these three pairs of glands are the parotid glands. The ducts of the large parotid (puh rot' id) salivary glands release saliva above the tongue, next to the second molar of the upper jaw. If you do not have wisdom teeth (the third molar), the second molar is the last one in line. The opening of the parotid duct feels like a small bump on the inside of your mouth beside the upper second molar. If you are outside for a while in cold weather, and the parotid glands, which are on the sides of your face in front of the ear grow cold, you can feel cold saliva enter your mouth if you just provide a little suction on them. Now you know where much of your saliva comes from. When a person has mumps, the puffiness of the cheeks is a result of a viral infection of the parotid glands, which causes inflammation and swelling. The ducts of the sublingual (sub leeng' wull) and submandibular salivary glands release saliva underneath the tongue. In addition to these three major pairs of glands, there are many small salivary glands in the tongue, cheeks, and even the lips.

Your salivary glands secrete about a liter of saliva every day. This secretion is controlled by the autonomic nervous system (ANS). The senses of taste and smell send messages to the medulla oblongata, which stimulates the autonomic nerves that control the salivary glands. You can see how this works the next time you are really hungry. Before you start eating, smell your food by inhaling deeply through your nose. What happens? Your mouth begins to fill with saliva, even though you haven't put food into it! The act of chewing can also stimulate the ANS to cause the salivary glands to secrete saliva. If you chew on something tasteless like wax, you will still generate saliva, because the act of chewing creates ANS reflexes that stimulate the salivary glands.

Once the teeth have cut, crushed, and ground the food, and once the food has been mixed with your saliva, the tongue moves the food around so that it forms a soft lump called a bolus (bowl' us). Now it is time for deglutition (dee' gloo tish' uhn).

Deglutition—The act of swallowing

Deglutition could be one of the most dangerous things that you do; yet, you do it safely all the time! Why is it dangerous? Look at Figure 13.2. The oral cavity leads to the pharynx, which opens to both the esophagus and to the larynx. The air that you breathe travels down the larynx, into the trachea, and into the lungs. Food must cross the airway to get to the esophagus. So, when you swallow, you put food right across your airway. If it would happen to go down the wrong tube, you would be in big trouble!

To make that food go down safely, then, the airway must be closed off. How does this happen? There are two steps that happen automatically. When you swallow, your soft palate rises up and closes off the nasal cavity, which opens into the upper part of the pharynx. That prevents you from breathing in through your nose. At essentially the same time, the larynx rises and the epiglottis drops. This seals off the larynx so that food *cannot* travel down into the trachea. If you put your hand on the front of your neck and then swallow, you can feel the larynx (which makes your adam's apple) rise up to meet the epiglottis.

When you were a kid, you probably had the experience of laughing while drinking milk. Of course, you found out that this was a bad thing because milk would come spraying out of your nose! This is because of the action of the soft palate. While you are breathing quietly, the soft palate hangs down, completely closing off your mouth. Even if your lips are open, you can breathe completely through your nose because the soft palate closes off your mouth. When you swallow, your soft palate lifts up, closing off your nasal cavity. If you happen to laugh while you swallow, the soft palate flutters, and milk that you are trying to swallow can travel into your nasal cavity because the soft palate is not sealing it off.

think about this

Have you ever wondered why you can blow up a balloon without holding your nose? When you try to blow out through your mouth, your soft palate lifts up and closes off your nasal cavity, just like it does when you swallow. This forces all of the air to leave through your mouth, filling up the balloon. This is also true for playing musical instruments.

Although the process of the soft palate rising to seal the nasal cavity and the epiglottis sealing the trachea is incredibly well-coordinated, every once in a while something goes wrong as food passes through the pharynx. When this happens, part or all of the bolus can fall near or into the larynx instead of the esophagus. However, God has designed a backup mechanism for this system. The linings of the larynx and trachea are *very* sensitive. If anything other than air passes down the larynx or even near it, a signal is sent to the brain, and a cough reflex occurs. This pushes any food that is in the larynx back into the pharynx. If you have ever eaten and then started coughing uncontrollably, someone probably asked you if your food "went down the wrong pipe." In fact, that's most likely what happened! Food probably got near your larynx, and your body's cough mechanism kicked in, making you expel the food.

To explain the cough reflex in detail: You inhale a large amount of air, and you then lift up your soft palate, blocking off the nose. Next you exhale forcefully through your mouth by contracting your abdominal muscles. Meanwhile, your diaphragm, which is for inspiration, relaxes, and so does the smooth muscle that forms the part of the trachea that lies against your esophagus. But, your vocal cords within your larynx contract, closing the glottis (passageway through the larynx). The sudden burst of air, powered by your contracting abdominal muscles, rushes out at high speed, literally "blowing out" the irritating material through the trachea and vocal cords. Whew!

There are three stages of deglutition: the voluntary oral stage, the pharyngeal (fair un jee' uhl) stage, and the esophageal stage. You know that there's a point of no return when you swallow. Up to a certain point, you can spit the food out if you don't want it. At some point, however, there's no way to stop the food from going down into your stomach. As long as you can still spit the food out, you are in the voluntary oral stage. Once there's no turning back, you have hit the pharyngeal stage.

In the voluntary stage, the bolus is pushed toward the back of the mouth by the tongue. As the bolus reaches the pharynx, the pharyngeal stage begins. That's when the soft palate lifts up and blocks the nasal cavity. As a result, you can't breathe during the time you swallow. At essentially the same time, the larynx lifts up to meet the epiglottis, closing off the larynx and trachea below it. In addition to the epiglottis, there are also true vocal cords (called vocal folds) that move together, forming a tight seal in the trachea. This provides more protection against food going "down the wrong pipe." You will learn more about vocal folds in the next module. After the soft palate seals off the nasal cavity and the larynx and trachea are also sealed, the pharyngeal muscles constrict to push the bolus toward the esophagus. Now, although that *sounds* pretty simple, it is actually a rather complex procedure involving the coordination of several muscles at once. This, in turn, involves several cranial nerves that originate at the base of the brain.

The last stage of deglutition is the esophageal stage. In this stage, which is also involuntary, rings of muscle contract and relax to push the bolus down the esophagus. This process is called peristalsis (per ih stal' sis).

Peristalsis—The process of contraction and relaxation of circular smooth muscle that pushes food through the alimentary canal

Peristalsis occurs in waves called, not surprisingly, peristaltic waves. The smooth muscle of the esophagus relaxes *below* the bolus to make room for it, and they *contract* right above the bolus. As the wave of contraction moves along behind the wave of relaxation, it pushes the bolus through the esophagus.

There are two sphincters, the upper and lower esophageal sphincters, which are at the top and bottom of the esophagus. These sphincters are rings of circular muscle that remain tightly contracted unless swallowing occurs. When the bolus comes down the pharynx, the upper esophageal sphincter relaxes in response to the peristaltic wave, making room for the bolus to enter the esophagus. Then, the peristaltic wave pushes the bolus down the esophagus. When the bolus reaches the end of the esophagus, the lower esophageal sphincter relaxes, again in response to the wave of relaxation, just long enough for the bolus to leave the esophagus and enter the stomach.

How is this all controlled? The reflex is initiated by the bolus. The pressure of the bolus at the pharynx sends a message to the pons and medulla oblongata. There are eight cranial nerves involved in swallowing, four on each side. They control the muscles involved. Skeletal muscles are involved in this process until about halfway down the esophagus. After that, the rest of the muscle is smooth.

Since there are eight cranial nerves involved in swallowing, even a moderate amount of nerve damage can affect a person's ability to swallow. Stroke victims and other people with nerve damage that affects the mouth and pharynx must have their deglutition reflex examined in order to make sure that they can swallow safely. Interestingly, speech pathologists are usually called in to examine a stroke victim's deglutition. The speech pathologist will have the person swallow a substance, and then the therapist will perform x-rays to find out how well the patient swallows. Since speech pathologists know so much about the mouth, pharynx, and larynx, they are often qualified to make such a diagnosis.

think about this

You've probably heard and maybe even used the saying, "That's hard to swallow," meaning that something was difficult to accept. Now, however, you will have a new appreciation for just how complicated the act of swallowing really is!

COLORING BOOK EXERCISE 13.2

For further review of the mouth, salivary glands, teeth, and esophagus, you can color pages 269-275 in your coloring book.

ON YOUR OWN

13.2 Scuba divers must breathe through their mouths while underwater. Is the soft palate raised or lowered when a scuba diver is underwater?

13.3 You have two samples of clear fluid. One is a collection of tears, and the other is saliva. What test could you do to tell them apart?

13.4 When you smell food or begin chewing, your salivary glands increase their secretion of saliva. Does the parasympathetic or the sympathetic divisions of the ANS control this increase in salivary secretion?

13.5 Why do you cough when you inhale smoke?

MOD 13

THE STOMACH

Once the bolus passes through the lower esophageal sphincter, it reaches the stomach, which is left of the midline and inferior to the skeletal muscle that controls breathing, called the diaphragm (dy' uh fram). Although you may not realize it, the stomach is *not* a major digestive area. It's more of a storage chamber. People can actually live without a stomach. It can expand considerably without much increase in pressure, meaning that it will just relax and get bigger instead of squeezing back. This explains why Thanksgiving dinner can stay put! It also acidifies the food entering it. This does two things. First, it kills most bacteria and other microorganisms that may be in the food. Second, the enzymes within the stomach that are used to digest proteins work better at an acidic pH. So, acidifying the food enhances the digestion of proteins, which, as we will see, begins in the stomach. Before we discuss the physiology, or function, of the stomach, let's look at a little bit of its anatomy, as seen in figure 13.4.

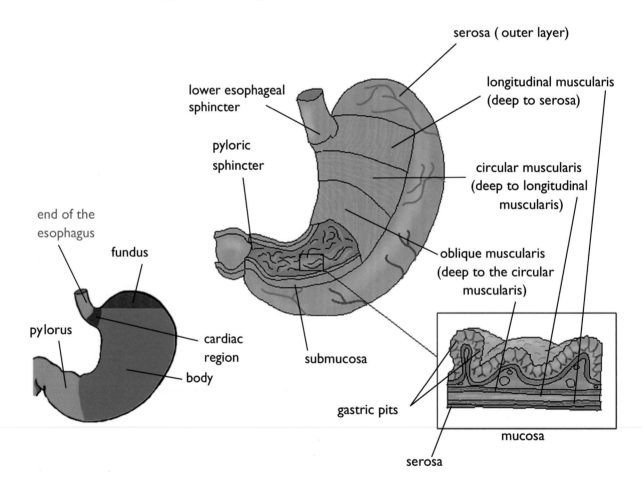

FIGURE 13.4
Anatomy of the Stomach
Illustration by Megan Whitaker

The stomach is separated into four main regions. As noted in the left-hand portion of the figure, they are the cardiac region, the fundus (fun' dus), the body, and the pylorus. The cardiac region contains the lower esophageal sphincter and the entrance into the stomach. The fundus is the portion of the stomach beside the cardiac region. The body is the largest part of the stomach, and the pylorus (which means "gatekeeper") joins the small intestine. The pyloric sphincter governs the flow of materials from the stomach into the small intestine.

The outer layer of the stomach is thin and slick. It is called the serosa (sir oh' sah), or specifically, the visceral peritoneum (pehr' ih toh nee' uhm). It is made of a thin layer of connective tissue and a thin layer of simple squamous epithelium, and it allows the stomach to move with little friction as it contracts. Underneath the serosa, there are three layers of smooth muscle. Collectively, these layers are called the muscularis. Right below the serosa, you find the longitudinal muscularis. Underneath that, you find the circular muscularis, followed by the oblique muscularis.

Beneath the muscularis layers are the submucosa and the mucosa. The submucosa is a layer of connective tissue that contains blood vessels and nerves. It loosely binds the muscularis to the mucosa. Notice in the figure that the mucosa contains many folds called rugae (roo' gee), which are only temporary folds. When the stomach is full, the mucosa is stretched out and relatively smooth, like a wrinkled paper sack that smoothes out as it is filled. As the stomach empties, it contracts, and the mucosa folds again into rugae. The epithelial tissue of the mucosa is made of simple columnar epithelium.

If you now look at the right side of the figure, you will see a magnified illustration of the mucosa. It consists of a layer of epithelium and many gastric pits. One important function of the stomach is secretion, and the gastric pits perform this function. They are the openings for gastric glands, which secrete two to three liters of gastric juice every day. Note that the word gastric means "stomach."

Gastric juice—The acidic secretions of the stomach

You can see from the definition that gastric juice is acidic. The pH ranges from about 1 to 3. Why doesn't this strong acid hurt the stomach? Well, there are cells near the top of the gastric pits that secrete an enormous amount of mucus. In fact, there is so much mucus lining the stomach that the gastric juice never actually touches the tissues of the stomach!

The acid in gastric juice is called hydrochloric acid (HCl). It kills most of the bacteria and other microorganisms that might be in the bolus. Of course, it does not kill *all* of the bacteria in food, or we would not get sick when we eat food that is spoiled. There are also certain strains of acid-resistant bacteria that gastric juice cannot effectively kill. Stomach ulcers, which are inflamed areas of the mucosa, are the result of an unusual acid-resistant bacterium known as *Helicobacter pylori*. The acid in gastric juice also activates the enzyme pepsin (pep' sin), which breaks proteins down into smaller chains of amino acids called peptides. Remember, to be absorbed, proteins must be broken down into amino acids. Pepsin does not do this. However, it starts the job by breaking the proteins down into smaller molecules that have fewer amino acids linked together.

There are actually five different groups of cells that make up the gastric glands. As a result, there is more in gastric juice than just HCl. For example, the gastric glands produce pepsinogen (pep sin' oh jen). This chemical, when mixed with HCl and other pepsin molecules, can be converted into pepsin. Why do you think there is an activation step? Why can't the gastric glands just secrete pepsin? A cell can't make an active enzyme that breaks down proteins because the *cell is full of proteins*. A protein-digesting enzyme would destroy the cell! To avoid this problem, the gastric glands make pepsinogen, which does not break down proteins. Then, once the pepsinogen gets into the stomach, HCl converts it to pepsin, which digests proteins.

Another very important chemical secreted by the gastric glands is intrinsic factor. As we mentioned before, you can live without a stomach; however, you would have at least one problem. Without intrinsic factor, your body could not absorb vitamin B_{12}. Intrinsic factor binds to vitamin B_{12} in order for it to be absorbed later on by the small intestine. If a person's stomach is removed because of a tumor or a very bad ulcer, the patient must get vitamin B_{12} injections. This is true also if the person's stomach has been bypassed surgically for body weight control. Finally, the stomach is controlled not only by the ANS but also by the endocrine system. There are hormones produced in the gastric glands in order to allow for endocrine control. Like other hormones, these hormones are secreted into the blood, not into the stomach itself.

To get a better look at the histology of the stomach, perform the following experiment.

EXPERIMENT 13.1
Histology of the Stomach

Supplies:
- Microscope
- Prepared slide: stomach (human)

Purpose:
The prepared slide of human stomach tissue will give you a good look at gastric pits and other features of the stomach's mucosa and submucosa.

Procedure:

1. Place the slide on the stage and focus at 40x magnification.

2. At this magnification, you should see the general structure of the mucosa and submucosa. You will see a thick layer of tissue that is stained dark purple. It should have many crisscrossing white channels running through the purple tissue. Those white channels are the gastric pits. Below the tissue that makes up the gastric pits, you will see a thin layer of tissue that is stained with a lighter purple color and is rather smooth. That is a layer of smooth muscle that forms the bottom of the mucosa. The thicker, pink tissue below is the submucosa.

3. Draw what you see, labeling the gastric pits, the smooth muscle of the mucosa, and the submucosa.

4. Increase magnification to 100x and refocus. Center a section of the tissue that contains the gastric pits. You should now see that there are different cells that line the gastric pits. The top cells are individually arranged. These are the surface cells that secrete the mucus that protects the stomach from the HCl in the gastric juice. You should also see dark purple ovals of cells. Those are the cells that make up the gastric glands.

5. Draw what you see, labeling the gastric pits, the surface mucous cells, and the gastric gland cells.

6. Reposition the slide to examine the submucosa. Notice that it has structure to it. There are many little ovals. Some are empty ovals surrounded by a wall of cells. Those are blood vessels. Others are ovals with cells inside and no distinct wall. Those are lymph nodules.

7. Increase to 400x magnification and examine all parts of the tissue. Note the differences in the cells of each layer.

8. Put everything away.

Before we move on to the other functions of the stomach, we want to point out that the stomach has many features in common with most of the rest of the alimentary canal. Remember, the stomach is covered in an outer layer called the serosa. Underneath that layer, there is a layer of muscle tissue called the muscularis. Beneath the muscularis, there is a layer of connective tissue called the submucosa, and finally, beneath the submucosa, you find the mucosa. These four layers, or tunics, are common to most of the alimentary canal. The stomach and intestines each have these same four tunics.

Now, of course, there are differences between each of the major organs in the alimentary canal. For example, most of the alimentary canal has only two layers of muscularis tissue: the circular muscularis and the longitudinal muscularis. The stomach has a third layer, the oblique muscularis. The esophagus and parts of the large and small intestines have adventitia (ad ven tish' uh) instead of serosa.

Adventitia—A thin layer of loose connective tissue that binds an organ to surrounding tissues or organs

Even though these differences exist from organ to organ, the major groups of tissue are the same throughout the alimentary canal.

So that's the basic anatomy and histology of the stomach. We've already discussed its secretory function. What about its other functions? Well, as we have already mentioned, the stomach is not a major digestive organ. Nevertheless, it does perform some motor functions. These are functions that involve the smooth muscle of the stomach. The first motor function is storage. As the stomach fills, the smooth muscle in the muscularis layer relaxes. The rugae unfold like smoothing out a wrinkled paper bag, and the stomach enlarges. This allows us to store food.

The stomach's next motor function is to mix the boluses with gastric juice to form a liquefied mixture called chyme. How does it do this? The smooth muscle of the stomach contracts and relaxes in a rhythmic pattern to form mixing waves. These waves, which occur about every 20 seconds when the stomach is full, blend the boluses with the gastric juice to make chyme. As the liquefied food mixes with the gastric juice, it also mixes with pepsin so that the proteins can be broken down into peptides.

While this mixing goes on, there's also a small amount of peristalsis, which forces the chyme down the stomach into the pylorus. That's another of the stomach's motor functions. The peristaltic waves that push the chyme along are weak. The mixing waves are the strong ones. So, the mixing waves swish the chyme back and forth in the stomach while slow, weak peristaltic waves push the chyme through the pyloric sphincter and into the small intestine a little bit at a time. The stomach, therefore, empties rather slowly. As we mentioned before, food spends as long as four hours in the stomach before it gets into the small intestine, depending on the amount and type of food entering it. A large, protein-rich and fatty meal, for example, "sticks to the ribs." This means that the stomach empties slowly because the proteins and fats slow down stomach emptying.

Vomiting is another motor function of the stomach. When the lining of the alimentary canal becomes irritated, action potentials travel to the medulla oblongata. If the action potentials are frequent enough, the vomit reflex is initiated by the medulla. At that point, you are reflexively forced to inhale; the larynx elevates; the soft palate closes off the nasal cavity; the upper and lower esophageal sphincters open; and the diaphragm and abdominal muscles contract strongly. This compresses the stomach, and since the esophagus is open, the contents of the stomach travel back up the esophagus and out the mouth.

Now remember, we have already mentioned that the stomach is controlled both by the nervous system and the endocrine system. From the lips to the end of the esophagus, all of the control comes from the nervous system. When you go to the level of the stomach, however, the control is mixed between the nervous system and the endocrine system. This means that both nerves and hormones control the stomach, liver, and pancreas.

One important hormone is gastrin, which is secreted by the stomach. One effect of gastrin is to increase lower esophageal sphincter tone. This makes the sphincter contract more strongly. That's important so that you don't have gastric juice backing up into the esophagus, which *causes gastroesophageal reflux*, or heartburn. That's a really painful situation that is well named. It can be confused with a heart attack because it hurts in the esophagus, which is in the chest. Gastrin also *decreases* the pyloric tone. This means the pyloric sphincter is loosened, and that increases the rate at which the stomach empties. Gastrin also increases the rate of secretion from the gastric pits, and it increases the rate of mixing waves of the stomach.

Although the secretory and motor functions of the stomach are the most important ones, the stomach does have absorptive functions as well. Water can go through the stomach wall and be absorbed into the blood. Alcohol can also travel through the stomach and be absorbed. One of the reasons that alcohol is related to ulcers is that, in going through the stomach wall, the alcohol irritates the stomach lining. To a certain extent, the stomach can also absorb aspirin, and that's why aspirin has a reputation for irritating the stomach.

Do you know why you belch? Well, there's air in your stomach. It gets in your stomach when you drink and eat. An increase in air pressure opens up the lower esophageal sphincter, and the air then travels up the esophagus and out the mouth. That's a belch.

Finally, have you ever wondered why your stomach growls? It can be very embarrassing, sometimes even when the stomach is not yours! Consider this limerick, attributed to President Woodrow Wilson:

I went to the palace for tea,
The Duchess of Windsor sat next to me.
Her rumblings abdominal
Were truly phenomenal
and everyone thought it was me!

What causes this? Control of the stomach is partly the job of the nervous system. So, sometimes low blood glucose, or even just thinking about food can cause your stomach to start generating mixing waves and peristalsis. If the stomach is empty, however, there is just air in it. The air vibrates in response to the motion of the stomach. Of course, vibrations of air cause sound, and when we hear that sound, we say that the stomach is growling.

THE SMALL INTESTINE

Once the chyme passes through the pyloric sphincter, it enters the small intestine. The overwhelming majority of digestion takes place here. Some digestion of starch takes place in the mouth, and some digestion of proteins takes place in the stomach. However, the majority of digestion takes place in the small intestine. Additionally, most of the nutrients from the food are absorbed here. The chyme that is not absorbed moves down the small intestine on its way to the large intestine. We can say that the small intestine has three main functions: to mix and propel the chyme, to digest the food, and to absorb the nutrients.

Let's start with the anatomy of the small intestine. Stretched out, the small intestine would be about 6 meters (20 feet) long. It can be split into three main regions. The duodenum (doo uh dee' num or doo oh duh' num) is the first region of the small intestine. It connects to the stomach and is about 0.25 meter (almost a foot) long. The term "duodenum" actually means "2 and 10" (inches). The jejunum (jeh jyou' num) is the next region and is about 2.5 meters (8 feet) long. The last region of the intestine, the ileum (ill' ee uhm), is about 3.25 meters (11 feet) long and empties into the large intestine.

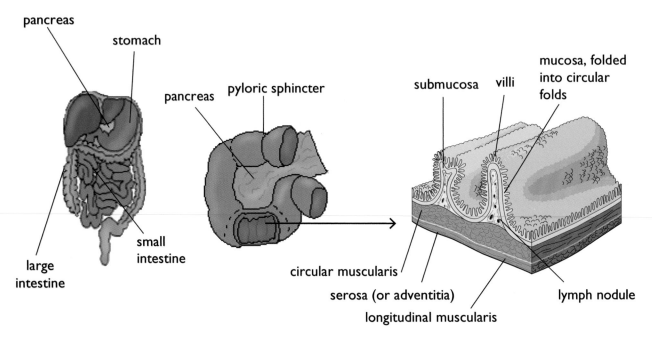

FIGURE 13.5
Anatomy of the Intestine
Illustrations (left and center) by Megan Whitaker | Illustration (right) by LifeArt

Notice from the right-hand side of figure 13.5 that the intestine has the same layers as the stomach, except it has no oblique muscularis and the duodenum has adventitia instead of serosa. As we mentioned when we discussed the stomach, most of the alimentary canal has these layers of tissue in common.

Since most of the nutrients in food are absorbed out of the small intestine into the blood, your small intestine needs a lot of surface area! God has designed specific features into the intestine to increase its surface area so that it can be as efficient as possible. First of all, it is long. So, the chyme stays in the intestine for a relatively long time. That, however, is not enough. In order to increase the surface area, there are rings of mucosa called circular folds, which increase the surface area. These folds are covered with little projections called intestinal villi (singular is villus).

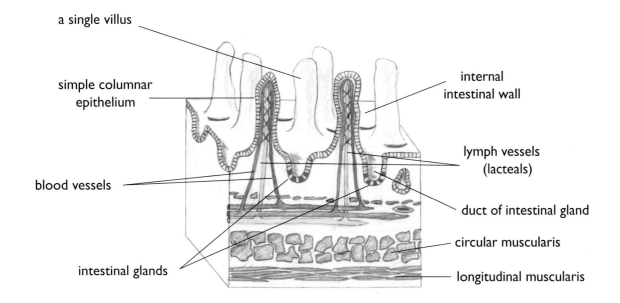

FIGURE 13.6
Intestinal Villi
Illustration by Megan Whitaker

Intestinal villi are not microscopic. They *are* small, however. If you take a piece of fresh intestine and wash off the mucus, it will look like velvet. The velvety appearance is due to the tiny hair-like villi projecting out of the mucosa. These villi increase the amount of intestinal surface that comes into contact with the food, speeding up the absorption process. Notice in figure 13.6 that the free surface (part exposed to the chyme) of the intestinal villi is composed of simple columnar epithelium, and that a blood capillary and a lymph vessel called a lacteal are found in the center of each villus. The nutrients absorbed through the simple columnar epithelium travel into the blood capillaries or lacteals so that they can enter the bloodstream and be distributed throughout the body.

The epithelial cells of the villi are covered with microvilli, which are microscopic extensions of the cell membrane. They increase the surface area of the cells themselves, further increasing the efficiency of nutrient absorption. If the inside wall of the small intestine were smooth rather than covered with villi and microvilli, the small intestine would need to be *2.25 miles long* in order to allow enough time for the absorption of nutrients!

The blood capillaries of the villi do not take up fatty acids (the components of fats) or other fat-soluble nutrients. Instead, lacteals carry fat-soluble nutrients to the blood by making them part of the lymph. When lymph ultimately gets returned the bloodstream, the fat-soluble nutrients enter the circulatory system as well. The term *lacteal* comes from the word meaning "milk." When fat-soluble nutrients are absorbed into lymph, it turns a whitish, milky color. Between the intestinal villi are intestinal glands. These glands secrete a number of products into the lumen.

Lumen—The space in the center of a tube

When we use the term lumen, then, we are referring the to empty space in a tube. In the case of the small intestine, the lumen is where the chyme can be found. In a blood vessel, the lumen is where the blood can be found.

There are both endocrine and exocrine glands in the intestine. Remember from module 2 that exocrine glands secrete through ducts. Mucous goblet cells are exocrine glands which secrete mucus. This mucus protects the tissue of the intestine from the chyme, as well as from the digestive enzymes, which break down the proteins, fats, and carbohydrates. Mucous goblet cells can be found all over the small intestine. Specifically in the duodenum, you find duodenal glands. These glands secrete an alkaline (basic) mucus. Why? Remember, the chyme has just come from the stomach and is very acidic. So, the alkaline mucus helps to neutralize the acidity of the chyme. This is one of *four* secretions that specifically neutralize the acid in chyme entering the small intestine; this is important because acid would irritate the intestinal lining. The intestinal glands mentioned above are also exocrine glands. They produce **fluid and enzymes**, which we will discuss in a moment.

The small intestine also has endocrine glands. In fact, the very first hormone ever discovered was secretin (seh' krit in), which is secreted by the duodenum. Instead of being secreted into the lumen like exocrine secretions, however, it is secreted into the blood capillaries within the wall of the duodenum. The secretion of secretin is controlled by the acidity of the chyme. The more acidic the chyme, the more secretin is released. This hormone inhibits the secretion of gastric juice, and it increases the secretions of substances that reduce the acidity of chyme. It also slows the movements of the stomach and, therefore, slows stomach emptying.

Cholecystokinin (koh' lee sis toh kye' nin) (CCK) is another hormone secreted by the endocrine glands of the small intestine, especially in response to fatty chyme. Its name means "gallbladder contractor." The term chole means "bile;" the term cystic means "sac;" and the term kinin" refers to "contraction." So, this hormone causes the gallbladder to contract, pushing bile into the intestine. It also powerfully inhibits gastric emptying, which is why fat in a meal slows stomach emptying. It also increases the secretion of digestive enzymes from the pancreas. If you think about it, stimulation of the gallbladder to release bile and stimulation of the pancreas to release more digestive enzyme will promote the digestion of fats. It is not surprising, then, that the secretion of CCK is stimulated by the presence of lipids in the chyme. If there are many lipids in the chyme, CCK is secreted to increase their digestion.

Now let's go back to the intestinal glands. Remember, these glands secrete fluid, about two liters a day. The pH of the juice is basic, and it is the second secretion that is used to neutralize the acidity of chyme (alkaline mucus from the duodenal glands was the first). Since most digestion takes place in the small intestine, there are also many digestive enzymes produced by the intestinal glands. We want to discuss these enzymes, but first we want you to remember that the name of an enzyme most often ends in -ase, and the first part of the name usually refers to the chemical on which the enzyme works.

The major digestive enzymes in intestinal juice are maltase (mall' taze), sucrase (soo' craze), lactase (lak' taze), peptidase (pep' tih daze), and enterokinase (en' ter oh kyne' aze). Maltase is the enzyme that digests maltose. The suffix -ose means "sugar." Sugars are carbohydrates, which can be monosaccharides, disaccharides, or polysaccharides. Maltose is a disaccharide, with two glucose molecules bonded together. Although that's not very big, it's too big to be absorbed. Maltase breaks up the maltose into two glucose molecules, each of which can be transported across the simple columnar epithelium of the intestinal villi.

The enzyme sucrase breaks down sucrose, which is table sugar. Sucrose is also a disaccharide, but this disaccharide is made up of two different monosaccharides: glucose and fructose. Since a disaccharide is too big to be absorbed, sucrase breaks sucrose down into glucose and fructose, both of which can then be absorbed by the intestinal villi.

The enzyme lactase breaks down lactose, which is milk sugar. Lactose is also a disaccharide, which is made up of one glucose and one galactose. Students commonly confuse lactose with galactose. Just remember that lactose is the *disaccharide,* and galactose is a monosaccharide that makes up half of lactose. Lactase is of interest because there's a fairly common condition called lactose intolerance. People who have this condition cannot digest most dairy products because they cannot make lactase. That is, they cannot digest lactose. This causes intestinal problems, which usually lead to diarrhea. If you are lactose intolerant, you can actually go to a pharmacy and get lactase pills that enable you to digest dairy products that you eat shortly after taking the pill. If you artificially add the enzyme lactase to your meals, you can eat dairy products without discomfort.

Now interestingly enough, even lactose-intolerant people were actually born with the ability to make lactase because they were nourished with their mother's milk. At that time, then, they obviously could digest lactose. What happened to change that? Well, lactase (like many other enzymes) is considered an inducible enzyme. This means that if we continue to use it (by drinking milk, for example), we continue to make it. If we cease drinking milk, however, the body may gradually stop making lactase. So, lactose intolerance can be a culturally caused problem. In cultures where people do not drink milk or use lactose-containing foods after babyhood, lactose intolerance is common.

Peptidase, as the name suggests, breaks down peptides. Remember, the stomach breaks down proteins into smaller chains of amino acids called peptides. Peptides are still too big to be absorbed, however, so peptidase breaks the peptides down into their individual amino acids. Those amino acids are then small enough to be absorbed. This is a very important point. In order for a protein to be absorbed, it must be broken down into individual amino acids. So, when you ingest a protein, your body does not absorb *that* protein. Instead, it just gets the amino acids from that protein. Once those amino acids are absorbed, the blood transports them to the cells, which use them to make *their own* proteins.

The last enzyme we want to discuss is enterokinase. This enzyme does not digest food molecules. Instead, it activates trypsinogen (trip sin' uh jen) into trypsin (trip' sin). Where does the trypsinogen come from? It is secreted from the pancreas. Trypsinogen itself, however, is inactive. Enterokinase activates it into trypsin, and trypsin breaks down proteins. The cells of the pancreas cannot produce and secrete a protein-digesting enzyme, since that would destroy the pancreatic cells. So, the cells produce the inactive molecule trypsinogen, which can be activated into the protein-digesting enzyme once it enters the small intestine.

All of the digestion and absorption that takes place in the small intestine requires a lot of mixing. After all, in order for the digestive enzymes to work, they must come into contact with the chemicals they are supposed to digest. Also, to be absorbed, the digested molecules must come into contact with the intestinal villi. Not surprisingly, in addition to absorptive and secretory functions, the small intestine has motor functions, just like the stomach. The smooth muscle of the small intestine contracts and relaxes to slosh the chyme back and forth. In addition, there are peristaltic waves that are slow and weak. These waves move the chyme down the small intestine very slowly on its way to the large intestine.

THE LARGE INTESTINE

The final part of the alimentary canal is the large intestine. It is actually composed of three parts: the cecum (see' kum), the colon (kole' un), and the rectum.

COLORING BOOK EXERCISE 13.4

To review the small intestine, follow the instructions on page 279 of the coloring book.

ON YOUR OWN

13.8 A highly stressed person typically has elevated activity in the sympathetic division of the ANS. The sympathetic division of the ANS decreases the activity of the duodenal glands. To what kind of intestinal problem can high stress lead?

13.9 One of the digestive enzymes found in the intestine (but secreted by the pancreas) is lipase. Based on the name, what kinds of molecules does lipase break down?

13.10 A person's secretin levels are high. What does that tell you about the acidity of the chyme in the small intestine?

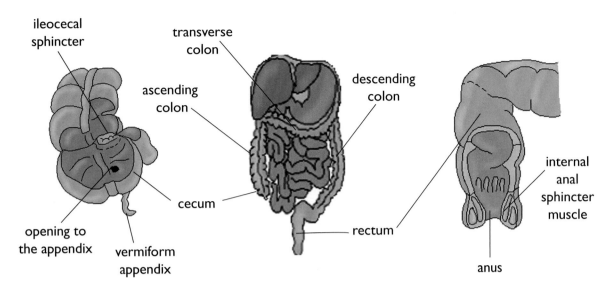

FIGURE 13.7
The Large Intestine
Illustration by Megan Whitaker

It is called the large intestine because its diameter is wider than the diameter of the small intestine. It is actually about one-fourth the length of the small intestine, or roughly a meter and a half (5 feet).

The cecum is at the beginning of the large intestine. It is a blind-beginning sac that connects to the small intestine through the ileocecal sphincter. This sphincter, as you might guess, regulates the amount of chyme leaving the small intestine. The cecum also attaches to the vermiform appendix.

The colon can be further divided into regions based on the arrangement of the large intestine in the body. The ascending colon is the portion of the colon in which chyme travels upwards. The portion of the colon in which chyme travels from the right side of the body to the left side at the level of the waist is called the transverse colon, and the portion in which the feces travels down to the rectum is the descending colon. By the time chyme is about halfway across the colon, it is renamed feces. Chyme is a liquid; feces are semisolid.

The main job of the colon is to take the liquid chyme coming from the small intestine and to form the feces, which are then eliminated through defecation. The main thing that must happen to transform chyme into feces is the absorption of water. Roughly one liter of water enters the large intestine every day, but only about one-tenth of that is actually eliminated in the feces. The rest is absorbed into the blood by osmosis through the wall of the large intestine. What causes this osmosis? Sodium ions are actively transported through the wall of the large intestine and into the bloodstream. As a result, the water follows by osmosis.

MOD 13

Although most of the digestion and absorption of nutrients occurs in the small intestine, a small amount of both occurs in the large intestine, as well. For example, there are many bacteria that live in the large intestine. These bacteria feed on the chyme that travels through the large intestine. Since they digest some of the chyme for their own life processes, the chyme is further changed, which aids the formation of feces. Not only that, but some of the by-products of the bacteria feeding on the chyme are useful to our bodies. Vitamins such as vitamin K, biotin, and folic acid are the by-products of bacteria feeding off the chyme in the large intestine. They are absorbed out of the large intestine and distributed throughout the body.

In addition to producing the beneficial vitamins listed above, the bacteria in the large intestine also break down other chemicals contained in the chyme. Bilirubin, a chemical produced in the liver, for example, is converted to urobilinogen (your' oh bil in' o gen) in the colon. This brown chemical is largely responsible for the brown color of feces. The bacterial breakdown of certain amino acids that are not absorbed in the small intestine results in chemicals that produce the strong odor associated with feces. Finally, carbohydrates that could not be broken down into monosaccharides in the small intestine are broken down by bacteria in the colon. This produces gas known as flatus, which is expelled through the anus. The amount of flatus produced depends on the person and the nature of the food eaten. Beans, for example, are laden with polysaccharides that do not all get digested in the small intestine. So, they can result in a lot of flatus being produced.

Without the bacteria living in your large intestine, your health would suffer. Just like the bacteria on your skin, the bacteria in your intestines help to keep you healthy. For example, "friendly bacteria" fight pathogenic bacteria. They also fight yeast organisms that are harmless as long as their populations are kept in check. In exchange, your body provides food for the bacteria. This mutual relationship is called symbiosis. *The total number of bacteria in your large intestines is over 100 trillion (100,000,000,000,000)! Together, they weigh about three pounds!*

Although your body benefits from having bacteria in your intestines, those same bacteria would be pathogenic in other parts of your body. In healthy individuals, then, the bacteria are confined to the intestines. However, if the walls of the intestines are torn or begin to leak, those bacteria that were being helpful can invade other parts of your body and cause serious damage! Even when they are in the large intestine, the body must protect itself from some of their by-products. Many of these bacteria produce acid, and this acid could damage the lining of the large intestine. However, the large intestine is completely lined with glands called crypts that contain goblet cells, which produce mucus. This mucus lines the walls of the large intestine, protecting it from the acid. It also helps bind the feces together. In addition, the crypts in the large intestine secrete bicarbonate, which is a weak base. This base neutralizes the acid produced by the bacteria.

Weak peristaltic waves are responsible for most of the movement in the colon. However, chyme is moved through the transverse and descending colons by strong, irregular peristaltic contractions known as mass movements. These mass movements occur only a few times per day and are usually triggered by food entering the stomach. or chyme entering the duodenum. Mass movements move feces (as it is called once it is in the middle region of the transverse colon) toward the rectum for later defecation. This helps clear the way for new chyme coming though.

COLORING BOOK EXERCISE 13.5
To review the large intestine, follow the instructions on page 281 of the coloring book.

ON YOUR OWN
13.11 Some pathogenic bacteria in food can survive the stomach and small intestine, reaching the large intestine. There, they attack the lining of the colon. This irritates the colon, and goblet cells in the colon are stimulated to produce more mucus. This extra mucus can inhibit water absorption through the colon. What common digestive abnormality does this cause?
13.12 Although there are bacteria in the small intestine and the large intestine, there are normally none in your stomach. Why?

The last part of the large intestine is the rectum. Feces collect there so that their elimination can be controlled. This is more evidence for the design that we see in the body. The feces have to be eliminated. However, it is much more convenient and sanitary for them to be eliminated once or twice a day rather than whenever they reach the end of the colon. So, the Designer built in a holding container (the rectum) that allows feces to collect. As the rectum fills with feces, it distends. This triggers the defecation reflex, which causes the internal anal sphincter to relax. Fortunately, the external anal sphincter, which surrounds the internal anal sphincter, is made of skeletal muscle. Its default position is to be tightly contracted, sealing off the anus. The conscious control of the skeletal muscle of the external anal sphincter allows us to relax it at the appropriate time and place. This allows the feces to exit the body through the anus. About one-third of a person's feces are composed of bacteria that were originally in the large intestine. Many of the bacteria are dead by the time they leave the body.

ACCESSORY ORGANS: THE LIVER, PANCREAS, AND GALLBLADDER

Although not a part of the alimentary canal (also called the gastrointestinal tract), the liver, pancreas, and gallbladder (illustrated in figure 13.8) are nevertheless organs of the human digestive system. The liver is, by far, the most complicated organ in the digestive system. It has an enormous number of jobs, yet it is able to perform them all with incredible efficiency. It is also the body's largest internal organ. Its main job in terms of digestion is to produce bile, which aids in the digestion of fats. The liver has many other jobs, however, and we will discuss them in this section. The gallbladder concentrates the bile produced by the liver. It stores it, and then secretes the concentrated bile into the small intestine, when needed.

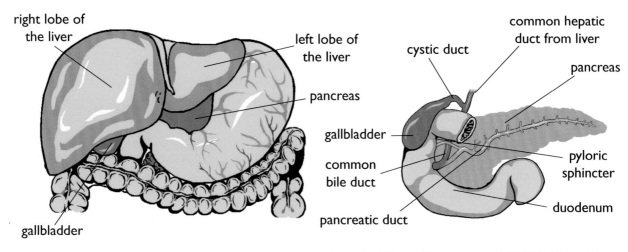

right lobe of the liver

left lobe of the liver

pancreas

gallbladder

Anterior View

cystic duct

common hepatic duct from liver

pancreas

gallbladder

common bile duct

pancreatic duct

pyloric sphincter

duodenum

Anterior View of Pancreas and Gallbladder with Liver, Stomach, and Large Intestine Removed

FIGURE 13.8
The Liver, Pancreas, and Gallbladder (Two Views)
Illustration by Future Graph Collection

The liver is composed of two major lobes, the left lobe and the right lobe, which are visible in the anterior view. The liver is supplied with oxygen through a large artery called the hepatic artery. The word hepatic means "associated with the liver." There is also a large vein, the hepatic portal vein, that brings blood into the liver. Why does the liver need two vessels to bring it blood? The hepatic artery brings oxygenated blood from the heart. This supplies the cells of the liver with oxygen. The hepatic portal vein, on the other hand, brings blood from the small intestine, stomach, spleen, and large intestine. This blood is deoxygenated, but it contains *many* nutrients—those that were absorbed mainly through the small intestine. This is necessary, as one of the liver's functions is to process nutrients from the digestive system.

Let's look at the microscopic structure of the liver. The tissue of the liver is divided into lobules, each of which has a specific structure.

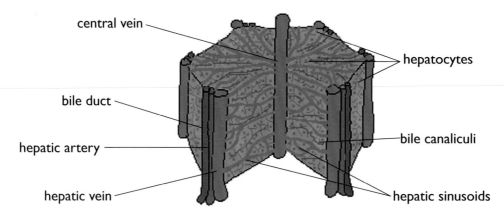

central vein

hepatocytes

bile duct

hepatic artery

hepatic vein

bile canaliculi

hepatic sinusoids

FIGURE 13.9
A Liver Lobule
Illustration by Future Graph Collection

A lobule is hexagonal in shape, with a portal triad at each corner. Typically, a portal triad has two blood vessels, one that branches from the hepatic portal vein, and one that branches from the hepatic artery. It also contains a bile duct that collects bile, which is to be sent to the common hepatic duct. A central vein runs through the center of each lobule. This vein joins other veins in the liver, eventually forming hepatic veins, which join together and empty into the inferior vena cava, and from there the blood returns to the heart.

The functional cells of the liver, called hepatocytes (huh pat' oh sites), radiate outward from the central vein in thin cords, like the posters displayed around one post or spokes on a wheel. These hepatic cords, as they are called, are separated by widened blood vessels called hepatic sinusoids (sign' uh soyds). The hepatic sinusoids contain phagocytic cells, whose function will be discussed in a moment.

As mentioned before, the hepatic portal vein brings nutrient-rich, oxygen-poor blood to the liver. This vein splits into many smaller veins, each occupying a portal triad. In addition, the hepatic artery brings oxygen-rich blood to the liver. It also splits into many vessels, each of which takes a position on a portal triad. The blood from these vessels then mixes in the hepatic sinusoids. This allows the hepatocytes to get the oxygen and nutrients that they need to survive. In addition, the hepatocytes also process the remaining nutrients, altering them for various functions throughout the body, as you will see. The blood then collects in the central vein and makes its way to the hepatic vein, where it exits the liver and enters into the inferior vena cava.

The third vessel in the portal triads carries bile, not blood. Hepatocytes produce and secrete bile. The bile travels in bile canaliculi (kan uh lik' you lye), which are in the hepatic cords. It flows into the hepatic ducts in the portal triad, and these ducts join together with the hepatic duct, which takes the bile to the cystic duct and then to the gallbladder. Notice that the flow of bile is *opposite* that of blood. Blood flows from the edge of the lobule (the portal triads) to the center of the lobule (the central vein). Bile, on the other hand, flows from inside the lobule (the hepatocytes) to the edge of the lobule (the portal triad).

As we mentioned before, bile production is one of the functions of the liver. The hepatocytes produce and secrete it, and it is collected in the common hepatic duct and sent to the gallbladder. Although *bile has no digestive enzymes*, it helps neutralize acid from gastric juice because it is quite basic. It is the third secretion that neutralizes acid chyme. It promotes the digestion of fats by emulsifying them. This means that chemicals within the bile, called bile salts, interact with large drops of lipids and separate them into smaller drops. This is important because the enzymes that digest fats are water-soluble. So, they can only interact at the *surface* of a droplet of fat. The smaller the droplets, the more surface that is exposed to the digestive enzymes. This speeds up the rate at which fats can be digested. In fact, without bile, as occurs when an abnormal gallstone blocks the common bile duct, fats remain undigested and much fat is lost in the feces. Even though it contains no digestive enzymes, the bile salts are essential for fat-digesting enzymes to be able to do their job.

Bile production is only one of many functions performed by the liver. Earlier, we mentioned that the liver processes the nutrients that come from the intestines. What does that mean? Well, first of all, if there is too much glucose in the blood, the hepatocytes can absorb it and convert it into glycogen, a polysaccharide. Remember, starches are polysaccharides, and since animals tend to make glycogen as the polysaccharide in which they store excess glucose, glycogen is often called animal starch. This is one storage function of the liver.

The hepatocytes can also convert certain types of nutrients to other types of nutrients. This is called nutrient interconversion, and it is another way in which the liver processes the nutrients that come from the intestines. For example, it changes the monosaccharides fructose and galactose into glucose, which is why blood sugar is essentially all glucose. Additionally, the hepatocytes can combine nutrients into more useful molecules. Phospholipids (the major component of cell membranes), for example, are produced in the liver from fats and other chemicals absorbed in the digestion process.

In addition, the liver is one of the body's main chemical manufacturing facilities. For example, the liver produces prothrombin, fibrinogen, and many blood coagulation factors. This is called the synthesis function of the liver.

All of the just-discussed functions of the liver are done by the hepatocytes, which are the amazingly versatile cells that form over 99% of the liver. But, the liver also engages in phagocytosis, because the hepatic sinusoids contain phagocytic cells. These white blood cells help the spleen destroy worn-out erythrocytes. They also remove worn-out white blood cells, bacteria, and other debris from the blood.

Finally, the liver also detoxifies the blood. Many of the body's natural processes result in byproducts that would be toxic to the body if they were allowed to accumulate. For example, ammonia is a byproduct of the breakdown of amino acids. If ammonia were to build up in the blood or the tissues, it would become toxic. The liver converts ammonia to urea, which is a simple molecule not nearly as toxic to bodily tissues. This urea ends up being taken out of the blood by the kidneys, and it leaves the body in the urine. Since God has designed the body so elegantly, it is very efficient and rarely wastes anything. So, many substances removed by the hepatocytes are then integrated into the bile. Cholesterol, for example, is secreted into the bile as a waste product.

Now that you have learned about the functions of the liver, the function of the gallbladder is easy to understand. The bile produced by the liver leaves through the common hepatic duct and backs up into the gallbladder through the cystic duct. It does not travel out of the common bile duct because there is a sphincter, which closes off the common bile duct from the duodenum. As the bile backs up into the cystic duct, it progressively enlarges the gallbladder. While the bile is in the gallbladder, salt is actively transported across the inner wall of the gallbladder, and water follows by osmosis. This concentrates the bile, making it more potent. When the intestine produces the right amount of the hormone CCK, the sphincter that closes off the common bile duct relaxes, and the gallbladder contracts. This releases bile into the duodenum.

Although the gallbladder plays a role in digestion, you can live without one. Many people have had their gallbladders removed due to gallbladder disease, which is on the rise in the United States. This usually means that gallstones have plugged the gallbladder or its ductwork. Gallstones are mostly cholesterol. They look like pea-sized hard, smooth, black balls. How do they form? Remember that the gallbladder removes water from the bile. Well, bile contains cholesterol. If enough water is removed from the bile, the cholesterol will fail to remain liquefied. Instead, it will solidify, forming a gallstone. If they stay in the gallbladder, they are usually harmless. However, if one leaves the gallbladder and plugs up a duct, it can cause pain and serious trouble. If it does not pass on its own, surgery is required. Usually the gallbladder is removed to prevent the problem from recurring. The bile then flows continuously from the common hepatic duct into the common bile duct and into the duodenum.

The last accessory organ we need to discuss is the pancreas. As we noted before, the pancreas is an endocrine gland, but in this module, we are interested in its exocrine functions. Remember, exocrine glands secrete through ducts, and the pancreatic duct is easy to see in figure 13.8. It joins with the common bile duct and empties into the duodenum. What does the pancreas secrete through the pancreatic duct? Pancreatic juice, of course!

The pancreas secretes more than a liter of pancreatic juice each day. The pH of this juice is generally basic because it contains bicarbonate. This ion helps neutralize the acidity of the chyme coming from the stomach. Pancreatic juice is the fourth basic secretion that neutralizes acid chyme. There are also many enzymes in pancreatic juice. The first three that we want to discuss are trypsinogen (trip sin' uh jen), chymotrypsinogen (kime' oh trip sin' uh jen), and procarboxypeptidase (pro' car box ee pep' tih daze). All three of these enzymes are inactive because they are used to digest proteins. As we have already mentioned, a cell cannot produce an active protein-digesting molecule, or it would digest itself. Trypsinogen is activated into trypsin in the small intestine by enterokinase and by other trypsin molecules, which we have already mentioned. Trypsin also activates the chymotrypsinogen into chymotrypsin, and it activates procarboxypeptidase into peptidase. Trypsin and chymotrypsin begin protein digestion by breaking proteins into peptides. Peptidase completes protein digestion, taking the peptides and breaking them down into their amino acids.

Another component of pancreatic juice is amylase, which breaks down polysaccharides into maltose. Maltose is then digested into the glucose molecules by maltase from the intestinal gland. Lipase is also found in pancreatic juice. As mentioned before, it breaks down triglycerides into fatty acids. After babyhood, the pancreas is the only significant source of this essential fat-digesting enzyme. People with chronic pancreatic disease often have the most difficulty with digesting lipids. Why? The mouth, stomach, and small intestine contain enzymes that digest protein and carbohydrates, but only the pancreas produces enough lipase to digest fat.

Now you might not think about it this way, but when you eat, you are usually eating cells. Whether you eat fruits, vegetables, meat, and so forth, you are eating cells. These cells contain a lot of nucleic acids (DNA and RNA). These are *huge* molecules that must also be broken down. Enzymes called nucleases (new' klee azes) are produced and secreted by the pancreas to accomplish the breakdown of nucleic acids.

EXPERIMENT 13.2
Histology of the Liver

Supplies:
- Microscope
- Prepared slide: liver (human)

Purpose: Your prepared slide will not be just one liver lobule. Instead, it will probably be a cross section of several. You will therefore probably not see the hexagonal shape of the liver lobules. Nevertheless, the main features of the liver's histology can be seen.

Procedure:

1. Place the prepared slide on the microscope stage and focus at 40x magnification.

2. Look for a large, roughly circular "hole" in the tissue. That is a central vein. Center on it, magnify to 100x, and refocus.

3. Notice the structure of the tissue that surrounds the hole. It is different than the rest of the tissue. That's the wall of the central vein.

4. Now examine the tissue away from the central vein. The purple dots are the nuclei of the hepatocytes. Notice the winding canals in between the hepatocytes. Those are the hepatic sinusoids and the bile canaliculi.

5. Draw a picture of what you see.

6. Search the slide at this magnification, looking for smaller holes in the tissue. Try to find a group of three holes near one another, surrounded by tissue that looks much like the tissue which surrounds the central vein. That's a portal triad.

7. Center on a portal triad, increase the magnification to 400x, and refocus.

8. Draw what you see.

9. Put everything away.

NUTRITION

Now that you have learned about the digestive system and how it works, we want to spend some time on the topic of nutrition. After all, you now know *how* your body digests food and absorbs it, so we want to spend some time discussing *what* your body actually needs to digest and absorb. We split nutrients into two categories: the macronutrients and the micronutrients.

> **Macronutrients**—The nutrients the body needs in large amounts: carbohydrates, fats, and proteins

> **Micronutrients**—The nutrients the body needs in small amounts, such as vitamins and minerals

COLORING BOOK EXERCISE 13.6
To review the liver and gallbladder, follow the instructions on pages 283 and 285 of the coloring book.

ON YOUR OWN

13.13 The liver performs at least six functions in the body. List them.

13.14 The common bile duct is open because the sphincter which closes it is relaxed. Most likely, is the level of CCK in the blood higher than average or lower than average?

13.15 Crash diets, especially those very low in fat intake, can result in gallstone formation. Why?

Macronutrients are the body's source of energy and building materials (that's why the body needs large amounts of them), while micronutrients are chemicals that support the many chemical processes that must occur efficiently throughout the body.

Let's start our discussion with the macronutrients. Carbohydrates are carbon-, hydrogen-, and oxygen-based molecules that the body can use as energy sources as well as for other purposes. Simple sugars, or monosaccharides, include glucose, fructose, and galactose. The liver converts all of these to glucose, so that the blood sugar is essentially glucose. Glucose is used as a fuel for most body cells. Other carbohydrates are parts of glycolipids and glycoproteins, which serve as markers on cells, so that the immune system can differentiate between self and non-self cells.

The general term used to refer to large polysaccharides is complex carbohydrates. Some complex carbohydrates can be digested with the help of amylase. Others, such as the plant carbohydrate cellulose, cannot be digested. Nevertheless, indigestible plant carbohydrates (fiber) are very healthy for you. The crunchiness of a carrot or a celery stalk is caused by its indigestible but beneficial fiber. Fiber stimulates the intestines by stretching them, which causes the intestinal walls to reflexively contract. This moves the chyme or feces along, which is beneficial, since feces contain wastes that need to be removed.

Lipids are oil-soluble molecules made up largely of carbon and hydrogen molecules, with oxygen in smaller proportions. The most common class of lipids in the human body is the triglycerides, composed of three fatty acid chains bound together in a long E shape by a three-carbon molecule called glycerol. The triglyceride is a compact way of storing fuel for later energy use in the mitochondria of cells. There are also other types of lipids that are part of every cell.

The first is cholesterol, which is a lipid. It's actually a chemical precursor of the sex hormones estrogen, progesterone, and testosterone, as well as the hormones of the adrenal cortex, including aldosterone. These are critical hormones for the body.

MOD 13

Also, as you learned in module 1, cholesterol is a critical part of every cell's plasma membrane. There is a tendency with the popular press to think of cholesterol as something bad. That's just not true! It's something that's absolutely necessary because it gives the cell membrane just the right rigidity. Of course, you can certainly overdo your fat intake and cause cholesterol to build up in your blood vessels, and *that* can have negative consequences. *Excess* cholesterol is the problem, not cholesterol itself.

We also want to mention phospholipids, which are the major components of a cell's plasma membrane. Phospholipids are *not* triglycerides; they have only two fatty acid molecules, not three. In place of the third fatty acid molecule, phospholipids have a phosphate group. This gives the phospholipid its special characteristic: It has two oil-soluble tails, but a water-soluble head formed by the phosphate group.

There are two fatty acids that are absolutely critical. Since the body *must* have them, they are called essential fatty acids. You can only get them by eating the right kinds of fat. One of these fatty acids, linoleic acid (also called the omega-6 essential fatty acid), is common in salad oils. If you are avoiding salad oils because you think they are bad for you, you're making a mistake. The other essential fatty acid is alpha linolenic acid (also called the omega-3 essential fatty acid). This is also found in plant oils. It's uncommon in the American diet, but you can get it by eating soy oil, pumpkin seeds, walnuts, and flax seeds or flax oil. Fish oils also contain beneficial omega-3 oils, called docosahexaenoic acid (DHA) and eicosapentaenoic acid (EPA). These are actually the omega-3 molecules that your cells need, but they are not considered essential. Why not? As long as you have alpha linolenic acid in your diet, along with several vitamins and minerals, your cells can change the alpha linolenic acid into EPA and DHA.

What do these essential fatty acids do? They form prostaglandins. Now, there are "good" prostaglandins and "bad" prostaglandins. The alpha linolenic acid, which is uncommon in the American diet, is the precursor of what are nicknamed "good" prostaglandins, and it also helps prevent the "bad" ones from being formed, among other things. The good prostaglandins reduce inflammation, and prevent excess blood clotting. In addition, essential fatty acids give just the right amount of flexibility to a cell's plasma membrane. They also help usher in oxygen through the cell membrane.

Proteins form the last class of macronutrients. As you know, proteins are long chains of amino acids. The digestive tract cannot absorb proteins. It must first digest it down to its amino acids. Then, it can absorb the amino acids. What does the body then do with those amino acids? Well, if we remove the nitrogen-containing amino group, your body can burn the remaining part for energy. However, the main thing the body does with amino acids is to make its own proteins. Remember, cells need to make lots of proteins. That's what the DNA codes for. To do this, the cells need amino acids. You get those amino acids by eating protein-rich foods.

There are 20 amino acids in the proteins of the human body. Your body can make 11 of these. However, the other 9 cannot be made. These amino acids are called essential amino acids, and the only way you can get them is to eat proteins that contain them. A protein that contains all 9 of the essential amino acids is called a complete protein. From a practical standpoint, the only complete proteins are animal proteins such as dairy products, eggs, fish, and meat. So, the easiest way to make sure that you are getting all of the essential amino acids that you need is to consume animal proteins.

What about vegetarians? Can a person get essential amino acids by eating a strictly vegetarian diet? The answer is yes, but they have to exercise care in choosing the plant foods that they eat. For example, a typical vegan (completely plant-based) meal combines grains and beans. Neither the grains nor the beans contain complete proteins, but the essential amino acids missing in the grains are found in the beans. Many cultures have meals that mix grains and beans in order to provide a healthy diet. For example, beans on a flour tortilla are common in the Mexican diet. Wheat flour provides grain proteins that have some of the essential amino acids, and the beans provide proteins that have the rest of the essential amino acids. The Native American dish called succotash blends corn, a grain, with lima beans, providing all of the essential amino acids. Even the humble peanut butter sandwich is a complete protein food, because the wheat in the bread is a grain, and peanuts are actually beans!

MICRONUTRIENTS

Micronutrients are nutrients that are essential, but we need them only in tiny amounts, usually less than a gram per day. Vitamins are micronutrients. They are highly complex organic molecules that our bodies must have but cannot synthesize. So, we need to get them in our food on a regular basis. They are *not* digested, however. If they were digested, they would lose their function. What is their function? Vitamins act mainly as regulators of the chemical processes that occur in the body. Many are coenzymes, which enable cellular enzymes to do their job. Vitamins are classified as either fat-soluble or water-soluble. A fat-soluble vitamin cannot be dissolved in water. It can only be dissolved in fat. A water-soluble vitamin cannot be dissolved in fat, but it can be dissolved in water.

The fat-soluble vitamins are vitamin A, vitamin D, vitamin E, and vitamin K. The water-soluble vitamins are vitamin C, the vitamin B group (B_1, B_2, B_3, B_5, B_6, B_{12}), biotin, folic acid, and pantothenic acid. The body cannot make most of these vitamins, so they must be eaten with our food. There are several exceptions. Although your body can also absorb it from food, vitamin D is actually manufactured in the body through the skin's exposure to sunlight. In addition, vitamin K is produced by bacteria in the large intestine, as are some B vitamins.

So what do these vitamins do? Well, each kind of vitamin has its own unique support roles within the human body. Vitamin A, for example, is a component of the process that allows your eyes to detect light. Without sufficient vitamin A, you would not see properly. It also maintains the cells that protect your body, such as skin cells. Vitamin D allows calcium that you eat and drink to be absorbed from the small intestine. Vitamin E is an *antioxidant*, which means it helps protect important chemicals (such as the essential fatty acids) from being destroyed through oxidation, which means damage by reacting with oxygen. The B vitamins help your cells in a number of different ways, as do biotin and folic acid. For example, they are involved in the mitochondria's production of energy from food molecules, and they also are involved in cell division. Vitamin C helps build collagen in bones and teeth, and it supports the immune processes that help us fight disease. Finally, as you learned in module 11, vitamin K is necessary for the synthesis of many blood clotting factors.

This is just a brief overview of what these vitamins do; in fact, recent research continues to show that individual vitamins have more than one role in the body. Vitamin D has been shown to reduce inflammation and to reduce the incidence of cancer. Another wonderful discovery is that folic acid reduces the risk of many different birth defects, if a woman takes in adequate folic acid very early in pregnancy.

Minerals are the other class of micronutrients. These are inorganic substances that your body needs to function properly. You get these from your food, as well. You usually don't eat them directly, of course, because they are inorganic. Instead you eat them as you eat organic (carbon-containing) materials. For example, when you drink milk, you are also drinking the calcium minerals that were in the cow's system.

The minerals you need the most are those that contain calcium, magnesium, phosphorus, iron, iodine, sodium, chloride, zinc, copper, sulfur, selenium, and potassium. Without enough minerals containing these elements, you would have problems. For example, too little calcium in your diet will lead to bone problems. Remember, calcium minerals are used to make bone matrix. Without enough calcium, bones will not form properly. A constant lack of calcium intake can, later in life, lead to a malady called osteoporosis. In addition to calcium, your bones need phosphorus and magnesium. Because they are used in bone, you need more of these minerals than the others. So, calcium, phosphorus, and magnesium are called bulk minerals. The other minerals are called trace minerals.

Iron is important in your diet so that the hemoglobin in your erythrocytes can carry enough oxygen to your tissues. With too little iron, your body would not be able to distribute oxygen efficiently. As a result, you would not be able to burn the macronutrients as quickly as needed. This leads to shortness of breath, dizziness, feeling worn-out all of the time, and a host of digestive problems. This malady is called iron-deficiency anemia. Yet, because the body recycles iron as old red blood cells are broken down, you still need iron only in trace amounts.

Iodine is needed in very small amounts for the thyroid gland. In addition, your body needs sodium and chloride. Because of the media attention, we tend to think of table salt (sodium chloride) as something bad. However, it is essential. The sodium in table salt is essential for nerve conduction and water balance, and the chloride is necessary for the pH balance of the blood and for gastric juice production. It is *excess* sodium intake that can cause problems, notably high blood pressure in some individuals. Zinc is used in many enzyme systems and is essential for carbon dioxide transport. Sulfur is a component for many of the hormones and proteins that the body makes. Copper is an essential part of hemoglobin production, and selenium is used in the production of many enzymes in the body. Potassium is important for proper muscle function. These minerals, then, are essential to the body's chemistry. Don't think they are unimportant because we use them in trace amounts!

We all know that we must eat in order to survive. Perhaps after reading this module, you will be motivated to make healthier choices when selecting food. The next time you chew your food, take time to contemplate the astonishing accomplishment that is about to happen. In fact, perhaps the mealtime prayer will even take on a deeper meaning for you.

ANSWERS TO THE "ON YOUR OWN" QUESTIONS

13.1 The alimentary canal includes the mouth, pharynx, esophagus, stomach, small intestine, large intestine, and anus. That's the "tunnel" which leads through the body. The accessory organs would be the salivary glands, the liver, the pancreas, gallbladder and the vermiform appendix. These are not a part of the tunnel, but they all play a role in digestion. The tongue and the teeth are in the tunnel, but some do not consider them a part of the tunnel. We would put them as a part of the accessory organs.

13.2 The soft palate is raised. If that were not the case, water would go in and out of the nose. For a scuba diver, that would be bad!

13.3 Test for amylase. Tears do not contain amylase; saliva does. Tears and saliva both contain mucus and lysozyme, although the salivary glands secrete a much higher proportion of mucus. The "stretchiness" of saliva is due to the mucus. Tears are never "stretchy."

13.4 In module 9, you learned that the parasympathetic division of the ANS stimulates the salivary glands to increase their secretion of saliva, while the sympathetic division of the ANS inhibits the secretion of saliva. So, the control in this case is by the parasympathetic division of the ANS.

13.5 The linings of the trachea and larynx are very sensitive. The particles that make up the smoke irritate the linings of the trachea and larynx because they are not gases—they are tiny solids.

13.6 The stomach is mostly full. As the stomach stretches out, the rugae begin to disappear.

13.7 Look for a layer of oblique muscularis. Only the stomach has that layer. The rest of the alimentary canal has longitudinal and circular muscularis only.

13.8 High stress can lead to a duodenal ulcer. If the duodenal glands are not active enough, chyme will not be neutralized, which can irritate the intestinal lining.

13.9 Lipase breaks down lipids. Lipids are fats.

13.10 Secretin acts to reduce the acidity of chyme by stimulating the release of substances that neutralize acid chyme. So, the acidity of the chyme is high.

13.11 This causes diarrhea. Remember, the large intestine absorbs water. If it cannot absorb all of the water it is supposed to absorb, the feces will be too watery.

13.12 The stomach is strongly acidic due to gastric juice. That acid is specifically designed to kill bacteria. Since the acid gets neutralized in the small intestine, bacteria can grow there and beyond. Most cannot grow in the stomach, however. (The bacteria that cause stomach ulcers are an exception; they are resistant to acid.)

13.13 The six functions of the liver are: bile production, storage of nutrients, nutrient interconversion, synthesis, phagocytosis, and detoxification.

13.14 The level of CCK is higher. Remember, CCK causes contraction the gallbladder to put bile into the small intestine. This cannot happen if the sphincter is closed, and CCK also relaxes the sphincter.

13.15 If you greatly restrict your intake of fat, the gallbladder is not stimulated by CCK to release bile into the small intestine. So, the bile stays in the gallbladder and gets more concentrated. Eventually, the cholesterol may fail to remain liquid, and a gallstone can be produced.

STUDY GUIDE FOR MODULE 13

1. Define the following terms:
   a. Mastication
   b. Digestion
   c. Deglutition
   d. Peristalsis
   e. Gastric juice
   f. Adventitia
   g. Lumen
   h. Macronutrients
   i. Micronutrients

2. Label the organs in the figure here:

Illustration from the Future Graph collection

3. For each organ in the figure (combine h, i, j; and combine p, q, r, s), answer the following questions:
   a. Is it a part of the digestive system?
   b. If it is a part of the digestive system, is it a part of the alimentary canal?
   c. If it is a part of the digestive system, what is (are) its function or functions?

4. What keeps food from going down into your larynx?

5. What digestive enzyme can be found in saliva? What does it do?

6. What is the soft palate's function in deglutition?

7. Starting from the outer layer and working inwards, list the tunics that are contained in most of the alimentary canal. What extra layer exists in the stomach?

8. What digestive enzyme is secreted by the stomach? What does it do?

9. Why doesn't the acid in gastric juice hurt the lining of the stomach?

10. Where is intrinsic factor secreted? What is its function?

11. Although the stomach mostly churns food, it also absorbs certain things. What three things are absorbed through the stomach?

12. What are the effects of the hormone gastrin?

13. List the three regions of the small intestine, starting with the region closest to the stomach and ending with the region closest to the large intestine. Which region is the shortest of the three?

14. What design features in the intestine increase the rate at which nutrients are absorbed?

15. List the three main hormones released by the small intestine, and list their effects.

16. List the major enzymes from the intestinal glands and their functions.

17. Why can't a cell produce an active enzyme that breaks down proteins?

18. What functions do the bacteria in the large intestine perform?

19. Many people find that they must defecate shortly after eating. Why?

20. In a liver lobule, what travels from the portal triads to the central vein? What flows the opposite way?

21. Is bile a digestive enzyme? What does it do?

22. Which organs produce amylase?

23. There are four secretions designed to reduce acidity in the alimentary canal. What are they?

24. What are the fat-soluble vitamins?

25. What kind of role do most vitamins play in the body?

26. Which two vitamins can the body absorb without eating food that contains those vitamins?

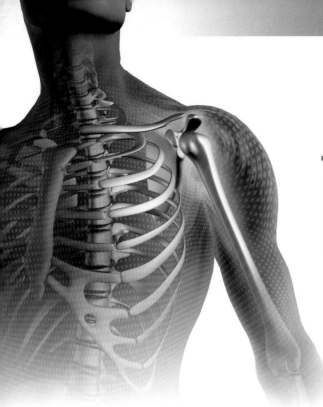

THE
RESPIRATORY SYSTEM

"Then the LORD God formed the man from the dust of the ground. He breathed the breath of life into the man's nostrils, and the man became a living person" (Genesis 2:7, NLT).

In this module you will be learning about your respiratory system and all of its life-giving properties. As you learn about your respiratory system, you will

heart of the matter

The "Breath of Life" is the essence of your existence. Why do we say that? There are multiple reasons. First, breathing keeps you alive on a minute-to-minute basis. You can't decide to hold your breath for ten minutes! Second, your breath is used when you express yourself as you speak, laugh, sing, sigh, and so forth.

probably learn answers to many questions you have had about the body. For example, you will learn about pneumonia and emphysema. You will also learn what triggers rapid breathing as a result of exercise, and why you tend to breathe through your nose rather than your mouth. Amazingly, the respiratory system is also critical to the acid-base balance in the body, so you will learn about that as well.

ANATOMY AND FUNCTIONS OF THE RESPIRATORY SYSTEM

We will spend most of the time in this module on the physiology of the respiratory system. However, before we can do that, we must first discuss the anatomy as seen in figure 14.1.

The respiratory system contains the nasal cavity, the paranasal sinuses, the pharynx, the larynx, the trachea (tray' kee uh), the bronchi (bron key'), and the lungs. Generally, we divide the respiratory system into two parts.

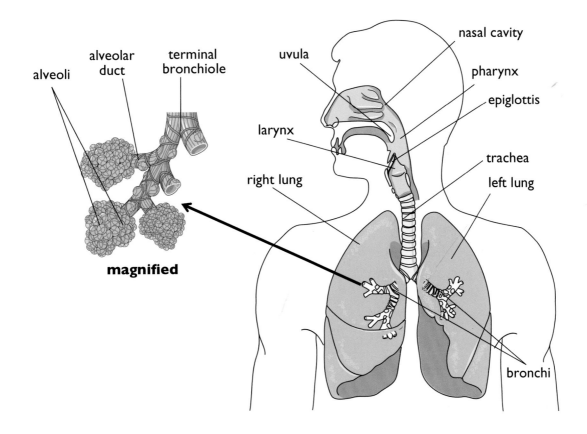

FIGURE 14.1
Anatomy of the Respiratory System
Illustration: LifeArt

Upper respiratory tract—The part of the respiratory system containing the nasal cavity, paranasal sinuses, and pharynx

Lower respiratory tract—The part of the respiratory system containing the larynx, trachea, bronchi, and lungs

Notice from figure 14.1 that the bronchi split into smaller and smaller tubes until they eventually end in microscopic **alveoli** (al vee' oh lie).

Each of the parts of the respiratory system has its own function or functions. The nasal cavity, for example, has two functions. First, it provides for olfaction. Remember from module 9 that in order to smell something, airborne chemicals must reach the olfactory epithelium in the upper part of the nasal cavity. This happens when you breathe in through the na sal cavity. So, olfaction is not only a function of the nervous system , but it is also a function of the respiratory system.

The nasal cavity also accomplishes something else when you inhale. It acts as an air conditioner! That is, it changes the inhaled air in a way that makes it more favorable to the body. How does it do that? First, there is quite a bit of surface area in the nasal cavity, and the tissue on that surface is very vascular. If you get a nosebleed, you'll agree that there are a lot of blood vessels in the tissue of the nasal cavity! That blood, of course, is warm. There is also a mucous membrane that is moist and sticky.

When you breathe in through the nasal cavity, then, the air is warmed by the blood in the vessels, moistened by the mucus, and cleansed of particles because particles stick to the mucous membrane. This air conditioning is very important because the air eventually reaches the alveoli, which are composed of delicate, simple squamous epithelium. If the air were not conditioned well, it would damage that tissue. If you have ever had to breathe through your mouth for an extended period of time, you might have felt a burning sensation in your chest. That sensation is due to irritation of the lungs caused by poorly conditioned air.

When the air passes through your nasal cavity, it enters your pharynx. You learned about the pharynx in the previous module. It is a passageway for both air and food. The superior (upper) part of the pharynx is called the nasopharynx (nay' zoh fare' inks). The nasopharynx ends at the uvula (you' vyou luh), a small process that hangs off of the soft palate. In cartoons, the uvula is usually shown dangling at the back of the throat when a person screams. It aids the soft palate in closing off the nasal cavity during deglutition (swallowing). The openings for the two eustachian (auditory) tubes are found in the nasopharynx, one from each ear. This allows air passage between the middle ear and the pharynx, which equalizes the pressure between the middle ear and the atmosphere.

Inferior to the nasopharynx, is the oropharynx (or' oh fare' inks). It extends from the uvula to the epiglottis. It is called the oropharynx because this is the place that the oral cavity opens to the pharynx. As a result, both food and air pass through the oropharynx. Two pairs of tonsils are located in this region of the oropharynx, one pair on either side, and the other on the back of the tongue.

Nearest the larynx is the laryngopharynx (luh ring' oh fare' inks). It is actually posterior to the larynx. When the epiglottis is not blocking the larynx, as it does during swallowing, air travels through the laryngopharynx to the larynx. When the epiglottis is closed, food passes from the laryngopharynx into the esophagus.

When air moves through the larynx, we encounter the second function of the respiratory system: voice. As you probably already know, the larynx, often called the voice box, contains the vocal cords, which give you your ability to make intricate sounds so that you can speak, shout, or sing. You will learn more about the larynx and the vocal cords in the next section.

Once air travels through the larynx, it enters the trachea, which is also called the windpipe. It consists of about 20 pieces of cartilage that are shaped like the letter C. Dense regular connective tissue and smooth muscle hold these pieces of cartilage together. Since the windpipe is a direct route to the lungs, it is a good place to point out the absolutely essential function of the respiratory system: ventilation.

Ventilation—The process of getting air into the lungs and back out

This word comes from the Latin word for window because when you open a window, air can travel into and out of a room.

The trachea splits into two bronchi (**bronchus is the singular of bronchi**), which each carry air to and from a lung. A little more than half of the air travels through the short, wide right primary bronchus into the right lung. A little less than half of the air travels through the slightly longer, narrower left primary bronchus into the left lung. Notice that the left lung and right lung are slightly different from one another. Each lung is composed of lobes, but the right lung is made up of three lobes while the left lung is made up of only two. Why the difference? Go back and look at figure 11.14. Notice that your heart is not exactly in the center of your body. It takes up more space on the left side as compared with the right side. So, your left lung is smaller because your heart takes up extra space on the left.

Once in the lungs, the two primary bronchi divide into smaller tubes called secondary bronchi. Each secondary bronchus goes to one lobe. So, there are three secondary bronchi in the right lung and two in the left lung. These tubes then split into smaller tubes called tertiary bronchi, and these eventually divide into even smaller tubes called bronchioles (bron' kee olz). The bronchioles continue to branch into even smaller tubes, until they become terminal bronchioles. These terminal bronchioles branch into tiny alveolar (al vee' oh lar) ducts, which open into many microscopic, balloon-like sacs called alveoli. The word alveoli actually means "hollow cavity," which makes sense, since the alveoli are, indeed, hollow. The tissue of the alveoli is composed of simple squamous epithelium, which is lined with capillaries.

The alveoli are involved with another absolutely vital function of the respiratory system: respiration. This process involves three specific steps. First is external respiration.

External respiration—The process of oxygen (O_2) and carbon dioxide (CO_2) exchange between the alveoli and the blood

The O_2 diffuses into the blood, and from there it can be sent to the cells. The CO_2 is released from the blood into the alveoli by diffusion and is exhaled back into the atmosphere.

Once external respiration has taken place, the next step of respiration, gas transport in the blood, takes place. As you already learned in module 11, oxygenated blood leaves the lungs and goes to the left heart and then to the body tissues, where it can supply the cells with O_2. At the same time, the blood picks up CO_2 from the cells. The CO_2 is then transported back to the lungs so that it can be eliminated from the body.

The final stage of respiration is internal respiration, which allows for the exchange of gases between the cells and the blood. Don't let this term confuse you; internal respiration occurs everywhere in the body, and does not directly involve respiratory structures.

Internal respiration—The process of O_2 and CO_2 exchange between the cells and the blood

Breathing is useless if the cells don't get oxygen and don't get relieved of their excess carbon dioxide. Even though you automatically think of the lungs when you think of respiration, remember that there is also internal respiration happening in your big toe! External respiration happens in the lungs, and internal respiration happens all over the body.

Why are external and internal respiration necessary? As you know, cells burn food to make ATP, which they then use for energy. In order to do this most efficiently, they must do this aerobically, and that requires O_2. One of the products of this process is

CO_2, which must be eliminated as waste. The process by which cells burn food for energy is actually called cellular respiration, and we will go over that in some detail later in this module.

VOICE

Animals have voices. You can recognize the friendly bark of a dog, its whimpering, or growling. You know the meow of a hungry cat or its contented purr, but only humans have language, and human language depends on the voice. Let's look at the anatomy and physiology of sound production. Do recognize that the language that humans can use so intricately depends on the brain, where we form the thoughts of speech and initiate the movements to form words and sentences.

First let's consider vocal cords, which are located in the larynx. There are actually two types of vocal cords in the larynx: true vocal cords (also called vocal folds) and false vocal cords (also called vestibular folds). Both are mucosa-covered ligaments and both are found in the upper portion of the larynx. The false vocal cords are superior to the true vocal cords. These two sets of vocal cords have different jobs. As discussed in the previous module, the false vocal cords help close the larynx to prevent food from traveling down the wrong pipe during deglutition. The true vocal cords are even more effective at closing off the larynx when you swallow, as they form a tight seal across the airway each time you swallow. And, the true vocal cords actually produce sound. Both the true vocal cords and false vocal cords are illustrated in figure 14.2.

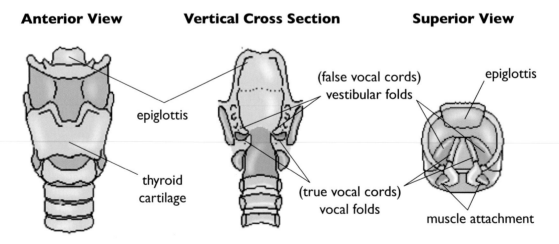

Anterior View   **Vertical Cross Section**   **Superior View**

epiglottis

thyroid cartilage

(false vocal cords) vestibular folds

(true vocal cords) vocal folds

epiglottis

muscle attachment

FIGURE 14.2
The Larynx
Illustration by Megan Whitaker

The illustration on the left shows the anterior view of the larynx. The most striking feature is the thyroid cartilage, the hyaline cartilage framework of the adam's apple, which you can easily feel on your neck, especially when you swallow. The center illustration is a vertical cross section of the trachea. In this illustration, you can see that the vestibular folds are superior to the vocal folds. The illustration on the right is a view through the opening into the larynx from above and behind. This passageway between the true vocal cords is called the glottis. Note the muscle attachment, where the delicate muscles that control the vocal folds are anchored.

How is sound created? Try humming a tune. What you did first was inhale. Then you used delicate skeletal muscles to move your true vocal cords into the airway, lightly closing the glottis. Next, you exhaled, which blew air past the two true vocal cords causing them to vibrate, since they were pulled to the center of the glottis. If you were humming a tune of different pitches, you were using the other delicate skeletal muscles to vary the tension and thickness of the true vocal cords, which in turn caused them to vibrate at different rates. We'll explain more about that soon.

Of course, you can do a lot more than just hum. You can vary the volume of the sound as well as the pitch. How is

think about this

When a speech therapist helps a child to learn better articulation (clearer speech), he or she will often start with the consonant sounds that are made by the lips and front teeth, because the child can see the therapist and can easily imitate the movements. Which consonant sounds do the lips make? Try making the sounds of *b, p, f, v,* and *m*. Now try the *d* and *t* sounds. Aren't they made behind the front teeth, using the tongue? The k and hard g sounds are made further back in the mouth. Some speech therapists say that the *r* sound is more difficult to teach than learn, because it is made in the back of the mouth, where it cannot be easily shown. Some speech therapists have kids smile and roar like a lion to position the mouth for the *r* sound!

that done? Well, the loudness of a sound is controlled by the *displacement* (how far the vibrating object moves) of the vibrations in the air. If you pluck a guitar string hard, it vibrates with a large displacement. This makes a loud sound. The larger the displacement, the louder the sound. In the larynx, the more forcefully that air passes through the vocal cords, the larger their displacement. Thus, you control the volume of your voice by controlling how forcefully air passes through the larynx. The more air you use, the louder your voice is. If you're going to yell at someone, you naturally take a deep breath, because you need a lot of air in order to raise the volume of your voice to that level.

Pitch is another important aspect to the sounds that you make. It is controlled by the *frequency* of the vibrations in the vocal cords. A guitarist can vary the pitch of a given string on the guitar by pinching off the string at different points. This varies the length of the string, which varies the frequency at which the string vibrates. The shorter the string, the higher the frequency of vibration and the higher the pitch. A musician can also vary the pitch of the guitar by plucking strings of different thicknesses. The thicker the string, the lower the pitch. Another way the musician can vary the pitch is by tightening or loosening the strings. That is usually done when the musician is tuning the guitar. The more tense the string, the higher the pitch.

You vary the pitch of your voice in much the same way that the musician varies the pitch of the guitar strings. You can vary both the thickness and the tension of your true vocal cords. The length of your vocal cords also affects the pitch just as it does in guitar strings, but you cannot change that. When you were young, the true vocal cords were relatively short. This gave your voices a high pitch. As you mature, your vocal cords grow. Typically, boys' vocal cords grow more than girls' vocal cords. So, as a boy matures, his voice gets deeper, because the longer the vocal cords, the lower the pitch. Although girls' vocal cords also grow, they do not grow as much. So, a girl's voice will typically get deeper as she matures, but not nearly as noticeably as that of a boy.

The length of your vocal cords affects the pitch of your voice, but you vary the pitch by changing the thickness and tension of your vocal cords. You do this through the action of some of the most delicate muscles in your body. Although the control of these muscles is unconscious, they are nevertheless skeletal muscles. The thinner you make your cords, the higher the pitch. You can also vary the pitch by adjusting the tension in your vocal cords. Skeletal muscles also do this. The higher the tension in the vocal cords, the higher the pitch.

Another aspect of voice is resonance. There are air chambers in the body (the chest cavity, the pharynx, and the paranasal sinuses in the skull), and air vibrates within those chambers. This gives the voice its resonance. The larger the cavities, the more the resonance. Think of the large tenors who sing opera. They get their strong, resonant voices from the large chambers in their bodies. An acoustic (non-electric) guitar gets its resonance from the air chamber that sits below the strings. The larger the chamber, the more the resonance of the guitar. Resonance adds volume to the voice.

Of course, there is more to your voice than resonance and the ability to change volume and pitch. You also need articulation, the ability to make the intricate sounds of speech. Although it is obvious that you use your tongue and lips for this, you might not be aware that you use your pharynx, larynx, palate, and teeth, as well. All of these are controlled by nerves that manipulate the muscles in just the right way to form the words you need when you speak.

COLORING BOOK EXERCISE 14.2
To review the structures just discussed, follow the instructions on page 259 of the coloring book.

ON YOUR OWN
14.3 When a person gets tense or uptight, the pitch of his or her voice often rises. Why?

THE MUSCLES AND MECHANICS OF VENTILATION
One of the vital functions of the respiratory system is ventilation, which brings air into the lungs and lets the air back out. To learn how this works, you need to learn the muscles of ventilation first. We will start with figure 14.3.

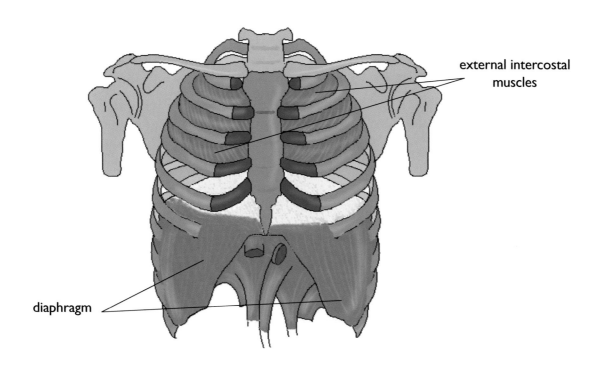

external intercostal
muscles

diaphragm

FIGURE 14.3
The Muscles of Principal Inspiration
Illustration by Megan Whitaker

We divide the muscles of ventilation into three groups: muscles of principal inspiration, muscles of forced inspiration, and muscles of forced expiration. The muscles of principal inspiration (shown in the figure), the diaphragm (die' uh fram), and the external intercostals, are used when we breathe in at rest. When we consciously take a deep breath or when we exercise vigorously, we use the muscles of forced inspiration, the sternocleidomastoid (ster' noh klee' doh mas' toyd) muscles, the scalene (skay' leen) muscles, and the pectoralis minor muscles, as well. When we consciously force ourselves to exhale, we use the abdominal muscles and internal intercostal muscles (deep to the external intercostal muscles), which are the muscles of forced expiration. Note that there are not really any muscles for resting expiration, because that happens when the principal inspiration muscles relax.

How do these muscles control ventilation? Let's start with the diaphragm. It is a broad, sheet-like muscle, and when we exhale, it's relaxed. That means it is as long as it can get. When we inhale, the diaphragm contracts, which causes it to shorten and pull downward. This pushes down on the abdominal organs below it, which increases the size of the cavity in the chest (the thoracic cavity). When this happens, the lungs expand, and that causes air to rush into them through the nasal cavity or the mouth. When the diaphragm relaxes, it gets longer, and the abdominal organs below it passively push it back up. This reduces the size of the thoracic cavity, which pushes in on the lungs. As a result, air flows out of the lungs and out through the nasal cavity or mouth. Figure 14.4 illustrates how this works.

MOD 14

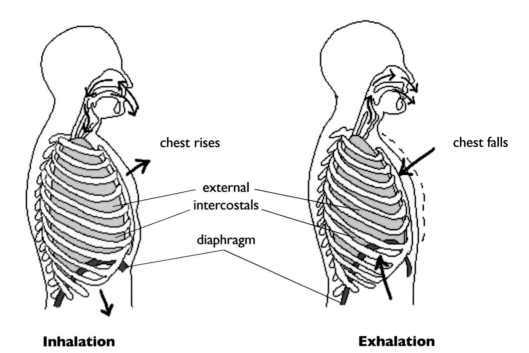

Inhalation

The diaphragm contracts and pushes the abdominal organs down. The external intercostals also contract, pulling the ribs up and out. This increases the size of the thoracic cavity.

Exhalation

The diaphragm relaxes, and the abdominal muscles push it up. The external intercostals relax, and the rib cage falls downward and inward. This decreases the size of the thoracic cavity.

FIGURE 14.4
The Action of the Diaphragm
Illustration by Megan Whitaker

Now remember, the diaphragm is only one of the muscles of principal inhalation. The other set of muscles that work during normal inhalation are the external intercostals. When they contract, they pull the ribs up and out. Once again, this increases the size of the thoracic cavity, and the lungs expand as a result. Muscles of inhalation, then, increase the volume of the thoracic cavity. For a big, forced breath, you have to use the muscles of forced inspiration, the sternocleidomastoid, pectoralis minor, and scalene muscles. These pull up either the ribs or the sternum when they contract, and that makes your thoracic cavity even larger. This increases the amount of air that you can inhale.

What about expiration? In order to exhale at rest, you just have to relax any of the inspiratory muscles. As we already discussed, when the diaphragm is relaxed, it gets longer. This reduces the size of the thoracic cavity as the abdominal organs passively push it up. If any of the other muscles of inhalation are contracted, relaxing them will further reduce the size of the thoracic cavity. When that happens, the lungs get pushed in, and air is forced out.

To expire more air than normal, you must reduce the size of the thoracic cavity even more. You can do that by contracting your abdominal muscles. When they contract, they push the abdominal organs up against the diaphragm, which further reduces the size of the thoracic cavity. In addition, contracting the internal intercostal muscles pulls the ribs in, making the thoracic cavity even smaller. So, normal expiration requires no muscle contraction. The principal inspiratory muscles must simply relax. To force more air out of the lungs, however, requires the contraction of the muscles of forced expiration, the abdominals and internal intercostals.

You can feel how all of this works yourself. Watch your chest as you inhale deeply. What happens? Your chest expands. So, the size of your thoracic cavity is increasing. Now exhale forcefully. What happens? Your chest collapses. This means the size of your thoracic cavity is decreasing.

How does this work? Why does air flow into your lungs just because your thoracic cavity increases in size? Why does air flow out of your lungs just because the size of your thoracic cavity decreases? It is the practical application of Boyle's Law. Boyle's Law says that at constant temperatures, the pressure of a gas increases with decreasing volume and decreases with increasing volume.

When your thoracic cavity gets smaller, there is less volume available to the air inside your lungs. This increases the air pressure in the lungs, in accordance with Boyle's Law. However, your lungs are connected to the outside world via your mouth and nasal cavity. The outside world is at atmospheric pressure. As a result, the pressure inside your lungs is now *higher* than the pressure in the outside world. This pressure difference causes air to rush out of your lungs. Think about it. When you blow up a balloon, the air inside the balloon is at a higher pressure than the air outside of the balloon. So, if you were to release the nozzle of the balloon, air would rush outside because air travels from areas of high pressure to areas of low pressure. In the same way, then, when the air pressure in your lungs climbs above atmospheric pressure, air will flow out of the lungs.

What about inspiration? When the diaphragm and the external intercostals contract, the thoracic cavity gets larger. As a result, there is *more* volume for the air in your lungs. This *reduces* the pressure in the lungs, making it *less* than atmospheric pressure. Since air travels from areas of high pressure to areas of low pressure, air rushes into the lungs, filling them. The airflow stops when the pressure within the lungs equals the atmospheric pressure.

ON YOUR OWN

14.4 Air is leaving the lungs. Is the diaphragm contracted or relaxed? Is the pressure in the lungs greater than, equal to, or less than atmospheric pressure? Are the external intercostals contracted or relaxed? What muscles might be contracted?

FACTORS THAT AID VENTILATION

Although the actions of the muscles that we discussed in the previous [section] driving force behind inspiration and expiration, there are other factor[s] these processes. For example, there are elastic fibers in the lungs. So, [they are] like balloons. They can be inflated because their elastic nature allows [them to] However, when nothing is forcing them to stretch what will they do? [They will] back to a smaller size. The elasticity of the lungs, therefore, aids in e[xpiration. As] the diaphragm and external intercostal muscles relax and the thoraci[c cavity] decreases, the pressure inside the lungs increases. This forces the air [out.]

Emphysema (em fuh see' muh) is unfortunately a common lung d[isease] caused by smoking or being exposed to excess air pollution. In this [case, some] of the tiny alveoli degenerate, and many tiny alveoli join together to [form]

alveolus (singular of alveoli). This causes two problems. The rate at which oxygen can be exchanged with the blood in the alveoli depends on the surface area over which blood is exposed to oxygen. Many tiny alveoli have more surface area than one large alveolus. So, the decrease in surface area causes less oxygen to be exchanged with the blood. The second problem is that, as the walls of the alveoli degenerate, the elastic tissue degenerates, as well. Typically, it is replaced with scar tissue. As a result, the lungs lose their elasticity. This causes a person with emphysema to have difficulty *exhaling*. It is common to think that people with emphysema have trouble breathing. Technically, that's not correct. They have no trouble inhaling. In fact, the root of the word emphysema means "puffed full of air." Why? People with emphysema have trouble exhaling because their lungs have lost elasticity and do not recoil normally.

In addition to the elasticity of the lungs, another factor also aids expiration: the surface tension of alveolar fluid. What does this mean? Let's start with the term alveolar fluid. The wall of an alveolus is lined with simple squamous epithelium. This tissue is delicate, and that's why smoking or chronic exposure to air pollution can damage it. Now, like any mucous membrane or any of the internal membranes, this tissue is *moist*. The fluid that causes this moistness is called alveolar fluid, and it covers the entire inner surface of the alveolus. The key thing to remember about this fluid is that its principal component is water. Examine figure 14.5.

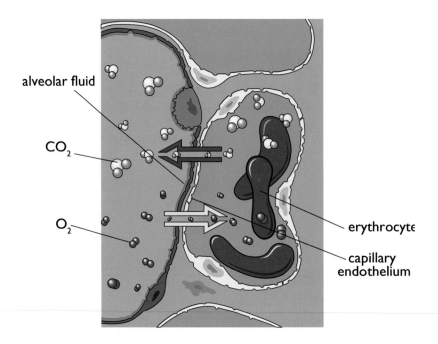

Figure 14.5
Alveolar fluid
Illustration: LifeArt

As you know, water is strongly attracted to other water molecules. In fact, it is more strongly attracted to other water molecules than to the molecules in the air. At the surface of any collection of water molecules, this creates surface tension. Have you ever made a needle float on the surface of a bowl of water? You can. Although the needle is made of metal and should sink, if you place it on the surface of water very carefully, you can get it to float. Why? The water molecules are so attracted to one another that the weight of the needle is not great enough to force them apart. So, the needle cannot get in between the water molecules, and it just floats on the surface. That's surface tension, and it is a powerful force.

When an alveolus inflates with air, the watery alveolar fluid has to "stretch" out to cover the increasing surface area of the simple squamous epithelium. This forces the water molecules to move farther apart from one another. The water molecules do not "want" to do that. Instead, they try to stay close together. This creates surface tension. The water is being pulled in one direction (out), but the molecules of the water are pulling in the other direction (in toward each other). As long as the force of the air inflating the alveolus is strong enough, the alveolus will expand. However, as soon as that force decreases, the alveolus will be pulled back by the surface tension of the alveolar fluid. So, the alveolar fluid aids in expiration because the water molecules of the alveolar fluid continuously pull on other water molecules, pulling to get the alveolus closed.

Just as there are two processes that aid expiration, there are also two processes that aid inspiration. These processes also keep the lungs from collapsing completely when you exhale. To understand the first of these processes, you need to learn one more detail about lung anatomy.

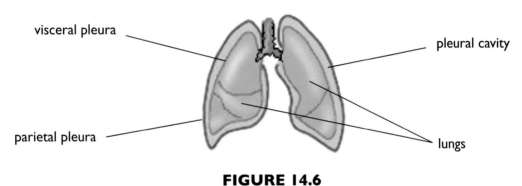

FIGURE 14.6
The Pleural Cavity
Illustration by Megan Whitaker

Look at figure 14.6. The surface of the lungs is covered with a thin, slick membrane called the visceral pleura (plur' uh). The surface of the chest wall and diaphragm is covered with another thin, slick membrane called the parietal (puh rye' ih tuhl) pleura. The narrow space in between these membranes is called the pleural (plur' uhl) cavity, and it contains a small amount of watery fluid called pleural fluid. The pleura adheres tightly to the lungs, and parietal pleura adheres closely to the chest wall and to the surface of the diaphragm.

The two pleural cavities (one around each lung) have no air in them, only pleural fluid, but nevertheless, their pressure is lower than atmospheric pressure. How can that be? The two factors that we just discussed—the elasticity of the lungs and the surface tension of the alveolar fluid inside each alveolus—cause the lungs to pull away from the chest wall. The ribs, though, are springy, and so tend to pull the lungs outward. Since each pleural cavity is literally sealed, the pull in opposite directions creates a vacuum seal, or, technically speaking, negative pleural pressure, since the pressure within each pleural cavity is lower than atmospheric pressure.

To observe this effect, put a couple of tablespoons of water in the palm of one hand. Now tightly clasp both palms together. Next, holding your palms together, try to pull the center of each palm away from the other. Can you feel the pull? That's negative pressure. Finally, pull your palms apart enough to make a whooshing sound as they break apart. That's the sound of air rushing into the vacuum seal that you had made as you clasped your palms and then pulled them apart.

How does the negative pressure within the pleural cavity help inspiration? Since the pleural cavity is at a pressure lower than atmospheric pressure, it puts suction on the lung, holding it open. So, even though the elastic nature of the alveoli and the surface tension of the alveolar fluid keeps pulling the lungs closed, the negative pressure in the pleural cavity acts as a counterbalance, keeping them from collapsing completely.

What happens if we lose the vacuum seal of the pleural cavity? Air will rush into the pleural cavity, giving it the same pressure as the atmosphere. When that happens, there is no longer a negative pressure holding the lung open, and the lung will collapse. That's called a pneumothorax.

Pneumothorax—Air in the pleural cavity, which leads to a collapsed lung

As we mentioned, the pleural cavities around each of our lungs are independently sealed. Thus, if the seal is broken around one lung, it will collapse. However, the other lung will be fine, unless its seal is also broken. One lung is enough to sustain life until healing occurs. The lung can be reinflated by medical intervention, or even on its own as the living pleural membranes heal.

In addition to the negative pleural pressure, a second process also aids inspiration and keeps the lungs from collapsing completely. This process counteracts the surface tension of the alveolar fluid. Remember, this surface tension aids the alveoli in collapsing, and it is quite a powerful force. It turns out that this force must be reduced in order to allow for proper breathing. How is it reduced? It is reduced by surfactant, a molecule secreted by specialized cells in the lungs.

Surfactant—A molecule with a hydrophilic (water-soluble) end
and a hydrophobic (oil-soluble) end

Surfactant is a detergent, and detergents are made of molecules in which one end dissolves readily in water (the hydrophilic end) and one end dissolves readily in nonpolar compounds (the hydrophobic end). A detergent, then, such as your dishwashing soap, is an example of a surfactant.

Cells in the lungs also produce a surfactant. What does this surfactant do? Well, its hydrophilic end gets very close to some water molecules in the alveolar fluid, and its hydrophobic end pushes the surrounding molecules away. This, in effect, isolates water molecules from one another. As a result, their mutual attraction goes down significantly. In the end, then, this *reduces the surface tension*. If you did the experiment we mentioned above where you floated a needle on the surface of a bowl of water, there was an easy way to get the needle to sink. All you had to do was add a drop of dish soap. The dish soap, being a surfactant, separated the water molecules from each other. This decreased the surface tension in the water, and the needle's weight was then strong enough to push through the surface and sink into the water.

The surfactant secreted by cells in the lungs decreases the surface tension in the alveolar fluid in the same way. As a result, the alveoli are far easier to inflate than they would otherwise be, and therefore, the presence of surfactant in the alveolar fluid aids inspiration.

Have you ever heard of infant respiratory distress syndrome? This problem used to be common in premature babies. It is characterized by the baby having great difficulty breathing. What makes it difficult to breathe? Well, if the baby is more than about four weeks premature, the baby does not have the ability to make the surfactant for the alveolar fluid. As a result, the surface tension of the alveolar fluid is at its strongest, and that surface tension fights against inflation. As a result, the newborn has a very hard time inhaling. If this situation is not treated, the newborn will die of exhaustion just trying to breathe.

How can this problem be treated? Well, if a baby is born prematurely, surfactant can be artificially put into the lungs via the trachea until the baby matures and the surfactant-secreting cells produce surfactant. However, if a physician thinks that a baby is going to be born prematurely, the physician can prescribe cortisol injections to the mother. Remember from module 10 that cortisol is a hormone normally secreted by the adrenal glands, especially during times of stress. It turns out that the fetus normally makes cortisol about a month before birth, which stimulates the formation of surfactant in the developing lungs. The cortisol injected into the mother will travel to the unborn baby, and it will stimulate the baby's lungs to start secreting the surfactant that the baby will need for inspiration after birth. That way, even though the baby is born prematurely, it may not need any surfactant treatments, as it will be able to make its own.

Since we are discussing babies, let's think for a moment about what happens when a baby is first born. Before birth, the baby is getting the oxygen and nutrients it needs from the mother. When the umbilical cord is cut, however, the baby must begin to breathe on its own. It turns out that the first breath is the hardest breath that the child will ever take. That's because the compliance of the lungs is low.

Compliance—The ease with which the lungs inflate

Why is that? Suppose you get a new balloon. The first time you inflate it you really have to blow hard, because the elastic material that composes it is stiff. But, if you blow it up and shoot it around the room a few times, after about the ninth or tenth time it's easy to inflate. We could say that the balloon's compliance increases after it has been inflated a few times. In the same way, the lungs are hardest to fill on the first breath. The second breath isn't quite perfect, nor is the third, but within two hours (or less) of birth, the baby's lungs have about the same compliance as adult lungs. Compliance of the lungs is the technical way of saying the old expression, "It's easy as breathing." Breathing is easy because the lungs are compliant soon after birth.

Before we leave this section, we need to mention something about airway resistance. Remember, the air flows into the lungs and ultimately to the alveoli through the bronchi, bronchioles, and alveolar ducts. Well, when air travels through a tube, the walls of the tube resist the flow. That's called airway resistance. Of course, the lower the airway resistance, the easier it is to get air into and out of the lungs. It turns out that most of the airway resistance occurs in the bronchioles, which are about one millimeter wide or less. Asthma is a disease that increases airway resistance. Although its cause is not always understood, we know that asthma results in a narrowing of the bronchi and especially the bronchioles. This increases airway resistance, making it harder for air to get to the alveoli. As a result, asthma causes wheezing, coughing, and shortness of breath. It can be treated with bronchial dilators, which are inhaled medications that relax the smooth muscles of the airways. That reduces airway resistance, making it easier for the person to breathe.

ON YOUR OWN

14.5 In first aid, you learn that when a person has a chest wound, the wound is more severe if it is a *sucking wound*. When you are treating a person with such a wound, you can hear air being sucked directly into the chest through the wound. What would cause air to be sucked into the chest, and why is that a problem?

EXTERNAL RESPIRATION

In module 9, we discussed olfaction, the sense of smell. In this module, we have discussed voice and ventilation. It is now time to discuss the essential function of the respiratory system: respiration. Now remember, respiration is composed of three steps: external respiration, transport, and internal respiration. We will begin our discussion of this process with external respiration.

Did you know that whether you are in good physical shape or in poor physical shape, your blood is virtually 100% oxygenated when it leaves your lungs? Of course, if you have some kind of lung or heart disease, that might not be true. However, as long as you have no serious abnormalities, the oxygenation level of your blood is virtually independent of your physical condition. This is independent of whether you are resting or exercising vigorously. There are six reasons for this interesting fact, and they all center around the process of external respiration.

As we defined it earlier, external respiration refers to the diffusion of oxygen from the alveoli into the blood and the diffusion of carbon dioxide from the blood into the alveoli. figure 14.7 illustrates the basics of external respiration.

On the left-hand side of the figure, you see a cross section of a single alveolus with three capillaries near it. Notice that the alveolus has a macrophage in it to destroy by phagocytosis any foreign invaders that make it to the alveolus. These macrophages are often called dust cells because they engulf tiny particles that may make it past the mucous membranes of the air passageways that precede the alveoli. Air fills the lumen of the alveolus, and gases can be exchanged across the respiratory membrane.

The right-hand side of the figure shows you the details of the respiratory membrane. The first layer is the alveolar fluid, which was mentioned before. This fluid, which has surfactant in it, coats the simple squamous epithelium of the alveolus. The gases in the air pass through this ultra-thin membrane on the way in and out of the alveolus. Below the simple squamous epithelium of the alveolus, you find the basement membrane of the alveolar epithelium. Beyond that, there is a tiny interstitial space separating the alveolus and the capillary. That space ends with the basement membrane of the capillary endothelium. (Endothelium is the name for epithelium that lines the inside of blood vessels.)

After that you find the simple squamous endothelium of the capillary, which leads to the lumen of the capillary. Notice the structure of this epithelium. The cells are spaced relatively far from one another, and a thin membrane connects one cell to another.

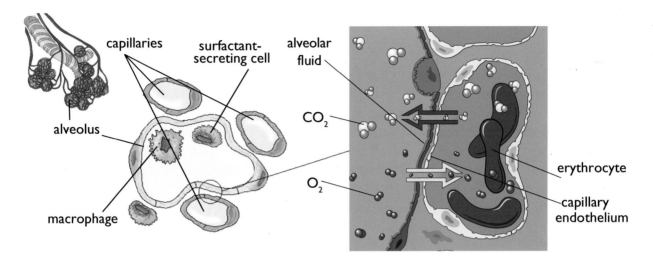

FIGURE 14.7
External Respiration
Illustrations by Megan Whitaker and LifeArt

When the alveolus fills with air, oxygen diffuses across the respiratory membrane and is picked up by the erythrocytes in the capillary. At the same time, carbon dioxide diffuses from the blood, across the respiratory membrane, and into the lumen of the alveolus. When the alveolus collapses as you expire (exhale), that carbon dioxide is forced out of the alveolus. When the alveolus is inflated again as you inspire (inhale), fresh oxygen comes in with the new air.

Okay, then, what makes this process so efficient that no matter what your physical condition your blood will be nearly 100% oxygenated? The first four reasons are ana-tomical in nature. First of all, despite its several layers, the respiratory membrane just discussed is particularly thin. It's pretty obvious that molecules will diffuse across a thin membrane much more easily than across a thick membrane. By contrast, farther up in the bronchial tree, the epithelium is not simple squamous epithelium. Instead, it is stratified squamous epithelium. No oxygen or carbon dioxide can be exchanged with the blood there because the epithelium is so thick.

The second factor is the very large surface area over which this exchange takes place. Much like the small intestine, God has designed the alveoli in such a way as to maximize the surface area. Let's put it this way: if we could take all of the respiratory membranes found in your lungs and spread them out like a carpet, they would cover a 25 X 35 foot room! Think about that! That's about half of a tennis court! That's how much surface area is available for gas exchange in the lungs.

think about this

How many connotations can you generate for the terms inspire and expire? Is it any wonder that we use the term inspiration to show an awakening, usually by divine influence, and the term expiration to show termination? How might you relate this to the act of breathing in life and breathing out your last breath?

Now remember, when a person has emphysema, not only do the lungs lack elasticity, but the small alveoli join together to make large alveoli. This *reduces* the surface area available for exchange because lots of tiny balloons have more surface area than one large balloon. So, people with advanced emphysema not only have trouble exhaling, due to the loss of elasticity, but their external respiration is also not nearly as efficient. As a result, their blood does not necessarily get 100% oxygenated in the lungs. Of course, our lungs are so incredibly well designed that we can deal with a significant amount of tissue loss. The truth is, an individual could live with half of one lung, which is one-fourth of the normal lung capacity. This person would not be able to exercise much, but he or she, with the proper behavioral restrictions, could still live reasonably well.

The third reason that exchange between the alveoli and the blood is so efficient rests in the fact that the capillaries are particularly narrow in the lung. What does this accomplish? It pushes the red blood cells right up against the capillary's endothelium. Instead of red blood cells being lost in a big "river" of blood, the capillaries are so narrow that red blood cells go through them in a single file. So, when an oxygen molecule gets into the capillary, it will immediately find a red blood cell to pick it up.

The fourth anatomical feature that increases the efficiency of gas exchange you already learned about in module 11. The shape of the red blood cell itself increases the surface area of the cell, making the absorption of oxygen more efficient. Remember, the red blood cell is shaped like a doughnut with a depression in the middle rather than a hole. This makes more surface area than you would find if the erythrocyte were round. Since there is more surface area, the oxygen can get into red blood cells more quickly than it could if they were spherical.

In addition to the four anatomical features that make external respiration efficient, there are two physiological processes that increase its efficiency as well. First, there is a controlled relationship between ventilation and capillary blood flow in the lungs. In other words, if your heart starts beating faster and harder, so that your blood starts flowing faster, reflexes coordinated in the medulla oblongata of your brain cause you to start breathing faster, also. That ensures that you can supply the right amount of oxygen to all the blood rapidly flowing through your lungs. Think about what happens when you exercise. Your heart starts pounding faster because your muscles need more oxygen and nutrients to do the work that you are asking them to do. As a result, you start breathing (ventilating) more. It's controlled completely by reflexes.

Of course, if this controlled relationship gets disrupted, bad things can happen. Suppose, for example, you get an obstruction of the airway. This can happen if, for example, you aspirate an object.

Aspirate—To take in by means of suction

When a person aspirates an object, the object is sucked down into the respiratory system by inhalation. We would say the person is choking. If this happens, the airway becomes blocked. This decreases the amount of air that can get into the alveoli. However, the heart is still pumping the same amount of blood. In fact, as the person gets stressed over the situation, the heart will start pumping even more blood. That blood cannot get the right amount of oxygen, however, because the alveoli are not getting enough air. What happens? The person usually turns blue due to the lack of oxygenated blood. The Heimlich maneuver is the technique that is used to dislodge such an object; it is a lifesaving skill that you can learn in a first aid class.

Pneumonia is another way that the controlled relationship between ventilation and blood flow can be compromised. Pneumonia is a general term that refers to an infection of the lungs. The infections can be viral, bacterial, or even the result of protozoa. These infections usually lead to mucus-like fluid collecting in the alveoli and poor oxygen exchange in the lungs. Once again, then, there is not enough air in the alveoli for the blood that is pumping through them. As a result, the tissues do not get enough oxygen, and the results can be deadly.

Of course, the opposite situation can happen as well. In module 11, we discussed the formation of an embolus. An embolus forms when a thrombus (blood clot) gets loose in the circulatory system. Usually it breaks loose from a vein, often in the leg. It moves through larger and larger veins until it enters the right heart. From there it goes via pulmonary arteries through smaller and smaller vessels, until it gets trapped in the lungs. There it clogs the capillaries. This reduces the blood flow in the lungs. Therefore, the controlled relationship between ventilation and blood flow is ruined, and even though there is plenty of air in the lungs, there is not enough oxygen getting to the body's tissues because there is not enough blood moving through the lungs.

As you can see, then, the controlled relationship between ventilation and blood flow is critical to the process of getting oxygen to the body's tissues. If something happens to interrupt this relationship, the consequences can be deadly! This principle is applied when you learn cardiopulmonary resuscitation (CPR). in the new hands-only CPR, you learn to compress the chest both to supply air, and to move blood out of the heart and to the lungs.

The second physiological process that aids in the efficiency of external respiration is the functional residual capacity of the alveoli. What does this mean? Well, even when you have exhaled, there is still air in your lungs. Typically, an adult's lungs have about two liters of air in them after he or she has exhaled normally. When an adult inhales at rest, usually the volume of air in the lungs increases by only half a liter or even less. This is referred to as the tidal volume.

Tidal volume—The volume of air inspired or expired during normal, quiet breathing

Under normal conditions, then, your lungs have somewhere between 2 and 3 liters of air in them. While you are breathing normally, the volume of air changes by only half a liter or less.

Because the tidal volume is small compared with the total volume of air in the lungs, there is a lot of air still in the alveoli when you have exhaled. So, even the red blood cells that pass through the alveoli while you are exhaling are exposed to plenty of oxygen. That's what we mean by functional residual capacity.

Functional residual capacity—The volume of air left in the lungs after a normal expiration

Even once you have exhaled, there is still enough functional residual air in the alveoli to transfer plenty of oxygen to the blood. This ensures that all of the red blood cells that pass through the alveoli become fully oxygenated.

Of course, the tidal volume is simply the variation of the air in the lungs during normal breathing. What happens when we breathe really hard? Most healthy adults can breath in over 3 liters additional air when they forcefully inhale. So, the volume of air in the lungs can change from just over 2 liters to about 5 or 6 liters (depending on size) when we forcefully inhale. This maximum volume of air that both lungs can hold is referred to as the total lung capacity.

Total lung capacity—The maximum volume of air contained in the lungs after a forceful inspiration

The total lung capacity for a healthy adult is usually about 5 to 6 liters.

Just as you are able to inhale more air than you usually do under normal conditions, you can also exhale more than you usually do under normal conditions. When you force-fully exhale, you expel as much air as possible from your lungs. Interestingly enough, you *cannot* empty your lungs of air. Even when you exhale as much as possible, a residual volume of air is left in your lungs.

Residual volume—The volume of air left in the lungs after a forceful expiration

For most adults, the residual volume of the lungs is about one liter.

Now remember, during external respiration, oxygen not only enters the blood, but carbon dioxide also leaves the blood and exits the body through the lungs. Even though we spent our time discussing how oxygen enters the blood during external respiration, don't forget that carbon dioxide does just the opposite at the same time. So, all of the anatomical and physiological features that make external respiration so efficient also apply to the process of exhaling carbon dioxide.

ON YOUR OWN

14.6 There are six separate parts of the respiratory membrane. List them in the order that they would be encountered by a molecule of carbon dioxide leaving the blood and entering the alveolus.

14.7 A person's lungs can hold 6 liters of air when maximally filled. He inhales as deeply as possible and then forcefully exhales into a device that measures the amount of air exhaled. Roughly what volume of air did he exhale?

EXPERIMENT 14.1
The Histology of the Lung

Supplies:
- Microscope
- Prepared slide: lung (human)

Purpose:
>   This experiment will give you a chance to see an alveolus, a capillary, and the respiratory membrane

Procedure:

1. Place the slide on the stage and focus at 40x. You will see that the slide looks like Swiss cheese because it is full of holes. Those holes are alveoli and capillaries.

2. The cross section of the slide is made so that you get at least one good look at an alveolus and a capillary. Search the slide for two or more ovals in the same vicinity. They should each be surrounded by tissue that sharply defines them from the rest of the tissue. The larger hole will be the alveolus. The smaller hole will be the capillary.

3. Draw what you see.

4. Center the ovals and increase magnification to 100x. Now you should be able to distinguish features of the tissue that surrounds the ovals. The capillary is surrounded by its endothelium, and the alveolus is surrounded by its epithelium.

5. Draw what you see.

6. Center the ovals and increase to 400x. Slowly scan from the edge of the alveolus to the edge of the capillary. Try to distinguish each layer of the respiratory membrane. You will not see the alveolar fluid, but the other layers should be there.

7. Draw a picture with all of the layers you found.

8. Put everything away.

GAS EXCHANGE DURING EXTERNAL AND INTERNAL RESPIRATION

In the previous section, you learned about external respiration, the exchange of oxygen and carbon dioxide between the alveoli and the blood. That, of course, is only the first stage of respiration. In the second stage (transport), the blood carries the oxygen to the tissues, and in the third stage (internal respiration), the oxygen leaves the blood and enters the tissues while carbon dioxide leaves the tissues and enters the blood.

Have you ever wondered how the oxygen and carbon dioxide "know" where to go? Why does oxygen enter the blood at the alveoli and exit at the tissues? Why doesn't the reverse happen? In the same way, what makes carbon dioxide leave the blood at the alveoli? Why doesn't it leave the blood at the tissues? The answer to these questions is surprisingly simple: *diffusion*! As you already know, substances diffuse from areas of high concentration to areas of low concentration. That's all it takes to explain why oxygen and carbon dioxide move into and out of the blood in the way that they do.

Let's think about external respiration. When dry, the air around us is about 78% nitrogen and 21% oxygen. The remaining 1% is a mixture of many, many gases, including carbon dioxide, which makes up about 0.04%. Of course, we never really breathe dry air. The air that we breathe has some water vapor in it, and that reduces the percentages of nitrogen and oxygen. Humidified air is typically 74% nitrogen, 20% oxygen, 6% water vapor, and still about 0.04% carbon dioxide. This is true of air at one atmosphere of pressure, which is about 760 mmHg.

When it comes to gases, we use the term partial pressure instead of concentration. In the following discussion, we define partial pressure. It might be helpful to think concentration when we say partial pressure, until you get the hang of it.

Dalton's Law states that the pressure exerted by a mixture of gases is equal to the sum of the partial pressure of each gas in the mixture. So, we can view a mixture of gases as a collection of individual gases, each exerting its own pressure. The partial pressure a gas exerts is simply proportional to the number of molecules of that gas present in the mixture. Using Dalton's Law, then, we can calculate the partial pressure of nitrogen in humidified air by taking the percentage of nitrogen in the air (0.74) and multiplying it by the total pressure exerted by the atmosphere (760 mmHg). The result is 562 mmHg. That's the partial pressure of nitrogen gas in humidified air, and it is a way of measuring how much nitrogen is in the air. If we perform the same calculation for oxygen and carbon dioxide, we will find that the partial pressure of oxygen in humidified air is 152 mmHg, and the partial pressure of carbon dioxide in that same air is 0.3 mmHg.

What do these numbers mean? They tell you *how much* of each gas is in the air. A higher partial pressure can be thought of as a higher concentration of the gas. When we breathe humidified air, we are breathing in nitrogen at a partial pressure of 562 mmHg, oxygen at a partial pressure of 152 mmHg, and carbon dioxide at a partial pressure of 0.3 mmHg. This tells us that there is almost four times more nitrogen in the air than oxygen. At the same time, we can tell from the partial pressure of carbon dioxide that there is about 500 times more oxygen in the air than there is carbon dioxide.

Okay, then, what happens when we breathe this air into our lungs? Well, the lungs have a functional residual capacity, remember? So, there is "old air" in the lungs. When we breathe in, the "new air" that we are breathing in mixes with the "old air" that is already there. What do you think will happen to the partial pressures of oxygen and carbon dioxide as a result? Remember, this "old air" has been giving up some of its oxygen to the blood and has been taking carbon dioxide from the blood. So, it has less oxygen and more carbon dioxide than the "new air." As a result, when the "new air" mixes with the "old air," the partial pressure of oxygen will be *lower* than it was in the "new air," and the partial pressure of carbon dioxide will be *higher* than it was in the "new air." It turns out that, on average, the partial pressure of oxygen in the alveoli of the lungs is about 104 mmHg, and the partial pressure of carbon dioxide in the alveoli is about 40 mmHg. Please remember those two numbers.

What do those numbers tell us? By themselves, they don't tell us very much; however, when compared to other numbers, they tell us quite a bit. What other numbers? These other numbers are those that show us the partial pressure of oxygen and carbon dioxide in the pulmonary *capillaries* around the alveoli. figure 14.8 will help you understand this concept further. Please note that in chemistry, we abbreviate partial pressure with a P, and the subscript on the P tells you what gas is being measured. So, P_{O_2} refers to the partial pressure of oxygen. In the figure, the letters in parentheses will correspond to the location on figure 14.8 that we are referring in the text.

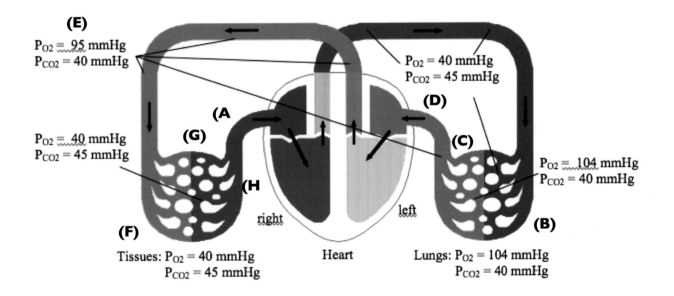

FIGURE 14.8
Partial Pressures of Oxygen and Carbon Dioxide in the Blood
Illustration: MasterClips Collection

The deoxygenated (blue) blood that returns to the lungs already gave up oxygen to the tissues. As a result, its partial pressure of oxygen is low—about 40 mmHg. At the same time, this blood had picked up carbon dioxide from the tissues. So, the pressure of carbon dioxide is relatively high—about 45 mmHg (A). Now let's compare *these* numbers to the partial pressures of oxygen and carbon dioxide in the alveoli. The partial pressure of oxygen in the alveoli is *higher* than the partial pressure of oxygen in the blood. As a result, diffusion requires that the oxygen must travel *out of the alveoli and into the blood*. On the other hand, the partial pressure of carbon dioxide in the alveoli is *lower* than the partial pressure of carbon dioxide in the blood. So, diffusion requires that carbon dioxide must travel *from the blood to the alveoli*. In the end, then, the gases really don't "know" which way they are supposed to travel. They travel the way that they do because diffusion demands it. (B)

When does diffusion stop? It stops when the concentration of the substance is the same everywhere, right? So, oxygen will travel out of the alveoli and into the blood until the partial pressures (think concentration) even out. Since the exchange of gases is so efficient as discussed previously, this happens rapidly. So, before the blood has left the lungs, it has gained enough oxygen so that the partial pressure of oxygen is 104 mmHg, just as it is in the alveoli. At the same time, the pressure of carbon dioxide in the blood quickly drops to 40 mmHg. (C)

The blood, now bright red in color, leaves the lungs and heads back to the left heart through the pulmonary veins, beginning the transport portion of respiration. As it does so, a small amount of deoxygenated blood mixes with it. Where does the deoxygenated blood come from? Well, the walls of the bronchi and bronchioles are made of living tissue and must get oxygen and nutrients. Veins that carry deoxygenated blood away from the bronchi and bronchioles dump into the oxygenated blood leaving the lungs. This reduces the pressure of oxygen to about 95 mmHg. (D) It raises the pressure of carbon dioxide only slightly, because carbon dioxide is more soluble in plasma than is oxygen, and can be carried in a chemically different form. In the end, then, the partial pressure of carbon dioxide is still about 40 mmHg after the blood leaves the lungs.

The red blood leaves the left side of the heart and is pumped through the aorta and to the body tissues. Throughout this transport, the partial pressure of oxygen remains at 95 mmHg, and the partial pressure of carbon dioxide remains at 40 mmHg. (E)

When the blood reaches the capillaries of the tissues, what happens? Well, the cells of the tissues have been *using up* their oxygen. Thus, the partial pressure of oxygen is low, averaging about 40 mmHg. At the same time, the process of using oxygen to convert food into energy (discussed in a later section) produces carbon dioxide. As a result, the partial pressure of carbon dioxide is high—about 45 mmHg. (F) As the blood flows through the thin-walled capillaries, then, oxygen diffuses from the area of high partial pressure (the blood) to an area of low partial pressure (the cells). At the same time, the carbon dioxide diffuses from an area of high partial pressure (the cells) to an area of low partial pressure (the blood). (G) This increases the partial pressure of carbon dioxide in the blood to 45 mmHg, and it lowers the partial pressure of oxygen in the blood to about 40 mmHg. (H) Do you recognize these two numbers from the beginning of this discussion? The blood, which is "blue" and deoxygenated now, is then sent back to the heart and then to the lungs to start the process all over again. Amazingly, all of the blood in

466

just the chemical information that you need. As you probably already know, the basis of organic chemistry is carbon. That's why the number of carbons in an organic molecule is a good way of keeping track of the molecule. So, in the reaction given above, and in all other reactions, we will give you the names of the molecules and then just the carbons and any other important elements in the chemical. The rest will be considered unnecessary information.

What do the words *specific enzymes* mean above the arrow? It just means that this reaction will not take place without the careful control of specific enzymes. So, the proper enzymes must be present for this reaction to occur. We are not going to name them.

Let's look at the box titled Glycolysis Step 1, then. Glucose is a molecule with six carbons. That's why there are six carbons shown below it. Fructose diphosphate also has six carbons, but in addition, it has a phosphate group (abbreviated as Pi) on each end of the carbon chain. That's what the symbol below fructose diphosphate means. Where did those phosphates come from? They came from ATP. Look at the equation. There are two ATPs on the reactants side, and there are two ADPs on the products side. What is the difference between ATP and ADP? The difference is a phosphate! The ATP breaks apart, releasing energy. This energy allows the phosphate that broke off of each ATP to bind to the carbon chain, making fructose diphosphate.

Now that we have fructose diphosphate, what happens? The second step is to break down the fructose diphosphate. Since this chemical has six carbons with a phosphate on each end, into what do you think it will be broken down? It will be broken in half, making two molecules that have three carbons, each with one phosphate on each end. This three-carbon molecule, phosphoglyceraldehyde, fortunately is called PGAL.

GLYCOLYSIS STEP 2

specific
enzymes

fructose diphosphate → 2PGAL

Pi-C-C-C-C-C-C-Pi   2 C-C-C-Pi

The third step is probably the most important step in glycolysis, at least from an energy point of view. The PGAL that is formed in the reaction above reacts with phosphate and a molecule abbreviated NAD^+ (nicotinamide adenenine dinucleotide). NAD^+ is formed in part by niacin and vitamin B_3. Other B vitamins are also involved in cellular energy production, which may be why your mom reminds you to take your vitamins if you sleep too late in the morning! NAD^+ is often called a *hydrogen accepter* because it is designed to pick up hydrogen atoms from other molecules.

GLYCOLYSIS STEP 3

specific
enzymes

2 PGAL + 2Pi + 2NAD⁺ → 2 D-PGA + 2 NADH
2-C-C-C-Pi   2Pi-C-C-C-Pi

Notice what happened here. Each PGAL has three carbons and one phosphate. By reacting with phosphate, it can add another phosphate on the other end of the chain so that we have a three-carbon molecule with phosphates on each end. That's D-PGA (diphosphoglyseric acid). That's the main reaction. Notice that NAD^+ turned into NADH. That means it picked up a hydrogen. Where did the hydrogen come from? It came from the PGAL. Think about it. If we want to stick a phosphate onto the PGAL, we need to take something off. What do we take off? We take off a hydrogen. Where does that hydrogen go? It goes to a hydrogen accepter. We say that the NAD^+ is reduced to NADH.

Now, we're almost done with glycolysis. In the fourth and final step, the two D-PGA molecules give up their phosphates to make pyruvate, which is a simple three-carbon molecule.

GLYCOLYSIS STEP 4

specific
enzymes

2 D-PGA + 4 ADP → 2 pyruvate + 4 ATP
2Pi-C-C-C-Pi 2-C-C-C

Once again, look what happened here. The two D-PGA each have two phosphates, for a total of four phosphates. Those molecules give up all four of their phosphates to four ADP molecules. What does ADP plus a phosphate make? It makes ATP, which is the energy molecule for cells. When the D-PGAs lose their phosphates, they become the simple, three-carbon molecule pyruvate.

That's the end of glycolysis. Let's look at the big picture now. What happened? Well, we started off with a six-carbon glucose molecule. In the end, that glucose molecule was broken into two three-carbon pyruvate molecules. It took two ATPs to get all of this going (step 1), but in the final chemical reaction (step 4), we produced four ATPs. Since ATP is the molecule in which cells store energy, this means that glycolysis actually produced some energy for the cell. It took two ATPs to get it started, but it yielded four ATPs, for a net gain of two ATPs. Now don't forget another thing that was made. In step 3, we made two NADH molecules. We will see those in a later stage of cellular respiration.

We want to point out a couple of things about glycolysis before we move on to the next stage of aerobic respiration. First of all, notice that no oxygen is used in any of the chemical reactions. Oxygen is *not* required for glycolysis. Thus, glycolysis is an anaerobic step. In addition, you need to realize that all of this takes place in the cytoplasm of the cell.

STAGE 2 OF CELLULAR RESPIRATION: OXIDATION OF PYRUVATE

After the pyruvate made during glycolysis goes from the cytoplasm into the mitochondrion to start the Krebs cycle, something happens in the mitochondrion to *prepare* the pyruvate for the Krebs cycle. We call that the oxidation of pyruvate stage, or it can also be called the acetyl coenzyme A formation stage. When the two pyruvate molecules enter the mitochondrion, they each give up a hydrogen to NAD^+. This causes the pyruvate molecules to break down, and one of the carbons in each pyruvate gets converted to CO_2. This leaves us now with a pair of two-carbon chains, which are called acetyl groups. The acetyl groups need something with which to bind, however. Carriers called coenzyme A bind to the acetyl group, and the result is called acetyl coenzyme A. Coenzyme A is formed in part from the B vitamin pantothenic acid, again giving us an example of how B vitamins enable us to produce cellular energy.

OXIDATION OF PYRUVATE
(Acetyl Coenzyme A Formation)

specific
enzymes

2 pyruvate + 2 NAD^+ + 2 coenzyme A → 2 acetyl coenzyme A + 2CO_2 + 2 NADH

C-C-C   C-C-enzyme   C

Now keep track of what went on here. The two pyruvates from the original glucose each have three carbons. They each give up a hydrogen to NAD^+. That makes 2 NADH. They also each lose a carbon to make CO_2. That leaves two molecules, each with two carbons, called acetyls. Those two-carbon acetyls bind to two coenzyme A molecules. This makes two acetyl coenzyme A molecules. That's the oxidation of pyruvate, which prepares pyruvate for the citric acid cycle.

Doesn't it seem like there's some waste going on at this stage? After all, we lose a carbon from each pyruvate as CO_2. We don't gain any ATP, as we did with glycolysis. Think of it like this: If you have a fireplace, have you ever had to cut off a small piece of the end of a log so it will fit into the fireplace? In a way, that's occurring at the oxidation of pyruvate stage. But as we will see, just as those pieces of log that you cut off could be used later, energy will be gained later from the hydrogen that bound to NAD^+, producing the two NADH.

This step happens as soon as the pyruvate molecules enter the mitochondrion. Since we are discussing the mitochondrion here, let's show you an illustration of it in figure 14.9 and point out some of its parts.

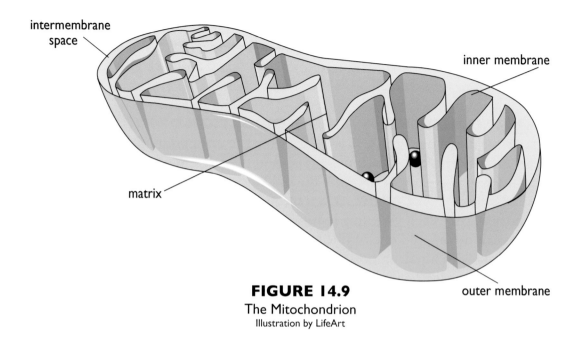

FIGURE 14.9
The Mitochondrion
Illustration by LifeArt

The oxidation of pyruvate (coenzyme A formation) occurs as the pyruvate molecules cross into the matrix of the mitochondrion.

STAGE 3 OF CELLULAR RESPIRATION: CITRIC ACID (KREBS) CYCLE

What happens next? Coenzyme A escorts the two-carbon molecules around the matrix of the mitochondrion to start the citric acid cycle. In the citric acid cycle, the two carbons of each acetyl group are converted to carbon dioxide. This happens in several steps, but we can simplify them into two basic steps. First, the coenzyme A molecules drop the two-carbon acetyls off. There, they join with a four-carbon molecule called oxaloacetic (ox al' oh uh see tik) acid. Since two carbons are being joined to four carbons, the resulting molecule, citric acid, contains six carbons.

CITRIC ACID CYCLE STEP I

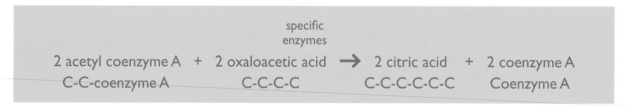

Notice that coenzyme A doesn't truly participate in the reaction. It is a carrier that "drops off" the two-carbon acetyl group so that it can bind to the four-carbon chain to make citric acid. The coenzyme A can then repeat the process with more acetyl groups.

You may have learned this as the *Krebs cycle*, after Sir Hans Krebs, the Nobel prize winner who did much of the intricate biochemical work on yeast to discover this process. Because citric acid is made in the first step it is also called the citric acid cycle. What happens in this cycle? Well, NAD^+ accepts hydrogen atoms from the citric acid. In addition, another "hydrogen-accepter," FAD (flavin adenine dinucleotide), also accepts hydrogen atoms from the molecules. In the end, each citric acid loses five hydrogen atoms and two carbon atoms. The hydrogen atoms are added to the NAD^+ and the FAD, and the carbon atoms are converted into carbon dioxide.

FAD is yet another molecule composed of a B vitamin. In this case, vitamin B_2, riboflavin, is the vitamin. You may have heard that the B vitamins work together to liberate energy. As you can see, they definitely do. And, various B vitamins are often found together in our foods. Why? Both plants and animals use cellular respiration to liberate energy, and their mitochondria must contain these B vitamins to do so.

CITRIC ACID CYCLE STEP 2

specific
enzymes

$$2 \text{ citric acid} + 2ADP + Pi + 2 FAD + 6 NAD^+ \longrightarrow 6 NADH + 2 FADH_2 + 2 ATP + 4CO_2 + 2 \text{ oxaloacetic acid}$$

C-C-C-C-C-C   C-C-C-C-C-C

Look at what happens in step 2. The two six-carbon chains each lose three hydrogen atoms to NAD^+. This makes a total of six NADH molecules. In addition, they each lose two hydrogen atoms to FAD, making two $FADH_2$ molecules. They also each lose two carbons to make carbon dioxide. Two ATP are produced per original glucose (from the two acetyls per glucose that enter the citric acid cycle). A total of four carbon dioxide molecules are produced. When these molecules each lose two carbons, how many carbons are left? Four. What four-carbon chain molecule have we just mentioned to start the citric acid cycle? Oxaloacetic acid is a four-carbon chain. Thus, the end of the citric acid cycle makes the oxaloacetic acid that is used to start the citric acid cycle again! So, the cells do not *use up* oxaloacetic acid, they just need some on hand to start the citric acid cycle. Since it is made again at the end, the cells never really run out of it. That's why it's called a cycle!

STAGE 4 OF CELLULAR RESPIRATION: ELECTRON TRANSPORT CHAIN

We now reach the fourth and final stage of aerobic respiration, the electron transport chain. This is actually the stage that produces the most energy by far. At this point, we no longer have any carbons left over from the original glucose. The glucose molecule had six carbons. In the oxidation of pyruvate, two carbons were converted to carbon dioxide. In the citric acid cycle, the other four carbons were each converted to carbon dioxide; so, all the carbon of glucose becomes CO_2. What happens then to the glucose you eat? You exhale it! (At least the carbons and oxygens of that glucose!)

What's left, then? Hydrogen atoms are left. Remember, part of what's been going on since the beginning is that NAD^+ and FAD have been accepting hydrogen atoms to make energy-rich NADH and $FADH_2$ which are both now "energy-rich", because of the hydrogens they have accepted. How many of these hydrogen atoms do we have? We actually have twelve.

How do we have 12 hydrogen atoms? In glycolysis, two NADH molecules were made from NAD^+. That's two hydrogen atoms. In the oxidation of pyruvate, two more NADH were made, giving us a total of four hydrogen atoms. Finally, in the citric acid cycle, six NADH were made (that's more hydrogen atoms), and two FADH$_2$ molecules were made (that's two more hydrogen atoms). In the end, then, we have a total of 12 hydrogen atoms, per original glucose.

Those hydrogen atoms are carried by the NAD$^+$ and FAD molecules that accepted them to the edge of the matrix, that is, the inner membrane of the mitochondrion. The hydrogen atoms then leave these carriers and split into H$^+$ ions and electrons:

ELECTRON TRANSPORT CHAIN STEP I

$$H \rightarrow H^+ + e^-$$

The electrons then travel through a chain of seven carrier molecules. Each time the electron is passed from one carrier molecule to another, some energy is released.

For what is that energy used? It is used to actively transport the H$^+$ ions across the inner membrane of the mitochondrion. What good does that do? Well, when the H$^+$ ions gather in the intermembrane space of the mitochondrion, they are forced by diffusion to go *back through* the inner membrane and into the matrix. The only way they can do that is to travel through special channels that have ADP and phosphate sitting on the other side. The ADP and phosphate use the energy of the H$^+$ ions traveling back into the matrix to combine, forming ATP.

ELECTRON TRANSPORT CHAIN STEP 2

$$\overset{\text{energy}}{\underset{\text{from } H^+ \text{ diffusion}}{}}$$
$$ADP + Pi \rightarrow ATP$$

This is the real energy-making step of aerobic respiration, and it is called oxidative phosphorylation (fos' for uh lay' shun). Each NADH contains enough energy to produce three ATPs by this process. Each FADH$_2$ has enough energy to make two ATPs by this process.

Now let's think about this for a moment. We have a total of ten NADH molecules. However, allow us to take away the two NADH molecules made during glycolysis. We will get back to them in a moment. Taking those two away, we have a total of eight NADH molecules, each of which makes three ATPs. So, 24 ATPs come from those NADH molecules. In addition, there are two FADH$_2$ molecules, each of which makes two ATPs. This gives us four more ATPs for a total of 28 ATPs. Now let's consider the NADH molecules made in glycolysis. They are made in the cytoplasm because that's where glycolysis happens. To be a part of the electron transport system, however, they must enter the mitochondrion. They lose energy when they do that, so they can only make two ATPs. So, those two NADH molecules make only four ATPs. This gives us a grand total of 32 ATPs. That's how many ATPs get made in the electron transport system.

We are not quite done, however. What happens to the H^+ ions once they get back into the matrix? Also, what happens to the electrons that were handed down from one carrier molecule to another? Well, that's where the *oxygen* comes in. Remember, aerobic respiration requires oxygen. At the end of the chain of carrier molecules, the electrons are passed to oxygen molecules. Those oxygen molecules then combine with the H^+ ions in the matrix to make water. Since there are 12 hydrogen atoms originally, there are enough hydrogen atoms to make six water molecules (H_2O).

We have reached the end of aerobic respiration. However, we need to tidy things up a bit. First, let's see what is used and made throughout this whole process. In glycolysis, glucose is used up. In addition, a net of two ATPs are made (four are actually made, but two were required to get it started, so the net gain is two ATPs). In the oxidation of pyruvate, two molecules of carbon dioxide are made. In the citric acid cycle, four more molecules of carbon dioxide are made, along with two more ATPs. In the electron transport system, oxygen is used up. Six water molecules are made as well as 32 ATPs. What's the overall result? Glucose and oxygen are used up, while six molecules of carbon dioxide, six molecules of water, and 36 ATPs are made. What's that sound like? It sounds like our original equation:

$$C_6H_{12}O_6 + 6O_2 \rightarrow 6CO_2 + 6H_2O + \text{energy in the form of 36 ATP}$$

The four stages of cellular respiration, then, add up to the simple equation above. As you now know, however, the process is *far* from simple. A summary is given in table 14.1.

Stage	Takes Place In	Makes
Glycolysis	Cytoplasm	2 ATP
Oxidation of pyruvate	Matrix of mitochondrion	2 CO_2
Citric acid cycle	Matrix of mitochondrion	2 ATP 4 CO_2
Electron transport chain	Inner membrane of mitochondrion	32 ATP 6 H_2O

TABLE 14.1
The Stages of Cellular Respiration

REVIEW OF CELLULAR RESPIRATION

This is probably one of the more technical things that we have covered in this course. So, we want to review it in a more visual way in figure 14.10.

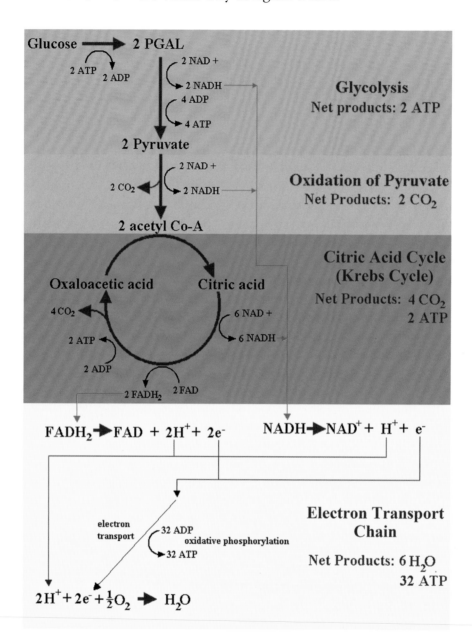

FIGURE 14.10
A Summary of Aerobic Respiration

This is a complex figure, but it is not that hard once you break it down. Look at the top section of the figure. That's the stage of glycolysis. What happens in glycolysis? Glucose is converted to fructose diphosphate and then to PGAL. Notice that this step involves two ATPs turning into ADP. That means two ATPs are used up. What happens

STUDY GUIDE FOR MODULE 14

1. Define the following terms:

   a. Upper respiratory tract
   b. Lower respiratory tract
   c. Ventilation
   d. External respiration
   e. Internal respiration
   f. Pneumothorax
   g. Surfactant

   h. Compliance
   i. Aspirate
   j. Tidal volume
   k. Functional residual capacity
   l. Total lung capacity
   m. Residual volume

2. Identify the structures in the figure below.

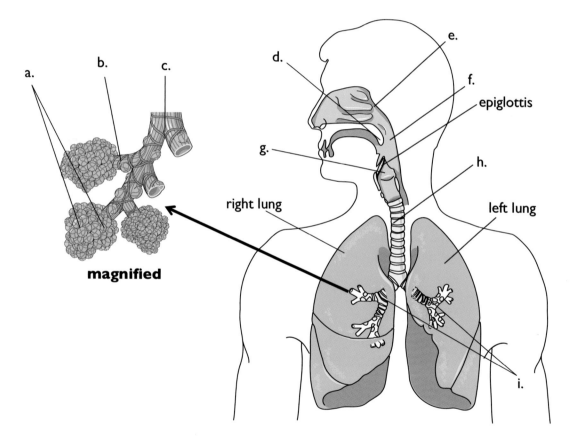

magnified

right lung

left lung

epiglottis

3. As air is exhaled, which structures are encountered first: the vocal folds or the vestibular folds?

4. What is the function of the vocal folds?

5. a. Name the muscles of principal inspiration.
    b. Name the muscles of principal expiration.
    c. Name the muscles of forced inspiration.
    d. Name the muscles of forced expiration.

6. A person inhales forcefully.
    a. Name the muscles that are contracted.
    b. What is the relative size of the thoracic cavity: large or small?
    c. What is the air pressure in the lungs as compared to the atmospheric pressure during this forceful inspiration?

7. What are the two factors that aid the collapse of the lungs during expiration? When one of these factors is missing or reduced, the result is a common disease. What is the name of the disease, and the lack of which factor causes it?

8. What are the two factors that help prevent total lung collapse and aid inspiration? When each of these factors is missing or reduced, two separate maladies result. What are the maladies, and with what factors are they associated?

9. When in a healthy person's life is lung compliance at its lowest?

10. What are the six factors that increase the efficiency of external respiration?

11. What are the six layers of the respiratory membrane? List them in order from the lumen (air sacs) of the alveolus to the lumen (fluid space) of the capillary.

12. What is pneumonia? What does it do to inhibit respiration?

13. The partial pressure of either carbon dioxide or oxygen in the blood is measured at the following places: right before the blood exits the lungs, in the pulmonary vein between the lungs and the heart, and in the inferior vena cava. Indicate which place corresponds to each measurement.
    a. $PCO_2 = 45$ mmHg
    b. $PO_2 = 104$ mmHg
    c. $PO_2 = 95$ mmHg

14. Suppose that, at some instant, the partial pressure of oxygen in blood near the tissues is about 70 mmHg. What can you conclude is happening to the blood? Would the partial pressure of carbon dioxide most likely be 35 mmHg, 43 mmHg, or 49 mmHg?

15. Describe the Hering-Breuer reflex.

16. What parts of the CNS control the muscles of breathing?

17. A student says that the body monitors the partial pressure of oxygen in your blood and then sends messages to the respiratory control centers to increase or decrease the rate and depth of ventilation based on the results of the monitoring. What is wrong with that statement?

18. If the pH of blood is on the increase, what will happen to the rate and depth of ventilation?

19. List the four stages of aerobic respiration as discussed in this module. Note the number of ATPs formed in each step, and note any carbon dioxide or water made as well. What is the total number of ATPs formed from one glucose molecule in aerobic respiration?

20. In the following figure, fill in the letters with the appropriate substances:

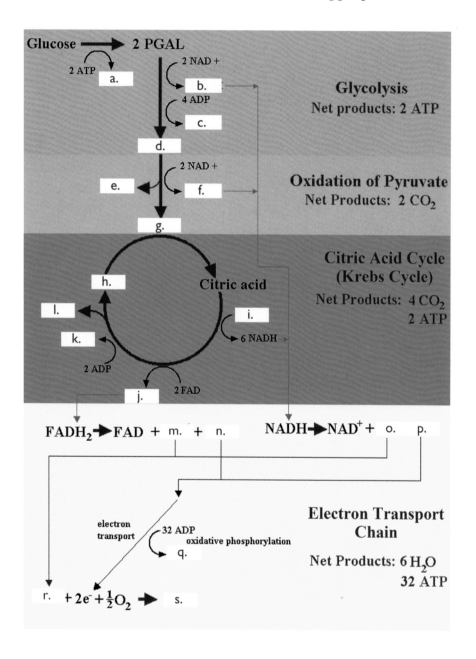

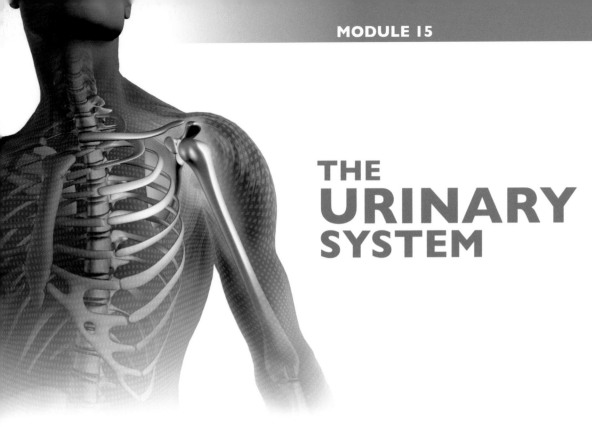

THE URINARY SYSTEM

Y ou have now studied nine of your body's organ systems. You've learned how calcium ions are a part of bone development, synaptic transmission, and blood coagulation. You know that sodium (Na^+) and potassium (K^+) ions are integral to the production of action potentials, but what you haven't learned yet is how your body maintains the proper level of these ions so that these various systems run smoothly. Also, even though you know that there is water in your blood, water in your lymph, water in your interstitial fluid, and water in your mucous membranes, you have not learned how your body maintains the proper amount of water for all of these systems. Finally, you've studied how your body controls blood pH through ventilation, but you have not yet learned the primary means that the body uses for pH control.

heart of the matter

Take a moment to consider a clothes washing machine. What does it do? It cleans something that you want to keep, your clothes, and removes things that you don't want or need, such as dirt and stains. It doesn't get rid of your clothes. In fact, it gives them back to you in a better condition than when you put them into the machine. Your urinary system is similar to the washing machine. It gets rid of the waste materials in your blood and forms urine, yet it also filters and saves those things that your body needs and can use again.

In this module we are going to discuss the urinary system. The urinary system is the main excretory system of the body. It is a continuous filtration system that maintains homeostasis by correcting imbalances in the composition of the blood. It is the primary means by which the body gets rid of toxins, controls the levels of ions in the body, controls the amount of water in the body, controls the pH of the blood, and controls red blood cell production. As an added bonus, the urinary system stores its waste, the urine, in a convenient sac, the urinary bladder, until it can be emptied voluntarily.

ANATOMY OF THE URINARY SYSTEM

The basic anatomy of the urinary system is shown in figure 15.1. The main organs of the urinary system are, of course, the kidneys. There are two of them, but notice that they are not exactly at the same position on the right and left sides of the body. The right kidney is slightly lower than the left because the liver takes up so much room on the right side of the abdomen.

Each kidney has a ureter (yur' eh ter) that takes urine out of the kidney and into the urinary bladder. The bladder holds urine. As urine collects, the urinary bladder can stretch because it is made of smooth muscle, and its mucosa is made of stretchy stratified transitional epithelium, as discussed in module 2. The urinary bladder empties through the urethra (you ree' thruh), which leads outside the body.

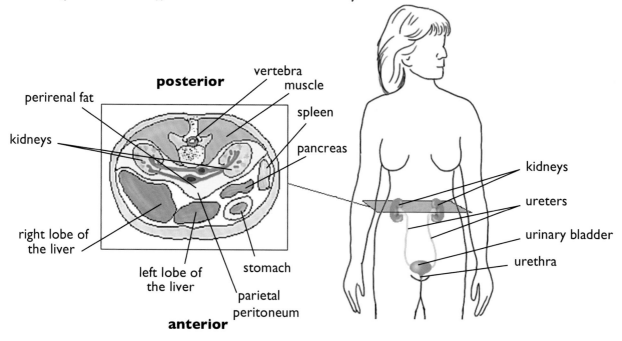

FIGURE 15.1
Anatomy of the Urinary System and Cross Section of the Kidneys
Illustration by Megan Whitaker

We'll focus on the kidneys in a moment. Before we do that, however, we need to show you where the kidneys are located relative to the other organs in the body. On the left side of figure 15.1, we illustrate a cross section of the abdomen as if you were looking down on it. The first thing you should notice is the large organ-filled cavity anterior to the kidneys. That is the peritoneal (puh rit' uh nee uhl) cavity. Its outer membranous boundary, the parietal (puh rye' ih tuhl) peritoneum (pehr' ih tuh nee' uhm), lies over the kidneys. It is composed of a serous membrane (see module 2) that secretes a small amount of fluid into the cavity. Most of the abdominal organs (liver, spleen, pancreas, and stomach, for example) are housed in the peritoneal cavity. Notice, however, that the kidneys lie behind it. As a result, they are called retroperitoneal (reh' troh pehr ih tuh nee' uhl) organs.

Retroperitoneal—Behind the parietal peritoneum

The organs that are housed within the peritoneal cavity are each closely encased in another smooth, slippery serous membrane called the visceral peritoneum. These two serous membranes (the parietal and visceral peritoneum) lubricate the organs so that they experience very little friction as they move against the body wall and each other, as, for example, when you bend or stretch.

Unlike most of the abdominal organs that are housed within the peritoneal membranes, the kidneys do not move much when the body moves. Instead, they are held firmly in place by a layer of adipose tissue (see module 2) called perirenal (pehr uh ree' nul) fat. Even thin people have perirenal fat. However, if a person gets *really* emaciated, he or she can lose perirenal fat, and the kidneys can slip as a result. While it is natural for many organs to move as your body moves, it can be devastating if it happens to the kidneys because the dropping kidney's ureter might get pinched, blocking off the flow of urine into the bladder.

**COLORING BOOK
EXERCISE 15.1**

To review the anatomy of the urinary system, follow the instructions on page 287 of the coloring book.

That's the basic anatomy of the urinary system. However, we want to concentrate on the anatomy of the kidneys themselves because that's where most of the urinary system's work is done.

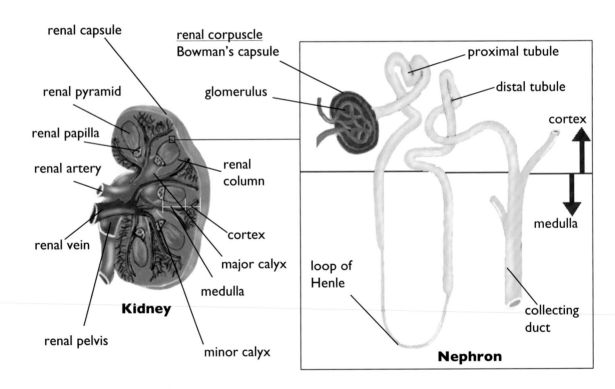

FIGURE 15.2
The Anatomy of a Kidney and a Nephron
Illustration by Megan Whitaker

Your kidneys are bean-shaped and are roughly the size of a clenched fist. They are each surrounded by a renal capsule, which is composed of fibrous connective tissue. The interior is split into two regions: the outer region, called the cortex, and the inner region, called the medulla. The medulla is composed of roughly cone-shaped structures called renal pyramids. The bases of these pyramids form the boundary between the medulla and the cortex. The tips of the pyramids are called renal papillae, and they point toward funnel-shaped structures called minor calyces (kal' ih seez). Urine formed in the renal pyramids enters into these minor calyces (singular is calyx, pronounced kay' liks). The minor calyces converge to form major calyces, and the major calyces converge to form the renal pelvis. The renal pelvis then narrows to form the ureter, which ultimately removes the urine from the kidneys. The renal pyramids are separated from each other by renal columns, which are essentially extensions of material found in the cortex that project into the medulla.

The functional unit of the kidney is the nephron (nef' ron), a microscopic filter bed that includes a precisely folded tubule. One nephron is illustrated on the right side of figure 15.2. Before we discuss the nephron itself, we want you to understand where nephrons are in the kidney. As shown in the figure, nephrons extend into both the medulla and the cortex. The blood enters the nephron at the renal corpuscle, which is in the cortex of the kidney. The tubular part of the nephron then extends into the medulla, leaves the medulla, and goes back into the cortex. There, it dumps into a collecting duct, which enters the medulla once more and leads to one of the minor calyces.

The renal corpuscle is the beginning of the nephron. It is a filter bed consisting of a capsule, called the Bowman's capsule, and a network of capillaries called the glomerulus (gloh mair' you lus). A proximal (meaning near) tubule runs from the renal corpuscle to a long tube called the loop of Henle (hen' lee). The loop of Henle dips into the medulla and then comes back into the cortex. In the cortex, the loop of Henle meets up with the distal (meaning far) tubule, which leads to the collecting duct. It turns out that only about 10% of the nephrons actually have a loop of Henle. This means 90% do not have one. Nevertheless, we are going to focus on the nephrons which do have a loop of Henle, because the loops of Henle enable nephrons that have them to concentrate the urine as necessary.

There are about *1.3 million* nephrons in each kidney. At the bare minimum, at least one-third of them must be functional. If fewer than one-third are functional, you simply cannot survive without medical intervention. This should tell you something about the kidneys. They are obviously super efficient! This is why you can donate a kidney. Even if one of your kidneys is removed, you still have roughly half of your nephrons. That's plenty to do the job.

To re-emphasize an important point, the nephron is the functional unit of the kidney. In the next section, we will explain the ins and outs of how the nephrons work. However, we just want to end this section by giving you the big picture, which is an overview of the urinary system's functions. We all know that the kidneys filter the blood to form urine. That's the first function of the urinary system: urine formation. However, have you ever thought about *why* the kidneys form urine? Urine is formed to remove waste from the blood. Now remember, waste can be either substances that should not be in the blood, like the urea produced in the liver, or it can be extra amounts of substances that should be in the blood. For example, most people in the Western world ingest far more sodium ions than they need. Sodium ion is a necessary ion in the blood, but too much of it would disrupt the homeostasis of many body processes. So, the kidneys remove the excess sodium ions, and the ions go into the urine. Water is another substance regulated by the kidneys. We certainly need to have water, but excess water must be removed. So, the kidneys remove excess water from the blood and put it in the urine, as well.

The next function of the kidneys is to control the pH of the blood. The kidneys can adjust the amount of H^+ ions in the blood, which determines the pH. The more H^+ in the blood, the lower the pH. The more H^+ the kidneys secrete into the urine, the lower the pH of the urine, but the *higher* the pH of the blood. The kidneys are very sensitive to pH changes, and they can adjust the pH of the blood, whether it is too low or too high. The third function of the urinary system is to regulate the blood pressure. We'll see that this third function is done via a group of cells called the juxtaglomerular (jux tuh gloh mair' you lur) apparatus.

The fourth function of the urinary system is to stimulate erythropoiesis (eh rith' roh poy ee' sis).

Erythropoiesis—The production of red blood cells (erythrocytes)

Cells in the kidneys detect low oxygen, and in response, they produce erythropoietin (eh rith' roh poy ee' tin), a hormone, which travels via the blood to the bone marrow, where it signals the red bone marrow to increase red blood cell production.

The fifth function of the urinary system is the activation of vitamin D. Vitamin D is produced with the interaction of sunlight on the skin. However, vitamin D gets activated to perform its hormonal functions by kidney cells. The sixth function is the transport of urine. That's done by the ureters. Finally, the seventh function of the urinary system is the storage and release of urine. That's done by the urinary bladder, which like the rectum, is really optional equipment. (Consider how easily babies exist without the conscious control of either!) Nevertheless, the Designer of the body gave you a urinary bladder so that you can store up urine and release it when it is convenient.

COLORING BOOK EXERCISE 15.2

To review the structures of the kidney and nephron, follow the instructions on pages 289 and 293 of the coloring book.

ON YOUR OWN

15.1 Starting at the collecting duct of a nephron, list the structures that urine encounters as it is transported out of the body.

15.2 Most of the abdominal organs are surrounded by a serous membrane. The kidneys are not. Why not?

URINE FORMATION: THE OVERALL SCHEME

One of the best analogies for kidney function is called the desk-drawer analogy. Suppose you need to clean out a desk drawer. There are basically two ways you could do it. You could open the desk drawer and start picking out the stuff you need to get rid of, like the cracker crumbs, the outdated stationery, the broken pencils, and so forth. When you are done picking out the junk, everything left in the drawer is good, and the drawer is clean. Alternatively, you could dump *everything*, the junk and the good stuff, onto a newspaper and then put the good stuff back in the drawer. Which way would be more efficient? Obviously, the second way. That's how the kidneys clean the blood. Plasma, minus its proteins, is "dumped" into the nephron, the good and bad alike.

Then, the "good stuff" is pulled back into the blood vessel. The rest becomes urine. This desk-drawer approach to cleaning the blood takes place in four basic steps, schematically illustrated in figure 15.3.

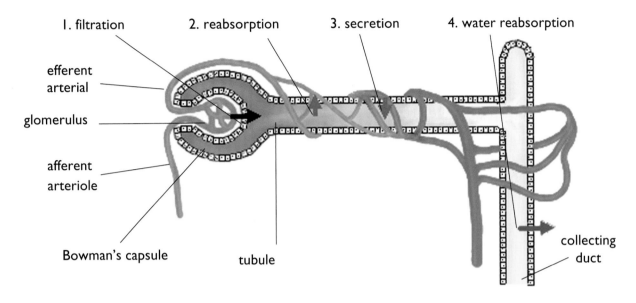

FIGURE 15.3
A Schematic Illustration of Nephron Function
Illustration by Megan Whitaker

The first step, filtration, occurs within the renal corpuscle. Fluid leaves the blood capillaries, called the glomerulus, and passes through a filtration membrane to enter the lumen of the Bowman's capsule. The filtration membrane is porous, but it keeps blood cells and proteins in the blood vessels. So, only the blood fluid and its nonprotein contents enter the nephron. This fluid is called filtrate, and it is like blood plasma, but without the proteins.

Filtrate—Blood plasma minus the proteins, filtered by the nephrons of the kidneys

The filtration doesn't really remove anything bad. It just keeps the blood cells and proteins in the blood vessel. Both the good and the bad chemicals in the filtrate flow through the filtration membrane and into the proximal tubule of the nephron. Although the filtrate is now in the functional unit of the kidney, it is *not* yet urine. In fact, upon entry into the proximal tubule, the fluid is essentially the same as the interstitial fluid that surround cells throughout the body. The next three steps turn this fluid into urine.

The second step is reabsorption, which means moving molecules out of the nephrons and back into the blood. As blood passes through the many blood capillaries that run *along* the nephron, the useful molecules that the blood needs are reabsorbed across the wall of the nephron. This reabsorption is controlled by a series of complex transport processes that ensure that useful molecules are reabsorbed and that they are reabsorbed to their proper levels. For example, even though sodium ion is a necessary component in blood plasma, if there is too much sodium ion in the nephron, it will not all get

MOD 15

think about this

reabsorbed into the blood. Instead, the reabsorption will occur only until the sodium ion levels in the blood plasma have reached their proper level.

In the desk-drawer analogy, then, we start by dumping out the desk drawer. Now all of the contents are on the newspaper. That's the filtration step in the kidneys. Put everything, the good and the bad, into the nephron (the newspaper), and then let the nephron sort it out. As you start taking useful items from the newspaper and putting them back into the desk drawer, you are mimicking the reabsorption step. You are "transporting" back into the drawer (the blood) the things you want to keep, and you are leaving the things that you want to throw away on the newspaper (the nephron).

The third step is secretion. In this step, certain chemicals still in the blood must be removed from the blood and put into the nephron for excretion in the urine. We don't want those chemicals in the plasma, so they must be secreted into the nephron. In our desk-drawer analogy, let's suppose you see a magnet stuck in the desk drawer. You notice that the magnet has all sorts of paper clips stuck to it. You have more paper clips than you need, so you remove some of the paper clips from the magnet and put them onto the newspaper. That's secretion. Some extra things are still in the drawer, so you must remove them. In the same way, harmful or excess molecules get secreted into the nephron in step 3. Compared to the amount of reabsorption that takes place in the kidneys, the amount of secretion that goes on is quite minimal. Nevertheless, secretion is vitally important. For example, the kidneys can adjust the blood pH by secreting H^+ ions if the blood is too acid.

ON YOUR OWN

15.3 A man is cleaning out a desk drawer by dumping its contents onto a newspaper and then putting the things he wants to keep back into the drawer. Consider the actions listed below. Which of the four steps in kidney function is analogous to each action?

a. The man dumps the desk drawer, but the built-in dividers that are part of the drawer don't fall out with the rest of the material.

b. The man finds some paper clips that got stuck in the drawer. He decides he just has too many paper clips. Therefore, he starts picking a few of them out of the drawer and putting them onto the newspaper.

The fourth step is water reabsorption. In principle, we could really group this as a part of step 2, reabsorption, and many books do. However, we like to consider it as a separate step, because it is so complex. The processes that occur in the nephron regulate the water volume in the body. The water enters the nephron, and then the blood reabsorbs exactly the amount of water it needs and leaves the rest. The remaining water is the principal component of urine.

We will look at each of these steps more closely, but first we want to make a point about how much blood the kidneys process. As you learned in module 11, the average adult has about 5 liters of blood, and that entire volume passes through the heart every minute. The blood flow to the kidneys is about 20% of that. So, about 1 liter of blood flows through the kidneys every minute. This called the renal blood flow rate.

Renal blood flow rate—The rate at which blood flows through the kidneys (1 liter/min)

So, the nephrons in the kidneys are performing this four-step process on about 1 liter of blood each minute. That's about 1,400 liters of blood *every day*!

URINE FORMATION, STEP 1: GLOMERULAR FILTRATION

The first step of urine formation is filtration of the blood. It occurs in the glomerulus, within the renal corpuscle, so it is called glomerular (gloh mair' er you lur) filtration. Figure 15.4 is a detailed illustration of a renal corpuscle, which is composed of the glomerulus and the Bowman's capsule.

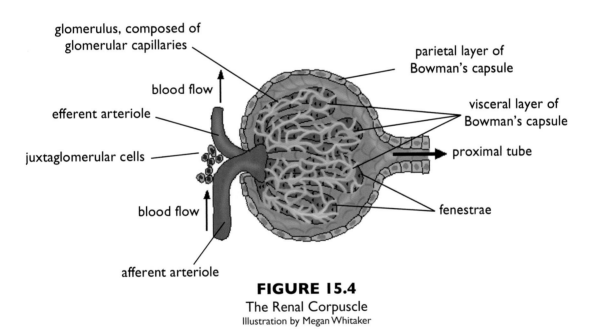

FIGURE 15.4
The Renal Corpuscle
Illustration by Megan Whitaker

First, notice that there are pores in the glomerular capillaries. These pores are called fenestrae (fen' es tray), and they make these capillaries more porous than most other capillaries within the body. Second, notice that there are two layers to the Bowman's capsule. The outer layer, the parietal layer, is a solid layer composed of simple squamous epithelium. The inner layer, called the visceral layer, is porous. It is composed of podocytes (poh' doh sights), which are specialized cells that actually attach to the glomerular capillaries by means of small processes called *foot processes*.

Since the glomerular capillaries are very porous, a huge amount of filtrate (about 20% of the total plasma that passes through the capillaries, leaves the capillaries and enters the Bowman's capsule *each minute*. To leave the capillaries, the filtrate must pass through the filtration membrane. The filtration membrane is composed of the porous wall of the glomerular capillaries, the basement membrane of the glomerular capillaries, and the podocytes. However, since the capillaries are so porous, they need to be held together. The podocytes perform that function. So, the podocytes act like netting. The netting is too "open" to serve as a true filter, but it holds things together so that the filtration membrane can work.

The filtration membrane keeps the proteins from leaving the capillaries because the proteins are too big to pass through the fenestrae. The truth is that a few proteins do slip through, but they're soon taken back into the blood by pinocytosis. As a result, we generally say that what flows into the Bowman's capsule, the filtrate, is blood plasma minus the plasma proteins.

The filtrate leaves the Bowman's capsule and enters the proximal tubule. The rate that this happens is truly amazing. The kidneys produce about 125 mL of filtrate every minute. This is called the glomerular filtration rate (GFR).

Glomerular filtration rate—The rate at which filtrate is produced in glomerular filtration (125 mL/minute)

If you do the math, you will see that this glomerular filtration rate means the kidneys filter about 180 liters of filtrate *every day*. Another way to look at this number is that *all* of your blood plasma is filtered *every 25 minutes,* on average. Think about how supereffiecient your kidneys must be to get all of that done!

How can the kidneys filter so much fluid so fast? Well, the first reason is that the filtration membrane is highly permeable. This allows the filtrate to leave the glomerular capillaries quickly. Second, there is relatively high blood pressure within the capillaries. It turns out that the blood pressure in the glomerular capillaries is higher than that of ordinary capillaries. While the pressure in ordinary capillaries is about 25 mmHg, the pressure within glomerular capillaries is about 50 mmHg. This extra pressure helps push the plasma through the filtration membrane. Since the pressure is higher than that of an ordinary capillary, filtrate flows out of glomerular capillaries more quickly than interstitial fluid flows out of ordinary capillaries.

Why is the pressure in glomerular capillaries high? It's the result of an anatomical feature of the arterioles that enter and leave the glomerulus. Look again at figure 15.4. Notice that there is an arteriole that brings blood into the Bowman's capsule. It is called the afferent arteriole. Notice also that there is an arteriole, called the efferent arteriole, which brings blood out of the glomerulus. This blood has a lot less plasma in it, since much of the plasma became filtrate while in the glomerulus. This plasma-poor blood is then sent in capillary networks down the length of the nephron, so that it can reabsorb the molecules sent to it by the nephron. Now, look at size of the afferent arteriole as compared to the efferent arteriole. The efferent arteriole is *narrower* than the afferent arteriole. What does this do? This causes a backup of blood, *increasing* the pressure of the blood behind it. So, the blood in the glomerulus is at a higher pressure than blood in other parts of the body because the efferent arteriole is smaller than the afferent arteriole.

This increased glomerular capillary pressure (GCP) allows the glomerular filtration rate (GFR) to be high, because pressure is continually pushing filtrate out of the glomerular capillaries. Now, of course, if the GCP goes down, the GFR will go down, as well. In the same way, if the GCP increases, the GFR will also increase. Thus, the rate of plasma filtration in the kidneys is influenced by changes in the glomerular capillary pressure.

Now, since blood is ultimately being pushed through the glomerular capillaries by the heart, the overall blood pressure in the body affects GCP. For example, if a person gets cut severely and bleeds profusely, that person's blood pressure will go down. That will also decrease the GCP, which will, in turn, decrease the GFR. If, on the other hand, a person drinks a lot of fluid, the volume of his or her blood will increase. This will increase blood pressure, which will, in turn, increase the GCP and the GFR. There are other factors that affect blood pressure, and each of these factors will affect the GCP, which will ultimately affect the GFR.

Why do we need to worry about GCP? We need to worry about it because, if the GCP decreases too much, the GFR will drop to zero. This results in renal shutdown, that is, no urine will be produced. How can this happen? There are two factors that oppose the GCP. First of all, the Bowman's capsule pushes back against the glomerulus. This results in capsular pressure, which fights against the GCP.

To understand capsular pressure, think of a leaking hose. To fix the leak, you could wrap it in duct tape. Would that fix the leak? Well, it would fix it a little, but water would still probably leak out. It just wouldn't leak out as fast. Why won't it leak out as fast? The duct tape exerts pressure against the flow of the water. This reduces the amount of water that can come out of the leak. The parietal layer of the Bowman's capsule acts like that duct tape. It exerts pressure against the filtrate flowing out of the glomerular capillaries. How much pressure does it exert? It exerts about 10 mmHg *against* the GCP.

The other factor that fights GCP is osmosis. Remember, the filtrate leaves the glomerular capillaries, but the proteins do not. So, the concentration of proteins becomes much higher inside the glomerular capillaries than outside. If the proteins could diffuse through the filtration membrane, this situation would be rectified right away. However, they cannot because they are too big. So, *osmosis* takes over. The water in the filtrate is attracted back to the higher concentration of proteins. As a result, it crosses the filtration membrane and goes *back into* the capillaries. This, of course, opposes the GCP, which is pushing the water *out* of the capillaries. The pressure caused by this osmosis is called colloid osmotic pressure, and it measures about 30 mmHg.

There are two factors, then, that oppose the GCP. Capsular pressure exerts 10 mmHg of pressure against the plasma being pushed out of the glomerular capillaries, and colloid osmotic pressure exerts another 30 mmHg. That's a total of 40 mmHg. However, as we stated above, the GCP is about 50 mmHg. So, the GCP is higher than the two factors that work against it, and the result is that plasma *can* leak into the Bowman's capsule to travel through the nephron.

However, suppose someone has a bout of dangerously low blood pressure. What will happen? The GCP will go down as well. If GCP goes down by only 10 mmHg to 40 mmHg, what happens? The GCP and the factors that work against it will be equal. As a result, no plasma leaks through the glomerular capillaries, and *filtration by the kidneys stops*! So, the GCP and the factors that affect it are very important. If GCP drops by only 10 mmHg (which is only 20% of the total), the kidneys cannot clean the blood. If this were to continue over a period of two to three days, the result would be death. However, such a drop only occurs under severe situations such as major hemorrhage or dehydration. In the short term (a few hours), this can actually be beneficial, because loss of urine can make the hemorrhage or dehydration worse.

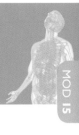

ON YOUR OWN

15.4 If the capillaries in the glomerulus were the same as ordinary capillaries, would the GFR be higher or lower?

MOD 15

URINE FORMATION, STEP 2: REABSORPTION

Once the filtrate enters the proximal tubule, the next step of urine formation, reabsorption, occurs. Remember, both the useful molecules and the excess or waste molecules are in the filtrate. The blood, therefore, must reabsorb the useful molecules and leave the excess or waste molecules in the filtrate, to be disposed of as part of the urine. This is a major process. How does it happen? In figure 15.3, you see that the efferent arteriole leaves the glomerulus and then forms capillaries that wrap around the tubules of the nephron. These capillaries are called peritubular (per ih tube' you lur) capillaries, and there is a great network of peritubular capillaries surrounding the tubules of the nephron. As the filtrate passes through the tubules of the nephron, substances that the blood needs pass across the wall of the tubule and back into the capillaries. That is why the process is called reabsorption. Molecules that have been filtered are absorbed back.

To make reabsorption efficient, the walls of the nephron tubules are thin. In the proximal tubule, the wall is composed of simple cuboidal epithelium. The epithelium must be cuboidal, not squamous, because there must be room for cellular machinery in the epithelium to facilitate the reabsorption. As is the case with the small intestine, the walls of the nephron tubules also have a lot of surface area in order to increase the rate of reabsorption. To accomplish this, the cells have a "brush border" on the inside wall of the tubule. These little extensions (the "bristles" of the "brush") increase the surface area of the cells significantly, which increases the rate of reabsorption.

Most of the reabsorption occurs immediately, in the proximal tubule. For example, about 65% of the water needed by the blood is reabsorbed in the proximal tubule, as is virtually 100% of the glucose that the blood needs. In addition to the proximal tubule, some nephrons have a loop of Henle, which is composed of simple squamous epithelium. All nephrons have a distal tubule, which is composed of simple cuboidal epithelium. Once the filtrate passes through those tubules, it enters the collecting duct, which is made of simple columnar epithelial tissue. When it reaches the end of the collecting duct, the final product, which has been altered along the way, is called urine.

Absorption in the tubules of the nephron occurs in two ways, active reabsorption and passive reabsorption. Active reabsorption requires ATP and a carrier. Passive reabsorption, on the other hand, occurs without any cellular energy being expended. It does not require ATP. We will begin with active reabsorption.

What kinds of substances must be actively reabsorbed? Basically, all of the nutrients and minerals that your body needs are actively reabsorbed. Thus, glucose, amino acids, water-soluble vitamins (vitamin C and B vitamins), and minerals (sodium ion, potassium ion, calcium ion, etc.) are all actively reabsorbed. These must have a carrier that takes them across the nephron epithelium, and the epithelial cells must expend energy to make that happen.

Although almost all of the active reabsorption that goes on in the nephron requires the presence of a carrier, there is one type of substance that does not. As we mentioned before, a few proteins do leak through the filtration barrier. Those must be reabsorbed. However, they are too big for carrier molecules. Instead, the cells take them in through pinocytosis, which we discussed in module 1. For those substances that are actively reabsorbed via a carrier, there is an interesting and medically important effect called tubular maximum (T-max).

Tubular maximum—The maximum rate of reabsorption by active transport through the nephron tubules

The tubular maximum of a substance limits how much of it can be reabsorbed in the nephron. Why would these substances have a tubular maximum? Think about it. Glucose is actively reabsorbed via a carrier. Normally, there is no glucose in urine because all of the glucose in the nephron gets reabsorbed back into the blood. However, if the blood glucose level gets too high, glucose will appear in the urine. Why? At some point, every carrier is being used to transport a glucose molecule. As a result, any glucose molecules left cannot get across because there are no more carriers available. So, the glucose is left behind in the urine. This, by the way, is a key sign of untreated diabetes.

Sodium ion, on the other hand, is usually found in urine. Why? You get so much sodium ion in your diet that it usually exceeds its T-max in the nephron. As a result, the nephron reabsorbs as much sodium ion as the body needs, but some sodium ion usually remains in the urine, as well. Unlike the situation with glucose, sodium ion in the urine is normal.

If you think about it, this is the way the kidney can control whether or not substances get reabsorbed into the blood, and at what level the reabsorption happens. After all, if a molecule requires active transport, but there is no carrier for it, the molecule will not be reabsorbed. It will leave the body in the urine. In other words, if a substance must be actively transported but cannot find a carrier, it is automatically a waste product because it will not get back into the blood. Also, the T-max of a substance limits how much of that substance can get back into the blood. So, if the T-max of a substance is low, the kidney is designed to limit the amount of that substance in the blood. If the T-max of a substance is high, the kidney is designed to allow for a high concentration of that substance in the blood. Amazing, isn't it?

The other kind of reabsorption in the nephron is passive reabsorption, which does not require ATP. Essentially, there is no absolute limit to what can be reabsorbed this way. Water is reabsorbed this way. Why? Well, water needs no carrier because it is a tiny molecule. Also, there is osmotic pressure attracting the water back into the peritubular capillaries. Remember, there are many proteins in the blood that could not get into the nephron. There are also many nutrient molecules that were actively reabsorbed into the peritubular capillaries, as well. As a result, osmosis caused by these molecules draws the water into the capillaries.

Now, there is an interesting problem associated with passive reabsorption. Consider what happens to the other molecules in the filtrate when water is passively reabsorbed. If the molecules are waste products, they begin to get more concentrated in the filtrate as the water leaves the nephron. Since they are waste products, they are not actively reabsorbed by the blood; therefore, there is a low concentration of them in the blood. Therefore, the concentration becomes high in the nephron and low in the blood. Let's further suppose that the molecule is small enough to *diffuse* through the wall of the nephron and into the peritubular capillary. What will happen? The waste products will move *into* the blood, even though the body does not need them!

Urea is a prime example of this. It is a waste product, which is filtered by the glomerulus. At the same time, however, it is a relatively small molecule. Thus, it can diffuse back into the peritubular capillaries. As water is passively reabsorbed, then, urea will flow back into the blood, as well, because diffusion will demand that it travel from an area of high concentration (the nephron) to an area of low concentration (the peritubular capillary). This means that a certain amount of urea will always be found in the blood, even though most urea does end up in the urine.

ON YOUR OWN

15.5 The reabsorption T-max of substance A is much higher than that of substance B. Assuming that the blood entering the kidneys has essentially equal concentrations of both, which substance will be more concentrated in the urine?

15.6 A waste product that is not a protein gets reabsorbed despite the fact that there is no carrier for it. What can you deduce about the relative size of the molecule?

Chloride ions provide another example of passive reabsorption. Sodium ions are actively reabsorbed because they are needed in the body. However, as those positive sodium ions are actively transported to the peritubular capillaries, a charge imbalance occurs. As a result, negative chloride ions diffuse into the peritubular capillaries, as well, because they are attracted to the net positive charge there. They, in effect, "hitch a ride" back into the blood.

URINE FORMATION, STEP 3: SECRETION

The next step in the formation of urine is secretion. In this step, waste products that did not get filtered are specifically sent into the nephron. In our desk-drawer analogy, this is similar to taking something somehow left in the drawer when you dumped it, and putting it onto the newspaper. For example, you decide that some of the paper clips that you find stuck in your drawer are extra; so you pick out some of the paper clips in the drawer, and add them to the junk pile.

Where does secretion occur? Mostly, it occurs in the distal tubule. What gets secreted? Not a whole lot. The volume of reabsorption is much, much higher than that of secretion. However, there are certain substances that get secreted. Some drugs, when broken down by the liver, can be secreted into the nephron. However, the two major substances are potassium ions (K^+) and hydrogen ions (H^+).

We will discuss this in more depth later on in this module, but secretion of H^+ is a powerful control of pH. Remember, the ability to donate H^+ makes a molecule an acid. Thus, if H^+ is added to water, the solution becomes more acidic. If H^+ is taken away, the solution becomes more basic. Thus, if the pH of blood in the peritubular capillaries starts to get too low, H^+ is secreted into the nephron. That way, the pH of the blood increases. Of course, if the pH of the blood is too high, that means it does not have enough H^+, and H^+ will not be secreted.

ON YOUR OWN

15.7 A person's urine has an unusually low pH. Had the blood in the capillaries near the distal tubule been too acidic or too basic?

URINE FORMATION, STEP 4: REABSORPTION OF WATER

Now, the fourth step of how the kidneys work is really one that we already mentioned: the reabsorption of water. Why do we separate it out when it is really a part of step 2? We do this because the amount of water in the body is a critical variable. Thus, the amount of water reabsorbed in the kidneys must be tightly controlled. If you drink a lot of fluid, for example, your kidneys must get rid of the excess water. On the other hand, if you are short on fluid, your kidneys must conserve water. So, the kidneys must regulate how much water is reabsorbed and how much is released as urine.

How do the kidneys accomplish this regulation? Well, the first thing that you have to realize is that the interstitial fluid deep in the kidneys is different from the interstitial fluid in most of the rest of the body: it is much more concentrated. Typical interstitial fluid has a solute concentration of 300 mOsm/kg. What does this number mean? The unit mOsm/kg is a measure of solute concentration. So, the larger the number, the more concentrated the solution is with solutes. If a fluid has a concentration of more than 300 mOsm/kg, it means that the fluid has more solutes in it than ordinary interstitial fluid. You do not need to know any more detail about this number; just use it as a point of comparison with the other numbers we will give you in this section.

If normal interstitial fluid has a concentration of 300 mOsm/kg, what is the concentration of blood plasma? It is about the same: 300 mOsm/kg. The concentration of solutes in the interstitial fluid of the kidney's cortex is also about 300 mOsm/kg. However, as you travel down into the medulla, you will find the concentration of solutes in the interstitial fluid increasing. By the time you are deep in the medulla, it reaches 1200 mOsm/kg. Why is the concentration of solutes so high in the medulla? There is a high concentration of urea in the interstitial fluid of the medulla. The interstitial fluid in the medulla has roughly four times the concentration of solutes as ordinary interstitial fluid, mainly because of the urea. In a moment, you will see that this is a critical part of the water reabsorption control mechanism.

Now let's talk about the details of how water reabsorption is controlled. For that, we will examine figure 15.5, which shows a nephron with a loop of Henle. Recall that only about 10% of all nephrons contain loops of Henle, but these are the nephrons that concentrate urine through reabsorption of water.

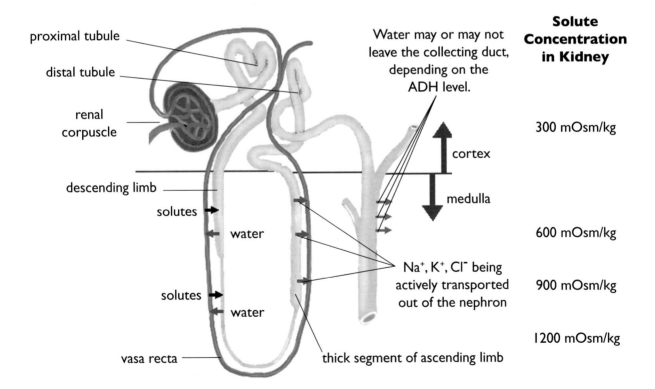

FIGURE 15.5
A Nephron and the Vasa Recta
Illustration by Megan Whitaker

Remember, the renal corpuscle of the nephron is in the cortex, as is the proximal tubule. The loop of Henle goes down deep into the medulla, where the concentration of solutes is 1200 mOsm/kg, and then it rises again to the cortex. The collecting duct then goes all of the way down into the medulla and to a minor calyx. Notice that the concentration of solutes increases steadily from the cortex to the medulla.

With these facts in mind, you can understand how water is reabsorbed. Let's start at the descending limb of the loop of Henle. This part of the loop is permeable to water and solutes. As the filtrate enters the descending limb of the loop, it has a solute concentration about equal to that of interstitial fluid (300 mOsm/kg). As it travels down into the medulla, however, the surrounding interstitial fluid increases in solute concentration. This pulls water *out* of the loop of Henle by osmosis, and it pulls solutes *into* the loop of Henle by diffusion. As the filtrate travels down the loop, then, it becomes more and more concentrated. By the time it reaches the bottom of the loop, it is just about as concentrated as the surrounding medullary interstitial fluid (1200 mOsm/kg).

Now before we go on, you need to understand where the water that had been in the loop of Henle went. It left the nephron and entered the interstitial fluid of the medulla, but it quickly ended up going into the vasa recta, which is the blood vessel shown in the figure. So, the blood has reabsorbed the water that left the nephron. That water, then, is returned to the body, and will not become urine. We're not done yet, however.

The thick segment of the ascending limb of the loop of Henle is *not* permeable to water or any other solutes. Thus, the only way anything can leave the thick segment of the ascending limb is through active transport. As the filtrate travels up the thick ascending portion, only three substances leave the nephron: sodium ions, potassium ions, and chloride ions. These three ions all have carrier molecules in the ascending limb of the loop and can be actively transported out. Where do they go? They go into the interstitial fluid and then diffuse into the vasa recta. In other words, they go back into the blood.

What happens to the concentration of solutes in the filtrate of the thick ascending limb during this stage of the process? It goes down. Think about it. Most often, water follows solutes. That is, if other molecules are transported across a cell membrane, water (a small molecule) will follow by osmosis. It is not unusual to have active transport of ions. However, it is *very unusual* for water to be unable to follow the ions. Nevertheless, that's how it is in the thick ascending limb of the loop of Henle. Water cannot follow the sodium, potassium, and chloride ions. Therefore, as sodium, chloride, and potassium ions are pumped out of the thick segment of the ascending limb, the fluid inside loses solutes. So, the total solute concentration decreases to about 100 mOsm/kg.

If sodium ions, potassium ions, and chloride ions are being pumped out of the filtrate, what is left? One of the main solutes left is urea. Remember, the filtrate had some urea in it before it reached the loop of Henle. Also, as the filtrate traveled down the descending limb of the loop, solutes diffused into the loop. One of the main solutes in the medulla is urea, so urea diffused into the loop, adding to the urea concentration in the filtrate.

This is the real genius behind the design of the kidney. You see, substances like sodium ions, potassium ions, and chloride ions are called electrolytes. As you know, this means that when electrolytes are dissolved in water, the water conducts electricity. Well, the electrolyte balance in your body is crucial. However, electrolytes tend to follow water. If this design feature of the thick ascending limb were not in the nephron, then any time a person drank a lot of fluid, the person would lose electrolytes. After all, if you drink a lot of fluid, you have to get rid of a lot of water. In the ascending limb of the loop of Henle, however, losing water without losing electrolytes is not a problem. The electrolytes get removed from the water and returned back to the blood at this point. The water, however, is retained in the nephron, keeping it out of the blood.

So, what happens next? The filtrate has traveled through the loop of Henle and is now in the distal tubule. Its solute concentration is low (100 mOsm/kg), less than that of interstitial fluid or blood, because electrolytes were actively transported out of the nephron, but the water was not able to follow. What happens next depends on the presence of antidiuretic hormone (ADH) produced in the posterior pituitary and controlled by the hypothalamus of the brain. We discussed this hormone in module 10, where we told you that ADH controls the amount of urine produced. When the blood contains too much water, ADH production is limited, and lots of urine is produced. When the body is low on water, the amount of ADH released increases, and less urine is produced. This hormone, then, enables us to conserve or get rid of water, depending on the body's needs.

How does ADH do this? *ADH makes the distal tubule and collecting duct permeable to water.* The more ADH present, the more permeable to water the distal tubule and collecting duct are. How does this help? Let's consider the case in which there is a shortage of water in the body. Thus, the blood needs to reabsorb as much water as possible from the nephrons. For this to happen, there must be a lot of ADH in the kidney. Why? When the filtrate reaches the distal tubule, its solute concentration is low, about 100 mOsm/kg. As the filtrate travels through the distal tubule and into the collecting duct, it goes deep into the medulla, where the solute concentration is high. Water, then, will move *out* of the distal tubule and collecting duct by osmosis because it is drawn there by the high solute concentration. Once out of the nephron, the water will enter the interstitial fluid and then the vasa recta. That is, water will be reabsorbed into the blood.

An increased level of ADH, then, leads to water leaving the nephron at the distal tubule and collecting duct and reentering the blood. That conserves water, because the water will not be a part of the urine. Instead, it will go back into the blood. Under these conditions, what can you say about the concentration of solutes in the urine? Well, if most of the water left the nephron and went back into the blood, there is not a lot of water in the urine. However, there are still plenty of waste solutes, because ADH does not affect the permeability of the nephron to solutes. Thus, the urine will be concentrated.

Now let's look at the other side of the coin. Let's suppose that the body has way too much water. That's a pretty common situation—just drink a couple of big glasses of water. Then what happens? In this circumstance, the hypothalamus and posterior pituitary will *decrease* the amount of ADH produced. This will decrease the permeability of the distal tubule and collecting duct to water. So, as the filtrate travels down the distal tubule and collecting duct, water might "want" to leave because the surrounding interstitial fluid is more concentrated with solutes, but it simply cannot leave. It is not permeable if ADH is absent. So, it stays in the nephron and is excreted as urine.

Okay, then, when water is plentiful, the distal tubule and collecting duct are not as permeable to water, and most of the water left simply passes through the nephron, through the collecting duct, and into a minor calyx. In this circumstance, what can we say about the concentration of solutes in the urine? The urine is dilute. After all, there is a lot of water in the urine, and that will dilute the solutes.

Again, do you see the genius of this design? One part of the nephron, the thick segment of the ascending limb, is *always* impermeable to water. In that part, active transport mechanisms make sure that there are enough electrolytes (sodium, potassium, and chloride ions) put back into the blood. Another part of the nephron is designed to get signals from the body in the form of ADH. If the body produces a lot of ADH, this "tells" the nephron that water needs to get reabsorbed into the bloodstream, so the distal tubules and collecting duct of the nephron become permeable to water, releasing the water by osmosis back to the blood vessels. If there is little ADH, this "tells" the nephron that there is plenty of water in the body, so the distal tubule and collecting duct of the nephron do not become permeable to water. Therefore, they will not release much water back into the blood. Instead, lots of water leaves the body as urine!

Since ADH is such an important part of the water-retention mechanisms in the kidney, you should probably know how it is produced. When you are relatively dehydrated, all your cells shrink slightly because they have less water in them. It turns out that the shrinking of cells in a particular part of the hypothalamus stimulates hypothalamic neurons, whose axons go to the posterior pituitary. This stimulation causes those hypothalamic neurons to release ADH.

ON YOUR OWN

15.8 A sample of filtrate taken from a nephron prior to the distal tubule has a solute concentration of 150 mOsm/kg. Was this sample most likely taken from the proximal tubule, the descending limb of the loop of Henle, or the ascending limb of the loop of Henle?

15.9 A person is excreting lots of dilute urine. Is the relative level of ADH in the body high or low? Is the person getting lots of fluid or only a little fluid?

STORAGE AND RELEASE OF URINE

Let's move on to the inevitable. Now that you've made the urine, you've got to store it and then get rid of it. That happens in the urinary bladder. Remember, the mucosa of the bladder is made of transitional stratified epithelium. So, it can stretch without tearing. A submucosa of connective tissue holds the mucosa to a muscularis of smooth muscle. The outermost layer of the urinary bladder is covered by serosa on the top and adventitia on the sides. The bladder is only as big as your thumb when it's empty. When it's full, it can get rather big. How big? That depends to a certain extent on your own anatomy. At any rate, it can certainly hold a reasonable amount of urine, perhaps up to half a liter.

When your bladder stretches as it fills with urine, information is sent to the spinal cord, and it's integrated there. Emptying the bladder is part of the "housekeeping" duties of the rest-repose division of the autonomic nervous system, the parasympathetic division. When the bladder is stretched to the point that it needs to be emptied, parasympathetic impulses contract the smooth muscle in the bladder, and the bladder empties through the urethra.

That part is all automatic. With babies, that's all that works for them, and they empty their bladders whenever this reflex tells them to do so. However, as you get older, you get myelination of your nervous system so that the spinal cord can send the message up to the cerebral cortex, and the cerebral cortex can decide what to do.

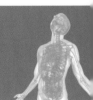

Now, the best thing about the bladder is that there is a ring of skeletal muscle around the external end of the uretha called the external urethra sphincter. This sphincter is normally contracted. As a result, the urethra stays closed, even when the bladder contracts. To empty the bladder, then, requires a conscious effort to *relax* the external urinary sphincter. That's how you learned to control urination

COLORING BOOK EXERCISE 15.3
A review of the urinary bladder can be found in your coloring book on page 291.

as a toddler. Of course, if nervous system damage occurs, you can lose that control. Oftentimes, elderly people who suffer from a general degeneration of the nervous system can lose control of the external urinary sphincter. When this happens, they cannot control when they urinate. We call this incontinence.

BLOOD PRESSURE CONTROL BY THE KIDNEYS

Although removing waste from the blood is the best-known function of the urinary system, it is not the only one. Surprisingly, the kidneys play a major role in blood pressure regulation, as well. This is because the volume of blood ultimately determines the blood pressure. This makes sense. When you put more water in a water balloon, what happens to the pressure inside? It goes up. Oppositely, when you let water out of the water balloon, the pressure goes down. In the same way, more fluid in the blood vessels increases blood pressure, and less fluid decreases blood pressure. (This is true if other variables remain the same, such as heart rate or vasoconstriction of the blood vessels.) Since the kidneys determine the amount of water in the blood, they affect the blood pressure. A drop in blood pressure or a decrease in blood sodium ion levels can be detected in the afferent arteriole by the juxtaglomerular cells (see figure 15.4). When these cells detect either of those changes, they respond by releasing renin (reh' nin). Renin is an enzyme, not a hormone. It activates an inactive protein of the blood that is made in the liver. This inactive protein is called angiotensinogen (an' jee oh ten sin' oh jen). The suffix -ogen means it's a precursor. The root angio means blood vessel. "Tensin" means tension. So, this protein has something to do with blood pressure, but it is a precursor. It is not the molecule that actually affects the blood pressure, but it leads to the molecule that affects blood pressure.

When renin interacts with angiotensinogen, it produces a peptide called angiotensin I. This peptide is not quite the one that affects blood pressure either, but it is close. When it circulates through the lungs, it encounters another enzyme that activates it, creating angiotensin II. This is the active substance, and it does four things. First, it increases vasoconstriction throughout the body quite powerfully. That's where the tensin part of the name comes from. When vasoconstriction increases, blood pressure increases. Second, it makes a person thirsty. This is another way of increasing blood pressure because more water makes a larger volume of blood, which will lead to a higher blood pressure. Third, it increases salt appetite, which is your desire for salt. After all, one of the things that the juxtaglomerular cells respond to is a decrease in sodium ion levels. Increasing the appetite for salt will hopefully alleviate the problem of low sodium ions. Finally, it causes the release of aldosterone, a hormone produced by the adrenal cortex that increases sodium ion reabsorption in the kidneys.

Now, believe it or not, the third and fourth effects of angiotensin II also aid in raising the blood pressure. How does it do that? Well, both of those effects will increase the amount of sodium ions in the blood. With more sodium ions, the blood will absorb more water because the water will be attracted to the increased concentration of solute. If water absorption is increased, blood volume will go up, which will once again lead to a higher blood pressure.

There's one hormone that produces the opposite effect. Atrial natriuretic (nay' tree you ret' ik) hormone comes from the atria of the heart. When blood volume is high, the excess blood actually stretches the two atria. This triggers the release of atrial natriuretic hormone, which inhibits the nephrons from reabsorbing sodium ions. What does that do? It decreases the amount of water reabsorbed, because water follows solutes. If the amount of solute is reduced, the amount of water reabsorbed is reduced. This lowers the blood volume, which lowers blood pressure.

ON YOUR OWN

15.10 The level of aldosterone in a person's blood increases. What will happen to the level of sodium ion? What will happen to the blood pressure?

ACID-BASE BALANCE IN THE BODY

As we mentioned before, the pH of blood is under very tight control. The normal range is from 7.35 to 7.45. That's a narrow range! It's also just slightly basic. If the pH of blood drops from 7.35 down toward 7.0, it's called acidosis, which obviously means too much acid. Please understand that blood need not drop below a pH of 7.0 to enter acidosis. Essentially any pH lower than 7.35 is acidosis because the pH is lower than it should be. The effect of acidosis is dramatic. It decreases nervous function, ultimately leading to coma and death. The diabetic coma, for example, is from acidosis. Blood is so sensitive to pH changes that a blood pH below 7.0 is not considered possible in a living person.

The opposite of acidosis is alkalosis. This happens when the pH of blood rises above 7.45. Once again, the blood is very sensitive to these changes. A blood pH above 7.8 is also not compatible with human life. What's the effect of alkalosis? Not surprisingly, it is the opposite of acidosis. Alkalosis causes over-excitation nervous system, which can lead to convulsions. Convulsions are uncontrolled skeletal muscle contractions that occur when the overly excited nervous system stimulates such activity. Of course, the ultimate result is the same because severe convulsions can end in death when the respiratory muscles fail to contract normally.

Now, please understand that we are talking about *blood* pH here. The pH of the cells is considerably more acidic because of the carbon dioxide they're always making. Typically, the pH within cells runs between 6.0 and 7.4. That's okay, though, because individual cells can tolerate that range of pH. The blood, however, cannot.

What can cause changes in blood pH? Prolonged gastric vomiting is one cause of pH imbalance. When you vomit, you lose a lot of stomach acid. What can this lead to? It can lead to alkalosis because losing acid will raise pH. Diarrhea also causes pH changes in the blood. In diarrhea, you lose bicarbonate from the intestine. Since bicarbonate is a basic substance, severe diarrhea can lead to acidosis. Intestinal vomiting is another way of losing bicarbonate, because you lose bile and pancreatic juice, which contain bicarbonate, which is basic. So, this can lead to acidosis, as well. Since your kidneys can control the amount of H^+ in the blood, kidney dysfunction can also change the pH of blood. This can cause the pH to rise or drop, depending on the diet. If the diet is high in acid, it will lead to acidosis because the kidney is not getting rid of the acid. Respiratory dysfunction can also lead to pH imbalances in the blood because, as we discussed in the previous module, the respiratory system exerts control over the pH of the blood because of its control of CO_2.

There are three ways that the body controls acid-base balance, two quick-fix ways, and one slower but complete way. The first way the body controls pH in the blood is through buffer systems.

Buffer system—A mixture of an acid and a base that resists changes in pH

The second means by which the body controls blood pH is through the respiratory system. We discussed that in detail in the previous module, so we will not add any more detail here. The third, more complete, way is through the action of the kidneys. Kidneys secrete H^+ into the filtrate. The more H^+ they secrete, the higher blood pH becomes, and the lower the urine pH. The opposite is also true.

It turns out that the first method, buffer systems, is the least effective method. Nevertheless, it is an important part of the overall blood pH regulation process, because it is the quickest, acting within a few seconds. To better understand what a buffer system is, perform the following experiment.

think about this

How does high altitude make for basic urine? Sometimes relationships in physiology are quite obvious, like the relationship between drinking more fluid and producing extra urine, or the opposite: not drinking much fluid and producing very little urine. Other times, the relationships are not quite so clear, but since physiology is a truly logical science, once we dig a little deeper we can appreciate the amazing design of the body. The relationship between high altitude and an increased pH of the urine is such an example.

At high altitude, the oxygen pressure is lower than at the normal altitudes that most people inhabit. In response, when a person travels to a high altitude, the lower oxygen pressure stimulates the rate and depth of ventilation. As the person breathes more heavily and deeply, though, he or she loses carbon dioxide at a higher rate. As you know, carbon dioxide in the body forms carbonic acid, and the lack of carbon dioxide creates a shortage of acid in the body—alkalosis. The person cannot tolerate the alkalosis created by the heavy ventilation, and so the usual response is for him or her to feel fatigued and lethargic during the adjustment to the higher altitude.

However, the kidneys compensate in a day or two by decreasing their secretion of H^+ and decreasing their reabsorption of HCO_3^- (bicarbonate, a weak base). Saving acid for the blood means that the urine becomes less acid (more basic). This response of the kidneys counterbalances the loss of acid through the loss of carbon dioxide, and the person is soon able to function well at the higher altitude.

EXPERIMENT 15.1
The Bicarbonate Buffer

Supplies:

- A few leaves of purple (some call it red) cabbage
- A small pan with which to boil water
- A stove
- Two juice glasses
- An eyedropper
- Baking soda
- A measuring teaspoon
- A tablespoon
- Distilled water (available at any supermarket)
- Clear vinegar
- Clear soda pop (not cola, lemon flavored, for example)

Purpose: The bicarbonate buffer is one of the buffers that helps control blood pH. This experiment will show you how this buffer system works.

Procedure:

1. This experiment will work correctly only if you avoid contamination. Everything must be clean before the experiment starts and stay clean throughout the experiment. Rinse your hands thoroughly (this means several times) with tap water. Then rinse the juice glasses, teaspoon, tablespoon, and pan thoroughly with tap water. Next, rinse your hands thoroughly with distilled water and do so with the juice glasses, teaspoon, tablespoon, and pan as well.

2. Take a few leaves of cabbage and put them into the pan. Add roughly 3 cups of distilled water. Don't use a measuring cup. Just estimate.

3. Allow the water to come to a boil. Let it boil for a minute or so and then turn off the heat.

4. Allow the pan to cool, and then pour about half the liquid into one juice glass, and pour the rest into the other. If cabbage leaves get into the juice glasses, just pick them out.

5. What you have in each glass is a solution of anthocyanin, which is an acid-base indicator. It turns blue in the presence of high pH and pink in the presence of low pH. In between, it turns a variety of colors. Right now, it should be a light purple, which indicates a pH of roughly 7.

6. Add half a teaspoon of baking soda to one of the glasses. You should see the color change toward green. That's because the bicarbonate ion in the baking soda is a base. The green color is anthocyanin's reaction to the higher pH.

7. Use the tablespoon to add one tablespoon of soda pop to the same glass in which you just put the baking soda. Use that tablespoon to stir the solution. Continue to add soda pop one tablespoon at a time (stirring in between) until the color of the solution roughly matches the color of the solution in the other glass (the one in which you haven't added anything). This juice glass now has a mixture of an acid (carbonic acid from the soda pop) and base (bicarbonate from the baking soda). This is the bicarbonate buffer.

8. You now have two juice glasses, each at roughly the same pH. One has a buffer solution the other does not.

9. Take the eyedropper and add two drops of vinegar to the glass that does not have the buffer. Swirl the glass to mix the vinegar in the solution. Note the color.

10. Next, take the solution of soda pop and baking soda and do the same thing. Note the color change, if any.

11. Alternatively, add two drops of vinegar to each solution, swirling in between. Compare how quickly the bicarbonate buffer solution changes colors to how quickly the other solution changes colors.

12. Clean everything up.

If all went well in the experiment, you should have seen that while the bicarbonate buffer solution did not change colors very quickly, the other solution did. Why? In each case, you were adding an acid to the solution. The bicarbonate buffer resists changes in pH. Thus, its color did not change very rapidly, because its pH did not change very rapidly. The other solution had no buffer in it. So, it changed pH rather quickly when vinegar was added to it. As a result, the color changed rapidly, as well. The experiment, then, should have demonstrated that buffer solutions really do resist changes in pH.

Why does a buffer system resist changes in pH? Well, a buffer solution contains a weak acid and a weak base. The buffer solution you used in your experiment had carbonic acid, H_2CO_3 (from the soda pop) and bicarbonate, HCO_3^- (from the baking soda). When acetic acid (from the vinegar) was added, it could react with anything in that solution. What would it react with? Well, acetic acid "wants" a base with which to react. Thus, it reacted with the HCO_3^-:

$$CH_3COOH + HCO_3^- \rightarrow H_2CO_3 + CH_3COO^-$$

acetic acid   bicarbonate   carbonic acid   acetate

Now remember, pH is a measure of the amount of free H^+ in solution. The higher the concentration of H^+, the lower the pH. Notice that in this reaction, there are no free H^+ ions in the products. Thus, there is no direct change in the concentration of H^+.

Compare this to what would happen if there were no bicarbonate with which to react. In that case, the acid would simply dissociate:

$$CH_3COOH \rightarrow CH_3COO^- + H^+$$

acetic acid   acetate

In this reaction, H^+ is a product. Therfore, this reaction lowers the pH because *free* H^+ affects the acidity of a solution. That's essentially what happened in the second juice glass. Since there was no bicarbonate in the second juice glass, any vinegar that was added directly lowered the pH.

Now, suppose we were to add OH^- (hydroxyl ion, a base) to the buffer solution you formed in your experiment. What would the base react with? As a base, it would "want" to react with an acid:

$$OH^- + H_2CO_3 \rightarrow HCO_3^- + H_2O$$

Notice that a H^+ from the carbonic acid binds with the OH^-, making water. So the added OH^- does not raise the pH very much.

Now you know why a buffer solution is resistant to changes in pH. In order to dramatically change the pH of a solution, you need to alter the H^+ concentration. A buffer solution contains a weak base and a weak acid. That way, if an acid is added, the weak base neutralizes the acid before it can lower the pH much. If a base is added, the weak acid neutralizes it before it can raise the pH much.

Notice that throughout this discussion, we qualified our statements. We said that the pH would not change *much*, or that the H^+ concentration was not *directly* affected. Why were we not definite in our discussion? Well, it turns out that even in a buffer solution, the pH will change when base or acid is added. Think about it. Suppose a base is added to a buffer. The weak acid in the buffer neutralizes the base. In the process, however, the weak acid is used up. Thus, the concentration of weak acid decreases. What will that do to the pH? It will *raise* the pH. After all, acids lower pH. If the solution loses some acid, the pH will rise.

Although this is an important effect, it is secondary because the acid in the buffer is weak. Thus, the buffer *resists* changes in pH, but it cannot entirely *prevent* them.

Although the base that is added is neutralized, the effect of that neutralization decreases the amount of weak acid in the buffer, and that raises the pH a bit. The opposite can be said when an acid is added to a buffer. The acid is neutralized, but in the process, this "uses up" some weak base. As a result, the pH of the buffer drops a bit. Once again, however, since the base is weak, the change in pH is small compared to what would happen if there was no buffer.

In the end, then, a buffer resists changes in pH, but it cannot prevent them. So, although buffer systems are an important part of the acid-base balance in the body, it is the least effective of the three acid-base regulation mechanisms. Although not as efficient as the other acid-base regulation mechanisms, the essential thing about buffers is that they work quickly. We could say that buffers are a quick fix response to changes in pH.

You need to know the names of three buffers in the body. The first is the bicarbonate buffer system, which you made in the experiment. It is composed of carbonic acid (H_2CO_3) and the bicarbonate ion (HCO_3^-). This buffer is found in the extracellular fluids. The carbonic acid neutralizes bases that find their way into the extracellular fluids, while the bicarbonate ions neutralize the acids that are found in the extracellular fluids.

The second buffer system you need to know is the phosphate buffer system. It is composed of dihydrogen phosphate ($H_2PO_4^-$) and monohydrogen phosphate (HPO_4^{2-}). The $H_2PO_4^-$ is the weak acid that will neutralize base that is added to the system, and the HPO_4^{2-} is the weak base that will neutralize any acid added to the system. This buffer system is found in two places. It is found inside the cells because phosphate is a common substance inside the cells. It is also found in the nephron tubules.

Finally, there is a protein buffer system, which is found inside the cells and in blood plasma. Proteins are actually single-molecule buffers because they are composed of amino acids. The amino part of the name refers to an amino group, which is a weak base. The acid refers to the acid group, which is a weak acid. An amino acid, then, is actually a molecule that has *both* a weak acid and a weak base. As a result, proteins can act as buffers.

As we said before, the buffer systems are the least effective but quickest line of defense against pH changes. The second line of defense, the respiratory system, is a little slower, but more effective because it is controllable through the ventilation rate. In the previous module, you learned that by changing the rate and depth of ventilation, the body controls the pH. Increased ventilation will reduce the carbon dioxide level in the blood, which will increase pH. Decreased ventilation will increase the carbon dioxide level in the blood, which will lower the pH. This happens because (as discussed in the previous module) changing the depth and rate of ventilation affects the amount of CO_2 in the blood. Since CO_2 combines with water in the blood to make carbonic acid, the amount of CO_2 in the blood affects the pH of the blood.

The last line of defense, the kidneys, is the slowest-acting defense, but it is the most effective because the kidneys can actually remove H^+ from the body, or retain H^+ if necessary. The cells of the distal tubules of the nephrons are directly sensitive to pH. When they detect a *decrease* in pH of the interstitial fluid (which reflects blood pH), they *increase* the amount of H^+ that they secrete into the urine. Remember, the third step of urine formation is secretion, where substances are taken *out* of the blood and *put into* the nephron. One of the substances secreted in this way is H^+. If the blood pH goes down, the blood needs to get rid of H^+. Thus, the secretion of H^+ into the nephron is increased.

This results in more H^+ ions getting into the urine, and fewer H^+ ions staying in the blood. This, then, raises the pH of the blood, and it lowers the pH of the urine.

At the same time, a decrease in blood pH will increase the HCO_3^- (bicarbonate ion) reabsorption that takes place in the nephron. Remember, the bicarbonate ion is a base. If more base is reabsorbed into the blood, what will happen to the pH of the blood? It will go up. After all, more base means higher pH. Once again, this will decrease the pH of the urine because, if bicarbonate is being reabsorbed into the blood, it is not staying in the filtrate, and that lowers the pH of the urine.

If the distal tubules sense an *increase* in blood pH, exactly the opposite occurs. Less H^+ is secreted by the nephron. This leaves more H^+ in the blood. So, the blood pH decreases because there is more H^+ in the blood. At the same time, the pH of the urine rises because there is less H^+ in the urine. In addition, an increase in blood pH will trigger the nephron to reabsorb less bicarbonate ion. Less bicarbonate in the blood will lower the blood pH. However, the urine pH will rise because more base will be present in the urine.

ON YOUR OWN

15.11 When an acid is added to a protein buffer, which part of the amino acid reacts: the amino group or the acid group?

15.12 A person's urine is unusually basic. Is the nephron increasing or decreasing the amount of H^+ secretion? Is it increasing or decreasing the amount of bicarbonate reabsorption?

15.13 Would the unusually basic urine described in 15.12 occur in response to prolonged gastric vomiting or to prolonged diarrhea?

Notice the pattern that happens, then. If the blood's pH falls, the nephron will secrete H^+ and increase the reabsorption of bicarbonate. This will raise blood pH and lower urine pH. If the blood pH is too high, the nephron will stop secreting H^+ and will decrease the amount of bicarbonate ion being reabsorbed into the blood. This will lower the pH of blood, but it will raise the pH of the urine. It is usual for the urine to be acidic, because the Western diet tends to produce acid, so most often the nephrons secrete excess H^+.

Based on its outward appearance (see Figure 15.1), you would think that the urinary system was pretty simple, wouldn't you? What do you think now? Look at the engineering that had to be done to make this system work! The filtering, reabsorption, and secretion in the kidneys are each marvels of biological design. The nephron itself is perfectly designed to regulate both the water levels and the solute levels in the blood. The very fact that it travels down into the medulla, back up to the cortex, and back down into the medulla shows that it has been perfectly placed in the kidney. The fact that the thick segment of the ascending limb of the loop of Henle is impermeable to water while the distal tubule and collecting duct vary their permeability based on ADH level is nothing less than inspired! All of these design features show an incredible amount of forethought and engineering prowess.

Not only is the urinary system designed well, but it also seamlessly interacts with other systems of the body. It works together with the respiratory system to regulate the blood pH, and it works with the circulatory system to regulate blood pressure. There are numerous negative-feedback mechanisms that ensure these regulation processes all work together at peak efficiency. This shows you that even an apparently "simple" system in the body is far from simple. God's creation is truly marvelous!

ANSWERS TO THE "ON YOUR OWN" QUESTIONS

15.1 The collecting ducts empty into minor calyces, which empty into major calyces, which empty into the renal pelvis, which empties into the ureter, which empties into the urinary bladder, which empties into the urethra, which takes the urine out of the body.

15.2 The kidneys are not surrounded by a serous membrane so that they cannot move easily, since movement might kink the ureters. Remember, a serous membrane lubricates an organ where it rubs against other organs. The kidneys are lodged in fat and thus do not move much. Therefore, they need no serous membranes. (The parietal peritoneum does lie over their front surface, but it does not surround them.)

15.3 a. This is like the filtration step. The glomerular filter keeps proteins and blood cells in the blood while the filtrate spills out, just like the built-in dividers in the drawer don't fall out while he is dumping everything else out.

  b. This is secretion. Paper clips are stuck in the drawer, but the man decided not to keep all of them. So, he picked through the drawer and removed them. When certain chemicals, such as H^+, are excess in the blood, they can be secreted if they are not needed.

15.4 One reason the glomerular filtration rate is high is due to the high permeability of the glomerular capillaries. If they were more like normal capillaries, they would not be nearly as porous. Thus, the GFR would be lower.

15.5 Reabsorption puts molecules back into the blood. So, the more reabsorption that occurs, the LESS of the chemical you will find in the urine. Since the T-max of A is higher, more A gets into the blood than B. This means that less A will be in the urine than B. So, B will be more concentrated in the urine.

15.6 The molecule must be small. If there is no carrier and this is not a protein, then the only way it can get through the nephron is if the nephron is permeable to it, allowing it to diffuse. This happens only for small molecules.

15.7 If the person's urine has a low pH, that means a lot of H^+ was secreted into the urine. So, the blood needed to get rid of H^+. This means that the blood was too acidic, so it got rid of acid to reduce the acidity.

15.8 At the beginning of the proximal tubule, the filtrate is essentially blood plasma without proteins. So, its concentration is close to 300 mOsm/kg. As it travels down the loop of Henle, it gets MORE concentrated. As it travels up the ascending loop of Henle, however, it gets less concentrated again because electrolytes are being pumped out of it, but water cannot follow. Thus, the filtrate came from the thick segment of the ascending loop of Henle.

15.9   Remember, ADH increases the permeability of the distal tube and collecting duct to water. This allows water to get back into the blood, leading to concentrated urine. Since the urine is dilute, not much water is getting back into the blood. This means that there is little ADH in the body. Since the body is getting rid of a lot of water, the person is getting a lot of fluid.

15.10   Aldosterone increases the amount of sodium that is reabsorbed in the blood. So, this increases the blood sodium level. This will also increase blood pressure because more sodium in the blood will attract more water in the blood, which will increase blood volume.

15.11   The amino group is the base. Bases react with acids. Thus, the amino group will react.

15.12   If the urine is unusually basic, that means there is not much H^+ secretion into the nephron. So, H^+ secretion has decreased. The fact that the urine is unusually basic also means that there is extra base in the urine. That means bicarbonate is not being put back into the blood as much as usual. So, the amount of bicarbonate reabsorption has decreased.

15.13   If the urine is unusually basic, that means that the kidneys are trying to rid the body of excess base. The body is in alkalosis. Prolonged gastric vomiting, in which too much acid is lost, can put the body into alkalosis, and the kidneys will attempt to correct the imbalance by retaining H^+ for the blood, thus producing a basic urine.

STUDY GUIDE FOR MODULE 15

1. Define the following terms:
    a. Retroperitoneal
    b. Erythropoiesis
    c. Renal blood flow rate
    d. Filtrate
    e. Glomerular filtration rate (GFR)
    f. Tubular maximum
    g. Buffer system

2. Identify the structures in the figure below:

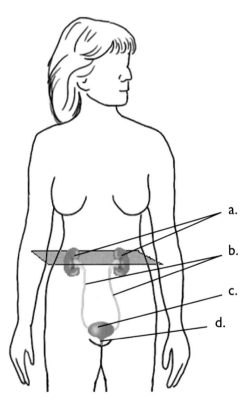

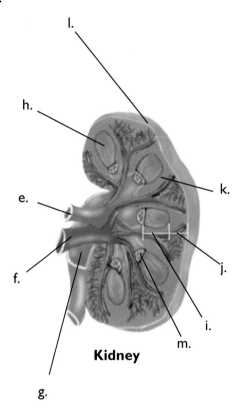

Kidney

3. Which structure above contains stratified transitional epithelium?

4. Between (i) and (j), which has greater concentration of solutes in the interstitial fluid? How much more concentrated do the solutes get compared with normal interstitial fluid?

5. List the seven functions of the urinary system.

6. Explain the desk drawer-analogy and how it relates to urine formation.

7. Label the structures in the figure below:

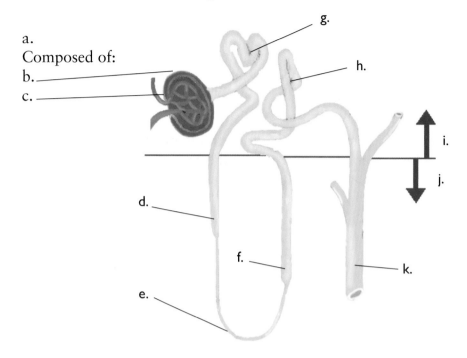

a.
Composed of:
b.
c.
g.
h.
d.
e.
f.
i.
j.
k.

8. Of the structures pointed out in the figure, which ones are always permeable to water? Which is never permeable to water? Which are permeable to water based on the amount of ADH present?

9. What are the four steps of urine formation. Which steps could be grouped together?

10. During glomerular filtration, what makes it past the filter and into the nephron? What doesn't make it past the filter?

11. What two factors assure a high GFR?

12. What causes a high GCP? What two factors oppose the GCP? What is the difference between these two pressures and the GCP? What happens when the GCP gets lower than the sum of the other two factors?

13. What two things are usually required for a substance to be actively reabsorbed? What exception exists to this general rule?

14. What is the main substance that is passively reabsorbed? What other two important substances are passively reabsorbed?

15. The reabsorption T-max for a particular substance is very high. In general, do you expect to find a lot of that substance in the urine or only a little?

16.   When a substance is secreted by the nephron, does its concentration in the blood increase or decrease?

17.   Compare the concentration of solutes in the filtrate to that of blood plasma at the following points in the nephron:
       a. The proximal tubule
       b. The bottom of the loop of Henle
       c. The thick section of the ascending limb of the loop of Henle
       d. The distal tubule

18.   What part of the bladder is controlled automatically by the parasympathetic division of the ANS for urination? What part of the urinary system can be controlled consciously so that we can decide when to urinate?

19.   What cells in the kidneys sense sodium ion levels and blood pressure in the blood and act to correct any large changes?

20.   What hormone is ultimately stimulated by the secretion of the cells in problem 19?

21.   What hormone discussed in this module decreases blood pressure and sodium ion levels in the blood?

22.   What is it called when blood pH drops below 7.35? What is it called when blood pH rises above 7.45?

23.   In the bicarbonate buffer system, which substance reacts if a base enters the blood? In the phosphate buffer system, what substance reacts when a base enters a cell?

24.   What are the three regulatory processes which control blood pH? List them in terms of their effectiveness, starting with the least effective one.

25.   List the pH control processes in terms of their speed in regulation, starting with the fastest.

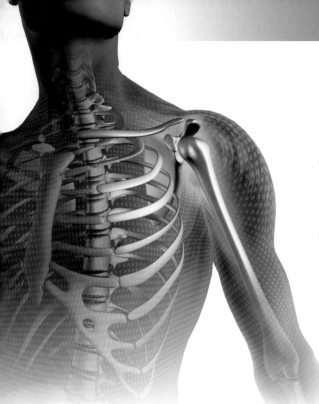

THE REPRODUCTIVE SYSTEMS

One of the characteristics of living organisms is that they reproduce. Multicellular organisms reproduce on two levels. They reproduce cells constantly by mitosis to grow, repair damage, and replace cells that have died. You learned about this process in module 1. Living organisms also reproduce as *whole* organisms. This can be done in one of two ways. Some multi-

heart of the matter

Thus far, we've taken you on a journey through cells, tissues, organs, and organ systems. It seems appropriate that the final organ system—reproductive—would lead back to the single cell. It is the cell that brings forth new life. Never lose sight of the mystery it holds.

You guided my conception and formed me in the womb.
— Job 10:10, NLT

cellular organisms (such as planaria) reproduce asexually. If we ignore the chance for mutations, asexual reproduction results in offspring that are genetically identical to the parent. Other multicellular organisms (such as humans) reproduce sexually. Sexual reproduction allows for the mixing of genetic material from two organisms. This produces offspring that are similar to, but far from identical to, the parents.

As you study the reproductive system, keep in mind that the reproductive system has four main functions. The first task is the production of gametes, which are the sperm in males and the ova (eggs) in females. This occurs through the process of meiosis, which we will discuss in detail later. The second purpose of the reproductive system is fertilization, which is the process that leads up to and includes the genetic material of the sperm joining with the main genetic material of the oocyte. So, the miracle of life begins with the formation of an original human being. The third function of the reproductive system is the development of the newly created individual inside the female, and in mammals this function continues after birth with the nourishment of the baby through milk production. The fourth function of the reproductive system is the production of reproductive hormones, which are essential for gender-specific functions. Since reproductive systems are different for each gender, we must discuss them separately. We will begin with the male reproductive system.

ANATOMY OF THE MALE REPRODUCTIVE SYSTEM

In order to understand how the male reproductive system works, you must first learn its anatomy, which is shown in figure 16.1. The testes (test' eez) (singular is testis) are really the functional centers of the male reproductive system. They are both endocrine and exocrine glands. Their exocrine function is to develop and secrete sperm, and their endocrine function is to produce and secrete sex hormones. Testosterone is the main sex hormone in males.

The testes are housed outside the abdomen in a sac called the scrotum (skroh' tum). During fetal development, however, they are formed within the abdomen retroperitoneally (behind the parietal peritoneum; see module 15), inferior to the kidneys. They are formed by two months after conception, but they do not descend into the scrotum until about eight months of development, about a month before birth. The descent of the testes into the scrotum is controlled by testosterone.

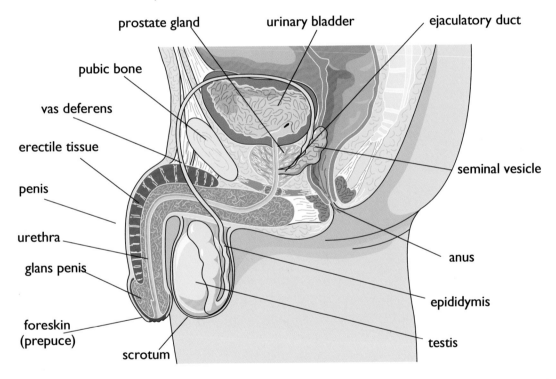

FIGURE 16.1
The Male Reproductive System
Illustration by LifeArt

Why do the testes descend into the scrotum? Why don't they just stay in the abdomen where they are well protected? Well, the primary reproductive function of the testes is the production and secretion of sperm. Spermatogenesis in the human cannot occur at normal body temperature. Instead, the enzymes required are most active at a temperature, around 95°F.

Spermatogenesis—The process by which sperm forms in the testes

The scrotum has a large number of sweat glands. In addition, it's outside the body. So, it is cooler than normal body temperature. This allows the testes to maintain a temperature that is ideal for spermatogenesis.

Not only is the scrotum cooler than the rest of the body, it can also regulate its own temperature. The cremaster (kree' mas ter) muscles are extensions of the abdominal muscles that descend into the scrotum on each side. When the scrotum is too cold, the cremaster muscles contract, pulling the testes nearer to the body to increase the temperature. If the scrotum gets too warm, the cremaster muscles relax, and the testes move farther from the body, decreasing their temperature.

Occasionally, one or both testes do not descend into the scrotum. If only one testis fails to descend, the man will not be infertile because he will still have one testis that can produce sperm (the one that did descend). If both testes fail to descend, he will be infertile because both testes will be too warm for spermatogenesis. However, even if a man is infertile because of two undescended testes, his testes will still produce and secrete testosterone, since the enzymes that control testosterone production are not nearly as temperature sensitive as those which control spermatogenesis.

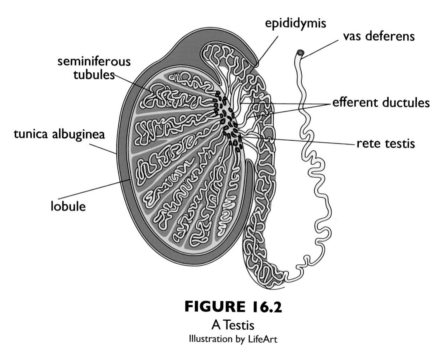

FIGURE 16.2
A Testis
Illustration by LifeArt

Figure 16.2 illustrates an internal view of a testis. It is covered with a thick connective tissue capsule called the tunica albuginea (al byou jin' ee uh). The inside of the testis is divided into several hundred lobules that are filled with tiny, coiled tubes called seminiferous (sem in if' er us) tubules. If you were to stretch the seminiferous tubules in a single testis out, they would span nearly *one-half mile!* The seminiferous tubules empty into the rete (ree' tee) testis.

The rete testis empties into the epididymis (ep' uh did' ih mus) (plural is epididymides). This is another coiled tube that, if stretched out, would be about 20 feet long. It is connected to the testis via efferent ductules. Sperm move from the testes to the epididymides and spend about ten days there to mature. Without this maturation, the sperm would not be able to fertilize an ovum. So, sperm are formed in the testes, but they mature in the epididymides.

Once mature, the sperm travel into the vas deferens (def' uh rens), which is also called the ductus deferens (see figure 16.1). These 18-inch long tubes (plural is vastus deferentia) are composed of smooth muscle and an inner lining of ciliated mucosa. During sexual activity, they move the sperm up around the bladder and to the ejaculatory ducts, which are connected to the seminal vesicles. The ejaculatory ducts push sperm out into the urethra so that it can leave the man and enter the woman for possible fertilization.

As you learned in the previous module, the urethra is the tube through which urine travels when the urinary bladder empties. In the male, however, the urethra is also the tube through which semen exits the body during sexual intercourse.

Semen—The mixture of secretions from the testes and other male reproductive glands that is released during sexual intercourse

Notice the Y in the tube that leads from the urethra to the bladder and the ejaculatory duct in figure 16.1. The portion of the Y which leads to the bladder has an internal urethral sphincter. During sexual arousal, the internal urethral sphincter constricts so that urine is not released during sexual intercourse.

The seminal vesicles are two large exocrine glands that open into the ejaculatory ducts. They secrete a fructose-rich, slightly basic fluid that mixes with the sperm. This fluid forms about 60% of the semen. The fructose serves as fuel for the sperm after ejaculation. The seminal fluid is also the swimming medium for the sperm, which are flagellated (see figure 16.6). They are, in fact, the only flagellated cells in the human species. They actively move forward by swimming with their flagella. In order to swim, however, they need a liquid medium. The secretions of the seminal vesicle help form that medium.

The prostate gland is an exocrine gland that surrounds the urethra at the base of the urinary bladder. It produces a fluid that also mixes with the sperm, contributing about 30% of the semen. Like the secretions from the seminal vesicles, prostatic fluid is slightly basic. It also provides a swimming medium for the sperm, but its main job is to reduce the acidity of the vagina, which is the canal in the woman through which the semen must travel. The vagina is normally acidic, but acid is damaging to sperm. The secretions of the prostate gland help to neutralize the acid in the vagina so the sperm can swim through it.

Two common problems associated with the prostate gland are benign prostate hypertrophy and prostate cancer. They both involve tumors in the prostate, but the diseases are very different. Benign prostate hypertrophy is not cancer. That's what the term benign means. However, it does lead to a swelling of the prostate gland, which compresses the urethra, slowing the stream of urine that leaves the bladder. It also compresses the bladder, causing frequent urination. This is more of an annoyance than anything else. On the other hand, prostate cancer can be deadly. In North America, it is the second leading cause of cancer death in men. Note that the prostate gland lies anterior to the rectum. Most prostate cancers occur in the posterior lobe of the prostate, which can be felt in a rectal exam. As men get older, regular rectal exams are advised to provide early detection of prostate cancer.

The other important glands in the male reproductive system are the two bulbourethral (bulb' oh you ree' thrul) glands. These little glands secrete mucus early in the stage of sexual excitation. This secretion is viscous and basic. It lubricates the urethra to make it easy for the semen to pass through it. Because it is basic, it also neutralizes any acid urine that may be in the urethra.

Most of the urethra is housed in the penis. The shaft of the penis is covered with skin that is loosely connected to the connective tissue that surrounds the penis. At the tip of the penis, called the glans penis, however, the skin is firmly attached. The glans penis is covered with a loose sleeve of skin called the foreskin, or the prepuce. In the Old Testament (Gen. 17:9-14, NIV), the Bible commands the Israelites to cut the foreskins of their male children. This process is referred to as circumcision, and it is a common surgical procedure in the United States. In the Acts of the Apostles, Peter makes it clear that circumcision is not required of the Gentiles who become Christians (Acts 15: 5-11, NIV).

The penis has three erectile tissues, which are vascular chambers surrounded by elastic connective tissue. When filled with blood, the erectile tissues cause the penis to enlarge and grow firm. This process is called erection, and it is an essential step in male sexual reproduction.

> **Erection**—The enlarged, firm state of the penis that results as the erectile tissues fill with blood

Erection is necessary for coitus (coe ee' tus), which is the process in which the man's penis enters the woman's vagina.

> **Coitus**—Sexual intercourse in the human (the process in which the erect penis enters the vagina)

If the penis were not firm, it could not be pushed into the vagina. Coitus, of course, is an important part of sexual reproduction because it allows the sperm to be transferred from the man to the woman.

What causes erection to take place? The erectile tissues must be filled with blood, and the blood must be trapped in the erectile tissues. In order for this to happen, parasympathetic activity causes vasodilation, which increases the blood flow into the erectile tissues. At the same time, the veins leaving the tissues are compressed, so the blood is trapped in the tissues. It is rare for parasympathetic neurons to innervate arterioles, but it does happen in the male reproductive system. What stimulates the parasympathetic division to initiate an erection? Stimulus can occur through touch receptors on the penis or through sexual thoughts.

Although the parasympathetic division of the ANS is responsible for erection, the next step of the male reproductive process is emission, and the sympathetic division of the ANS controls it.

> **Emission**—Movement of the male reproductive secretions toward the urethra

Remember, the seminal vesicles, the prostate gland, and the bulbourethral glands all secrete fluids to aid the sperm as it travels to the egg. Emission is the process in which those secretions, together forming the semen, begin to enter the urethra. Since the sympathetic division of the ANS controls this process, both divisions are a part of the reproductive process. The last stage in the male reproductive process is ejaculation.

> **Ejaculation**—The movement of semen out of the urethra

Movement of the penis within the vagina causes stimulation to the parasympathetic division of the ANS and the somatic motor system. This stimulation climaxes with contraction of skeletal muscles of the pelvic floor that push the semen out of the ejaculatory ducts.

The semen enters the woman's vagina, and the sperm make their way toward the uterine tubes for possible fertilization of an ovum. After ejaculation, the man experiences a period of resolution in which the penis returns to its ordinary size again, and he has a feeling of satisfaction. He will not be able to have an erection again for several minutes to several hours, depending on the man.

Before we leave this section, let's summarize a few things about semen. When the man ejaculates, he releases about 3 to 4 milliliters of semen. As we have already mentioned, about 60% of this is made up of the fructose-rich seminal fluid, which is mostly used as fuel for the sperm. Another 30% or so comes from the prostate gland, which helps neutralize the acidity of the vagina. Because of the secretions of the seminal vesicles, the prostate gland, and the bulbourethral glands, semen is slightly basic, with a pH of about 7.4.

COLORING BOOK EXERCISE 16.1

An overview of the male reproductive system can be found on pages 295 - 299 of your coloring book.

ON YOUR OWN

16.1 Starting with the testes, name all of the structures through which the sperm travel as they mature and eventually leave the body.

16.2 Sperm are extracted from a testis. They appear to be normal, but they cannot engage in fertilization. Why not?

MEIOSIS

As we mentioned before, sexual reproduction involves combining the genetic material of one parent with the genetic material of the other parent. This mixing results in an offspring that is genetically similar to both parents, but not genetically identical to either. As you already know, healthy humans have 23 chromosome pairs for a total of 46 chromosomes. There are 44 autosomes (non-sex chromosomes) and two sex chromosomes (Chromosomes that determine the gender of the individual. Females have two X chromosomes and males have an X and a Y chromosome). The chromosomes in diploid cells are in homologous pairs (similar but not identical). Figure 16.3 is a human karyotype that shows homologous chromosomes lined up together.

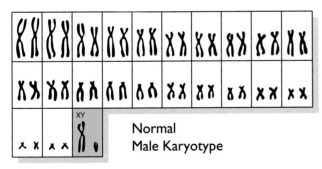

Normal Male Karyotype

Normal Female Karyotype

Figure 16.3
Male and Female Karyotypes
Illustration: LifeArt

Chromosomes contain the primary genetic information of the cell on coding sequences called genes. Remember that you inherit one copy of a gene from your mother and the other copy of that gene from your father. Those different versions of the gene are called alleles. The two chromosomes of each pair have the same *set* of alleles, but those alleles can be different. So, the *locations of alleles* in each chromosome of a homologous pair are identical, but the alleles themselves need not be identical.

For example, the gene that determines ABO blood type is on the ninth chromosome in humans. Each person has two alleles for every gene on the autosomal chromosomes. This includes the ABO blood type gene. In a given person, the first chromosome in the pair (inherited from one parent) might have the allele for type A blood, and the second chromosome in the pair (inherited from the other parent) might have the allele for type B blood. So, each chromosome has an allele for blood type; however, the alleles themselves are different: One is for type A blood, and the other is for type B blood. The person's blood type, then, is AB.

In meiosis, the goal is to split up the homologous pairs so that the resulting cell has only one chromosome from each pair. These resulting cells (gametes) are called haploid cells because they have only one representative of each chromosome pair, or half the amount of DNA. What does this give the cell? It gives the cell *one allele for every gene on the autosomal chromosomes*. This is important and we cannot stress it enough. The significance of meiosis is that it provides for constancy of the chromosome number from generation to generation. Given that humans have 46 chromosomes and each parent contributes to the DNA of the offspring, it makes sense that each parent can contribute only 23 chromosomes. How are the alleles split in order to make cells that have one allele per gene? That's what meiosis does, and it is reviewed for you in figure 16.4. It is important for you to realize that meiosis occurs only in the male testes to produce sperm or in the female ovaries to produce oocytes. The resulting sperm and oocytes are called gametes.

think about this

In 2003, the Human Genome Project completed sequencing the three billion chemical base pairs that make up human DNA, and the project has thus far identified more than 20,000 genes in human DNA!

Meiosis I

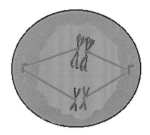

1. Early prophase I
The chromosomes and centriole replicate and the centrioles begin to move.

2. Late prophase I
The chromosomes line up in homologous pairs and the spindle begins to form.

3. Metaphase I
The chromosomes line up on the equatorial plane. The microtubules attach to one homologue each.

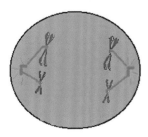

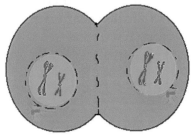

4. Anaphase I
The microtubules of the spindle pull the homologues apart.

5. Telophase I
The plasma membrane constricts, and the chromosomes become surrounded by nuclear material.

6. End of Meiosis I
Two haploid cells result. They still have replicated chromosomes, however, so they must enter meiosis II.

Meiosis II

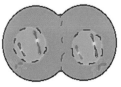

1. Prophase II
Both cells replicate centrioles.

2. Metaphase II
The chromosomes of each cell line up on the equatorial plane.

3. Anaphase II
The microtubules pull the replicates from the originals.

4. Telophase II
The plasma membranes constrict, and nuclei form.

5. End of Meiosis II
Four haploid cells (gametes), each with single chromosomes, result.

FIGURE 16.4
Meiosis
Illustration by Megan Whitaker

It is important to note that the process of meiosis produces a different end product for males and females, and we will discuss these details in separate sections. We'll start with males.

SPERMATOGENESIS: DEVELOPMENT OF SPERM

Spermatogenesis occurs in the walls of the seminiferous tubules of the testes (See figure 16.2). The process, illustrated in figure 16.5, begins with diploid cells (cells containing 46 chromosomes) called spermatogonia (sper' mat uh goh' nee uh). Spermatogonia do not undergo meiosis. Instead, they undergo *mitosis*. One of the two cells that result from mitosis remains a spermatogonium (singular of spermatogonia), and the other is a primary spermatocyte (sper mat' oh sight), which is the cell that actually undergoes meiosis.

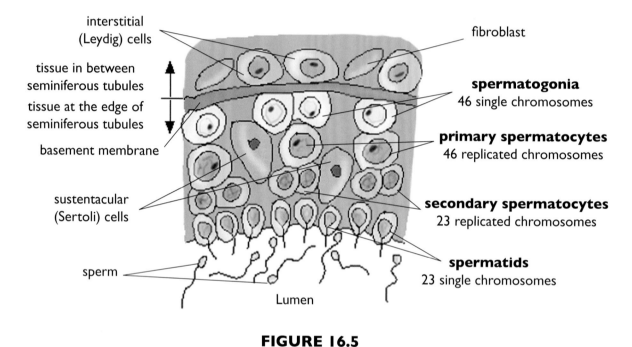

FIGURE 16.5
Spermatogenesis
Illustration by Megan Whitaker

Each primary spermatocyte, which has 46 replicated chromosomes, undergoes meiosis I to make two secondary spermatocytes. These cells have only one chromosome from each homologous pair, but those chromosomes are replicated. So, they have 23 replicated chromosomes. You can think of it as having two copies of the same magazine. Despite the extra copy, there is no additional information. They therefore undergo meiosis II to separate the replicates. This makes a total of four spermatids, each with 23 chromosomes, none of which are replicated. The spermatids, then, have only one allele for every gene. This process occurs as the developing cells are pushed from the edge of the seminiferous tubules toward the lumen (space) in the middle.

Once formed, the spermatids develop specific features, as illustrated in figure 16.6. When these features develop, the sperm enter the lumen of the seminiferous tubules where they are moved into the epididymides to become fully mature. (At this point they cannot move on their own.) The entire process of spermatogenesis takes about 70 days. Once fully mature, a sperm can live for several weeks inside the male, where it does not move at all under its own power. Instead, it is moved along by smooth muscle contractions of the various ducts. Once in the vagina, however, it can live for only a few days, but it can swim.

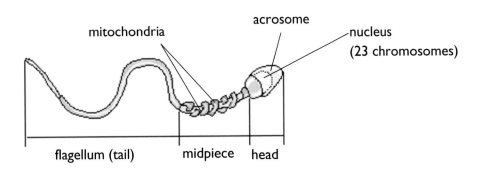

FIGURE 16.6
Sperm Structure
Illustration by Megan Whitaker

Sperm can be divided into three basic sections: the head, the midpiece, and the flagellum (tail). The tip of the head has a cap called an acrosome (ak' roh sohm), which contains digestive enzymes. These enzymes are capable of digesting away the covering of the ovum. In normal fertilization, many sperm will bury their heads in an ovum, and their acrosomes will work together to get rid of that covering. The first sperm to get in will then fertilize the egg. The rest of the head houses the nucleus, which contains 23 chromosomes. The midpiece contains mitochondria. There is a lot of energy involved in sperm movement, so the sperm need many mitochondria. Finally, sperm beats its flagellum back and forth to be able to swim toward the ovum.

You need to appreciate the design that you see in a sperm. The sperm has one job and one job only: to get to an ovum and fertilize it. In order to do this, it must first be highly mobile. Look how much of the cell is taken up by the flagellum. Since the flagellum is such an enormous part of the sperm, it is obviously *very* mobile. As we already mentioned, the sperm needs a lot of energy to swim, so it has a "power pack" of mitochondria to provide it with the energy. Finally, when it reaches the ovum, it must break through the ovum's outer protective barrier. It has its own "drill" to do just that: the acrosome. The Designer has outfitted the sperm with just what it needs to get the job done. It is important to note that the flagellum and midpiece of the sperm do not penetrate the outer protective layer of the ovum, and therefore, will not contribute mitochondria to the fertilized cell.

All of this incredible engineering is housed in a tiny space. Sperm are the smallest of all human cells. To give you an idea of how small they are, there are 60 to 90 *million* sperm in a single milliliter of what is ejaculated from the average healthy man. That's an amazing number, isn't it? If the number of sperm per milliliter drops significantly below 40 million, the man is said to have a low sperm count. If the numbers of sperm per milliliter of ejaculate drop to about 20 million, the man is usually infertile.

Two specific types of cells aid spermatogenesis. The first type, sustentacular cells (also called Sertoli cells), can be thought of as "nursemaid" cells. They form a liquid-tight enclosure called the blood-testis barrier around the developing sperm within the walls of the seminiferous tubules. This is necessary because during development, sperm can create antigens that will be attacked by the body's immune system. So, the blood-testis barrier seals off the developing sperm so that this doesn't happen. Of course, since the developing sperm are sealed off from the blood supply, they are also sealed off from nutrients and oxygen. The sustentacular cells, however, supply them with the nutrients and oxygen that they need.

In addition to supplying the developing sperm with nutrients and oxygen, the sustentacular cells produce a hormone called inhibin, which is involved in a complex sequence of hormone secretions that ultimately control the rate of spermatogenesis. We will discuss that more in the next section of this module. The other type of cell, called interstitial cells (also called Leydig cells), secrete testosterone, which we will also discuss in the next section. Interstitial cells are found *outside* the seminiferous tubules in the testes, which is how they got their name.

EXPERIMENT 16.1
Spermatogenesis and Sperm

Supplies:
Microscope
Prepared slide: Testis (human)
Prepared slide: Sperm (human)
Prepared slide: Blood smear (human)

Purpose:
This experiment will help you see the structure of the seminiferous tubules and how spermatogenesis takes place in them. It will also allow you to see sperm and compare their size to other cells in the body.

Procedure:
1. Place the testis slide on the microscope stage and focus at 40x magnification.

2. You will see several ovals surrounded by cells. These are cross sections of seminiferous tubules. Center one and increase magnification to 100x. Focus again.

3. At this magnification, you should be able to see that some of the ovals have some stringy tissue in the center of the lumen. Center one of those and increase magnification to 400x. Focus again.

4. Look at the edge of the oval. You should see a line of distinct tissue that surrounds the entire oval. That is the basement membrane. In between the basement membranes of two different ovals, you find the interstitial tissue.

5. Notice that there are many cells in the basement membrane and interstitial tissue. Many of them are fibroblasts. The cells with lots of space between the cell membrane and the nucleus are the interstitial cells.

6. Directly underneath the basement membrane, you will find the spermatogonia.

7. Beneath the spermatogonia, you will find the primary and secondary spermatocytes. These cells are roughly circular.

8. In this region, you will probably see some cells with irregularly shaped nuclei. Those are the sustentacular cells.

9. Near the center, you should see what look to be tiny filaments. Those are the tails of the developing sperm.

10. Draw what you see, labeling the cells.

11. Set the magnification back to 40x, remove the slide, and place the prepared slide of sperm on the stage. You will need to scan the slide carefully, as the sperm are small. You are looking for a light-pink line of tissue.

12. When you find the light-pink line of tissue, center, focus, and increase magnification to 100x.

13. Center, focus, and increase magnification to 400x.

14. Search for a few small dots and center them. Adjusting the fine focus carefully, look for a thin filament connected to the dot. The dot is the head of the sperm, and the filament is the tail.

15. Draw what you see. Take special note of the size because you will be looking at other cells next, so as to get an idea of the relative size of sperm.

16. Bring the microscope back to 40x magnification and remove the sperm slide. Now put in the blood smear slide. Center some blood cells and focus.

17. Increase the magnification to 100x and refocus. Notice that, already, the red blood cells are larger than the sperm were at 400x!

18. Increase the magnification to 400x and refocus. Try to draw a red blood cell next to one of the sperm that you already drew and directly compare the size.

19. Clean everything up.

COLORING BOOK EXERCISE 16.2

A review of spermatogenesis can be found on page 299 of the coloring book.

ON YOUR OWN

16.3 The sperm cell of an animal has 21 chromosomes in it. How many chromosomes are in this animal's nonreproductive cells?

16.4 A mother has type B blood and a father has type A blood. They have a baby who has type A blood. What blood type allele was in the sperm cell that produced the child? What allele was in the ovum? Remember from module 11 that the alleles for A and B are dominant over the allele for type O, and that A and B do not dominate one another.

HORMONAL CONTROL OF MALE REPRODUCTION

The principal male sex hormone is testosterone, which has wide-ranging effects in the male body. At conception, the sex chromosomes (pair 23; see figure 16.3) determine the gender of the child. If the baby has two X chromosomes, the child is female. If the baby has an X chromosome and a Y chromosome, the child is a male. Genetically, then, we are male or female from the moment of conception. However, the male embryo must produce testosterone to form the male reproductive organs before two months of gestation have gone by. If a male embryo does not produce testosterone in those two months of gestation, the testes would not descend, and he would have no male reproductive organs. While he would still be genetically male, he would, essentially, appear to be a girl. So, the first two functions of testosterone occur in the womb. Testosterone controls the formation of the male reproductive organs and the descent of the testes.

The other functions of testosterone occur after birth. Testosterone levels affect the male secondary sex characteristics.

Secondary sex characteristics—The characteristics that appear at puberty and tend to distinguish men from women. In the male, these include body shape, pitch of the voice, and the distribution of body hair, including growth of the beard.

Puberty—A series of events that transform a child into a sexually mature adult

Testosterone also helps to maintain the male reproductive organs. This means it helps regulate their size, their ability to perform their functions, and their health.

In adolescence, testosterone affects the anabolism that occurs in the body.

Anabolism—All of the synthesis reactions that occur in the body

In addition to causing puberty, testosterone has an especially strong effect on the anabolism reactions that build muscles and bones. Have you heard the term *anabolic steroids*? These are chemicals that artificially enhance anabolism in the body. Anabolism is the opposite of catabolism.

Catabolism—All of the decomposition reactions that occur in the body

Anabolism requires energy, while catabolism produces energy. In addition to all of the other functions discussed, testosterone also regulates male sexual behavior and is necessary for spermatogenesis.

How are testosterone levels controlled in the male body? Testosterone release begins with the hypothalamus, which releases gonadotropin releasing hormone (GnRH). This hormone then stimulates the anterior pituitary to release the gonadotropins, which are luteinizing hormone (LH) and follicle stimulating hormone (FSH). These hormones are called gonadotropins because they affect the gonads, which are the reproductive organs. They are the same hormones as the gonadotropins in women, but they have different target organs in women. They are actually named after their functions in the female. Also, in women the secretion of gonadotropins is in a monthly cycle, but in men it is not.

The interstitial cells in the testes are stimulated by LH to release testosterone. The level of testosterone in the blood causes a negative feedback to the hypothalamus, which controls the secretion of GnRH.

The other hormone, FSH, affects the sustentacular cells within the seminiferous tubules, stimulating them to increase spermatogenesis. The sustentacular cells also produce a negative feedback by releasing the hormone inhibin, which inhibits the release of FSH. This process can be a little complex, so we want to finish this section with figure 16.7.

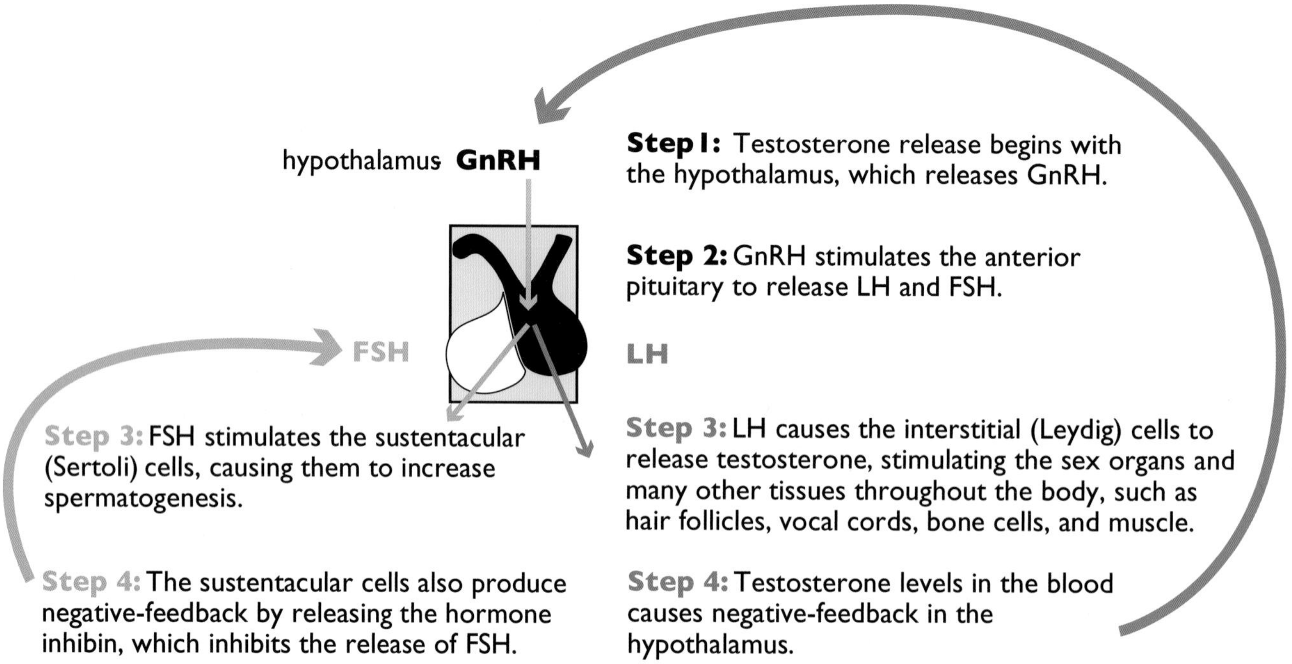

hypothalamus **GnRH**

Step I: Testosterone release begins with the hypothalamus, which releases GnRH.

Step 2: GnRH stimulates the anterior pituitary to release LH and FSH.

FSH

LH

Step 3: FSH stimulates the sustentacular (Sertoli) cells, causing them to increase spermatogenesis.

Step 3: LH causes the interstitial (Leydig) cells to release testosterone, stimulating the sex organs and many other tissues throughout the body, such as hair follicles, vocal cords, bone cells, and muscle.

Step 4: The sustentacular cells also produce negative-feedback by releasing the hormone inhibin, which inhibits the release of FSH.

Step 4: Testosterone levels in the blood causes negative-feedback in the hypothalamus.

FIGURE 16.7
Hormone Regulation of Male Reproduction
Illustration by LifeArt

ON YOUR OWN

16.5 The rate of spermatogenesis becomes too slow. Assuming that everything is working well, what will happen to the levels of the following hormones?

GnRH, FSH, LH, inhibin, testosterone

ANATOMY OF THE FEMALE REPRODUCTIVE SYSTEM

The male and female reproductive systems are complementary in their functions. Only in the reproductive systems do we see structures in one sex that require structures in the opposite sex for function. While the man provides half of the genetic material to the offspring, the woman, in addition to providing her half of the genetic material, also nourishes and protects the developing child.

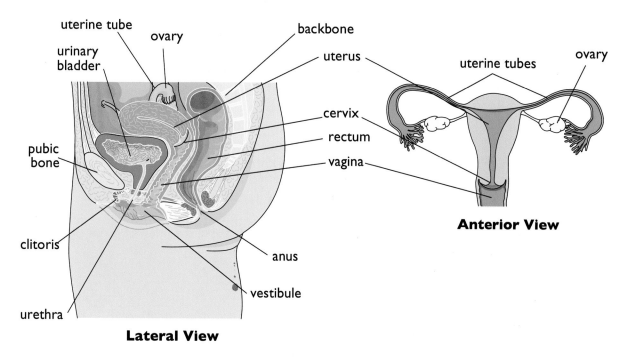

FIGURE 16.8
The Female Reproductive System
Illustration by LifeArt

We will start with the female reproductive anatomy on the right-hand side of figure 16.8. Let's begin with the ovaries. The main functions of the ovaries are to produce the female gamete, which is called the ovum, or egg cell, and to produce the major female hormones, estrogen and progesterone. We will deal more with this soon, but basically, the ovaries contain follicles, which are tiny sacs of cells that surround and then release the developing (but unfertilized) ovum. These follicles also produce the hormones mentioned above.

The uterus (you' ter us), or womb, is expandable to accommodate the unborn child's development. In the nonpregnant state, it is about the size and shape of an upside-down pear. It is composed of three layers: the inner endometrium (en' doh mee' tree uhm), the muscular myometrium (my' oh mee' tree uhm), and the thin outer perimetrium (pehr' uh mee' tree uhm). The endometrium is a thick layer of vascular epithelium. When the sperm fertilizes the ovum, the resulting zygote (the newly conceived child) implants within this layer of the uterus to develop. The myometrium is a layer of smooth muscle, remarkable for its ability to grow larger while still maintaining its thickness. During a full-term pregnancy, it grows to many times its normal nonpregnant weight and volume. Amazingly enough, within six weeks after pregnancy, it involutes (shrinks) back to its nonpregnant size and volume. The perimetrium is the thin outer layer of the uterus. It is part of the visceral peritoneum—the thin serous membrane that covers many of the abdominal organs. The perimetrium allows for the uterus to move easily around as the bladder fills or the intestines contract.

The uterine tubes, also called fallopian (fah loh' pee an) tubes, are like the vastus deferentia in that they are composed of smooth muscle and ciliated epithelium. Peristaltic movements of the smooth muscle and beating of the cilia slowly move the ovum from the ovary into the uterus. If fertilization occurs, it will occur in the uterine tube. Therefore, the uterine tube is called the site of conception. Why here? An unfertilized ovum lives only one day or less, but it takes three days for the uterine tube to transport the ovum into the uterus. Sperm must be able to swim "upstream" to fertilize the ovum within one day of ovulation. At that time, the ovum is still in the uterine tube.

The vagina (vuh jye' nuh) is a smooth, muscular tube with connective tissue on the outside and moist stratified squamous epithelium on the inside. This inner tissue is like the mucous membrane of the mouth. The functions of the vagina are to allow for coitus and to provide a canal through which the baby travels at birth. So, the vagina is often called the birth canal during the birthing process. The opening between the vagina and the uterus is a ring of smooth muscle, covered with epithelium, called the cervix.

Notice that, unlike in the male, the urethra is not a part of the female reproductive system. In the female, the urethra leads out of the body from the urinary bladder and opens into the anterior portion of the vestibule. The uterus, on the other hand, leads out of the body from the vagina and opens into the posterior portion of the vestibule. Even though both sperm and urine travel through the male urethra to exit the body, the female urethra performs no reproductive tasks.

The clitoris (klit' uh ris) can be found anterior to the vestibule. This is the erectile tissue of the female reproductive system. It provides much of the sexual stimulus for a woman during the sex act, as it is filled with sensory receptors. Typically, as sexual tension increases in a woman, her clitoris enlarges, so as to increase its contact with the penis during coitus. As in the male's penis, the blood vessels of the clitoris are also innervated by parasympathetic ANS neurons.

COLORING BOOK EXERCISE 16.3

A review of the female reproductive system can be found on pages 303 and 307 in the coloring book.

ON YOUR OWN

16.6 After sexual intercourse, sperm travel through the female reproductive tract. List the following structures in the order in which the sperm encounter them.

uterine tubes, uterus, vagina, ovum, cervix.

OOGENESIS: DEVELOPMENT OF THE OVUM

Although meiosis forms the basis of both ovum development and sperm development, these two processes are somewhat different. The development of the ovum starts with oogenesis (oh' oh jen' uh sis).

Oogenesis—The production of haploid germ cells by the ovary

Oogenesis begins with oogonia (oh' oh goh' nee uh), which are diploid cells (23 pairs of chromosomes) as illustrated in figure 16.9. Amazingly, by the fourth month of development in the womb, a female fetus has roughly five million oogonia. Most of these degenerate before birth, but the rest begin meiosis. They stop, however, during prophase I. At this point, the cells are called primary oocytes (oh' oh sites).

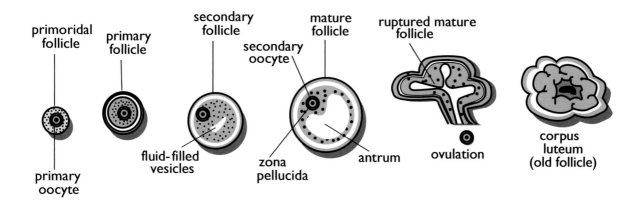

FIGURE 16.9
Development of an Ovum and Ovulation
Illustration by LifeArt

These primary oocytes are each surrounded by a single layer of cells called granulosa (gran you loh' suh) cells. This is the beginning of a follicle, so it is called a primordial follicle. The primary oocytes stay encased in their primordial follicles in the ovary and many actually degenerate until a girl enters puberty. At that point, she has about 400,000 primordial follicles. After puberty, only a few primary oocytes each month will continue with the development of an ovum.

Since the formation of an ovum starts with a primary oocyte, a girl baby is born with all of the oocytes that she will ever have. Note how different this is from spermatogenesis. In a man, the spermatogonia continue to perform mitosis to make more spermatocytes. So, a man continually makes sperm. A woman, on the other hand, has only a certain number of oocytes and cannot make more.

What happens when a girl enters puberty? At that point, the cyclic release of FSH from the anterior pituitary gland will stimulate about 20 of the primordial follicles to develop into primary follicles. In primary follicles, the granulosa cells enlarge and become cuboidal. Then, clear material, called the zona pellucida (pel oo' sih duh), is layered in between the primary oocyte and the follicle. Under the influence of FSH, the primary follicles begin to secrete estrogen.

A few of the primary follicles then transform into secondary follicles, which increase their production of estrogen. In a secondary follicle, the granulosa cells form several layers, and a large fluid-filled space begins to form. This fluid-filled space, called the antrum, pushes the primary oocyte off to one side. When the antrum is fully formed, the follicle is considered a mature follicle. Usually, only one mature follicle forms each monthly cycle. The other follicles degenerate, or they may continue to develop during the next cycle.

As the follicle matures, the primary oocyte completes meiosis I. Remember, meiosis began before birth but stopped during prophase I. The primary oocyte now finishes that process. This important process results in two cells, each with 23 chromosomes, though each cell contains replicates of its chromosomes. So, the cells are now haploid. The division of the cells' cytoplasm is unequal, however. One of the cells is much larger than the other. This cell, the secondary oocyte, is the one that continues ovum formation. The smaller cell, called a polar body, contains the genetic material not needed by the secondary oocyte. It will usually complete meiosis II, making a total of two polar bodies, and then both will disintegrate.

The secondary oocyte begins meiosis II. Interestingly, however, the process stops at metaphase II. At that point, the secondary oocyte is still encased in the mature follicle. Once again, note the differences between this process and spermatogenesis. Spermatogenesis produces mature sperm. Oogenesis does not produce a mature ovum. Instead, it produces a secondary oocyte that is "stuck" in metaphase II. This secondary oocyte is often called a germ cell because it *can* develop into an ovum, but most likely, it will not. Why not? You will see in a moment.

As the secondary oocyte matures, the follicle around it continues to fill with fluid and swell. In a matter of hours, it bursts, and the secondary oocyte is released from the follicle. This event is called ovulation (ahv' you lay' shun).

Ovulation—The release of a secondary oocyte from a mature follicle

When the secondary oocyte is ejected from the follicle, some of the granulosa cells stay around it. This layer of cells is now called the corona (kor oh' nuh) radiata (ray dee' ah tuh). Now remember what we have at this point. The secondary oocyte is stuck in metaphase II. Thus, the cell is haploid. It has only 23 chromosomes. However, those chromosomes are still replicated. The cell must finish metaphase II, anaphase II, and telophase II before those replicates are separated from one another.

After ovulation, the secondary oocyte is pushed down the uterine tube toward the uterus by the movements of smooth muscle peristalsis and by the beating of cilia. If fertilization occurs, it will occur in the uterine tube. Interestingly enough, if fertilization does not occur, the *cell will not finish meiosis II!* If fertilization does occur, the secondary oocyte will complete meiosis II as soon as the sperm penetrates its outer coating. Even though there are two cells as a result of meiosis II, the ovum will get most of the cytoplasm, and the other cell will be a tiny polar body that contains the cast-off genetic material. It will simply die off. In the end, then, from one oogonium, only one ovum is produced. This is yet another difference between spermatogenesis and oogenesis. In spermatogenesis, one spermatogonium leads to four sperm. In oogenesis, one oogonium leads to only one ovum.

Do notice that a total of three polar bodies are produced. So, it is correct to say that, while *mitosis* results in two diploid cells, *meiosis* results in four haploid cells. In the female, only one of those haploid cells, the ovum, is functional for reproduction.

ON YOUR OWN

16.7 A secondary oocyte has only one of each chromosome from the homologous pairs. So, it has only 23 chromosomes. In terms of chromosomes, what is the difference between a secondary oocyte before meiosis II and a secondary oocyte after meiosis II?

What happens to the follicle that is left over after the secondary oocyte is ejected from it? It continues to have an important job. It quickly transforms into a corpus luteum (loo' tee uhm), which secretes estrogen, as it did when it was a follicle. In addition, however, it secretes large amounts of the hormone progesterone.

THE MENSTRUAL CYCLE

Now that you know how the ovum develops, we want to look at its development in the larger context of its cyclic control. The development of the ovum, the release of hormones at various times, and the growth and shedding of the endometrium form the menstrual (men' stroo uhl) cycle. This cycle, which averages about 28 days, occurs regularly in women once they have reached sexual maturity, or puberty. The cycle is naturally interrupted by pregnancy and lactation (lack tay' shun).

> **Lactation**—The process by which a female mammal produces and secretes milk to feed her young

Physical problems such as excessive weight loss can also cause temporary loss of the menstrual cycle. The menstrual cycle stops permanently at menopause.

> **Menopause**—The last menstruation; the time of life after which a woman no longer ovulates

Menopause, which occurs when a woman is in her late 40s or early 50s, marks the natural end of her ability to reproduce.

Let's start our discussion of the menstrual cycle with figure 16.10, which integrates the development of the ovum, the changes in hormones, and the growth and shedding of the endometrium throughout one nonpregnant cycle.

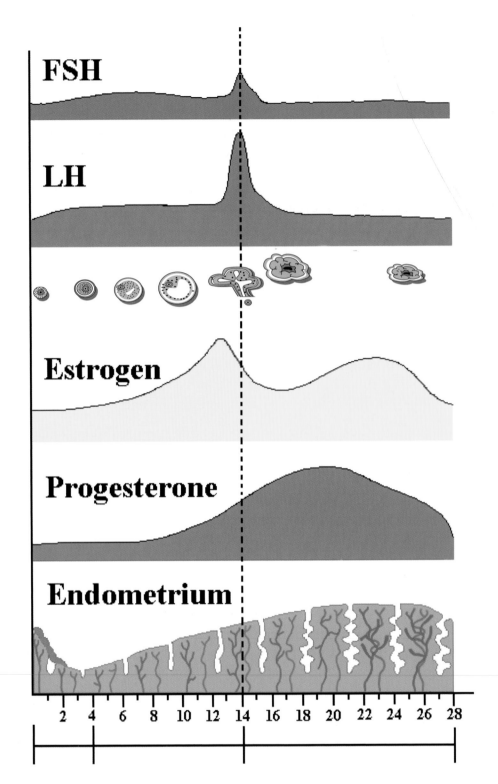

FIGURE 16.10
The Menstrual Cycle and Related Hormones
Illustration by Megan Whitaker and LifeArt

Notice what this figure illustrates. The top two graphs show the levels of follicle stimulating hormone (FSH) and luteinizing hormone (LH) in the blood. These two hormones are secreted by the anterior pituitary gland in response to gonadotropin releasing hormone (GnRH), which is secreted by the hypothalamus. Since FSH and LH stimulate the follicles for the development of the ovum, the stages of ovum development as discussed in the previous section are illustrated below the FSH and LH graphs. The next two graphs illustrate the levels of estrogen and progesterone over the same time period. The follicles in the ovaries secrete estrogen until ovulation. After ovulation, the corpus luteum secretes both estrogen and progesterone. Finally, the graph at the bottom illustrates the development of the endometrium (inner vascular layer) of the uterus.

By convention, the menstrual cycle starts with menses (men' seez).

Menses—Periodic shedding of the uterine endometrium which results in blood loss from the vagina

Menses begins because the uterus can no longer maintain the endometrium, which has grown thick with vascular tissue throughout the other phases of the menstrual cycle. As a result, some of it is shed. This sloughing off is evidenced by bleeding from the vagina, which is generally called menstruation. Typically, women refer to this as their "period," since it occurs on a periodic basis. If this is a bit of a mystery to you at this point, don't worry. You will understand why it occurs once we have discussed the other events of the menstrual cycle.

The first stage of the menstrual cycle, which actually includes the menses, is called the follicular phase. During this stage, the anterior pituitary gland begins to increase its production of follicle stimulating hormone. As its name implies, FSH stimulates some of the primordial follicles to continue oogenesis. As a result, about 20 primordial follicles become primary follicles. These follicles begin secreting small amounts of estrogen. This estrogen stimulates the endometrium of the uterus to begin proliferating so that it starts to thicken. Meanwhile, the release of GnRH from the hypothalamus increases, which increases the amount of both FSH and LH secreted by the anterior pituitary gland. As the follicular stage continues, the follicles continue to develop, but only about five of them actually reach the stage of becoming a secondary follicle.

Toward the end of the follicular stage, FSH and LH have reached their maximum in the blood, as you can see by their peaks on the graph. Why? A positive-feedback loop occurs for a few hours near the end of the follicular phase. It occurs because of a change in the hypothalamus. Estrogen from the follicle during this time causes *more* GnRH to be released, which causes *more* FSH and LH to be released from the anterior pituitary gland. This stimulates *more* estrogen, which stimulates *more* GnRH, and so forth. As we have mentioned before, positive-feedback mechanisms like this are rare in the body, and they escalate until something "gives." In this case, the rapidly swelling follicle "gives" in response to the high levels of LH, and the ovum is released. Ovulation, the big event of the female cycle, ends the positive-feedback.

The free end of the fallopian tube picks up the ovulated ovum, and the ovum is moved toward the uterus. If a sperm in the fallopian tube does not fertilize it, it will die within

24 hours. Since we are discussing a nonpregnant cycle, we will assume that the unfertilized ovum has died.

Of the roughly five or so secondary follicles produced in the follicular stage, usually just one ovulates. Ovulation begins the second stage of the cycle: the luteal (loo' tee uhl) (post-ovulatory) phase. During this phase, the follicle rapidly changes into the corpus luteum, which produces both estrogen and progesterone. This now has a strong negative feedback on GnRH release, and as a result, the levels of FSH and LH in the blood decrease. Estrogen continues to be produced, but progesterone production rises, and progesterone is the dominant hormone of the luteal phase. A follicle does not release progesterone until after ovulation, when it develops into the corpus luteum.

The increased level of progesterone stimulates the further development of the endometrium in the uterus. During this development, the endometrium increases in thickness and develops endometrial glands, which secrete a small amount of fluid rich in glycogen. At the same time, the blood vessels that supply the tissue increase in size to provide plenty of oxygen and nutrients to the endometrium. Why is the endometrium developing like this? It is preparing for possible fertilization (conception). If the ovulated ovum is fertilized, a new life has been conceived, and that new individual will need to develop. To do that, he or she will need oxygen and food. For the first few days after fertilization, the newly conceived embryo remains in the uterine cavity, nourished by the glycogen-rich fluid, which is called *uterine milk*. Once it implants into the endometrium (about a week after conception), it will get oxygen and nutrients from the vascular tissue of the endometrium. So, the endometrium is developing during the luteal phase so that the embryo will have a place to develop if the ovum gets fertilized.

As we said, if the ovum is not fertilized within 24 hours after ovulation, it will die. In a nonpregnant cycle, about 12 to 14 days after ovulation, the corpus luteum degenerates because there is now little LH to maintain it. The resulting drop in estrogen and progesterone causes the endometrium to be lost, and that brings on another menses. During menses, the endometrium is sloughed off, and menstrual bleeding occurs.

Now please understand that even though the typical menstrual cycle is depicted as a 28 day cycle, it normally varies from woman to woman. In general, longer cycles are more frequent than shorter cycles, but both exist. Also, even though the luteal phase lasts about 12 to 14 days, the unfertilized ovum only survives about eight to 24 hours after ovulation. So, there is a very short window of time in which fertilization can occur. Remember, however, that a sperm can live inside a woman's reproductive tract for a few days. So, sexual intercourse does not have to happen during this eight to 24 hour time frame in order for fertilization to occur. As long as sexual intercourse has occurred during that time or *a few days before*, fertilization can occur.

If fertilization does occur, profound changes are triggered by the presence of the embryo. First the cells of the embryo begin secreting the human chorionic (koh ree on' ik) gonadotropin (HCG). This hormone signals the corpus luteum to increase secretion of estrogen and progesterone. As a result, the levels of those hormones rise, and the endometrium is not sloughed off. Instead, it grows thicker, ensuring that the endometrium will be a nourishing place for implantation and development. Of course, the menses will not occur. Traditionally, "missing a period" is a sign of pregnancy, though stress, illness, or being underweight can disrupt the delicate hormonal balance and prevent ovulation. In such cases, the period may be absent or delayed, since no ovulation has occurred.

There is one more item that we must note before we leave this section. The main function of progesterone is to build up the endometrium for pregnancy. It also causes the uterine muscle to relax during the pregnancy. You can now understand the meaning of the name. The gest portion of the word progesterone refers to gestation, which is the development of the fetus in the womb. The pro means that it promotes that. So, progesterone is pro-gestation. It rises to very high levels during pregnancy.

Although progesterone's main function is found within the luteal phase of the menstrual cycle and then continues into pregnancy, estrogen has functions beyond the scope of the menstrual cycle. It maintains the female reproductive organs. It also initiates the female secondary sex characteristics. In other words, estrogen is responsible for female puberty. The breast development, the growth spurt, pubic and axillary hair, and the pattern of fat accumulation are all secondary sex characteristics that are produced by estrogen. Estrogen levels also rise significantly during pregnancy.

ON YOUR OWN

16.8 Of the two sex hormones secreted by the ovaries, which dominates the follicular stage of the menstrual cycle? Which dominates the luteal stage?

16.9 A corpus luteum has formed. Which stage of the menstrual cycle is this? Has ovulation occurred yet?

FERTILIZATION, DEVELOPMENT, AND PARTURITION

The miracle of an individual's life starts at fertilization, which is also called conception. As we mentioned before, it takes several sperm to get through the covering of the egg cell, as shown in figure 16.11.

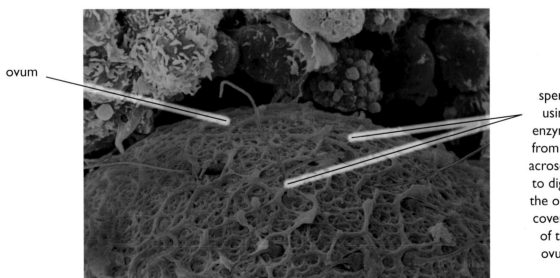

ovum

sperm using enzymes from the acrosome to digest the outer covering of the ovum

FIGURE 16.11
Several Sperm on the Surface of an Ovum
Photo by Dr. Y. Nikas © Phototake

Once that outer layer is breached, however, only one sperm will fertilize the ovum. When that happens, a new and unique human being is conceived. At that point, the fertilized ovum is called a zygote, which means, *paired*. It gets 23 chromosomes from the sperm and 23 chromosomes from the ovum, for a total of 46 chromosomes. Notice from the figure the relative size of the sperm and ovum. This shows you that despite the fact that the zygote gets equal amounts of nuclear genetic material from the ovum and the sperm, the vast majority of its cytoplasm comes from the ovum. Since the mitochondria within the ovum's cytoplasm also contain DNA, all human mitochondrial DNA is inherited from the mother. You learned about this in module 1.

The ovum is fertilized in the uterine tube, and the resulting zygote must travel down to the uterus to implant into the endometrium. The cilia push it along, as do peristaltic contractions of the uterine tube. At fertilization, every genetic aspect of the child is determined, including the gender. Now remember, the gametes (sperm and egg) get *one* chromosome of each homologous pair (a simplification). Since a woman has two X chromosomes, the ovum will *always* have an X chromosome because that's the only possibility. However, since a man has an X and a Y chromosome, the sperm might have an X *or* it might have a Y, depending on which chromosome it got from the pair. So, if an X sperm fertilizes the egg, the result is a girl, since the zygote will have two X sex chromosomes. However, if a Y sperm fertilizes the egg, the result is a boy, since the zygote will have an X and a Y chromosome.

This is the stage at which fraternal twins can be produced. Usually only one ovum is ovulated. However, on rare occasions, more than one ovum is ovulated. This means there will be more than one ovum that can be fertilized. If a second ovum is fertilized, two zygotes are produced and two babies can develop. These babies will not be genetically identical, however, because they are the result of two different ova (plural of ovum) being fertilized by two different sperm. They will be born at the same time, but they will not have identical genes.

What about identical twins? How are they formed? They are formed as a result of the mitosis that occurs after fertilization. The first few stages in this process are shown in figure 16.12.

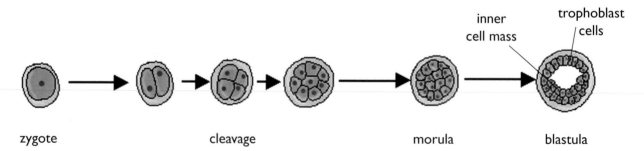

inner
cell mass

trophoblast
cells

zygote   cleavage   morula   blastula

FIGURE 16.12
Cleavage, Morula, and Blastula Stages
Illustration by Megan Whitaker

In order to develop, the zygote must produce more cells. So, within about 18 to 36 hours after fertilization, the zygote undergoes mitosis to make two cells. This begins the cleavage stage of development. The two cells continue cleavage by once again undergoing mitosis to make four cells. This process continues so that more cells are produced. Interestingly enough, the developing embryo does *not grow* during the cleavage stage. It simply makes more cells and packs them into the same-sized ball.

Occasionally during the early stages of cleavage, the dividing cells do not stay together very well. If the cells separate, they will go on to develop two different embryos, rather than just one. This is what forms identical twins. Since both twins come from the same zygote, they have identical genetic information. Of course, genetics do not determine everything about a person. There are developmental, environmental, and spiritual factors that also contribute to the person's makeup. So, even though identical twins have identical genes, they are not identical in all respects.

Once the developing zygote produces enough cells, it forms a rough sphere. This is called the morula (mor' you luh) stage. Morula actually means *mulberry* because the developing embryo looks a bit like a mulberry during this stage. It usually takes about three days to go from zygote to morula, and at this point, the embryo is still in the uterine tubes.

The next stage of development is the blastula stage, which happens 4 to 7 days after fertilization. As the cells of the morula continue to divide, the embryo now begins to grow. The cells press against one another, forming a fluid-filled cavity called a blastocele (blas' toh seel). This results in a hollow sphere called a blastocyst. The blastocyst contains a single layer of outer cells called the trophoblast (troh' foh blast), which means, feeding layer. The trophoblast soon develops into the placenta, the umbilical cord, and the amniotic sac that surrounds the embryo. It's called the feeding layer because it provides oxygen and nutrients to the embryo via the placenta that will be formed. A flat arrangement of cells at one end of the blastocyst is called the inner cell mass, and it is the actual embryo.

During the blastula stage, the blastocyst embeds itself into the thick, vascular layer of the endometrium of the uterus. This is called implantation, and it usually occurs seven to nine days after fertilization.

Implantation—Burrowing of the blastocyst into the endometrium

Implantation generally occurs high in the uterus, away from the cervix. To implant into the endometrium, the trophoblast cells of the blastocyst secrete digestive enzymes that allow the blastocyst to "move in." Now, the developing embryo has access to nutrients and oxygen brought by the mother's blood. After implantation, a new cavity, the amniotic sac, forms from the trophoblast cells.

The next stage of development is called the gastrula (gas' truh luh) stage. In this stage, the embryo (inner cell mass) of the blastocyst begins to change shape. The cells also differentiate into three germ layers: the ectoderm, the mesoderm, and the endoderm. These germ layers will give rise to all of the parts of the body. The ectoderm will produce the skin, nervous system, and some glands. The endoderm will give rise to the lining of the digestive tract, the lining of the respiratory system, most glands, and the digestive accessory organs. The mesoderm gives rise to the circulatory system, muscles, and most of the bones. The lists we just gave you are not exhaustive, but they hit the highlights of what each germ layer becomes.

The next stage of development is the neurula (ner' you luh) stage. In this stage, the neural tube forms. The flat, three-layered embryo folds inward and closes like a zipper to form the neural tube, which becomes the brain and spinal cord. This happens three to six weeks after fertilization. During and after the neurula stage, organogenesis occurs.

Organogenesis—The formation of organs in a developing embryo

Organogenesis is a broad term, and occurs from the second to the eighth week after fertilization. During this time, all organs are formed, though many are still nonfunctional since they are not fully developed. After eight weeks, we stop calling the developing baby an embryo and use the term fetus, which means *young one*. Organogenesis is surprisingly rapid. Figure 16.13 shows a developing fetus only nine weeks after fertilization. Notice that you can already see bones forming!

FIGURE 16.13
Human Fetus Nine Weeks After Fertilization
Photo © Phototake/Dr. Y. Nikas

With the fetus encased in the amniotic sac, you might wonder where he or she gets food and oxygen, as well as how wastes are removed. Most pregnant mammals (including humans) produce a placenta, an organ that allows nutrients and waste to be exchanged between the mother and the child. Amazingly enough, this nutrient-waste exchange system *does not* involve the mixing of blood between the mother and the fetus. Instead, the mother's capillaries run very close to the baby's capillaries in the placenta. This allows nutrients, oxygen, wastes, and carbon dioxide to be exchanged across thin membranes, but no blood gets exchanged. The fetus's blood then returns to the fetus through the umbilical cord. In addition to being an exchange mechanism for nutrients and wastes, the placenta also produces a large number of hormones, including estrogen and progesterone. It's the source of estrogen and progesterone for most of the pregnancy, even though in early pregnancy it's the corpus luteum that produces these two hormones.

The length of human gestation (pregnancy) averages eight months plus three weeks, or 266 days from conception to birth. After the full gestation period, the baby is born. This is called parturition (par ter ih' shun).

Parturition—The process of childbirth

Parturition begins with labor. Surprisingly, it is the fetus's hormones, not the mother's, that start parturition. Stress hormones from the adrenal cortex of the fetus increase toward the end of the pregnancy as the fetus begins to need more nutrients and space to support its growth. These hormones travel through the blood via the placenta and affect the mother, causing a drop in her progesterone. Her estrogen levels then increase, as does her oxytocin, which is the hormone from the posterior pituitary that causes the uterus to contract.

During labor, the contraction of the uterus causes a positive-feedback system that further increases the contractions of the uterus. As the uterus contracts, the fetus is pushed against the cervix. This gradually causes the cervix to stretch open, which it must do in order to let the baby out. As long as the cervix has not stretched enough to allow the baby to pass through, receptors in the cervix send messages to the spinal cord, which relays those messages to the hypothalamus. These messages result in more oxytocin being secreted. The positive-feedback continues, raising the level of oxytocin, until the cervix stops stretching, which is not until the baby has been born. Most often, labor lasts from one to 20 hours, but it varies considerably from woman to woman. Usually, it is shorter in women who have already given birth, but other factors, such as the size of the woman's pelvic inlet and the position of the baby, affect it, as well. Labor is well named; it is *strenuous!*

Final Project
Fetal Pig Dissection

Introduction:

The fetal pig is an excellent choice for dissection as you complete your studies in human anatomy and physiology. Of course it differs in many ways from the human, but it is also a mammal, and therefore has many similarities to the human body. You will focus on those similarities. The fetal pig dissection enables you to integrate the topics of reproduction and development with a review of many of the organ systems you have studied so far.

Purpose: Hog farmers know that pigs take three months, three weeks, and three days from breeding (fertilization) to birth, and fetal pigs are by-products of pregnant sows that are butchered. Preserved in a mild solution, they are useful for study. As you will see, they contain a wealth of fascinating anatomy. You will use a generally regional approach as you dissect the fetal pig while considering the organ systems that you can observe.

Procedure:

1. Before you dissect, first look at the external animal, its head and teeth, its hair and hooves. Take the time to review the tissue types as you do so. From there, carefully dissect the thorax and abdomen. In the thorax, you will be able to observe the lungs, tiny and collapsed, yet fully formed. The heart can be seen within its delicate pericardial sac. The large pulmonary trunk and aorta, as well as the superior vena cava, are all easily identifiable. The thymus gland, quite large in the fetus, will also stand out.

2. Below the muscular but nonfunctional diaphragm, you can identify the liver, and even the miniature gallbladder beneath it. The stomach and spleen are evident. You will be able to pull out the mesenteries, the delicate membranes that suspend the small intestine, and marvel at the radiating pattern of blood vessels that supply the intestines. You will also be able to see many tiny lymph nodes along the small intestine.

3. The large intestine in the pig is shaped differently than in the human, and is called the spiral colon. It is indeed coiled up. Its long length enables the pig, after birth, to absorb nutrients very efficiently. Pigs are bred to convert feed to meat in a high ratio. That long spiral colon is evidence of its ability to do so.

4. Once you remove the intestines, you can see the kidneys lying between the aorta against the body wall, covered by parietal peritoneum. In the lower belly, the urinary bladder can be moved so that you can observe the route of the fetal blood vessels, the umbilical arteries, and umbilical vein, which form the three vessels of the umbilical cord.

5. If you have a male pig, you can identify the scrotum, testes, and urethra, and even the large seminal vesicles—all, marvelously, in the fetal pig. If your pig is a female, the uterus, ovaries and vagina will be present and observable.

6. We encourage you to take the opportunity to dissect and study the fetal pig. No, it is not human, but it certainly will help you to deepen your understanding of the mammalian body, and therefore of the human body, as well.

Well, you've done it! You have completed your study of human anatomy and physiology. We certainly hope that you have enjoyed it. More than that, however, we hope that you have developed a deep appreciation for the wonder of God's creation. The human body is the pinnacle of design and engineering. No matter what wonders human science can create, it will never be able to make anything that matches the elegance, efficiency, resiliency, and functionality of the human body.

For you created my inmost being; you knit me together in my mother's womb.
I praise you because I am fearfully and wonderfully made; your works are wonderful,
I know that full well. My frame was not hidden from you when I was made in the secret place,
when I was woven together in the depths of the earth. Your eyes saw my unformed body;
all the days ordained for me were written in your book before one of them came to be.
—Psalm 139: 13-16, NIV

COLORING BOOK EXERCISE 16.5
A review of fertilization and development can be found on pages 311-315 of the coloring book.

ON YOUR OWN

16.10 Put the following stages of development into their proper chronological order:

cleavage, neurula, zygote, gastrula, blastula, morula

16.11 During which of the stages listed above can identical twins be formed?

16.12 List all the organs mentioned in the dissection, and classify each as to the organ system to which it belongs. (Hint: some organs, such as the diaphragm, belong to more than one organ system.)

ANSWERS TO THE "ON YOUR OWN" QUESTIONS

16.1 The sperm are formed in the testes. Then, they move to the epididymides to mature. During emission, they travel through the vastus deferentia to the ejaculatory ducts. Upon ejaculation, they move through the urethra and out of the penis.

16.2 They cannot fertilize an egg because they have not matured in the epididymides. That maturation step is crucial for sperm to be able to do their job.

16.3 Since there are 21 chromosomes in the sperm, that is the *haploid number*. A non-reproductive cell has twice that number, or 42 chromosomes.

16.4 Since the mother is type B, her possible genotypes are BB and BO. If her genotype is BB, all eggs will get the B allele. If she is BO, half of her eggs will get the B allele, and the other half will get the O allele. Since this father is type A, his possible genotypes are AA and AO. If his genotype is AA, all sperm will get the A allele. If he is AO, half of his sperm will get the A allele, and the other half will get the O allele. So, the baby will get B or O from the mother and A or O from the father. It has type A blood. Its only possible genotypes are AA or AO. The mother has no A's to give, so the baby's genotype is not AA. Thus, the baby got an A from the father and an O from the mother. So, the sperm had the A allele, and the egg had the O allele. As a result, we know that the mother has a genotype of BO.

16.5 If spermatogenesis is too slow, inhibin will decrease. Since high levels of inhibin normally signal enough spermatogenesis, in response to low levels of inhibin, the secretion of GnRH, FSH, LH, and testosterone will all increase. In response, spermatogensis will increase.

16.6 The sperm enters through the vagina. It then moves through the cervix to the uterus and into the uterine tubes. In the uterine tubes, if an ovum is present, the sperm can fertilize it.

16.7 Before meiosis II, the chromosomes are replicated. Meiosis II separates the replicates into single chromosomes. So, the difference is that the secondary oocyte has its 23 chromosomes replicated, whereas after meiosis II, the chromosomes are no longer replicated because the replicates are in the polar body that results from meiosis II.

16.8 The ovaries secrete estrogen and progesterone. LH and FSH are secreted by the anterior pituitary gland and thus are not a part of the question. In the follicular stage, estrogen dominates. In the luteal phase, progesterone dominates.

16.9 This is the luteal stage of the menstrual cycle. Ovulation has occurred, since the corpus luteum forms from the empty follicle.

16.10 The fertilized egg is a zygote. It then increases its number of cells via cleavage followed by the morula. When it forms into a hollow sphere, it is at the blastula, stage. The blastula stage is followed by the gastrula stage and then the neurula stage.

16.11 Identical twins can be formed during cleavage.

16.12 Muscular: heart, diaphragm

Cardiovascular: heart, aorta, pulmonary trunk, superior vena cava, other blood vessels, including the umbilical arteries and veins

Respiratory: lungs, diaphragm

Digestive: liver, gallbladder, stomach, small intestine, spiral colon

Lymphatic: thymus gland, spleen, lymph nodes

Urinary: kidneys, urinary bladder, urethra

Endocrine: thymus gland, testes, ovaries

Reproductive: scrotum, testes, seminal vesicles, urethra (male); uterus, ovaries, vagina (female)

STUDY GUIDE FOR MODULE 16

1. Define the following terms:
   a. Spermatogenesis
   b. Erection
   c. Coitus
   d. Emission
   e. Ejaculation
   f. Semen
   g. Secondary sex characteristics
   h. Puberty
   i. Anabolism
   j. Catabolism
   k. Oogenesis
   l. Ovulation
   m. Menopause
   n. Lactation
   o. Menses
   p. Implantation
   q. Organogenesis

2. Identify the structures in the following figures:

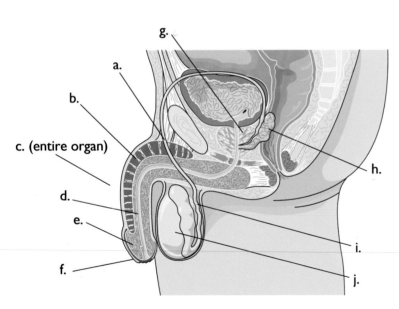

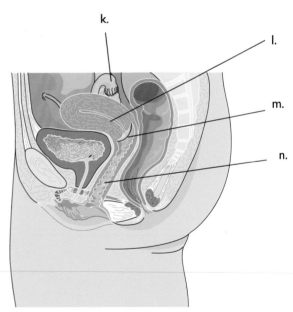

3. Track the path of a sperm cell through the following structures from formation to fertilization:
   uterine tube, male urethra, testis, vagina, epididymis, uterus, vas deferens

4. Why must the testes be in the scrotum for the male to be fertile?

5. List the number of chromosomes in each of the following cells. Assume they all come from humans.
    a. Spermatogonia
    b. Primary spermatocytes
    c. Secondary spermatocytes

6. What are the primary functions of sustentacular (Sertoli) cells and interstitial (Leydig) cells? Where is each cell type located?

7. What cells does FSH principally affect in men? What cells does LH principally affect in men?

8. How many sperm can be formed from one primary spermatocyte? How many ova (eggs) can be formed from one oogonium?

9. In terms of the number of gametes that they can form, what is the difference between men and women?

10. LH and FSH are on the rise in a woman's blood. What stage of the menstrual cycle is she currently experiencing? Has she ovulated yet?

11. The amount of progesterone in a woman's body is increasing and the amount of estrogen is decreasing. Is the endometrium thickening or getting thinner? What stage of the menstrual cycle is she experiencing?

12. If fertilization does not occur, what happens to the endometrium within 12 to 14 days of ovulation? Why?

13. How do fraternal twins form? How do identical twins form?

14. It is said that the father controls the sex of the child. Why is this true?

15. Briefly describe each of the developmental stages below:
    a. Zygote
    b. Cleavage
    c. Morula
    d. Blastula
    e. Gastrula
    f. Neurula

16. During what stage does the embryo implant into the uterus?

17. What cells form the placenta?

GLOSSARY

A-Band—Length of the myosin myofilament in a sarcomere

Abdomen—The area between the thorax and pelvis, commonly called "belly"

Abduction—A movement that is away from the midline

Acetylcholine (ACh)—A neurotransmitter

Acrosome—The head of the sperm containing enzymes to help it penetrate the ovum

Acquired immunity—An immune response targeted at a specific pathogen or toxin

Action Potential—A change in membrane potential that acts as an all-or-none signal

Adenosine Diphosphate (ADP)—Adenosine with two phosphate groups attached to it

Adenosine Triphosphate (ATP)—Adenosine with three phosphate groups attached to it. The energy stored in ATP is used in reactions in cells.

Adipose—fat

Adventitia—A thin layer of loose connective tissue that binds an organ to surrounding tissues or organs

Aerobic Respiration—The breakdown of glucose, in the presence of oxygen, to create carbon dioxide, water and ATP

Afferent neurons—Neurons, which transmit action potentials from the sensory organs to the central nervous system

All-or-none law of skeletal muscle contraction—An individual muscle fiber contracts with equal force in response to each action potential.

Anabolism—All of the synthesis reactions, which occur in the body

Anatomical position—The position acquired when one stands erect with the feet facing forward, the upper limbs hanging at the sides, and the palms facing forward with the thumbs to the outside

Antigen—A protein or carbohydrate that, when introduced in the blood, triggers the production of an antibody

Apocrine glands—Exocrine glands that have cytoplasm in their secretions

Appendicular skeleton—The portion of the skeleton that attaches to the axial skeleton and has the limbs attached to it

Arteries—Blood vessels that carry blood away from the heart

Arterioles—The smallest arteries that still have three tunics

Articular cartilage—Hyaline cartilage that covers the ends of a bone in a joint

Aspirate—To take in by means of suction

Association neuron—A neuron that conducts action potentials from one neuron to another neuron within the central nervous system

Autonomic nervous system—The system that transmits action potentials from the central nervous system to the smooth muscles, cardiac muscles, and glands

Axial skeleton—The portion of the skeleton that supports and protects the head, neck, and trunk

Basement Membrane—Layer of specialized material that separates the epithelial cells from the connective tissues

Belly—The largest part of the muscle, which actually contains the muscle cells

Buffer system—A mixture of an acid and a base, which resists changes in pH

Callus—A mass of tissue that connects the ends of a broken bone

Cancellous bone—Bone with many small spaces or cavities surrounding the bone matrix

Capillaries—Tiny, thin-walled blood vessels that allow the exchange of gases and nutrients between the blood and cells

Cardiac cycle—One complete round of systole and diastole

Catabolism—All of the decomposition reactions, which occur in the body

Cell-mediated immunity—Immunity, which comes from the actions of T-lymphocytes

Chemoreceptors—Sensory receptors that respond to chemicals

Chemotaxis—Attraction of cells to chemical stimuli

Chondrocytes—Mature cartilage cells

Coagulation factors—Proteins in blood plasma, which help, initiate the blood coagulation process

Coitus—Sexual intercourse (the process in which the erect penis enters the vagina)

Commissures—Connections of nerve fibers, which allow the two hemispheres of the brain to communicate with one another

Compact bone—Dense bone matrix enclosing only a few small spaces

Complement—A series of 20 plasma proteins activated by foreign cells or antibodies to those cells. They (1) lyse bacteria, (2) promote phagocytosis, and (3) promote inflammation.

Compliance—The ease with which the lungs inflate

Cranial nerves—Nerves that originate from the brain

Cutaneous receptors—Receptors in the skin

Decussation—A crossing over

Deglutition—The act of swallowing

Dermis—Dense irregular connective tissue that forms the deep layer of the skin

Diapedesis—Passage of any formed element of blood through the blood vessel and into the tissue spaces

Diastolic phase—The phase of the cardiac cycle in which the ventricles relax

Diffuse lymphatic tissue—Concentrations of lymphatic tissue with no clear boundaries

Digestion—The breakdown of food molecules into their individual components

Edema—A buildup of excess fluid in the tissues, which can lead to swelling

Effector—A structure in the body that can change the value of a variable

Efferent neurons—Neurons, which transmit action potentials from central nervous system to the effector organs

Ejaculation—The movement of sperm out of the urethra

Emission—Movement of the male reproductive secretions towards the urethra

Endocrine glands—Ductless glands that secrete hormones into the bloodstream

Endocytosis—The process by which large molecules are taken into the cell

Epidermis—The outer portion of the skin, formed by epithelial tissue, which rests on the dermis

Erection—The enlarged, firm state of the penis, which results as the erectile tissues fill with blood

Erythrocytes—Red blood cells, which carry the oxygen in blood

Erythropoiesis—The production of red blood cells (erythrocytes)

Excitability—The ability to create an action potential in response to a stimulus

Exocrine glands—Glands that secrete substances outward through a duct

Exocytosis—Transportation of material from inside the cell to outside the cell

External respiration—The process of O_2 and CO_2 exchange between the alveoli and the blood

Extracellular matrix—The chemical substances located between connective tissue cells

Extrinsic hand muscles—Muscles in the forearm, which create motion in the hands

Fibroblasts—Spindle-shaped cells that form connective tissue proper

Filtrate—Blood plasma without proteins, found in the nephrons of the kidneys

Foramen—A hole

Formed elements of blood—The cells and cell parts of blood produced by the bone marrow

Functional residual capacity—The volume of air left in the lungs after a normal exhalation

Ganglia—collections of neuron cell bodies, which are outside of the central nervous system

Gastric juice—The acidic secretion of the stomach

Glomerular filtration rate—The rate at which filtrate is produced in glomerular filtration (125 mL/minute)

Gray matter — Collections of nerve cell bodies and their associated neuroglia

Gross anatomy—The study of the macroscopic structures of an organism

Hematoma—A localized mass of blood that is confined to an organ or some definable space

Hemopoiesis—The process by which the formed elements of blood (blood cells) are made in the body

Hemostasis—The process by which the body stops blood loss

Histology—The study of tissues

Holocrine glands—Exocrine glands whose secretions are made up of disintegrated cells

Homeostasis—A state of equilibrium in the body with respect to its functions, chemical levels, and tissues

Humoral immunity—Immunity that comes from antibodies in blood plasma

Hypodermis—Loose connective tissue underneath the dermis, which connects the dermis to muscle or bone

Immunological defense—The process by which the body protects itself from pathogenic invaders such as bacteria, fungi, parasites, and foreign substances

Implantation—Attachment of the blastocyst to the endometrium

Innate immunity—An immune response that is the same regardless of the pathogen or toxin encountered

Insertion—The point at which a muscle's tendon attaches to the moveable bone

Interferon—Proteins secreted by cells infected with a virus. These proteins stimulate nearby cells to produce virus-fighting substances.

Internal respiration—The process of O_2 and CO_2 exchange between the cells and the blood

Intrinsic hand muscles—Muscles within the hand, which create motion in the hand

Labile cells—Cells that undergo mitosis regularly and quickly

Lactation—The process by which a female mammal produces and secretes milk to feed her young

Leukocytes—White blood cells, which perform various defensive functions in blood

Lower respiratory tract—The part of the respiratory system containing the larynx, trachea, bronchi, and lungs

Lumen—The hole in the center of a tube

Lymph—Watery liquid formed from interstitial fluid and found in lymph vessels

Lymph nodes—Encapsulated masses of lymph tissue found along lymph vessels

Lymph nodules—Lymphatic tissue arranged into compact, somewhat spherical structures

Lymph tissue—Groups of lymphocytes and other cells, which support the lymphocytes

Macronutrients—The nutrients the body needs in large amounts: carbohydrates, fats, and proteins

Mastication—The process of chewing

Maximal stimulus—A stimulus, which is strong enough to create action potentials in all the motor neurons innervating a whole muscle

Meatus—A passageway

Mechanoreceptors—Sensory receptors that respond to movement

Menopause—The last menstruation; the time of life after which a woman no longer ovulates

Menses—Periodic shedding of the uterine endometrium which results in blood loss from the vagina

Merocrine glands—Exocrine glands that secrete without losing cellular material

Micronutrients—The nutrients the body needs in small amounts, such as vitamins and minerals

Microscopic anatomy—The study of the microscopic structures of an organism

Motor unit—One motor neuron and all the muscle fibers it innervates

Muscle tone—The state of partial contraction in a muscle, even when the muscle is not being used

Nerves—Bundles of axons and their sheaths, which extend from the central nervous system

Neuron—The functional unit of the nervous system, a nerve cell

Neurosecretory cells—Neurons of the hypothalamus that secrete neurohormone rather than neurotransmitter

Neurotransmitter—A chemical released by a neuron. This chemical travels across the synaptic cleft, allowing the neuron to communicate with another cell.

Nociceptors—Sensory receptors that respond to pain or excess stimulation

Oogenesis—The production of haploid germ cells by the ovary

Organ—A group of tissues specialized for a particular function

Organogenesis—The formation of organs in a developing fetus

Origin—The point at which a muscle's tendon attaches to the more stationary bone

Ossification—Bone formation

Osteoblast—A bone-forming cell

Osteoclast—A large, multinucleated cell that breaks down bone

Osteocyte—A mature bone cell surrounded by bone matrix

Ovulation—The release of a secondary oocyte from a mature follicle

Parasympathetic division—Division of the autonomic nervous system that regulates resting and nutrition-related functions such as digestion, defecation, and urination

Parenchymal cells—Cells that provide the actual function of the tissue

Parturition—The process of childbirth

Peristalsis—The process of contraction and relaxation of circular smooth muscles, which pushes food through the alimentary canal

Permanent cells—Cells that cannot undergo mitosis

Photoreceptors—Sensory receptors that respond to light

Physiology—The study of the functions of an organism and its parts

Plasma—The fluid portion of the blood, which is mostly water

Platelets—Cell fragments in blood, which helps prevent blood loss

Pneumothorax—Air in the pleural cavity, which leads to a collapsed lung

Potential difference—A measure of the chsarge difference across the cell membrane

Process—A projection on a bone

Proprioceptors—Receptors in the muscles and tendons

Prostaglandins—Biologically active lipids which produce many effects in the body, including smooth muscle contractions, inflammation, and pain

Puberty—A series of events, which transforms a child into a sexually mature adult

Pulmonary circulation—Circulation of the blood over the air sacs of the lungs

Pyrogens—Chemicals, which promote fever by acting on the hypothalamus

Renal blood flow rate—The rate at which blood flows through the kidneys (1 liter/min)

Residual volume—The volume of air left in the lungs after a forceful exhalation

Retroperitoneal—Behind the parietal peritoneum

Sarcomere—The repeating unit of a myofibril

Secondary sex characteristics—The characteristics that appear at puberty and tend to distinguish men from women. These include the development of breasts, hairline patterns, facial shape, body shape, and the distribution of body hair.

Selective permeability—The ability to let certain materials in or out while restricting others

Semen—A milky-white mixture of sperm and the secretions of the testes, seminal vesicles, prostate gland, and bulbourethral glands

Sensory receptor—An organ, which responds to a specific type of stimulus by ultimately triggering an action potential on a sensory neuron

Sinus—A hollowed out space in a bone

Somatic motor nervous system—The system that transmits action potentials from the central nervous system to the skeletal muscles

Somatic receptors—Sensory receptors in the skin, muscle, and tendons

Special receptors—Sensory receptors in specific locations

Spermatogenesis—The process by which sperm form in the testes

Spinal nerves—Nerves that originate from the spinal cord

Stable cells—Cells that do not regularly undergo mitosis but are able to if the need arises

Stromal cells—Cells that provide structure or support for parenchymal cells

Submaximal stimuli—Stimuli of increasing strength that create more action potentials along more neurons

Subthreshold stimulus—A stimulus too small to create an action potential in a neuron

Surfactant—A molecule with a hydrophilic end and a hydrophobic end

Suture—A junction between flat bones of the skull

Sympathetic division—Division of the autonomic nervous system that generally prepares the body for physical activity

Synapse—The interface between a nerve cell and another cell

Systemic circulation—Circulation of the blood through the other tissues of the body

Systolic phase—The phase of the cardiac cycle in which the ventricles contract

Thermoreceptors—Sensory receptors that respond to heat or cold

Threshold stimulus—A stimulus strong enough to create one action potential in a neuron

Tidal volume—The volume of air inhaled or exhaled during normal, quiet breathing

Tissues—Groups of cells specialized for a particular function

Total lung capacity—The maximum volume of air contained in the lungs after a forceful inhalation

Tubular maximum—The maximum rate of reabsorption by active transport through the nephron tubules

Upper respiratory tract—The part of the respiratory system containing the nasal cavity, paranasal sinuses, and pharynx

Veins—Blood vessels that carry blood back to the heart (337)

Ventilation—The process of getting air into the lungs and getting it back out

Venules—Small veins that do not have three tunics but instead have only an endothelium, a basement membrane, and a few smooth muscle cells

Visceral receptors—Sensory receptors in the internal organs

Viscosity—The resistance to flow and alteration of shape due to cohesion

Vital functions—Those functions of the body necessary for life on a short-term basis

White matter — Bundles of parallel axons and their sheaths

Yellow Marrow—Connective tissue (mainly fat) that fills the cavities of bones

Z Disk—Structure at the end of each sarcomere where actin myofilaments attach

Zona Pellucida—A surrounding layer of the oocyte

Zygote—The diploid cell that is the product of the union of sperm and oocyte

INDEX

A

W

X

Y

Z

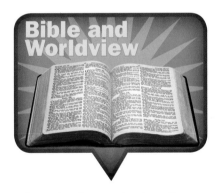